ELEMENTS OF ELECTRONICS

SECOND EDITION

ELEMENTS OF

McGRAW-HILL BOOK COMPANY, INC.

NEW YORK
TORONTO
LONDON
1961

ELECTRONICS

HENRY V. HICKEY

Chief Electronics Technician, United States Navy
Member, Institute of Radio Engineers

WILLIAM M. VILLINES, Jr.

Lieutenant, United States Navy
Member, Institute of Radio Engineers

Foreword by NELSON M. COOKE
Author, Basic Mathematics for Electronics, Second Edition

FOREWORD

During the years since the beginning of World War II the training of enough engineers and technicians to fill the needs of the rapidly expanding field of electronics has presented the armed forces, industry, and educators with a formidable problem. In spite of the fact that more men are being trained every year, it appears that the demand for competent engineers and technicians will exceed the supply for many years.

Many different curricula and methods have been employed in efforts to train more technicians in less time, keep courses up to date, and, without relaxing standards, make them less difficult, thereby attracting more applicants. I have yet to meet an instructor worth his salt who failed to produce within a few minutes of discussion his own curriculum or ideas on how to do the job. This is all to the good; it denotes thought and devotion to his calling. The problem may, however, be intensified by a program that trains the student only to locate and correct trouble within certain types of equipment, at the expense of a good grounding in fundamentals. Such a program may save time; it does not produce a technician. The graduate's chance of ever becoming a technician is remote until he learns those fundamentals.

I have known the authors of this book for several years. We have shared experiences in the training of technicians, and we have discussed at length our ideas and beliefs. The certainty that a good grounding in fundamentals is necessary for continued growth has always been foremost in our minds and eventually led to the writing of the First Edition of this book. Again, in this Second Edition, the authors have attempted to present the essentials with brevity but without sacrificing the coverage of fundamentals. I believe that they have again achieved their goal and that this new edition will fill a long-felt need.

Nelson M. Cooke

v

PREFACE

In this age of missiles, rockets, and man-made satellites, we have truly arrived at the threshold of conquering space. Few scientific achievements have received the acclaim accorded recent developments in that field. And there are few men who would deny that these achievements have been largely dependent upon success in a closely related field—the field of electronics.

With the advent of this era, more and more electronics technicians are being trained in schools and colleges, through correspondence courses, and on the job. However, even with the intensified training programs, the number of competent technicians is insufficient for the proper maintenance of newly developed electronics equipment. Therefore, there are many openings for those interested in making a career of electronics, since few industries do not employ electronic devices of some sort.

The task of turning a student of average intelligence into a qualified technician within a reasonable length of time continues to be a problem, especially when different educational backgrounds and future goals have to be considered. Moreover, if 100 professional educators were asked what material they considered essential to the successful training of an electronics technician and what nonessential, 100 different answers would probably be given.

Based upon the authors' experience in actual practice, this text presents the minimum amount of material necessary for training students in the fundamentals of electronics. The methods and sequences followed have been successfully used for a great number of years by the authors in producing trained technicians for the Armed Forces. Students with only intermediate-level education have become capable of carrying out simple maintenance procedures or of progressing to any of the specialized branches of this field.

Mathematics is not treated as a separate subject but is integrated into the text where necessary and appropriate.

The text has been divided into chapters of approximately equal length as an aid to either the instructor or the home-study student. However, this division is only a suggestion and may be utilized or disregarded. The division was based upon the authors' experience in teaching the fifty chapters in ten weeks by covering one chapter each day. While this may not always be practical, it is recommended that the division be followed and the course outlined for completion in some multiple of ten weeks.

Before revising this text, the authors queried numerous instructors for comments and recommendations. The material deleted or added represents a composite opinion, and grateful acknowledgement is made to those who have contributed so much toward making this a better text. Although every author attempts to turn out a perfect product, some ambiguities and conflicting statements will often crop up; those pointed out by the users have been clarified. A great majority of users wanted additional questions, problems, and photographs or diagrams; accordingly, nearly two hundred questions and problems and fifty photographs and diagrams have been added. Moreover, in compliance with requests by those who use this text extensively, material has been added regarding detectors, wave propagation, headphones, microphones, transmission lines, cathode-ray oscilloscopes, terrestrial magnetism, and hi-fi amplifiers. Most important, this revised edition provides a more comprehensive treatment of transistors that includes the circuitry and operation of a transistor radio.

In all cases the revised edition has been up-dated to conform with current terminology and ASA standards. The commercial equipment depicted is actually on the market today.

The questions and problems included at the ends of chapters summarize the preceding material in almost all cases and are designed to be an aid to instructors and students. In a few instances, questions have been included which may require minor outside research on the part of the student. These have been purposely included as an aid to instructors in dealing with higher-caliber students. Actual values and conditions are presented in so far as practicable.

Since this text is designed to cover sufficient material to prepare the intermediate-level student to advance to any of the branches of this field, it is not considered necessary to include reference lists for supplementary reading, which are readily available elsewhere.

Like most technical texts, this one is based upon lecture notes accumulated by the authors over a period of years. The material has been drawn from many sources. Where the origin is known, credit is gratefully given. To the many scientists, engineers, authors, and others in this field whose contributions have made this text possible, the authors give their sincere thanks.

Numerous industrial organizations have been highly cooperative in furnishing photographs, material, and data concerning their products. Their assistance is gratefully acknowledged. Notable among these are the following: International Resistance Company; P. R. Mallory and Co., Inc.; Centralab Division of Globe-Union Inc.; Radio Corporation of

America; Sylvania Electric Products, Inc.; Ohmite Manufacturing Co.; W. M. Welch Manufacturing Co.; Bell Telephone Laboratories; Ziff-Davis Publishing Co.; Electronic Instrument Co., Inc.; J. W. Miller Co.; Allied Radio Corporation; Universal Scientific Co., Inc.; Philmore Manufacturing Co.; Conant Laboratories; Heath Company; Hammarlund Manufacturing Co.; National Co.

The authors are particularly indebted to Nelson M. Cooke, without whose assistance the writing of this text would have been a much more difficult task. All mathematical parts of this text, in addition to other material and diagrams pertaining to the solution of a-c circuits, are either taken verbatim from, or based on, his book *Basic Mathematics for Electronics*, Second Edition, McGraw-Hill Book Company, Inc.—a book that is strongly recommended as a source of additional and amplifying information concerning the mathematical parts of *Elements of Electronics*. It is also considered the best of its kind for the student requiring a mathematical background prior to studying any phase of electronics.

It is a pleasure to express gratitude to Francis Lazenby, Saunders Radio and Electronic School, Inc.; J. L. Duffy, International Business Machines Corporation; Frank A. Keegan, Keegan Technical Institute; and C. F. Veraldi and I. V. Hohenstein, Penn Technical Institute, for their excellent suggestions and comments towards improving the second edition. The authors also wish to thank the late Dr. J. B. Hershman, president of Valparaiso Technical Institute, for his valuable assistance, and C. A. Meyer, Radio Corporation of America, for his cooperation in supplying an unusual amount of material. Special credit is due Robert N. Reed, Electronics Technician Chief, U.S. Navy, for his work in connection with the typical equipment referred to in this text.

Henry V. Hickey
William M. Villines

CONTENTS

CHAPTER 1

FUNDAMENTALS OF ELECTRICITY

The concept of the nature of electricity is purely theoretical. However, modern science has developed laws and theories which explain electrical action beyond any contradiction. This has been accomplished because electrical phenomena follow a clear-cut pattern. To the student who takes a mathematical approach to most problems, accepting pure theory as fact may be difficult. It must be remembered, however, that

Fig. 1·1   The Atomium.

1

practically all these concepts of the theories of electricity have been proved mathematically; the remainder have been proved through the manifestations of electrical action.

The word *electronics* applies to the field that deals with the emission, flow, and effect of electrons in vacuum, gases, and semiconductors. However, since electricity is considered to be a movement of electrons through similar media, the field involving electricity has recently been considered generally within the electronics field. Because electronics involves the sources and movements of electrons through certain media, an understanding of the nature and action of the electron is necessary before proceeding with the study of its effects.

1·1 Composition of Matter. Since the electron is an integral part of the atom which comprises all matter, the composition of matter will be considered first in order to visualize its relation to the electron.

Matter, according to science, is anything that occupies space and has the attributes of gravity and inertia. Matter can be liquid, gas, or solid. All matter is composed of either an *element* or a combination of two or more elements. An element is a substance which contains the single material and cannot be formed or decomposed by chemical or other means known to science. Three examples of elements are gold, silver, and iron. At present there are over 100 known elements of which all matter is comprised. If matter is made up of more than one element, it is known as a *compound*. Wood, stone, paper, glass, etc., are examples of substances formed of more than one of the known elements. The many combinations possible from the numerous elements explain the presence of so many different compounds on earth.

The Atomium in Fig. 1·1, erected at the Brussels World's Fair to symbolize the atomic age, represents man's concept of the structure of matter. Each sphere, enlarged billions of times, represents one of the atoms that combines with billions of others to form the elements or compounds of which matter is comprised. An *atom* is the smallest particle into which an element can be broken down and still retain all its original properties. The smallest particle into which a compound can be divided and still retain its original characteristics is called a *molecule*. Each molecule contains some of the atoms of each of the elements forming the compound. Figure 1·2 represents the structure of a simple compound known as salt, formed by combining sodium and chlorine atoms.

1·2 The Atom. An atom is basically composed of *electrons, protons,* and *neutrons*. (Although other particles are known to exist in the atom, an understanding of their characteristics is not essential to the purpose of this text.) The protons and neutrons form the nucleus of the atom, around which the electron revolves in an orbit similar to that of the earth around the sun. The physical dimensions of these bodies, although extremely minute, are now definitely known. The mass of a proton is 1.672×10^{-24} g when at rest, or about 1,836 times that of an electron. The electron occupies approximately 2,000 times as much space as the proton and has a mass of 9.108×10^{-28} g when at rest.

1·3 Electrons, Protons, and Neutrons. An electron is the unit particle of *negative* electricity and a proton is the unit particle of *positive* electricity. The neutron is a combination of an electron and a proton, containing no charge and therefore *neutral*. Both the proton and neutron are present in the nucleus of the atom, their position relative to the electrons being com-

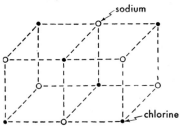

FIG. 1·2 Arrangement of atoms in salt, a compound composed of sodium and chlorine.

parable to that of the sun in the solar system. Therefore, matter can be imagined as made up of elements, or compounds, composed of bodies of atoms. The atoms are further imagined as made up of minute quantities of positive, negative, and neutral particles. As may be determined by study of the Tables of the Chemical Elements in Appendix I, each element is identified by an *atomic weight* and *atomic*

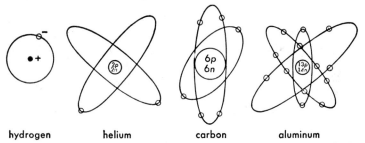

| hydrogen | helium | carbon | aluminum |

FIG. 1·3 Structure and electron orbits of hydrogen, helium, carbon, and aluminum atoms.

number. Atomic weight is determined by the number of both electrons (or protons) and neutrons. Atomic number is determined by the number of electrons present in the atom. Figure 1·3 shows the atomic structure and electron orbits of four common elements. From this it is seen that the various elements are formed of atoms containing different numbers of protons, electrons, and neutrons.

1·4 Balanced Atoms. The atom can be imagined as a minute solar system, with the protons and neutrons forming the heavier part of the atom called the *nucleus* around which revolve the electrons. These electrons revolve in orbital paths and are sometimes called *planetary* electrons since their paths and positions correspond to those of planets around the sun. An atom having an equal number of protons and electrons is said to be *balanced*, or normal, and possesses no electric charge. Any element composed of balanced atoms will neither attract nor repel another neutral element. However, an atom with more than a normal number of electrons, that is, with more electrons than protons, is an unbalanced atom and is called a *negative ion*. Conversely, one that has fewer electrons than protons is also an unbalanced atom and is called a *positive ion*. Basically, an ion can be considered as an *electrified* atom, or one that is unbalanced.

1·5 Static Charge. When the electrons remain in their own orbit in any element, that is, around the nucleus of the parent atom, they are considered to be in a *static* condition. If some electrons are displaced

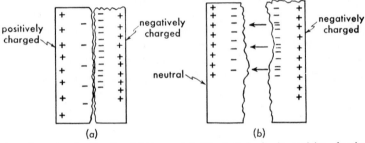

(a)   (b)

FIG. 1·4   Charging bodies by friction. (*a*) The left body is positive, having lost three electrons to the right body, which is now negative, since it has gained three electrons. (*b*) Attraction between two unevenly charged bodies. If the negatively charged body shown in (*a*) is placed in the vicinity of a neutral body, an attraction will exist between the two. If the two bodies touch, electrons will travel from one to the other until they have equal charges.

from their parent atoms through friction, as shown in Fig. 1·4a, or through the effect of some outside source, an electric charge will exist on the element. This produces an unbalanced condition and causes it to be a source of *static electricity*.

There are several examples of static electricity produced by friction in routine daily occurrences. As a person walks across a heavy rug, electrons are removed from the rug and attracted to the body. If a neutral object is then touched, the excess electrons will rush from the body to the object with an accompanying spark and slight electric shock to the person. The same thing happens when a person slides across the seat covers of an automobile and then touches the door handle or any neutral object. Friction between the two causes electrons to be drawn from one to the other, building up a slight charge that will flow to the next neutral object touched. If a comb is run rapidly through hair and immediately placed in the close vicinity of small bits of paper, the paper will be

attracted to the comb.   This is because a negative charge is built up on
the comb due to friction.   The comb then attracts the bits of paper,
which contain no charge but are, effectively, oppositely charged with
respect to the comb.

1·6   Law of Charges.   If an element or compound contains an excess
of electrons, it is said to be negatively charged; if it contains a deficiency
of electrons it is said to be positively charged.   If a pith ball is suspended
by a silk thread and touched with a negatively charged ebonite rod, some
of the excess electrons will be transferred from the rod to the ball and it
will become negatively charged.   Since both objects are now negatively
charged they will repel one another.   If a positively charged rod is
touched to another pith ball, some of the electrons will leave the ball
and be transferred to the rod.   Now the ball will be positively charged,
and if it is placed in the vicinity of the positively charged rod, they will

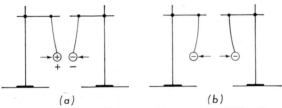

(a)   (b)

FIG. 1·5   Law of charges.   Unlike charges (a) attract, and like charges (b) repel.

repel one another.   If the ball is placed near the first pith ball, which was
negatively charged, they will attract one another as shown in Fig. 1·5a.
Two negatively charged objects will repel one another as shown by the
two balls in Fig. 1·5b.   This demonstrates the law that *unlike charges
attract and like charges repel.*

Another example of this law is in the action of common lightning.
When a cloud loses some of its electrons, it becomes positively charged.
Since the earth is negatively charged with respect to the cloud, a force
of attraction exists between them.   Electrons will be drawn from the
earth to supply the deficiency in the cloud in order to establish neutral
conditions.   This movement of electrons is known as *static discharge.*

1·7   Conductors and Insulators.   All elements in their normal state
contain an equal number of protons and electrons.   The electrons revolve
around the nucleus in orbital paths.   The number of orbits is dependent
upon the number of electrons in the element.   For example, the hydrogen
atom is composed of only one proton and one electron; there is only one
orbit.   In the case of the carbon atom containing six electrons, there
are two orbits of two and four electrons at progressive distances from
the nucleus.   Since the orbits of planetary electrons vary in distance
from the nucleus, each orbit can contain only a limited number of elec-

trons.   At the same time, it is possible for less than the maximum number of electrons to be present in the outer orbit.   As an example, aluminum contains 13 orbital electrons in three orbits of 2, 8, and 3 electrons (Fig. 1·3).   While it is possible for the outer orbit to contain more electrons due to its greater distance from the nucleus, it contains only three.

The modern concept of *current* in a material is a movement or flow of electrons.   In order to function as a good *conductor* the material should allow this movement of electrons with ease; to function as a good *insulator* the material should oppose the movement of electrons.   It has been found that a material whose atoms contain less than half the maximum number of electrons in its outer orbit tends to be a good conductor. If the outer orbit contains more than half the maximum number of electrons, it will tend to act as a good insulator.   Since electric current is a movement of electrons, the fewer the electrons in the outer orbit of an atom, the less their opposition to moving electrons.

1·8   Current.   Certain phenomena indicate that a large number of electrons are free in any conductor without the application of any external

Fig. 1·6   Path of a free electron through a conductor.

pressure.   They are imagined as being cast free from their parent atoms through inertia and moving about the conductor from atom to atom in elliptical paths, as shown in Fig. 1·6.   As soon as one electron sets itself free, it leaves an unbalanced atom which will attract other motional electrons from the atom adjacent, and so on.   These electrons are known as free electrons, and their motion does not constitute current.   Current, or electron flow, is considered to exist only when the majority of electron movement is in the same direction.   It results from an external pressure, or force, applied to the conductor.   This "pressure" results when one end of the conductor is oppositely charged with respect to the other.   If the two ends of a wire are connected to a *battery* or *generator*, the free electrons will move in a definite direction through the conductor from the negative terminal of the battery or generator to the positive terminal. Consider the battery in Fig. 1·7a, whose chemical action has forced many electrons out to the negative terminal, leaving a deficiency of electrons at the positive terminal.   If the battery is connected as shown, the electrons on the negative terminal will follow the law of charges and repel one another.   Since the positive terminal is deficient in electrons, it will attract some of those from the negative terminal.   The result is a continuous circulation of electrons around the conductor in a negative-to-positive direction, which is known as electric current by *conduction*.

1·9 Current Requirement. In order to maintain a steady flow of electrons through a conductor, or medium, a constant electrical pressure must be applied. This pressure is known in the field of electronics as *voltage* and is measured in units called *volts*. This is not a measure of quantity, but rather the difference in *potential* that would exist between the outer terminals of a conductor. If, for example, a battery rated at 6 volts was connected to a conductor, electron movement through the conductor would result. This movement of electrons would be dependent upon the difference in potential, or voltage, between the two battery terminals. Battery voltage is determined by the number of electrons in excess at the negative terminal as compared with the number deficient at the positive terminal. Now, if a 12-volt battery was connected to a similar conductor, there would be twice as much current, since the difference in potential between the two terminals would be twice as great.

For most purposes, voltage is measured relative to the earth, or *ground*, which is considered being at zero voltage, or having no charge. Although other reference points may be used, a negative voltage is usually measured as being a certain number of volts below ground and a positive voltage as being a certain number of volts above ground.

While there is a fine distinction between the terms *voltage*, *potential*, and *potential difference*, it is not essential to the scope of this text, and they will be used interchangeably.

1·10 Sources of Voltage. Although it is possible for a static charge to provide a great potential difference, the actual flow of electrons is of such short duration that very little usable electrical energy is thus obtainable. For almost all electrical applications a source of voltage that will maintain current for a great number of hours or days is required.

One of the methods of producing a voltage is through *chemical* means, such as with *cells* or *batteries*, which are combinations of one or more cells. In this method, shown in Fig. 1·7a, two dissimilar metals are immersed in a solution, called the *electrolyte*, which chemically decomposes the metals by different amounts. The terminal connected to one metal will have an excess of electrons and the terminal to the other a deficiency of electrons. When connected to an external wire, or conductor, electrons will flow steadily through the conductor by the continuous action of the electrolyte on the dissimilar metals.

Another method of producing a voltage is by *magnetic* means, as shown in Fig. 1·7b, and is the way most voltage-generating devices operate. Moving electrons set up a magnetic *field* at right angles to the direction of current, and, conversely, a moving magnetic field produces a current at right angles to the magnetic field. If a closed conductor is moved through the *lines of force* between two magnets, or the lines of force in the field of another conductor, a current will be produced in it. The amount of electricity obtained from alternators and generators (explained in later chapters) at relatively low cost and the ease with which it is produced make this means the most practical and widely used of all sources of electricity.

A third method of producing electric current in a conductor, or a difference of potential between the two ends of a conductor, is by *thermal* means (Fig. 1·7c). If two dissimilar metals are heated at their junction point, one will give up more electrons than the other because of differences in their molecular construction. As one metal loses electrons, it becomes positively charged with respect to the other, thus causing a

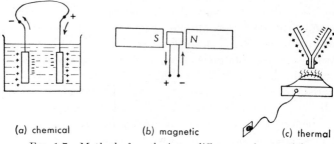

(a) chemical   (b) magnetic   (c) thermal

FIG. 1·7   Method of producing a difference of potential.

difference of potential to exist between the two. The amount of electricity produced by this method is very small and this limits its uses. Some of the more practical applications of this method are in protective devices, meters of various types, and temperature-indicating devices where remote indications are required because of the high temperatures being measured.

1·11 Types of Current. There are several types of current, although all are basically the same. For all practical purposes they can be considered as either *alternating current* or *direct current*. Direct current, usually obtained from d-c generators or batteries, is current whose direction remains the same. Alternating current, produced by several methods to be discussed later, is current whose direction reverses at fixed intervals. Alternating current varies in intensity from zero to some positive value, then reduces to zero and rises in intensity to some negative value before again reducing to zero.

1·12 Effects of Current. The flow of electrons through a conductor produces several effects, three of which are most important in that they can be employed for the measurement of current or voltage. The *thermal*, or heating, effect is due to the collision of electrons with atoms as they are forced to move through a conductor. This collision acts as a *resist-*

ance that is offered to the current, and the electrical energy expended in overcoming this resistance will heat the conductor. Another effect of current is the *chemical* effect, which is the process of breaking down the molecules of a compound into its basic elements. Called *electrolysis*, this is the electrolytic action that takes place in a solution containing two or more dissimilar materials. The third important effect of current is the *magnetic* effect, which produces a magnetic force around the conductor. The strength of this magnetic force is proportional to the rate of electron flow through the conductor.

Measuring the intensity of the effect of current indicates the amount of current or the voltage causing it.

1·13   Mathematics. The *powers of ten*, used in Sec. 1·2 in stating the relative size and mass of electrons and protons, are sometimes referred to as the "engineer's shorthand" and provide a simple means of using convenient whole numbers for working problems.

Some of the multiples of ten expressed in terms of powers are represented in the accompanying table.

Number	Power of ten	Expressed in English
0.000001	10^{-6}	ten to the negative *sixth* power
0.00001	10^{-5}	ten to the negative *fifth* power
0.0001	10^{-4}	ten to the negative *fourth* power
0.001	10^{-3}	ten to the negative *third* power
0.01	10^{-2}	ten to the negative *second* power
0.1	10^{-1}	ten to the negative *first* power
1	10^{0}	ten to the *zero* power
10	10^{1}	ten to the *first* power
100	10^{2}	ten to the *second* power
1000	10^{3}	ten to the *third* power
10,000	10^{4}	ten to the *fourth* power
100,000	10^{5}	ten to the *fifth* power
1,000,000	10^{6}	ten to the *sixth* power

From this it is seen that any *decimal* may be expressed as a whole number times some negative power of ten, and a large number expressed as some smaller number times the proper power of ten. This may be seen by the following rule:

RULE: *To express a decimal as a whole number times a power of ten, move the decimal point to the right as far as is desired. (A useful convention is to form a number between one and ten.) To find the power of ten which multiplied by this number gives the original, count the number of places the decimal point has been moved. This number, prefixed with a minus sign, is the exponent of ten.*

To express a large number as a smaller number times a power of ten, move the decimal point to the left as far as is desired. The number of places the decimal point has been moved will be the proper power of ten.

Examples:

$$0.00482 = 4.82 \times 10^{-3}$$
$$0.0000683 = 6.83 \times 10^{-5}$$
$$0.212 = 2.12 \times 10^{-1} \text{ or } 21.2 \times 10^{-2}$$
$$0.00789 = 7.89 \times 10^{-3} \text{ or } 78.9 \times 10^{-4}$$
$$234 = 2.34 \times 10^{2}$$
$$487,000 = 48.7 \times 10^{4}$$
$$2,792.4 = 2.7924 \times 10^{3}$$
$$3,722 = 3.722 \times 10^{3}$$

Multiplication with Powers of Ten. In multiplying with powers of ten the exponents are additive.

Example 1: Multiply 10,000 by 100,000.

Solution: $10,000 = 10^4$ and $100,000 = 10^5$
Then

$$10,000 \times 100,000 = 10^4 \times 10^5 = 10^{4+5} = 10^9$$

Example 2: Multiply 0.00001 by 0.0001.

Solution: $0.00001 = 10^{-5}$ and $0.0001 = 10^{-4}$
Then

$$0.00001 \times 0.0001 = 10^{-5} \times 10^{-4} = 10^{-9}$$

Division with Powers of Ten. In dividing with powers of ten, the converse of the multiplication is applicable in that the exponents are subtractive. Like exponents in numerator and denominator may be canceled, and powers of ten may be transferred from denominator to numerator, or vice versa, if the sign of the exponent is changed.

Example 1: Divide 10^6 by 10^3.

Solution: $\dfrac{10^6 \text{ (numerator)}}{10^3 \text{ (denominator)}} = 10^{6-3} = 10^3$

Example 2: Divide 64,000 by 0.0008.

Solution: $\dfrac{64,000}{0.0008} = \dfrac{64 \times 10^3}{8 \times 10^{-4}} = \dfrac{64}{8} \times 10^{3+4} = 8 \times 10^7$

Example 3: Divide 19,600,000 by 1,400,000.

Solution: $\dfrac{19,600,000}{1,400,000} = \dfrac{196 \times 10^5}{14 \times 10^5} = \dfrac{196}{14} \times 10^{5-5} = 14 \times 10^0 = 14$

PROBLEMS

Express the following as numbers between 1 and 10, times the proper powers of 10:

1. 0.0138

2. 15

3. 0.000260

4. 47,800

5. 0.0000000000123

6. 0.380

7. 261×10^{-4}

8. 42,400,000

9. 0.245×10^{-6}

10. 123×10^{-8}

11. 456,000,000

12. 3456

13. 0.0567

14. 0.000000789

15. 49,200

Multiply:

1. $68,000,000 \times 0.00000035 \times 0.000055$

2. $10^{-3} \times 25,000 \times 0.328 \times 0.00029 \times 10^5$

3. $500 \times 10^4 \times 782 \times 10^{-8} \times 10^{-6} \times 0.000037$

4. $0.485 \times 10^6 \times 4930 \times 10^{-12} \times 38.6$

5. $10^{-4} \times 597,000 \times 0.00000000793 \times 10^8 \times 3 \times 683 \times 10^{-6}$

6. $100,000 \times 10,000 \times 0.0001$

7. $10^5 \times 1,000 \times 0.00001$

8. $0.00025 \times 104,000$

9. $45 \times 10^8 \times 0.0000002 \times 10^{-3} \times 23$

10. $0.0005 \times 0.000017 \times 0.0000084$

Divide:

1. 1 by $6.28 \times 500 \times 10^{-12} \times 750$

2. 159×10^3 by $56 \times 10^{-6} \times 250 \times 10^{-12}$

3. 1 by $6.28 \times 452 \times 10^3 \times 1550 \times 10^{-7}$

4. $36,000 \times 0.00042$ by 0.009000

5. 1 by $0.000125 \times 8,000$

6. $0.000025 \times 5,000$

7. 1 by $563 \times 10^{-3} \times 248,000 \times 0.0000903$

8. 0.0058×0.000983 by 0.0000071

9. 0.000079×0.00036 by 58×10^{-8}

10. $593 \times 10^5 \times 793 \times 10^4$ by $78 \times 37 \times 10^8 \times 10^7$

REVIEW QUESTIONS

1. Briefly describe the concept of the structure of matter.

2. Explain the difference between an element and a compound.

3. What is the relation between matter, elements, and compounds?

4. What is the difference between an atom and a molecule?

5. Briefly describe the structure of an atom.

6. Name six elements and eight compounds.

7. State the law of charges.

8. (*a*) What is an ion?   (*b*) What is the difference between a negative and a positive ion?

9. How does an atom become unbalanced?

10. Explain how electricity can be produced by friction.

11. How does the electron compare with the proton in weight and mass?

12. Explain the three important effects of current in a conductor.

13. Describe in detail the three main sources of potential.

14. What is static electricity and how can it be produced?

15. What is the difference between a conductor and an insulator?

16. What is current?

17. What is the difference between negative voltage, positive voltage, and ground?

18. Explain the difference between alternating and direct currents.

19. What external evidence proves that a wire offers resistance to current?

20. How may the effects of electron flow be used to measure difference of potential?

21. Explain how electric current is produced in a conductor by thermal means.

22. What is electrolysis?

CHAPTER 2

INTRODUCTION TO VACUUM TUBES

The *vacuum* tube, sometimes known as the electron or *thermionic* tube, has limitless applications in the electronics field. In view of the numerous types of tubes being produced and the many purposes for which they are being used, the study of their construction and operation appears complex; however, the fundamental operating principles of all electron tubes are the same. The primary difference is in their particular mechanical construction and electrical characteristics.

The electron tube is a marvelous and versatile device. Its basis of operation is the flow of electrons and its importance lies in its ability to control electron flow instantaneously with a minimum of control energy.

2·1 Edison Effect. The basic principle of operation of the electron tube has been known as the *Edison effect*. This is in acknowledgment of a discovery made in 1883 by Thomas Edison while conducting experiments with the incandescent lamp. Having learned that his filament material would give off light and have satisfactorily long life only if enclosed in a partial vacuum, he was troubled with frequent burnouts at the positive ends of the carbon filaments in use. Constructing a special lamp, he experimentally placed a second electrode inside and found that when the filament was heated and a sensitive current-indicating device connected between the two electrodes, a current was indicated. Furthermore, the direction of the current was indicated as being in one direction—from the filament to the second electrode, or plate.

Being busy with the development of his lamp, Edison merely made a record of his discovery, and it remained a mystery until 1889, when J. J. Thomson formulated the now-accepted theory that the phenomenon was due to the heated filament's giving off electrons.

2·2 Emission of Electrons. *Emission* is roughly analogous to boiling. It is the process of causing electrons to remove, or separate, themselves from a substance in the form of a cloud much like the steam produced by boiling water.

The atom of any body is composed of one or more planetary electrons revolving around the nucleus. Even though a material has a large num-

13

ber of free electrons, few will ever leave the surface without the application of an outside source of energy. Under ordinary circumstances the electrons and atoms of a substance possess some energy due to a constant state of motion. The electrons cannot escape into space because of the attraction exerted by the oppositely charged protons in the nucleus of the atom. In order to overcome this attraction and escape from the substance, the electron must do work in the form of *kinetic*, or motional,

FIG. 2·1   Typical vacuum tubes.   (*Radio Corporation of America.*)

energy. For all known substances, the escape of electrons at normal temperatures would require more energy, or ability to do work, than the electron possesses. Therefore, they have to be forcibly emitted from the substance by the application of heat or energy supplied from outside. Applying heat will cause the orbital speed of the electrons to be increased. As their speed is accelerated, the diameter of their orbits is increased until nuclear attraction is overcome and they fly into space. This action, where the energy necessary to release electrons is supplied in the form of heat, is utilized in most electron tubes.

Once the electrons free themselves of the nuclear attraction and are projected into space, they also free themselves of the force that caused the original acceleration. The atoms losing electrons exert an attraction for those in the vicinity of the emitting substance. The electrons which are cast free from their parent atoms and the emitter then exert a repelling action on the newly emitted electrons. This action causes some to return to the emitter while others remain in the vicinity to produce an effect known as *space charge*.

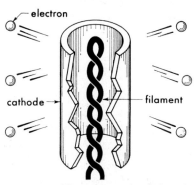

Thermionic Emission. The application of heat energy to a substance which results in electron emission is referred to as *thermionic emission* to distinguish it from other types. Any device employing this method of emission is called a *thermionic* device. The substance emitting the electrons is called a thermionic *emitter* or *cathode*, while that receiving the electrons is called a *plate* or *anode*.

Fig. 2·2 Electrons emitted by the cathode of a vacuum tube when heat is applied to the filament (thermionic emission).

Photoelectric Emission. It has been found that in a few materials the energy necessary to produce electron emission can be obtained simply by exposing them to light of certain wavelengths. For example, zinc is one of the many photosensitive materials that will give off electrons quite freely if exposed to ultraviolet rays. Since ultraviolet rays do not carry any electric charge and, therefore, cannot supply a charge to the body they illuminate, the emitted electrons can result only from the illumination of the surface. This phenomenon is known as *photoelectric* emission. The photoelectric cell used in television and sound motion-picture equipment is one of the many devices operating on this principle.

Secondary Emission. The forcing out of electrons from a substance by the impact of other electrons against it is called *secondary emission*. Although this is an undesirable type of emission in an ordinary electron tube, it is used to advantage in more advanced types. It occurs when the outside force causing electrons to flow within the vacuum is too great. The heavy bombardment of the anode by primary electrons from the cathode results in secondary electrons being knocked out. The electrons removed from the anode by bombardment are referred to as *secondary electrons* and tend to set up a repelling action against the oncoming negative charges being emitted from the cathode.

Cold-cathode Emission. Another type of emission, the application of which is beyond the scope of fundamentals, is *cold-cathode* emission. In this method the principle of the law of charges is utilized in attracting electrons from an unheated emitter. If an extremely strong positive charge is placed in the vicinity of some materials, electrons will be forcibly torn from them and attracted to the source of this charge.

2·3   The Diode Tube.   Although Edison actually discovered the principle of the two-element tube in 1883, he never realized that fact. In 1896 J. A. Fleming investigated the *Edison effect* and developed a two-element tube then referred to as the Fleming valve. At that time the name was adequately descriptive of the tube, although today it is known as the *diode*. This is the simplest of all electron tubes and consists of only two elements, or *electrodes*, for emitting and collecting electrons.

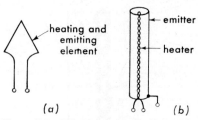

(a)   (b)

Fig. 2·3 Filament and indirectly heated types of cathodes.

The emitting electrode is known as the *emitter*, or *cathode*, while the collecting electrode is known as the *plate*, or *anode*.

2·4   Construction of Diode.   In the construction of the diode, as in other types of electron tubes, it is sometimes found advantageous to heat the emitter indirectly. In most vacuum tubes the thermionic cathode is one of two types: (1) the filament type, shown in Fig. 2·3a, in which the heating current is passed directly through the element that emits the electrons; and (2) the indirectly heated type, shown in Fig. 2·3b, which emits electrons as a result of heat from an adjacent source. In generally accepted terminology, the emitting element is known as the cathode while the heating element is known as the *filament*, or heater. However, in the case of filament-type emitters where one element

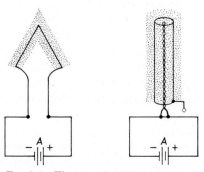

Fig. 2·4 Electron cloud formed around two types of emitters when heated by potential from battery A.

does both heating and emitting, the emitter is known as a cathode. Electron clouds produced by the two types of emitters are shown in Fig. 2·4.

Types of Emitters.   The different types of material used for emitters depend mainly upon the purpose for which they are to be used. The three most commonly used are (1) pure tungsten, (2) thoriated tungsten, and (3) oxide-coated alloys.

Directly heated tungsten cathodes are made from the pure metal and are used where large power-handling tubes are required, such as in the output stages of high-powered radio transmitters. Although its emission efficiency is very low, the advantage of tungsten as a cathode material lies in its ruggedness and ability to withstand high operating temperatures without melting.

Thoriated-tungsten cathodes are made of tungsten slugs impregnated with thorium. When the cathode is activated by the application of heat in the tube, a thin layer of thorium forms on the surface of the tungsten. Because of this layer of thorium many more electrons are emitted at a moderate temperature than would be emitted from pure tungsten. Thoriated-tungsten cathodes have an emission efficiency greater than that of pure tungsten and are used in medium-power applications.

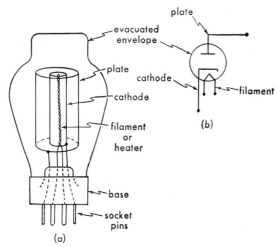

FIG. 2·5   (a) Construction of a typical diode employing an indirectly heated cathode. (b) Circuit schematic of diode.

The most commonly used of the three types of emitters is the oxide-coated. The directly heated type of coated emitter consists usually of a nickel-alloy wire, or ribbon, coated with a mixture containing barium or strontium. The indirectly heated type consists of a thin metal sleeve of similar material and coating, with a heater element contained within, but insulated from the sleeve. The heater element is usually made of tungsten wire and is used for heating the coated sleeve to a temperature sufficient for emitting electrons. Through the application of heat a layer of barium boils to the surface. This gives greater emission properties at low operating temperatures than would result from the use of pure metal. The advantages of this type of emitter are its high emission efficiency, low operating temperature, and relative freedom from filament burnout.

Physical Construction.   Figure 2·5a shows the physical construction of a typical diode employing an indirectly heated cathode. The electrodes are sealed in an evacuated enclosure, which removes gases and also prevents the filament from burning out through oxidation when it is heated to incandescence. The evacuated enclosure, from which all electric connections are brought to external pins, can be made from either metal, glass, or a combination of both.

The heating wires are shown as fitting inside the cathode. When current passes through them, the sleeve is heated, causing emission to start. The anode is often in the form of a hollow cylinder which fits around the emitter, as shown. It is made of one of several metals meeting the requirements of heat dissipation, physical rigidity, and ability to absorb gas. Some of the more common types of anodes are made of tungsten, graphite, molybdenum, tantalum, or nickel. Mechanical properties of an anode material are very important. With currents in excess of normal in the anode, it will heat considerably; therefore, it must

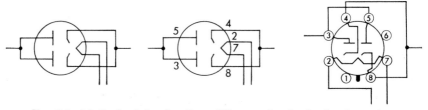

FIG. 2·6   Methods of showing three different tubes in circuit schematics.

be constructed from a metal that will retain its shape when subjected to high operating temperatures.

Circuit Schematic. Electron tubes, like all other electronic components, are usually represented by a *symbol* in what is known as a *circuit*. Figure 2·5*b* shows a diode as it would appear in a *schematic* of a circuit. A circuit, in its simplest form, is defined as the entire course traversed by an electric current. A symbol is defined as that which represents something, while a schematic is a diagrammatic outline of a circuit. Figure 2·6 shows how other tubes will appear in circuit schematics.

2·5 Operation of Diode. A diode employing a directly heated cathode is shown in Fig. 2·7*a*. The purpose of battery *A* is to provide a voltage between the two outer terminals of the conductor to which the cathode is attached. Application of voltage produces a current through the cathode and heats it to the temperature required for emission. This causes the electrons to free themselves from the surface and gather in a space charge adjacent to the emitter. While switch *S* is open, the electrons will remain near the emitter in the form of a cloud. Under these conditions none of the electrons will be attracted to the plate because it possesses no charge and, therefore, exerts no attraction for them. In Fig. 2·7*b*, switch *S* is closed, the anode is made positive, and a return

path is provided between cathode and anode. Since the anode is connected to the positive terminal of battery B, closing switch S will cause
the plate to be positive with respect to the cathode, and electrons will be
attracted to it. This simple arrangement is called a *circuit* and shows
electron flow from a source, through an external circuit, and back to its
original source. In this example, electrons may be thought of as beginning to flow at the cathode, continuing through the external circuit
consisting of the anode, battery B, switch S, and battery A, and then
flowing back to the cathode.

The amount of current can be increased by varying either the cathode
or the plate voltage. An increase in cathode voltage will cause the
electrons to be emitted in greater amounts. Owing to the increase in
volume, a greater number will be attracted to the plate. Also, increasing

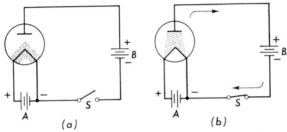

Fig. 2·7   (a) Diode tube with voltage applied only to cathode. Electrons form cloud
around emitter. (b) Diode in (a) with plate voltage applied. Electrons are now
attracted to plate and flow in external circuit back to source.

the plate potential to a higher value will exert a greater positive attraction
and cause more electrons to be collected by the anode. Conversely,
reducing plate potential will lower the attraction, and fewer electrons
will be collected.

Therefore, electron flow in a diode can be controlled by varying either
the plate or the cathode potential. However, a point will be reached,
when potentials are high, at which an increase in plate potential cannot
result in an increase in current. This is called *saturation*.

2·6   Tube Socket and Base. Although some electron tubes have
longer life than others, their life span is unpredictable and replacement is
usually required after prolonged operation. To permit easy removal and
replacement in electronic equipment, the tubes are made with a *base*
that fits into an appropriate *socket* permanently attached to the equipment chassis. All electric circuits are wired to the socket to allow
replacement with duplicate tubes should tube failure occur. Sockets
are designed for all types of tubes to accommodate the different number of
pins projecting from the tube base. The number of pins is usually

determined by the number of electrodes within the tube to which they are electrically connected. (Refer to Fig. 2·10 for socket wiring.)

Information on types of tubes to be used in each particular circuit can be obtained by reference to any manufacturer's tube manual.

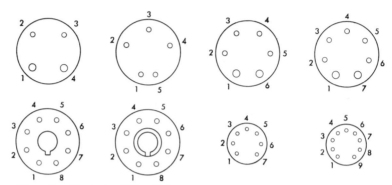

FIG. 2·8 Methods of identifying pin numbers of various types of tubes.

Tube-electrode Identification. To prevent improper placing of tubes in sockets, all tubes are provided with means of ensuring correct insertion. This is done in several ways, one of which uses an aligning key on the tube base that fits into a keyway in the tube socket. In another method

FIG. 2·9 Photograph of tube sockets. (*Sylvania Electric Products, Inc.*)

the tube is fitted with two pins larger than the others, and in a third method the base pins are spaced at varying distances. In all instances, some means is provided to ensure proper connection between the tube electrodes and associate electronic circuits.

Tube manuals and circuit schematics show that tube electrodes have identifying numbers that correspond to the associate socket. This facilitates wiring to proper socket terminals in the absence of the tube and ensures proper electrode-circuit connections after the tube is inserted. To determine pin numbers of a tube, hold the tube upside down and count from either the large pin or the pin adjacent to the aligning key. Pins are numbered in a clockwise direction, as shown in Fig. 2·8. Typical tube sockets and bases are shown in Fig. 2·9.

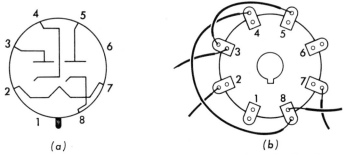

(a) (b)

Fig. 2·10 (a) Typical tube as shown in tube manual or circuit schematic. (b) Actual wiring of socket for base of tube shown in (a).

2·7 Mathematics. Before progressing to the study of practical problems concerning electronics, it is necessary to understand some of the more common electrical terms associated with circuits and the units in which they are expressed.

The *volt, ampere, ohm, mho, watt,* and other terms discussed in subsequent chapters must sometimes be expressed in units smaller or larger than practical, or basic, units. For example, the unit of circuit *inductance* is called a *henry* and is so large it must often be expressed in terms of smaller multiples or fractions. Another unit that must sometimes be expressed in other than basic units is the *farad.* This is a unit of circuit *capacitance* so large that even the largest capacitors are rated in millionths of a farad.

Conversion of Units. The use of some power of ten is a convenient method of converting to larger multiples or smaller fractions of the practical units; therefore, most of the terms encountered will be expressed in either megunits, kilounits, milliunits, microunits, or micromicrounits.

The *megunit* is used mainly for expressing ohms and cycles, due to the large number normally involved. It is usually abbreviated M and is 1,000,000, or 10^6, basic units. Thus, 1 megohm is equal to 1,000,000 ohms, or 10^6 ohms, and 1 megacycle is equal to 1,000,000 cycles, or 10^6 cycles.

The *kilounit* is equal to 1,000 basic units and is used to express watts, cycles, volts, amperes, and volt-amperes. It is abbreviated k. Thus, 25 kw (kilowatts) equals 25,000 watts, and 2 kv (kilovolts) equals 2,000 volts.

The *milliunit* is one-thousandth of a unit and is commonly used in connection with volts, amperes, watts, and henrys. It is abbreviated m. Thus, 20 mh (millihenrys) equals 0.02 henrys, and 100 mw (milliwatts) equals 0.1 watt.

The *microunit* is one-millionth of a unit and is commonly used in connection with volts, ohms, henrys, farads, amperes, and mhos. It is expressed by the Greek letter μ. Thus, 1 volt is equal to 1,000,000, or 10^6, μv (microvolts), and 5,000,000 μf (microfarads) equals 5 farads.

The *micromicrounit* is one-millionth of one-millionth of a unit and is seldom used to express anything but farads. It is written as $\mu\mu$ and, with farads, $\mu\mu$f. Thus, 1 farad is equal to 1,000,000,000,000, or 10^{12}, $\mu\mu$f.

The accompanying conversion table shows unit conversion in simplified form.

Multiply	By	To obtain
units........................	10^3	milliunits
milliunits...................	10^3	microunits
units........................	10^6	microunits
units........................	10^{12}	micromicrounits
microunits..................	10^6	micromicrounits
micromicrounits.............	10^{-6}	microunits
micromicrounits.............	10^{-12}	units
microunits..................	10^{-6}	units
microunits..................	10^{-3}	milliunits
milliunits...................	10^{-3}	units
kilounits...................	10^3	units
units........................	10^{-3}	kilounits
megunits....................	10^6	units
units........................	10^{-6}	megunits
kilounits...................	10^{-3}	megunits
megunits....................	10^3	kilounits

Example 1: Convert 6 μf to farads.

Solution: $$6\mu f = 6 \times 10^{-6} \text{ farad}$$

Example 2: Convert 750 ma to amperes.

Solution: $$750 \text{ ma} = 750 \times 10^{-3} = 7.50 \times 10^{-1} = 0.750 \text{ amp}$$

Example 3: Convert 2,500 watts to kilowatts.

Solution: $$2,500 \text{ watts} = 2500 \times 10^{-3} = 2.5 \text{ kw}$$

Example 4: Convert 300,000 ohms to megohms.

Solution: 300,000 ohms $= 300,000 \times 10^{-6} = 0.3$ megohms

Example 5: Convert 0.000250 henry to microhenrys.

Solution: 0.000250 henry $= 0.000250 \times 10^6 = 250$ μh

PROBLEMS

Express answers as numbers between 1 and 10, times the proper power of ten.

1. 0.05 amp = ＿＿μa = ＿＿ma
2. 3.82 amp = ＿＿ma = ＿＿μa
3. 3.42 amp = ＿＿mv = ＿＿μv
4. 0.042 volt = ＿＿mv = ＿＿μv
5. 25 ma = ＿＿amp = ＿＿μa
6. 0.00025 μf = ＿＿ farad = ＿＿$\mu\mu$f
7. 358 mh = ＿＿μh = ＿＿henry
8. 13.5 kv = ＿＿volts = ＿＿μv
9. 150 μh = ＿＿henry = ＿＿mh
10. 350 $\mu\mu$f = ＿＿farad = ＿＿μf
11. 0.0045 megohm = ＿＿ohms = ＿＿μ-ohms
12. 165,000 ohms = ＿＿megohms = ＿＿μ-ohms
13. 250 watts = ＿＿kw = ＿＿mw
14. 4.3 kv = ＿＿volts = ＿＿mv
15. 0.000000035 farad = ＿＿μf = ＿＿$\mu\mu$f
16. 36.4 kw = ＿＿watts = ＿＿mw
17. 30 $\mu\mu$f = ＿＿farad = ＿＿μf
18. 16.2 μa = ＿＿ma = ＿＿amp
19. 125 μh = ＿＿mh = ＿＿henry
20. 0.002 μf = ＿＿farad = ＿＿$\mu\mu$f

REVIEW QUESTIONS

1. Explain electron emission.
2. Explain how an electron can become free from its parent atom.
3. Explain thermionic emission.
4. Explain photoelectric emission.
5. How do electron tubes basically differ?
6. What is space charge?
7. Explain the principle of secondary emission.
8. Explain the principle of operation of a diode tube.
9. What is the difference between a filament and a cathode?
10. What is the purpose of a circuit schematic?
11. What determines the type of materials used for tube emitters?
12. Explain how heat can cause electrons to leave the surface of an emitter.

13. What is the advantage of the pure tungsten over the thoriated tungsten cathode?

14. What is the purpose of tube sockets?

15. Why are symbols used in circuit schematics?

16. Explain how the effect known as space charge is produced.

17. Explain the construction of a typical diode tube.

18. What effect does anode potential have upon electron flow through an electron tube?

19. Increasing cathode potential in a positive direction will have what effect upon electron flow through an electron tube?

20. What is the most important feature of an electron tube?

21. Explain Edison effect.

22. Explain the two types of thermionic cathodes.

23. What is a circuit?

24. What is meant by saturation in an electron tube?

25. Explain how tube electrodes are identified.

CHAPTER 3

ELECTRIC CIRCUITS

Thus far, a study has been made of the atomic structure of matter and the charges that are inherently a part of that matter. These charges will now be discussed in terms of their use or application. In daily occurrences there is proof that basic charges peculiar to the different types of matter are continually at work making living more pleasant and productive.

These charges will now be considered in terms of practical situations and the relationship that exists between electron flow, charges, and the opposition or aid offered to the flow of electrons through a material.

3·1 The Volt. The charge between two points or between two objects is often termed the potential difference between them; potential, because that charge is potentially capable of doing some work. The charge itself is a form of stored or potential electrical energy.

In honor of an Italian named Volta, who performed numerous experiments with charges and their capabilities, the unit which denotes potential difference was named the *volt*. *The volt is that potential which will produce a current of one ampere in a resistance of one ohm.* Through general usage, the electric force (attraction or repulsion) that exists between two points is often called a *voltage difference*, or simply *voltage*. This text will use the expressions potential, or potential difference, interchangeably with voltage, or voltage difference.

Polarity. In the study of charges it was learned that a positively charged object has a deficiency of electrons, while a negatively charged object has a surplus of electrons. If these two charges come into contact with each other, the excess electrons on the negatively charged object remove themselves to the positively charged object. Finally, a point is reached where both have the same number of electrons and the relative potential between the two objects is eliminated. Hence, if it can be known beforehand which object is positive and which is negative, the direction of electron travel can be predicted. Therefore, a voltage difference between two points is said to have a directional quality. This quality is known as *polarity*.

25

3·2 The Ampere. A famous French scientist named Ampère performed many valuable experiments in measuring the rate of electron movement through materials. In his honor, the unit of electron flow, or current, is called the *ampere*. *There is one ampere of current in a resistance of one ohm when a potential of one volt is applied across the resistance.* If two objects at a given distance are connected by a conductor and have a voltage difference between them, there will be a certain amount of current in the conductor. If the voltage is increased or the distance decreased, current will increase. However, the *direction* of the current will be governed solely by the polarity of the voltage.

3·3 The Ohm. A German physicist named Ohm experimented even further and found that the ratio of voltage and current was constant for a given conductor. This ratio was later called *resistance*. He also learned that electron flow could be varied for a given voltage by the use of different conducting mediums. While it was known that air was a very poor conductor of electrons, Ohm learned that metals such as copper, iron, gold, and silver would easily allow electron movement. Ohm also discovered that by varying the size of the medium, the resistance to electron flow could be varied. In his honor, the unit of resistance, or the *amount of resistance which will permit one ampere of current at a potential difference of one volt,* is called the *ohm*.

Ohm's Law. The foundation of circuit analysis is known as Ohm's law and is expressed: *one volt of pressure is required to force one ampere of current through one ohm of resistance.* Or

$$R = \frac{E}{I}$$

where R = resistance, ohms [often expressed as Ω (Omega)]
      E = potential difference, volts
      I = current, amp

Transposing,

$$E = IR$$

and
$$I = \frac{E}{R}$$

The reciprocal of resistance is *conductance*, in mhos, represented by G.

NOTE: Refer to Appendix III for abbreviations and symbols.

3·4 Electrical Power. The unit of electrical power is the *watt*. Power is basically a *rate of work*, or the rate of producing or consuming energy. Electrical energy is measured in watts or kilowatts. Thus, a lamp may be rated 150 watts at 110 volts or a battery 100 amp at 12 volts. Electrical energy is expended at the rate of 1 watt-sec every second when

1 volt produces a current of 1 amp. Therefore, *one watt of power results when one volt produces a current of one ampere.* This relation is expressed as

$$P = EI$$

where P = power, watts
E = voltage, volts
I = current, amp
Also, since $E = IR$, IR may be substituted for E in the above equation. Thus

$$P = (IR)I$$
or $$P = I^2R$$

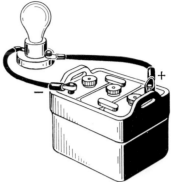

Fig. 3·1   Simple electric circuit.

This equation is useful when only current and resistance are known.

If only voltage and resistance are known, the value of I may be substituted. Thus

$$P = E\left(\frac{E}{R}\right)$$
or $$P = \frac{E^2}{R}$$

3·5 Relation of Electrical to Mechanical Power. In terms of mechanical work, power is a force exerted over a unit distance for a unit length of time. In electrical work it can be shown to be exactly the same. The unit expressing the quantity (Q) of electrons flowing is the *coulomb*. Time is expressed by the letter t. Current is defined as the *rate* of electron flow or, in units, amperes = coulombs per second. One coulomb is equivalent to 6.28×10^{18} electrons. Thus, if one coulomb of electrons passes a point in one second, a current of one ampere exists.

With respect to mechanical work, the amount of work performed, in foot-pounds, is the product of the force exerted, in pounds, and the distance, in feet, over which the force is applied. Or

$$\text{Work} = \text{force} \times \text{distance}$$
Also $$P = \frac{W}{t}$$

where P = power, ft-lb per sec
W = work performed, ft-lb
t = time expended, sec
With respect to electrical energy,

$$P = EI$$

Since current is expressed in coulombs per second, or $I = Q/t$, this value can be substituted for I. Thus

$$P = E\frac{Q}{t}$$

where P = power, watts
E = voltage, volts
Q = charge, coulombs
t = time, sec

As an example of the close relationship that exists between mechanical and electrical energy, 550 ft-lb per sec = 1 hp (horsepower). Further, 1 hp = 746 watts.

3·6 Electric Circuit. An electric circuit is considered to be the course that is followed by electron flow from the negative to the positive side of the voltage applied. Basically, there are three parts to any electric circuit: the voltage applied, the low-resistance medium through which electrons will flow freely, and the resistance that will oppose the current. The voltage applied is referred to as the *source* voltage, the medium as the *conductors*, and the resistance as the *load*.

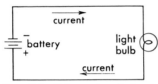

current

battery

light bulb

current

FIG. 3·2 Schematic of circuit in Fig. 3·1.

An example of a simple electric circuit would be a source voltage, connecting wires, and light bulb as shown in Fig. 3·1 and schematically in Fig. 3·2.

Measuring Devices. The three most commonly used instruments for measuring circuit conditions are the *voltmeter, ammeter,* and *ohmmeter.* The voltmeter is usually a very high-resistance instrument that will measure potential difference between two points, while taking practically no current from the circuit. An ammeter is an instrument designed to offer as little resistance as possible to the current being measured. An ohmmeter is an instrument designed to measure the resistance of a circuit in ohms.

3·7 Conductor Resistance. Many factors affect the resistance offered to current by a conductor. Normally, conductors are chosen with a view to offering a negligible value of resistance.

Cross-sectional Area. Electron flow through a conductor is analogous to water flow through a pipe. With the same water pressure a small pipe permits less flow than does a larger pipe. Similarly, the smaller the conductor, the less electron flow permitted. Therefore, it is seen that the resistance of a conductor will increase as the cross-sectional area decreases.

Conductors are identified and classified as to their cross-sectional areas. Since most wire is manufactured in circular form, it is fitting that a circular unit be used for measuring wire size. For example, a wire having a diameter of 2 mils ($\frac{2}{1000}$ in.) has a cross-sectional area of 4 mils (circular mils). The circular mil is established as the square of the mil for convenience. Squaring the diameter in mils of any wire will give its cross-sectional area in circular mils. Conversely, the diameter may be determined by extracting the square root of the cross-sectional area.

Conductors are further identified by number. The number assignments

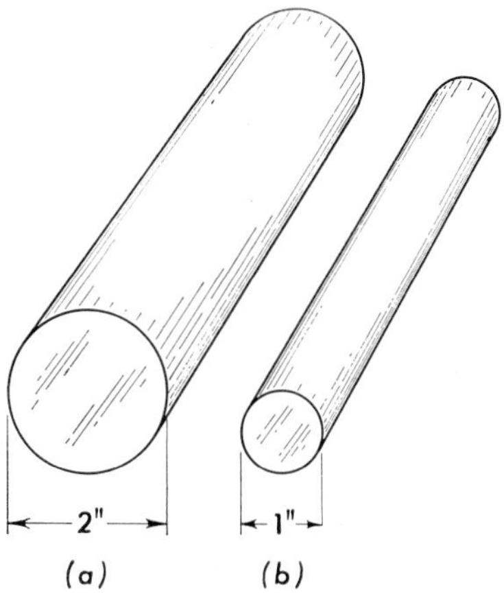

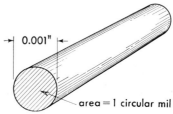

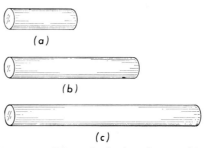

FIG. 3·3 Effect of cross-sectional area on resistance. Wire (b) has one-fourth the cross-sectional area of wire (a) and four times the resistance.

FIG. 3·4 Method of determining cross-sectional area.

have an inverse relationship to cross-sectional area. For example, No. 20 wire has a greater cross-sectional area than No. 30 wire. A table of copper-wire sizes, areas, and resistances per thousand feet at a certain temperature will be found in Appendix XI.

Length. Since electron flow encounters increased opposition as distance is increased, the resistance will vary directly with length for a uniform cross-sectional area.

Temperature Effects. In most conducting materials an increase in temperature will bring about an increase in resistance. This might appear to be a contradiction, since metals expand with the application of heat and expansion provides a larger circular area. If this were the only consideration, resistance and temperature would have an inverse, rather than a direct, relationship. However, heat causes an increase in the molecular activity within the metal. This increase in molecular activity

FIG. 3·5 Effect of wire length on resistance. Wire (b) is two times as long as wire (a) and has twice the resistance. Wire (c) is three times as long as wire (a) and has three times the resistance.

tends to retard the flow of electrons.   Therefore, resistance increases with temperature by an amount that more than compensates for any decrease resulting from expansion.   Any material offering an increased resistance with an increase in temperature is said to have a *positive temperature coefficient.*   Conversely, any material whose resistance varies inversely with temperature changes has a *negative temperature coefficient.*

Copper is a good example of a material with a positive temperature coefficient, while carbon has a negative coefficient.   Figure 3·6 shows the reaction to temperature of two materials of equal resistance but having opposite temperature coefficients.

There are often occasions where one particular material is used in a circuit simply because of the way it reacts to temperature variations. For example, if one part of an electric circuit reacts positively to temperature changes, it is common to insert in another part of the circuit some

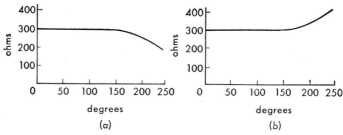

(a)   (b)

Fig. 3·6   Curves showing temperature coefficients.   (a) Material having negative temperature coefficient.   (b) Material having positive temperature coefficient.

material having the opposite reaction to maintain constant resistance regardless of temperature changes.

3·8   Insulators.   *An insulator is a material whose purpose is to isolate any given electric circuit.*   Any material having atoms with outer orbits more than half full of electrons will make a good insulator, or poor conductor.   However, since no known material has atoms with outer rings completely full, there is no perfect insulator.   In practical applications, current in most materials classed as insulators is so minute that it can be disregarded.   Some of the more common insulating materials are glass, mica, rubber, Bakelite, asbestos, vitreous enamel, and dry air. Conditions such as weather, heat, space available, and economy must be taken into consideration before deciding upon the type of insulator to be used.

Breakdown Voltage.   If the voltage across an insulator is increased to a large enough value, the attraction between the points of applied voltage will be so great that free electrons will dislodge other electrons from their parent atoms.   In a very short time a steady stream of free electrons will flow and the insulator will have become a conductor.   When this occurs, the *breakdown voltage* of the insulator has been exceeded.   Each insulating material has a characteristic breakdown voltage, which in part depends on the size and shape used in a particular installation. The greater the distance between points of stress, or between the points of applied voltage, the more voltage required to break down the insulator.

Insulating materials can be found in any number of sizes, shapes, and forms. For example, there are strain insulators several feet in length used to suspend antenna wires at some distance above the ground.

Leakage Resistance. Insulating materials, especially those covering current-carrying wires, are sometimes limited in use by what is termed their *leakage resistance*. For example, an insulated wire might "leak" current at random places along its length through the insulation. Therefore, if the wire is extremely long and has a low leakage resistance, the accumulation of leakage current could alter circuit conditions considerably.

3·9 Resistors. *Any resistor can be considered as a conductor across which a high voltage will produce only a small current.* Resistors have many uses but can be considered as incorporated into a circuit to produce certain conditions. For example, a resistor may be used to limit current in one circuit, lower the voltage at a given point within another, or provide several values of voltage from a common supply in another circuit. Figure 4·8 shows several types of resistors.

Carbon. A resistor often encountered in low-power, nonprecision applications is the carbon type. Usually constructed of a mixture of carbon and clay molded into a cylindrical form with short lengths of wire embedded in the ends, this type of resistor ranges in ohmic value from a fraction of an ohm to approximately twenty million ohms. The ratio of carbon to clay determines the amount of resistance offered. The short lengths of wire, called *pigtails*, are for solder connections to the circuit in which the resistor is being used.

Film or Metalized. This type is made by depositing a film of metal or carbon on a glass or ceramic tube and enclosing this in another tube of glass or ceramic. Most manufacturers attach the pigtails to metal tabs at the ends of the resistor or make ferrule-type resistors to be mounted in clips in the same manner that tubular fuses are installed. Film-type resistors, though made in approximately the same range of resistance values as the carbon type, are generally more accurate. The film, or metalized, is also a comparatively low-power resistor.

Composition. The composition type is very similar to the carbon type; the only dissimilarity is that some material other than clay is used in mixture with the carbon. Composition resistors are for use in applications where a negative temperature coefficient is not desirable. Since carbon has a negative temperature coefficient, mixing with a material having a positive temperature coefficient will result in a steady value of resistance for any temperature change within certain limits.

Wire-wound. In applications where a high degree of accuracy is required, the wire-wound type is most suitable. Most wire-wound resistors consist of turns of wire wound on fiber, ceramic, or some other insulating material, with either metal tabs or pigtails at the ends. This type is generally used where a large amount of power is developed. Spacing between turns of wire allows ventilation and thus prevents overheating. Clips are often used for mounting in lieu of tabs or pigtails. The sealing material either is of the same material as the insulated core or is a coating of vitreous or other insulating enamel.

3·10 Mathematics. The law that expresses the relationships that exist between source voltage, current, and resistance, or load, in an electric circuit is used as a formula for solving for all conditions within the circuit. If any two values are known, the third may be found by transposing and solving for the particular value that is unknown in terms of the two known factors.

Methods of Solution. The general procedure for solving by Ohm's law discussed in this chapter is applicable to the solution of individual circuit problems. In addition, a neat, simplified schematic diagram of the circuit should be drawn for each problem. This removes the problem from the class of pure mathematics to a combination of mathematics and electronics. The diagram should be properly labeled with all known values of the circuit. In this manner the problem and circuit can be visualized and more readily understood. A resistor is represented by the symbol used at the right side of Fig. 3·7.

Example 1: How much current will there be through a resistance of 25 ohms if the applied voltage across the resistance is 110 volts?

Solution: The circuit is represented in Fig. 3·7.

Given: $E = 110$ volts, $R = 25$ ohms.
Find: I.

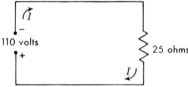

$$I = \frac{E}{R} = \frac{110}{25} = 4.40 \text{ amp}$$

Fig. 3·7   Schematic for solving I.

Example 2: A voltmeter connected across a resistance reads 220 volts, and an ammeter connected in series with the resistance reads 1.1 amp. What is the value of the resistance?

Solution: The circuit is represented in Fig. 3·8.

Given: $E = 220$ volts, $I = 1.1$ amp.
Find: R.

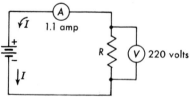

$$R = \frac{E}{I} = \frac{220}{1.1} = 200 \text{ ohms}$$

Fig. 3·8   Schematic for solving R.

Example 3: A current of 2 amp flows through a resistance of 300 ohms. What should be the reading of the voltmeter across the resistance?

Solution: The diagram of the circuit is shown in Fig. 3·9.

Given: $I = 2$ amp, $R = 300$ ohms.

Find: E.

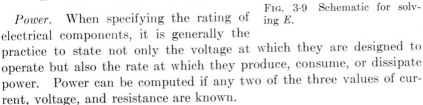

$$E = IR = 2 \times 300 = 600 \text{ volts}$$

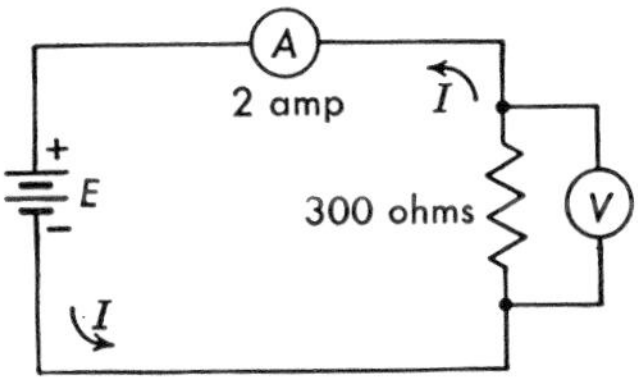

Fig. 3·9   Schematic for solving E.

Power. When specifying the rating of electrical components, it is generally the practice to state not only the voltage at which they are designed to operate but also the rate at which they produce, consume, or dissipate power. Power can be computed if any two of the three values of current, voltage, and resistance are known.

Example 1: An applied voltage of 200 volts produces a current of 1.5 amp. What is the power expended?

Solution: Diagram depicting conditions is shown in Fig. 3.10.

Given: $E = 200$ volts, $I = 1.5$ amp.

Find: P.

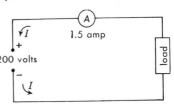

$$P = EI$$
$$= 200 \times 1.5 = 300 \text{ watts}$$

Fig. 3·10   Schematic for solving P.

Example 2: A resistor of 10 ohms carries a current of 3 amp. What power is being dissipated by the resistor?

Solution: The diagram of the circuit is shown in Fig. 3.11.

Given: $I = 3$ amp, $R = 10$ ohms.

Find: P.

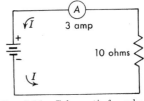

$$P = I^2R$$
$$= 3 \times 3 \times 10 = 90 \text{ watts}$$

Fig. 3·11   Schematic for solving P.

Example 3: A 150-volt source voltage is applied across a 100-ohm resistor. What power is being dissipated by the resistor?

Solution: The circuit is shown in Fig. 3.12.

Given: $E = 150$ volts, $R = 100$ ohms.

Find: P.

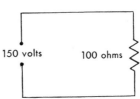

$$P = \frac{E^2}{R}$$
$$= \frac{150 \times 150}{100} = 225 \text{ watts}$$

Fig. 3·12   Schematic for solving P.

REVIEW QUESTIONS

1. Explain the requirements of a basic circuit.

2. What is meant by polarity?

3. What is the difference between current and voltage?

4. How is it possible to predict the direction of electron travel?

5. Define Ohm's law.

6. How is electrical power related to mechanical power?

7. For a given voltage, what effect will an increase in resistance have on current?

8. With resistance remaining constant, what effect will a decrease in voltage have on current?

9. How does the cross-sectional area of a wire affect its resistance?

10. If a wire 10 ft in length has a resistance of 20 ohms, what will be the resistance of a wire 110 ft in length?

11. Define current.

12. How are watts related to foot-pounds per second?

13. What are the relations between power, current, voltage, and resistance?

14. What is a coulomb?

15. Name three commonly used measuring devices and explain their purpose.

16. How do the properties of a good conductor differ from those of a good insulator?

17. (a) What is meant by negative temperature coefficient? (b) Positive temperature coefficient?

18. Explain leakage resistance.

19. Explain the difference between a carbon and a metalized resistor.

20. How is the circular mil area of a wire determined?

21. How much current will 440 volts force through an 80-ohm resistor?

22. A meter connected in series with a resistor reads 15 ma, and a voltmeter connected across the resistor reads 4.5 volts. What is the value of the resistance?

23. The voltage across a 600-ohm resistor is 1.73 volts. How much current flows through the resistor?

24. What is the voltage across a resistor of 10,000 ohms when 2.5 ma flow through it?

25. A buzzer requires 150 ma at 2.5 volts for operation. How much resistance does it represent?

CHAPTER 4

SIMPLE CIRCUITS

It is the purpose of almost any electric circuit to perform work of some nature. To accomplish this purpose, effective control over the three parts that comprise an electric circuit must be obtained. For a given voltage, current can be controlled by a variation of the resistance offered to electron movement. Therefore, resistance is purposely introduced into electric circuits for definite purposes, depending upon the particular type of circuit and the purpose for which it is designed.

Although some resistance may be found in any conductor, the term *resistor* will be used only for a device whose specific purpose is to reduce or control the amount of current or vary the voltage within a circuit.

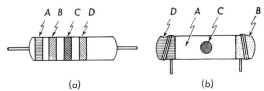

Fig. 4·1   Color-code arrangement for resistors.   (*a*) Axial-lead.   (*b*) Radial-lead-dot.

4·1 EIA Color Code. The resitance of a conductor is dependent upon the material of which it is made. The numerous types and sizes of resistors are marked with a *color code* that denotes resistance value and *tolerance*, or allowable variation from the actual rated value.

In 1938 a system of marking resistors was established by the Electronics Industries Association (EIA) that has been universally accepted by the electronics industry. The two distinctive arrangements in general use are the *axial-lead* and *radial-lead-dot* methods of marking resistors. The axial-lead resistors employ the use of four bands of different colors. With radial-lead-dot resistors, the body color, dot, and two bands of different colors enable identification. These two types are shown in Fig. 4·1. In Fig. 4·1*a* band A represents the first figure of the resistance value, band B the second figure, and band C the number of zeros following the first two figures. In Fig. 4·1*b* the body color A represents the first figure, tip B represents the second figure, and band C, or a dot, represents the number of zeros following the first two figures.

Tolerance. The degree of accuracy of a resistor is indicated by the color of band D in Fig. 4·1*a* and *b*. In most electronic equipment, resistors within 20 per cent of rated value are usually acceptable; however, in some equipment, such as measuring devices, the resistance must be accurate to within a few per cent. Tolerance is indicated by band D as follows: no color, 20 per cent; silver, 10 per cent; gold, 5 per cent.

Color Identification. The numbers that correspond to the colors on resistor bands are as follows: Black: 0; Brown: 1; Red: 2; Orange: 3; Yellow: 4; Green: 5; Blue: 6; Violet: 7; Gray: 8; White: 9.

Example 1: Band A, red; band B, green; band C, yellow; band D, gold.
Resistance = 250,000 ohms; tolerance = 5 per cent.

Example 2: Band A, blue; band B, black; band C, orange; band D, no color.
Resistance = 60,000 ohms; tolerance = 20 per cent.

4·2   Circuit Arrangements.   Although this part of the text is primarily concerned with the simple circuit, the four types of arrangement of

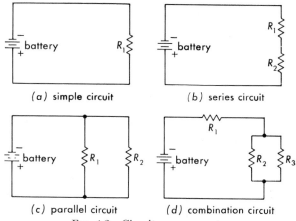

(a) simple circuit   (b) series circuit

(c) parallel circuit   (d) combination circuit
Fig. 4·2   Circuit arrangements.

resistors in a circuit should be indicated here. Figure 4·2*a* shows a *simple* circuit consisting of the three essential parts: the source of power, conductors to transmit the current, and the resistor that is to use the electrical energy. Figure 4·2*b* shows an arrangement known as a *series* circuit. In addition to the three essential parts of which a simple circuit is comprised, there is another resistor in series with that shown in *a*. These two resistors may or may not be of the same value, depending upon the purpose for which the circuit is designed. In Fig. 4·2*c* another resistor arrangement is shown in what is called a *parallel* circuit. In this arrangement the amount of voltage applied across the two resistors will be equal to that of the battery voltage, while the current will divide because of the two separate paths provided. The arrangement in Fig. 4·2d is known as a *combination* circuit, since it combines the features of both a simple and parallel circuit. This is, in effect, a series-parallel circuit, since the parallel circuit is in series with the other.

4·3 The Simple Circuit. The part of a simple circuit that is to use the electrical energy can be one of many different household appliances. Since all materials have some resistance, the heat generated as a result of current through resistance can be made to perform work. Waffle irons, toasters, electric blankets, stoves, soldering irons, and coffee percolators are some of the many appliances making use of this principle.

In order to design an electric circuit for some particular function it is necessary to calculate the ohmic value of resistance, amount of voltage, and current. For each circuit application, these will vary. As an example, to operate an electric iron and a light bulb from the same source requires resistance in different amounts to compensate for the different heat requirements and current. One requires much more energy than the other; therefore, it is necessary to incorporate two different values of resistance into the circuit to meet these requirements.

The key to solving complex circuits is in the analysis and application of Ohm's law in the solution of simple circuits. This law, reduced to simple terms, states the relation between voltage, current, and resistance as follows: *the voltage across any part of a circuit is proportional to the product of the current through that part of the circuit and the resistance of that part of the circuit.*

Example 1: What will be the current through a resistance of 20 ohms if the applied voltage across the resistance is 110 volts?

Solution:
$$E = IR$$

Transposing,
$$I = \frac{E}{R}$$
$$= \frac{110}{20} = 5.5 \text{ amp}$$

Example 2: A voltmeter connected across a resistor reads 220 volts, and an ammeter connected in series with the resistor reads 2.6 amp. What is the value of the resistor?

Solution:
$$E = IR$$

Transposing,
$$R = \frac{E}{I}$$
$$= \frac{220}{2.6} = 84.6 \text{ ohms}$$

Example 3: There is a current of 1.4 amp in a resistance of 450 ohms. What would be the reading of a voltmeter connected across the resistor?

Solution:
$$E = IR$$
$$= 1.4 \times 450 = 630 \text{ volts}$$

Figure 4·3 represents a simple circuit consisting of a 100-volt battery as a source of energy, a 10-ohm resistor to dissipate the energy, and con-

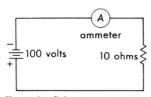

ductors to carry the energy. For the calcula-tion of circuit values at this early stage of the text, conductor resistance and internal resist-ance of the source will not be taken into consideration due to their negligible values. Conductor resistance in most electric circuits amounts to no more than a few ohms per 1,000 ft and is, therefore, of no mathematical importance.

Fig. 4·3   Schematic for solv-ing P.

In terms of Ohm's law, the relation between voltage, current, resistance, and power in the circuit of Fig. 4·3 is as follows:

$$I = \frac{E}{R} = \frac{100}{10} = 10 \text{ amp}$$

Check:
$$E = IR = 10 \times 10 = 100 \text{ volts}$$

Also
$$R = \frac{E}{I} = \frac{100}{10} = 10 \text{ ohms}$$
$$P = EI = 100 \times 10 = 1,000 \text{ watts}$$

4·4 The Series Circuit. Essential to the understanding of the more complex circuits is a thorough knowledge of Ohm's law applied to series circuits. So far, only one resistor has been taken into consideration in the circuits studied. In useful circuits, many resistance-offering devices will be involved. For illustration purposes, these will be shown as simple resistors.

In the series circuit the various resistances across the source voltage are so connected that the electrons must flow through each before return-ing to the other side of the source. Ohm's law must be applied to each part of the circuit and the following three rules remembered.

RULE 1: *The total voltage in a series circuit is equal to the sum of all volt-ages across the different parts of the circuit.*

RULE 2: *The current in a series circuit is the same in all parts of the circuit.*

RULE 3: *The total resistance of a series circuit is equal to the sum of the resistances of the different parts.*

Rule 1 is practically self-evident. If the sum of all the voltages around the circuit were not equal to the applied voltage, there would be a surplus voltage which would result in an increase in current. This increase in current would continue until it caused enough voltage drop across some resistance to balance the applied voltage. Hence

$$E_t = E_1 + E_2 + E_3 + \cdots$$

where E_t = total voltage

E_1 = voltage drop across resistance 1

E_2 = voltage drop across resistance 2

E_3 = voltage drop across resistance 3

Rule 2 is evident because the same electrons have to flow through all parts of the circuit, which are their only path back to the source.

To explain Rule 3, which may not be self-evident, it has been determined that the current is the same in all parts of a series circuit (Rule 2) and total voltage is the sum of all voltage drops (Rule 1). Therefore, if

$$R = \frac{E}{I}$$

and

$$E_t = E_1 + E_2 + E_3$$

then

$$R = \frac{E_t}{I}$$

Dividing each member of the equation for Rule 1 by I,

$$\frac{E_t}{I} = \frac{E_1}{I} + \frac{E_2}{I} + \frac{E_3}{I}$$

Substituting R for E/I, since R is equal to E/I (Ohm's law), then

$$R_t = R_1 + R_2 + R_3$$

By way of further explanation, consider Fig. 4·4, in which a 100-volt battery is providing the potential to two 5-ohm resistors. The electrons leaving the negative terminal of the battery have but one path to follow to the positive terminal. Therefore, there must be the same amount of current in both R_1 and R_2 (Rule 2). With a certain value of current in two resistors, each will dissipate power in proportion to the resistance it offers to the current. Thus, the sum of the voltage drops across R_1 and R_2 will be equal to that supplied by the 100-volt battery (Rule 1). Further, if the sum of the drops across the two resistors equals the applied voltage, then the total resistance must be equal to the quotient of total

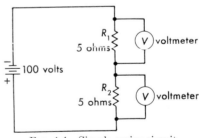

Fig. 4·4 Simple series circuit.

voltage divided by current. Therefore, total resistance is equal to the sum of R_1 and R_2 (Rule 3).

4·5 Calculation of Values. For further familiarization with the application of Ohm's law in solving circuit values, and to analyze various typical circuits, the following examples and solutions are given.

Example 1: If three resistors of 16.5, 45.6, and 67.9 ohms are connected in series across a generator, and a voltmeter connected across the 45.6-ohm resistor

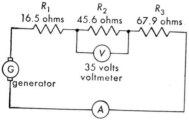

reads 35 volts, what will be the generator voltage? (See Fig. 4·5.)

Solution: $I = \dfrac{E}{R} = \dfrac{35}{45.6} = 0.768$ amp

$R_t = R_1 + R_2 + R_3$
$\quad = 16.5 + 45.6 + 67.9 = 130$ ohms

Therefore

$E_t = IR_t = 0.768 \times 130 = 99.8$ volts

FIG. 4·5   Schematic for solving generator voltage.

Example 2: In Fig. 4·6, three resistors of 20, 50, and 30 ohms are connected in series across a generator. The current through the circuit is 2.5 amp.

(a) What is the generator voltage?
(b) What is the voltage across each resistor?
(c) How much power is expended in each resistor?
(d) What is the total power?

NOTE: $P_t = P_1 + P_2 + P_3$.

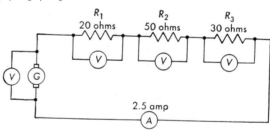

FIG. 4·6   Schematic for solving E and P.

Solution:
(a) $R_t = R_1 + R_2 + R_3 = 20 + 50 + 30 = 100$ ohms
         $E = IR = 2.5 \times 100 = 250$ volts
(b) $E_1 = IR_1 = 2.5 \times 20 = 50$ volts
         $E_2 = IR_2 = 2.5 \times 50 = 125$ volts
         $E_3 = IR_3 = 2.5 \times 30 = 75$ volts
Check: $E_t = E_1 + E_2 + E_3 = 50 + 125 + 75 = 250$ volts
(c) $P_1 = E_1 I = 50 \times 2.5 = 125$ watts
         $P_2 = E_2 I = 125 \times 2.5 = 312.5$ watts
         $P_3 = E_3 I = 75 \times 2.5 = 187.5$ watts
(d) $P_t = P_1 + P_2 + P_3 = 125 + 312.5 + 187.5 = 625$ watts

4·6 Variable Resistors. In previous examples and illustrations resistors were shown as having fixed values. However, there are many instances when it is desired to introduce a variable into the circuit that will allow external control of current. There is more than one type of variable resistor, but all can be described as having resistance that can be varied between a prescribed maximum and minimum value. They are made from the same type of material as fixed resistors and possess the same relative accuracy, power limitations, and temperature coefficients.

The *rheostat* and *potentiometer* are two of the more common types of variable resistors. It is the prime function of the rheostat to control the amount of current in a particular circuit. The function of the potentiometer is to govern the voltage delivered to a resistance; however, in some cases it also controls current through changing voltage. Ordinarily, it produces only voltage changes with no current change involved. Both rheostats and potentiometers are variable resistors, and in many instances

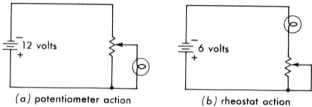

(a) potentiometer action   (b) rheostat action

Fig. 4·7   Difference between rheostat and potentiometer action in circuits.

they are interchangeable; their main difference lies in the particular job being performed.

In the physical construction of variable resistors and on circuit schematics the center member is the sliding contact, or arm, while the remaining two members are the extremes. They are referred to in terms of maximum resistance, since approximately 0 ohms is the minimum point of resistance. For example, a 50,000-ohm potentiometer is one whose value of resistance can be varied from 0 to 50,000 ohms. A 1,000-ohm rheostat provides a resistance of from 0 to 1,000 ohms.

Variable resistors are usually classified as to linearity, or rate of resistance change from minimum to maximum. Since practically all rheostats and potentiometers are circular in physical construction, arm movement follows a circular path. Some provide the change from minimum to maximum resistance in 180° of arm movement, while others utilize nearly 360°. One that produces this change in 180° has a greater change in resistance per degree than one producing the same resistance change in, say, 350°.

Figure 4·7 shows two examples of the brilliance of a light bulb varied through use of variable resistors. The volume control on a radio receiver is a typical example of the potentiometer, while the speed control on an electric motor typifies rheostat action.

4·7 Wattage. Resistors used in a particular circuit are first chosen for ohmic value, then for power-handling capabilities. When there is a current in a resistor, electrical energy is converted into heat. The amount of heat developed is proportional to the product of the current in

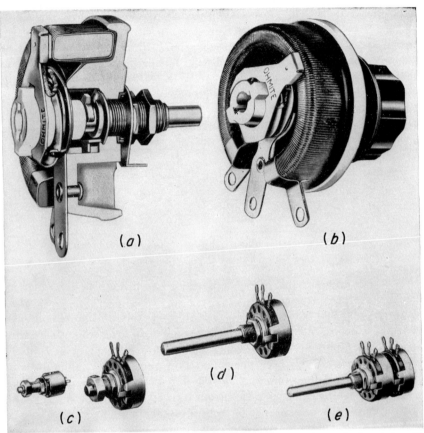

Fig. 4·8   Rheostats and potentiometers. (a) Cutaway view of rheostat. (b) Vitreous enameled rheostat. (c) One-half-watt potentiometers. (d) Two-watt potentiometer. (e) Potentiometer with ON-OFF switch. (*Ohmite Mfg. Co.*)

the resistor and the voltage causing the current. This product, measured in *watts*, is the unit for measuring electrical power utilized or expended in a circuit. In circuit design the amount of power to be developed has to be previously calculated and resistors chosen for suitable power-handling capabilities. The physical size is a determining factor in the ease with which power can be dissipated as heat. Since the heat must be dissipated to the surrounding air as fast as it is produced, the more surface exposed to air, the faster the cooling.

Power Analysis. Power is the amount of work done per unit time, or, in electrical terms, the rate at which electrical energy is consumed or produced. Where one person could do a job in ten minutes, it might take another person thirty minutes. Therefore, in doing the same job one has worked at a certain number of foot-pounds per minute while the other worked at a lesser rate.

In electric circuits, power is computed as the amount of electrical energy dissipated as heat or consumed in the performance of useful work per unit time. The power consumed by a lamp or resistor, for example, can be multiplied by time and watt-hours determined. This can be found mathematically by the following formula:

$$\text{Energy} = \text{power} \times \text{time}$$

where energy is expressed in watt-hours, power in watts, and time in hours.

Example 1: How much electrical energy would be consumed by a 60-watt lamp burning steadily for 5 hr?

Solution:
$$\text{Energy} = \text{power} \times \text{time}$$
$$= 60 \times 5 = 300 \text{ watt-hr}$$

NOTE: For practical use, the watt is a rather small unit. The consumption of electrical energy is usually expressed in kilowatts, or 1,000 watts. One kilowatt-hour (kwhr) equals 1,000 watt-hr.

Example 2: How much electrical energy would be consumed by a 100-ohm resistor in which there was a current of 2 amp for 10 hr?

Solution:
$$P = I^2R = 2 \times 2 \times 100 = 400 \text{ watts}$$
$$\text{Energy} = PT = 400 \times 10 = 4 \text{ kwhr}$$

PROBLEMS

1. Three resistors—$R_1 = 6.87$ ohms, $R_2 = 9.13$ ohms, and $R_3 = 205$ ohms—are connected in series across a 220-volt generator. What is the voltage across each resistor?

2. Three resistors—$R_1 = 20$ ohms, $R_2 = 50$ ohms, and $R_3 = 30$ ohms —are connected in series across a generator. The current through the circuit is 2.5 amp. What is the voltage across each resistor?

3. A 300-ohm relay must be operated from a 120-volt source. How much resistance must be added in series with the relay coil to limit the current to 250 ma?

4. Three resistors—$R_1 = 16.5$ ohms, $R_2 = 45.6$ ohms, and $R_3 = 67.9$ ohms—are connected in series across a generator. A voltmeter connected across R_2 reads 35 volts. What is the voltage of the generator?

5. An arc lamp that is designed to operate on a current of 5.7 amp is to be used in a 220-volt circuit. If the operating resistance of the lamp is 13.2 ohms, how much resistance must be connected in series with the lamp?

6. A 110-volt soldering iron which is rated at 300 watts is to be used on a 220-volt line. (*a*) How much resistance must be connected in series with the iron to limit the current to the proper value? (*b*) How much power will be expended in the added resistance?

Fig. 4·9   Assorted resistors.   (*Ohmite Mfg. Co.*)

7. If there is a current of 10 amp in a 25-ohm resistor, (*a*) how much power is expended in the resistor, and (*b*) what is the voltage across the resistor?

8. Three lamps of equal voltage and power ratings are connected in series across a 200-volt line. If the current through the lamps is 58 ma, what is the resistance of each lamp?

REVIEW QUESTIONS

1. Why is resistance introduced into electric circuits?

2. Why is it necessary to color-code resistors?

3. Explain the two most universally accepted systems of marking resistors.

4. Why is it necessary for most circuits to contain resistances of several different values?

5. What is the difference between a parallel and a combination circuit?

6. What is the resistance value of resistors having the following colors?

(a) Band A, brown; band B, green; band C, blue

(b) Band A, blue; band B, brown; band C, orange

(c) Band A, gray; band B, green; band C, brown

(d) Body color, brown; tip B, green; dot, blue

(e) Body color, blue; tip, orange; dot, yellow

(f) Body color, violet; tip, white; dot, blue

7. What is the relation of voltage to current across resistances in a parallel circuit?

8. Explain the three rules that apply to series circuits.

9. Why is it advisable to construct a simple schematic of the circuit being solved by Ohm's law?

10. (a) What is the prime purpose of rheostats? (b) Potentiometers?

11. Why is tolerance indicated on resistors?

12. What determines the amount of power that a resistor will dissipate as heat?

13. What will be the relation of current through the parallel portion of a combination circuit to that through the series portion?

14. What will be the relation of voltage drops across the parallel portion of a combination circuit to the drops across the series portion?

15. What effect of current in a resistor enables the electric circuit to perform work?

16. What would be the amount of electrical energy consumed by a resistor of 250 ohms at a potential difference of 110 volts in 5 hr?

17. What is the relation of voltage, current, and resistance as applied to any *part* of an electric circuit?

18. In calculating circuit values, why is conductor resistance *not* taken into consideration?

19. Explain the four basic types of circuit arrangements.

20. Name several purposes for which electric circuits are designed.

21. How much power would be consumed by two parallel resistors of 25 and 50 ohms each at a potential difference of 220 volts in 4 hr?

22. What is meant by linearity?

CHAPTER 5

TRIODE VACUUM TUBES

In designing electric circuits to perform work, the vacuum tube plays the most important role. To accomplish work with the minute negative charges that make up a part of matter, some means of control has to be provided. The amount of electron flow through a circuit must be governed according to power-handling capabilities and other design features.

The importance of the electron tube is its ability to control almost instantly the flow of electrons. In a two-element tube this was accomplished by varying either the cathode or anode potential. In 1906 Lee De Forest added a third element to the diode developed by Fleming and found that electron flow could be controlled by varying the potential on this third element, or electrode.

5·1 The Grid. The third element placed between the cathode and plate of an electron tube is known as the *grid*. To further distinguish between other grids later discussed, in this text the grid located nearest the cathode will be known as the *control grid*. With the addition of this third element, the tube is known as a *triode*, the family name for all three-electrode tubes.

The control grid is usually a spiral of fine wire placed around the entire length of the cathode. Although they may be one of several types, control grids are usually like one of those shown in Fig. 5·1a. The physical location of the control grid is between the cathode and plate, nearer to the cathode. Figure 5·1b shows actual tube construction.

Materials from which grids are constructed are chosen for low emission properties, high tensile strength, and good qualities of ductility. Spacing of grid wires is a matter of design and is such that few emitted electrons will strike the wires.

5·2 Control-grid Action. The action of the control grid on electron flow through a tube is based upon the law of charges. If a positively charged object is placed in the path of oncoming electrons, the attraction will cause the electrons to be accelerated in their travel. In an electron tube where electrons are liberated from the cathode through the application of heat, the number emitted may be increased by the addition of a

46

positively charged electrode near the cathode. The force of attraction will cause more electrons to escape from their parent atoms. Conversely, placing a negatively charged electrode near the cathode will cause a repelling effect and fewer electrons will be emitted. This is the basic principle of operation of the control grid in a triode.

If a control grid is placed in a tube but not attached to any source of voltage, it will contain no charge and have no controlling effect on current. The number of electrons traveling between cathode and plate will be determined solely by cathode and plate voltages. If the control grid is

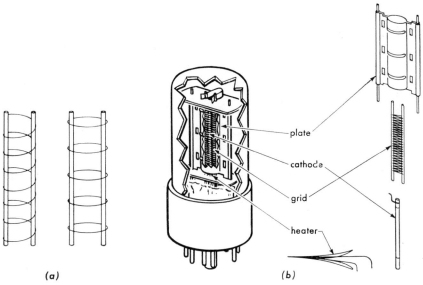

(a)   (b)

Fig. 5·1   Triode-tube construction.

connected to a source of voltage that is negative with respect to the cathode, it will exercise a repelling action against emitted electrons and plate current will be reduced. Increasing control-grid voltage in a negative direction will increase the repelling action, and plate current will further decrease. In this manner it is possible to negatively increase control voltage until plate current is completely cut off.

If the control grid is connected to a source of voltage that is positive with respect to the cathode, more electrons will be attracted from the emitter and plate current will increase. A continued increase in positive grid voltage will increase current until either secondary emission occurs or the control grid acts as an anode. When the latter condition exists, the grid attracts some of the electrons which flow through the grid circuit and back to the cathode as shown in Fig. 5·2c. When the plate no longer attracts electrons at the same rate they are emitted by the cathode, a condition has been reached called *plate-current saturation*. Examples of the effects of grid voltage on plate current are shown in Fig. 5·2.

Bias. A common term to which considerable reference will be made is *bias*, which is considered as a difference in potential that exists between cathode and grid for the purpose of controlling current. A tube is biased if the cathode is connected to a source of voltage positive with respect to the grid, or if the grid is connected to a source of voltage negative with respect to the cathode. The term bias is commonly used to refer to both positive and negative bias. Therefore, a tube would be positively biased if the grid was at ground potential and the cathode was connected to a *NEG* positive voltage. It would be negatively biased if the cathode was at ground potential and the grid was connected to a negative voltage.

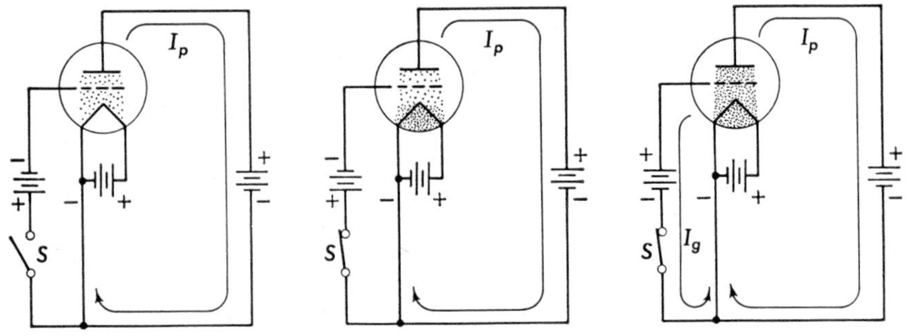

FIG. 5·2   Effects of grid voltage on plate current. (*a*) Grid circuit open; electron flow normal. (*b*) Control grid negative; electron flow reduced. (*c*) Control grid positive; electron flow increased, and tube drawing grid current.

Increasing the bias on a tube is construed as making the grid more negative with respect to the cathode, or the cathode more positive with respect to the grid.

5·3   Tube Characteristics. Although a more detailed discussion is included in a later chapter, it is important here to consider briefly some of the *characteristics* of an electron tube. This is a term used to identify the distinguishing electrical features and values of a tube in order to select one for a particular purpose. In some instances it may be desirable to use a tube which provides a high degree of control of electron flow, whereas in another application this feature would be of less importance.

In order to determine the actual performance of a tube under operating conditions, its characteristics are obtained from electrical measurements when the tube is in various circuits and under definite conditions of voltage. There are two types of tube characteristics, *static* and *dynamic*. Static characteristics are values obtained with d-c potentials applied to the tube electrodes. Dynamic characteristics are values obtained with an alternating voltage on the control grid and direct voltages on cathode and anode.

Amplification Factor. One of the most important characteristics of an electron tube is its amplification factor, written μ. The amplification factor of a tube denotes the relative effectiveness of grid and plate voltages to control plate current. This characteristic is determined by the physical dimensions of the tube, spacing of the grid mesh, and spacing of the electrodes. Since the grid is located in some portion of the space charge, it exercises greater effectiveness in controlling plate current than does plate voltage. Within certain limits, an increase in distance between grid and plate will result in an increase in the amplification factor. The amplification factor can be defined as the *ratio of change in plate voltage to a change in control-grid voltage necessary to give the same change in plate current.*

FIG. 5·3 Photograph of a miniature triode. (*Radio Corporation of America.*)

The amount of electron flow in a triode is measured as plate current in the external circuit from plate back to cathode. If, for example, plate current was 30 ma in a tube with a fixed value of grid voltage, an increase of 50 volts plate potential might result in a plate-current increase of only 5 ma. At the same time, if the plate voltage was held constant and the

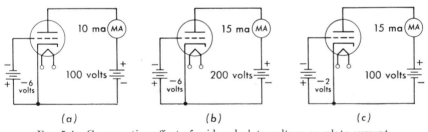

FIG. 5·4 Comparative effect of grid and plate voltage on plate current.

grid voltage increased by 5 volts, the same plate-current increase could result. Therefore, in this example the tube would have an amplification factor of 10. Since the plate required 10 times as much change in voltage to produce the same change in plate current, the grid would be 10 times as effective in controlling plate current.

Figure 5·4*a* shows a tube through which a 10-ma current is flowing. The control-grid bias is −6 volts and the plate potential 100 volts. In *b* the plate potential has been raised to 200 volts, and an increase in plate current to 15 ma is noted on the milliammeter. In c the plate potential has been reduced to the original 100 volts and the control grid has been decreased to -2 volts. The milliammeter again shows a plate current of 15 ma. To bring about a 5-ma change in plate current, plate voltage was increased by 100 volts and grid voltage was decreased by 4 volts. Thus, the grid is 25 times as effective in changing plate current as is plate voltage. The amplification factor, or μ, of this tube is 25. It can be determined by the following formula:

$$\mu = \frac{\Delta E_p}{\Delta E_g} \quad \text{(with } I_p \text{ constant)}$$

NOTE: Greek letter Δ (delta) is used to mean difference, or change.

where ΔE_p = change in plate voltage, volts
ΔE_g = change in control-grid voltage, volts

Example 1: What is the amplification factor of a tube that requires 10 volts increase in grid voltage to produce a change in plate current equal to that resulting from a 50-volt increase in plate voltage?

Solution: $\qquad \mu = \dfrac{\Delta E_p}{\Delta E_g} = \dfrac{50}{10} = 5$

Example 2: What change in grid voltage would be necessary in a tube having an amplification factor of 30 to produce a change in plate current corresponding to a 120-volt increase in plate voltage?

Solution: $\qquad \mu = \dfrac{\Delta E_p}{\Delta E_g}$

Transposing,

$$\Delta E_g = \frac{\Delta E_p}{\mu} = \frac{120}{30} = 4 \text{ volts}$$

Example 3: In a tube having an amplification factor of 12, what plate-voltage change would cause a plate-current change equal to that produced by a 3-volt increase in grid voltage?

Solution: $\qquad \mu = \dfrac{\Delta E_p}{\Delta E_g}$

Transposing,

$$\Delta E_p = \mu \Delta E_g = 3 \times 12 = 36 \text{ volts}$$

Plate Resistance. Another important characteristic of an electron tube is its plate resistance. Just as a resistor offers opposition to electron flow, an electron tube offers resistance to the flow of electrons within it from cathode to plate when the tube is operating with an alternating voltage on the grid. Since the number of electrons flowing to the plate varies, so does the internal resistance of the tube.

Plate resistance is the *ratio of change in plate voltage to change in plate current with grid-voltage constant.* It can be expressed by the following equation:

$$R_p = \frac{\Delta E_p}{\Delta I_p}$$

where R_p = plate resistance, ohms
ΔE_p = change in plate voltage, volts
ΔI_p = change in plate current, amp

Plate resistance varies with different types of tubes, ranging from 2,000 ohms for some tubes to 100,000 ohms for others.

Example 1: What is the plate resistance of a tube through which a change in plate voltage from 150 to 200 volts produces a 5-ma change in plate current?

Solution: $$R_p = \frac{\Delta E_p}{\Delta I_p} = \frac{50}{0.005} = 10,000 \text{ ohms}$$

Example 2: If the plate resistance of a tube is 5,000 ohms and plate voltage is changed from 250 to 150 volts, what is the change in plate current?

Solution: $$R_p = \frac{\Delta E_p}{\Delta I_p}$$

Transposing,

$$\Delta I_p = \frac{\Delta E_p}{R_p} = \frac{100}{5,000} = 20 \text{ ma}$$

Transconductance. The third important tube characteristic is its transconductance, or, as it is sometimes termed, *mutual conductance,* written G_m. This is a factor that combines in one term the amplification factor and plate resistance. It is an indication of the design merit of the tube and a measure of how much control the grid voltage has over plate current. Transconductance can be defined as the *ratio of a small change in plate current to a small change in grid voltage* and is expressed by the formula

$$G_m = \frac{\Delta I_p}{\Delta E_g} \qquad \text{(with } E_p \text{ constant)}$$

NOTE: Transconductance is usually expressed in micromhos, or 10^{-6} mhos. (*Mho* is *ohm* spelled backwards.)

This important characteristic of a tube is called *mutual* because it expresses a relationship between plate circuit and grid circuit, and *conductance* because it is a ratio of current to voltage. It is also referred to as control-grid-plate transconductance or, more commonly, simply as transconductance. The G_m of a tube is also a measure of the ease of electron movement through it.

Example 1: What is the transconductance of a tube in which a change of 50 ma results from a change of 5 volts on E_g?

Solution: $$G_m = \frac{\Delta I_p}{\Delta E_g} = \frac{0.05}{5} = 10,000 \text{ micromhos}$$

Example 2: In a tube having a transconductance of 250,000 micromhos, what change in E_g would cause a 0.3-amp change in I_p?

Solution: $$G_m = \frac{\Delta I_p}{\Delta E_g}$$

Transposing,

$$\Delta E_g = \frac{\Delta I_p}{G_m} = \frac{0.3}{0.25} = 1.2 \text{ volts}$$

Example 3: If $G_m = 500,000$ micromhos and $\Delta E_g = 2$ volts, what is the value of ΔI_p?

Solution: $$G_m = \frac{\Delta I_p}{\Delta E_g}$$

Transposing,

$$\Delta I_p = G_m \times \Delta E_g = 0.5 \times 2 = 1 \text{ amp}$$

5·4 Triode as Variable Resistor. In previous portions of this text it was seen that a variable resistor could be placed in a circuit, causing the amount of current to vary under a constant source of applied potential. If a 10- to 100-ohm rheostat was placed in a circuit to which 100 volts was applied, the current would be 1 amp at maximum resistance and 10 amp at minimum resistance. By varying the resistance through its range, current could be varied between 1 and 10 amp.

The triode electron tube can be considered in the same category as a variable resistor. Tube cathodes are usually operated at a fixed value of voltage specified by the manufacturer to ensure long life. Plate voltage is also specified for the same purpose. Therefore, the control-grid voltage is varied within certain specified limits to control current. This has the same effect upon plate-current as a variable resistor would have on current in an ordinary circuit.

5·5 Mathematics. To determine the characteristics of various tubes for suitability of application, a family of characteristic curves should be consulted. These are made by the manufacturer and represent measurements of the tube under certain values of voltage. This permits the selection of a tube for a definite purpose and also indicates operating conditions and performance data. The curves are pictured graphically, a *graph* being defined as a *pictorial representation of the relation existing between two or more quantities.*

In constructing a graph there must be two lines of reference, or axes. The horizontal axis is generally known as the x axis and the vertical axis

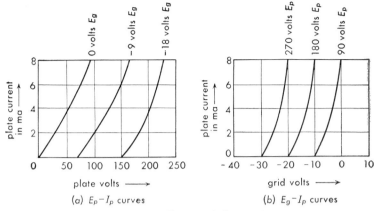

FIG. 5·5   Characteristic curves.

FIG. 5·6   Construction of typical triode.   (*Radio Corporation of America.*)

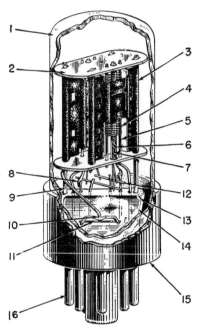

1. Envelope—lime glass
2. Spacer—mica sprayed with magnesium oxide
3. Plate—carbonized nickel or nickel-plated steel
4. Grid wires—manganese-nickel or molybdenum
5. Grid side-rods—chrome copper, nickel, or nickel-plated iron
6. Cathode—nickel coated with barium-calcium-strontium carbonates
7. Heater—tungsten or tungsten-molybdenum alloy with insulating coating of alundum
8. Cathode tab—nickel
9. Mount support—nickel or nickel-plated iron
10. Getter support and loop—nickel or nickel-plated iron
11. Getter—barium-magnesium alloys
12. Heater connector—nickel or nickel-plated iron
13. Stem lead-in wires—nickel, dumet, copper
14. Pressed stem—lead glass
15. Base—Bakelite
16. Base pins—nickel-plated brass

the y axis.   In most tube curves the y axis represents an increase in plate current while the x axis represents a change in grid or plate voltage. Since the electron tube is primarily concerned with the control of electron flow, plate current is considered the dependent variable and is usually calculated along the y axis, plotted against changes in grid and plate voltage on the x axis.

For example, Fig. 5·5a shows a family of E_p–I_p curves for three different values of grid voltage. With 0 volts on the grid and on the plate, plate current is also zero. As E_p is increased to 25 volts, I_p increases to approximately 2 ma. At 60 volts E_p, I_p has increased to 4 ma, and at 75 volts E_p, I_p has further increased to 6 ma. With −9 volts on the grid and plate voltage at 70 volts, I_p is zero. Increasing E_p to 100 volts causes an increase in I_p to 2 ma. A further increase in E_p to 150 volts causes I_p to increase to 6 ma. With −18 volts E_g, 220 volts E_p is required to produce an I_p of 6 ma. In Fig. 5·5b I_p is plotted against E_g for three different values of E_p. With +270 volts on the plate and −30 volts on the grid of the tube whose characteristics are shown graphically, I_p is zero. Holding E_p constant and reducing E_g from −30 volts to −20 volts, I_p rises to 8 ma. With 180 volts E_p and −20 volts E_g, I_p is zero, but when E_g is changed from −20 to −10 volts, I_p rises to 8 ma. With only 90 volts E_p, −10 volts on E_g will cause the tube to be cut off (no current), but when E_g is reduced to zero, I_p rises to 8 ma.

REVIEW QUESTIONS

1. Explain the action of the control grid in controlling electron flow in a triode.

2. What advantage does a triode electron tube have over a diode?

3. What is meant by (a) positive bias? (b) negative bias?

4. Explain the effect that bias has upon current.

5. What determines the amplification factor of a triode?

6. Explain the difference between static and dynamic tube characteristics.

7. If a tube requires a 20-volt increase in grid voltage to produce a change in plate current equal to that resulting from a 100-volt increase in plate voltage, what is its amplification factor?

8. In a tube having an amplification factor of 15, what change in grid voltage would be necessary to produce a change in plate current corresponding to a 300-volt increase in plate voltage?

9. Explain plate resistance and its effect upon current in a triode.

10. What is the plate resistance of a tube through which a change in plate voltage from 100 to 200 volts produces a 10-ma change in plate current?

11. Changing the plate voltage of a tube from 300 to 150 will produce what change in plate current if the plate resistance of the tube is 2,000 ohms?

12. Explain transconductance and its effect upon current in a triode.

13. What is the transconductance of a tube in which a change of 25 ma results from a 5-volt change on E_g?

14. What change in E_g would cause a 0.5-amp change in I_p in a tube having a transconductance of 500,000 micromhos?

15. Explain how a triode can be compared to a variable resistor.

16. What is a graph? Explain.

17. How are the characteristics of a tube determined?

18. Referring to the graph shown in Fig. 5·5a, what value of E_p would be required to produce 2 ma I_p with −18 volts E_g?

19. What is the main purpose for which tube characteristic curves are used?

20. Explain the relation between R_p, G_m, and μ of a triode.

21. What would probably occur within a tube if its grid was chosen from a material possessing high emission properties?

22. In the operation of an electron tube, what usually governs the value at which plate and cathode potentials are fixed? Why?

23. In an electron tube, what type of bias would result if the cathode was at ground potential and the grid was connected to a positive voltage?

24. What is meant when a tube is said to have a μ of 20?

25. What is meant by plate-current saturation?

CHAPTER 6

PARALLEL CIRCUITS

Most of the systems employed for the distribution of electrical energy consist of parallel circuits. The source voltage is connected through a pair of conductors, or feeders, to various loads, which use the energy. They can be motors, lighting circuits, toasters, television sets, or any of the many other appliances whose operation is dependent upon current.

A parallel circuit can best be described as several electrical paths between two points. The two points can be considered as the outer terminals of the source voltage and the paths the apparatus that use the electrical energy. In a series circuit, current has but one path from source through the external circuit and back to the source; in a parallel circuit it has many.

6·1 Voltage in Parallel Circuits. If two resistor loads are connected across a 25-volt battery as shown in Fig. 6·1, the voltage applied to *both* resistors will be equal to that of the source voltage, or 25 volts. If the source voltage can be imagined as a pressure like that resulting from water in a tank and the resistors as outlet pipes beneath it, then it can be seen that equal pressure will be applied to both. Therefore the following rule must be considered in solving for voltage across a parallel circuit.

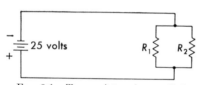

FIG. 6·1   Two resistors in parallel.

RULE: *The voltage is the same across all branches of a parallel circuit.*

6·2 Current in Parallel Circuits. The amount of current in any circuit is dependent upon the source voltage causing it and opposition offered to it. For a given voltage, a decrease in resistance will increase current. If the source voltage is considered as a constant pressure across two resistors and the resistors as two outlet paths instead of one, it is apparent that current will divide between them. There will be only a certain amount of current in a circuit having fixed values of voltage and resistance. Therefore, in the circuit shown, two separate paths are provided and the current will divide. If the resistors are of different values, current through them will be proportional to their resistance. The majority of electron movement will be through the resistor offering the smaller amount of resistance, while the remainder will be through that offering the larger resistance. Thus current will follow the path of least resistance. The following rule must be considered in solving for current in a parallel circuit.

RULE: *The total current in a parallel circuit is the sum of the currents of all the branches.*

6·3   Resistance in Parallel Circuits. In Fig. 6·1 it was found that current divided and appeared in both resistors. Since the current in each is considerably less than would appear in a single resistor of equivalent value, the total resistance offered is also less. This maintains Ohm's law of relationship between voltage, current, and resistance. In a parallel circuit the addition of paths for current effectively increases the cross-sectional area of the conductor and therefore reduces resistance. If two resistors of equal value are placed in a circuit in parallel, the resistance of both will be one-half that offered by a single resistor of the same value. Twice as much current will appear across the two resistors; therefore, the resistance offered will be halved. Further, the resistance of three equal-value resistors in parallel will be one-third the value of a single resistor. Four equal resistors in parallel will have an equivalent resistance equal to one-fourth that of one resistor. Therefore, *the more resistors in parallel, the smaller the equivalent resistance of the circuit, due to the additional paths provided.* And the equivalent resistance will be less than that of the smallest resistor.

6·4   Ohm's Law in Parallel Circuits. The relationship between voltage, current, and resistance applies in parallel as well as in series circuits. Total current in a parallel circuit is expressed as $I_t = I_1 + I_2$, where I_t is the total current in branches R_1 and R_2 through which appear currents I_1 and I_2. The total resistance in a parallel circuit is the equivalent resistance of the parallel combination. Since the source voltage is the same throughout the circuit, the relationship between the three parts of a parallel circuit can be expressed by Ohm's law as

$$E = I_t R_t$$

where E = source voltage
I_t = total current of all branches
R_t = equivalent resistance of all branches

6·5   Resistors in Parallel. The solution of a parallel circuit resolves to the reduction of the circuit to an equivalent single resistance that would replace the parallel combination without any change in voltage or current. Once equivalent resistance has been determined, solving for remaining values is simply a process of applying Ohm's law.

Figure 6·2 represents two resistors, R_1 and R_2, connected across a source voltage E. If the battery is capable of producing 12 volts, then 12 volts

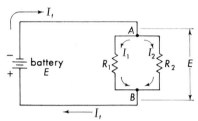

will be applied across both resistors. The total current I_t delivered by the battery in the indicated direction enters the parallel combination at junction A, divides between the two resistors, and leaves the parallel combination at junction B. Thus, the sum of currents I_1 and I_2, through R_1 and R_2, respectively, is equal to the total current I_t. From these facts, Ohm's law can be applied to show how parallel resistances combine. Thus,

FIG. 6·2 Two resistors in parallel. Current divides between R_1 and R_2, while voltage across both members of combination is equal to source voltage.

$$I_1 = \frac{E}{R_1} \qquad I_2 = \frac{E}{R_2} \qquad I_t = \frac{E}{R_t}$$

where R_t = joint resistance of R_1 and R_2. If

$$I_t = I_1 + I_2$$

the value of the currents E/R can be substituted for I, and thus

$$\frac{E}{R_t} = \frac{E}{R_1} + \frac{E}{R_2}$$

Dividing the above equation by E,

$$\frac{1}{R_t} = \frac{1}{R_1} + \frac{1}{R_2}$$

This equation states that *the reciprocal of the total resistance of a parallel circuit equals the sum of the reciprocals of the resistances in each branch.*

Since the reciprocal of resistance is *conductance*, which is the ease with which electrons flow through a conductor, it can be stated that *the total conductance of a parallel circuit is equal to the sum of the conductances in all the branches.* Or, by equation,

$$G_t = G_1 + G_2$$

Example 1: What is the joint resistance of the circuit in Fig. 6·2 if R_1 is 5 ohms and R_2 is 10 ohms?

Solution:
$$\frac{1}{R_t} = \frac{1}{R_1} + \frac{1}{R_2}$$
$$= \tfrac{1}{5} + \tfrac{1}{10} = 0.2 + 0.1 = 0.3$$

Transposing

$$R_t = \frac{1}{0.3} = 3.33 \text{ ohms}$$

Alternate Solution: A more convenient formula for determining equivalent resistance of two parallel resistances is obtained by solving for R_t in the equation

$$\frac{1}{R_t} = \frac{1}{R_1} + \frac{1}{R_2}$$

Thus

$$R_t = \frac{R_1 \times R_2}{R_1 + R_2}$$

This states that *the joint resistance of two resistors in parallel is equal to their product divided by their sum.*

Example 2: Using the alternate solution, determine the equivalent resistance of Fig. 6·2.

Solution:
$$R_t = \frac{R_1 \times R_2}{R_1 + R_2}$$

$$= \frac{5 \times 10}{5 + 10} = 3.33 \text{ ohms}$$

Example 3: What is the equivalent resistance of Fig. 6·2 if R_1 is 21 ohms and R_2 is 15 ohms? If the battery supplies 120 volts, what is the value of I_t?

Solution:
$$R_t = \frac{R_1 \times R_2}{R_1 + R_2}$$

$$= \frac{21 \times 15}{21 + 15} = 8.75 \text{ ohms}$$

$$I_t = \frac{E}{R_t} = \frac{120}{8.75} = 13.7 \text{ amp}$$

This example has an alternate solution: Since the source voltage of 120 volts exists across both resistors, the current through each may be found and added to obtain total current.

Current through R_1,

$$I_1 = \frac{E}{R_1} = \frac{120}{21} = 5.7 \text{ amp}$$

Current through R_2,

$$I_2 = \frac{E}{R_2} = \frac{120}{15} = 8 \text{ amp}$$

Therefore total current

$$I_t = I_1 + I_2 = 5.7 + 8 = 13.7 \text{ amp}$$

Proving,

$$R_t = \frac{E}{I_t} = \frac{120}{13.7} = 8.75 \text{ ohms}$$

From the foregoing it is evident that the two resistors of 21 and 15 ohms could be replaced with a single resistor of 8.75 ohms and the battery would be operating under the same load conditions.   Power in R_1 is determined by $P_1 = EI_1$; power in R_2 by $P_2 = EI_2$.

From these examples it should be apparent that current in a parallel circuit divides between the branches in inverse proportion to their resistance.   Also, as additional load resistances are added, current divides between all the paths and the equivalent resistance is reduced.

PROBLEMS

1. Find the equivalent resistance of a parallel combination containing 5 and 10 ohms.

2. A resistance of 50 ohms is connected in parallel with a resistance of 200 ohms.   What is the equivalent resistance?

3. Find the joint resistance of 300 and 250 ohms connected in parallel.

4. What is the joint resistance of 8 and 12 ohms connected in parallel?

5. Find the total resistance of two 200-ohm resistors connected in parallel.

6. State a general formula for the total resistance R_t of two equal resistors of R ohms connected in parallel.

7. In the circuit of Fig. 6·2 how many volts would be required to produce a total current of 12 amp through a parallel combination of 12 and 18 ohms?

8. How much power would be expended in the 12-ohm resistor of Prob. 7?

9. In the circuit of Fig. 6·2, $R_2 = 8.2$ ohms, $E = 32.8$ volts, and $I_t = 4.1$ amp.   What is the value of R_1?

10. How much power is expended in R_2 of Prob. 9?

11. In the circuit of Fig. 6·2, the total current of the combination is 5 amp. $R_1 = 45.3$ ohms, and the current through R_2 is 3.7 amp.   What is the resistance of R_2?

12. How much power is expended in R_2 of Prob. 11?

13. What is the equivalent resistance of 100 and 100,000 ohms connected in parallel?

14. A resistance of 440 ohms is connected across a generator that maintains a constant potential of 220 volts.   How much resistance must be connected in parallel with the 440-ohm resistor to raise the generator current to 1 amp?

15. How much power is expended in the added resistance of Prob. 14?

6·6 Three or More Resistances in Parallel.   The procedure for deriving a general equation for the equivalent resistance of three or more resistors is the same as for only two resistors.   If three resistors are connected in parallel, total current will divide among them. Then

$$I_1 = \frac{E}{R_1}, \qquad I_2 = \frac{E}{R_2}, \qquad I_3 = \frac{E}{R_3}, \qquad I_t = \frac{E}{R_t}$$

where R_t is the equivalent resistance of the parallel combination. Since

$$I_t = I_1 + I_2 + I_3$$

by substituting,

$$\frac{E}{R_t} = \frac{E}{R_1} + \frac{E}{R_2} + \frac{E}{R_3}$$

Dividing by E,

$$\frac{1}{R_t} = \frac{1}{R_1} + \frac{1}{R_2} + \frac{1}{R_3}$$

In similar fashion, it can be demonstrated that the equivalent resistance R_t of any number of resistances connected in parallel is

$$\frac{1}{R_t} = \frac{1}{R_1} + \frac{1}{R_2} + \frac{1}{R_3} + \frac{1}{R_4} + \frac{1}{R_5} + \frac{1}{R_6} + \frac{1}{R_7} + \cdots$$

Example 1: What is the equivalent resistance of the circuit in Fig. 6·3 if $R_1 = 5$ ohms, $R_2 = 10$ ohms, and $R_3 = 12.5$ ohms?

Solution:

$$\frac{1}{R_t} = \frac{1}{5} + \frac{1}{10} + \frac{1}{12.5}$$
$$= 0.2 + 0.1 + 0.08$$
$$= 0.38$$

Transposing,

$$R_t = \frac{1}{0.38} = 2.63 \text{ ohms}$$

It is also possible to find the equivalent resistance of any number of resistances in parallel by arbitrarily assuming voltage to exist across the combination. The currents through the individual branches that *would* exist if the assumed voltage were actually impressed are added to obtain the total line current. The assumed voltage divided by the total current always results in the equivalent resistance of the combination. To avoid decimal quantities of current, the assumed voltage should be numerically greater than the highest resistance of the parallel branch.

Example 2: Three resistors of 10, 15, and 45 ohms are connected in parallel. What is the value of equivalent resistance?

Solution: $E = 100$ volts across the combination (assumed voltage). Current in R_1,

$$I_1 = \frac{E}{R_1} = \frac{100}{10} = 10 \text{ amp}$$

Current in R_2,

$$I_2 = \frac{E}{R_2} = \frac{100}{15} = 6.67 \text{ amp}$$

Current in R_3,

$$I_3 = \frac{E}{R_3} = \frac{100}{45} = 2.22 \text{ amp}$$

Total current,

$$I_t = 18.89 \text{ amp}$$

Equivalent R,

$$R_t = \frac{E}{I_t} = \frac{100}{18.89} = 5.3 \text{ ohms}$$

PROBLEMS

1. Find the equivalent resistance of 10, 20, and 30 ohms connected in parallel.

2. Find the total resistance of 4, 8, and 12 ohms connected in parallel.

3. Find the resistance of 200, 250, and 300 ohms connected in parallel.

4. Find the resistance of 2.5, 5, and 3.33 ohms connected in parallel.

5. What is the equivalent resistance of 10, 20, 30, and 35 ohms connected in parallel?

6. What is the equivalent resistance of 250, 350, 450, and 550 ohms connected in parallel?

7. What is the resistance of 4.5, 8.2, 6.5, and 24.2 ohms connected in parallel?

8. What is the equivalent resistance of (*a*) three 20-ohm resistors connected in parallel and (*b*) four 20-ohm resistors connected in parallel?

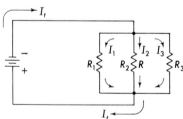

9. What is the equivalent resistance of (*a*) three 60-ohm resistors connected in parallel, (*b*) four 60-ohm resistors connected in parallel, and (*c*) five 60-ohm resistors connected in parallel?

10. State a general formula for the total resistance R_t of n equal resistors of R ohms connected in parallel.

FIG. 6·3   Three resistors in parallel.

11. In the circuit of Fig. 6·3, $R_2 = 20$ ohms, $R_3 = 90$ ohms, $I_t = 10$ amp, and $E = 110$ volts. Find the resistance of R_1.

12. In the circuit of Fig. 6·3, $E = 100$ volts, $R_1 = 80$ ohms, $R_3 = 50$ ohms, and $I_2 = 5$ amp. Find (*a*) I_t, (*b*) I_1, (*c*) I_3, and (*d*) R_2.

6·7 Mathematics. On numerous occasions the term *formula* has been used, and it will continue to be used throughout this text. The many relationships between the various quantities in electrical use are expressed as formulas. *A formula is the rule by which certain functions vary or according to which certain actions or changes take place.* It shows a scientific relationship between quantities and can be expressed by means of letters, symbols, and constant terms. The usual formula is expressed in terms of other quantities; it is often useful to solve for any quantity it contains.

Exponents and Subscripts. In several of the formulas previously used, resistors have been represented as R_1 and R_2. This is a method of distinguishing between several resistors being used in the same circuit. They could as easily have been represented as R_a or R_b, although the number designations are more commonly used.

R_1 and R_2 are read as "R sub one" and "R sub two" or simply as "R one" and "R two." Several electron tubes could be distinguished by being represented as V_1, V_2, and V_3, several switches by S_1, S_2, S_3, etc. The large letters are circuit symbols, which are defined in the appendix. They are used for ease of reference or in circuit drawings where space is a limiting factor. The small numbers or letters written at the right of and below the large letters are called *subscripts*.

Care must be taken to distinguish between *subscripts* and *exponents*. For example, R^2 is an indicated operation that means the quantity R to the second power, or $R \times R$, while R_2 is used to distinguish one quantity from another, as from R_1 or R_3.

In solving for one quantity in a formula it is often necessary to transpose the formula until the unknown quantity is the quotient or product of two or more known quantities. Once this is done, solving becomes a problem of simple multiplication or division or both.

Example 1: In the formula for Ohm's law, if E and R are known, solve for I. Given: $E = I \times R$.
Solution: Dividing both sides by R,

$$\frac{E}{R} = \frac{I \times R}{R}$$

Cancel like quantities in divisor and dividend.

$$\frac{E}{R} = \frac{I \times \cancel{R}}{\cancel{R}}$$

Therefore

$$I = \frac{E}{R}$$

where I = quotient of E/R, or result obtained by division

$\quad E$ = dividend, or number to be divided

$\quad R$ = divisor, or number by which dividend is to be divided.

Example 2: In the formula for Ohm's law, if E and I are known, solve for R. Given: $E = I \times R$.

Solution: Dividing both sides by I,

$$\frac{E}{I} = \frac{I \times R}{I}$$

Cancel like quantities in divisor and dividend.

$$\frac{E}{I} = \frac{\cancel{I} \times R}{\cancel{I}}$$

Therefore

$$R = \frac{E}{I}$$

Example 3: Given the formula, $I = \dfrac{E}{R}$, solve for E if I and R are known.

Solution: Multiplying both sides by R,

$$I \times R = \frac{E \times R}{R}$$

Cancel like quantities in divisor and dividend.

$$I \times R = \frac{E \times \cancel{R}}{\cancel{R}}$$

Therefore

$$E = I \times R$$

where E = product of factors I and R

Example 4: Solve for C, in the formula $X_C = \dfrac{1}{2\pi fC}$.

Solution: Dividing both sides by X_C,

$$\frac{X_C}{X_C} = \frac{1}{2\pi fCX_C}$$

Cancel like quantities in divisor and dividend.

$$1 = \frac{1}{2\pi fCX_C}$$

Multiplying both sides by C and canceling like quantities,

$$C = \frac{1\cancel{C}}{2\pi f\cancel{C}X_C}$$

Therefore

$$C = \frac{1}{2\pi fX_C}$$

In the following problems an attempt has been made to use formulas familiar to the field of electronics. Familiarization with methods of solving these formulas is an important consideration.

PROBLEMS

Given	*Solve for*	*Given*	*Solve for*
1. $R_t = R_1 + R_2 + R_3$	R_2	**2.** $Z^2 = R^2 + X^2$	R^2
3. $E = IZ$	I	**4.** $f = \dfrac{PN}{120}$	P
5. $R = \dfrac{KL}{m}$	L	**6.** $X_C = \dfrac{1}{2\pi fC}$	f
7. $X_L = 2\pi fL$	L	**8.** $\dfrac{E_p}{E_s} = \dfrac{N_p}{N_s}$	N_s
9. $\dfrac{I_p}{I_s} = \dfrac{N_s}{N_p}$	N_s	**10.** $F = HLi$	L
11. $Q = 0.24EIt$	t	**12.** $Gm = \dfrac{\mu}{R_p}$	μ
13. $Y_f = Y_b - 2m$	Y_b	**14.** $I_p E_p = I_s E_s$	I_s
15. $C = \dfrac{Q}{V}$	Q	**16.** $C = 0.08842K\dfrac{A}{d}$	K
17. $Q = \dfrac{\omega L}{R}$	R	**18.** $L = 1.26N^2P \times 10^{-8}$	P
19. $H = \dfrac{4\pi N_i}{L}$	N_i	**20.** $e_p = E_p - iR_L$	R_L

REVIEW QUESTIONS

1. How do parallel and series circuits basically differ?

2. Why is voltage the same across all branches of a parallel circuit?

3. What is the relation between current and the several resistances that form a parallel circuit?

4. Explain how an increase in the number of individual resistors will decrease the equivalent resistance of a parallel circuit.

5. What is conductance and how is it related to resistance?

6. When voltage is not known, how is it possible to find the equivalent resistance of a parallel combination by assuming that a certain value of voltage exists across the combination?

7. Define formula.

8. Explain exponents and subscripts, and distinguish between them as to use.

9. How is Ohm's law applicable to parallel as well as series circuits?

10. Why do parallel circuits enjoy more common usage than series circuits?

CHAPTER 7

COMBINATION CIRCUITS

Electric circuits are by no means limited to simple series circuits and simple parallel circuits. The two are often combined in order to utilize the advantages of both within the same circuit while minimizing their disadvantages. As circuits become more complex, circuit tracing and methods of calculating values of circuit components under different conditions become important considerations. However, it must be remembered that *all circuits are comprised of nothing more than series and parallel arrangements.*

7·1 Combination Circuit. A combination circuit is so named because it consists of both series and parallel circuits. Figure 7·1 shows a series

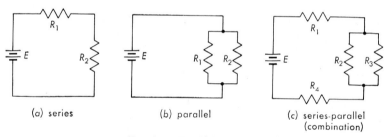

| (a) series | (b) parallel | (c) series-parallel (combination) |

FIG. 7·1 Typical circuits.

circuit, a parallel circuit, and a combination of the two. Series circuits have the same current through all members, and the sum of all voltage drops throughout the circuit is equal to the source voltage. In parallel circuits the sum of the currents in all members equals the total current, while voltage across any particular member is equal to the source voltage and to the voltage across any other member. Combining the features of these two circuits is the key to solving for values in combination circuits.

7·2 Voltage across a Combination Circuit. In Fig. 7·1c, with R_2 and R_3 of equal value, the voltage drop across R_2 is equal to the drop across R_3. As in any series circuit, the source voltage is equal to the total of the drops across all parts of the circuit. In order to determine the voltage drop across each part of the circuit shown, it is necessary first to determine the drop across the series resistors, then to add it to the drop across the parallel branch. Because two resistors in parallel are involved, it is necessary to apply Ohm's law for either resistor in order to determine equivalent resistance. Since current is the same in all parts of the series members, this current appears at the junction of the parallel members which are in series with the remainder of the circuit. The current divides into two paths upon entering the parallel network, one path through R_2 and the other through R_3. If the current through one path and the resistance of the path are known, then Ohm's law will apply in solving for the voltage drop across that resistor. Further, since it is a parallel network, the voltage drop will be the same across the other parallel resistor. The sum of the drops across the parallel branch and those across the series parts will equal source voltage.

7·3 Resistance in a Combination Circuit. The total resistance of a combination circuit can be computed by first determining the equivalent resistance of all parallel branches and then adding this to the series resistances. The sum of all series and equivalent resistances is the total resistance of the circuit. Referring to Fig. 7·1c it is evident that if the voltage is distributed across each resistance and current is constant, then resistance must also be a distributed factor. Therefore, although total voltage in a combination circuit is a product of total resistance and total current, individual voltage drops must be computed across individual resistances.

The following rule should be considered in solving for circuit values in a combination circuit.

RULE: *Regardless of the type of combination circuit involved, first reduce the parallel branches to equivalent series circuits and then combine these with the series parts.*

7·4 Solving Combination Circuits. The process of solving for both conditions and component values in a combination circuit is merely an expansion of the methods employed for series or parallel systems. Although no complete set of rules can be formulated for the solution of all types of combination circuits, the following examples are intended to cover most of the circuits likely to be encountered.

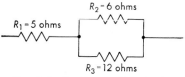

FIG. 7·2 Series-parallel circuit.

Example 1: Find the total resistance of the circuit shown in Fig. 7·2.

Solution: Since the parallel branch is in series with R_1 and the equivalent resistance of the parallel branch is

$$\frac{R_2 \times R_3}{R_2 + R_3}$$

the circuit resolves itself into two resistances in series, the total resistance of which can be expressed by

$$R_t = R_1 + \frac{R_2 \times R_3}{R_2 + R_3}$$

$$= 5 + \frac{6 \times 12}{6 + 12} = 9 \text{ ohms}$$

Example 2: Find the total resistance of the circuit shown in Fig. 7·3.

Solution: This circuit is similar to that shown in Fig. 7·2, except for the addition of another parallel branch. Therefore, after the equivalent resistances of the two parallel branches are found, the circuit is resolved into three series resistances. Thus,

$$R_t = R_1 + \frac{R_2 \times R_3}{R_2 + R_3} + \frac{R_4 \times R_5}{R_4 + R_5}$$

$$= 10 + \frac{8 \times 4}{8 + 4} + \frac{15 \times 20}{15 + 20} = 21.2 \text{ ohms}$$

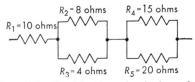

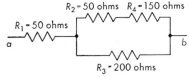

FIG. 7·3 Combination circuit for solving R_t.

FIG. 7·4 Combination circuit for solving R_t.

Example 3: Find the total resistance between points a and b in Fig. 7·4.

Solution: Since R_2 and R_4 are in series, they must be added before combining with R_3 to determine equivalent resistance of the branch. After equivalent resistance has been determined, the circuit is reduced to two resistances in series. Therefore, the total resistance can be found

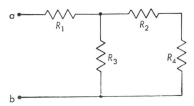

FIG. 7·5 Equivalent circuit of Fig. 7·4.

by

$$R_t = R_1 + \frac{R_3 \times (R_2 + R_4)}{R_3 + (R_2 + R_4)}$$

$$= 50 + \frac{200 \times (50 + 150)}{200 + (50 + 150)} = 150 \text{ ohms}$$

Note that the circuit in Fig. 7·4 is identical to that in Fig. 7·5, although it may at first appear different. As shown in Fig. 7·5, it is known as a *T pad*.

Example 4: What is the total resistance between points a and b in Fig. 7·6?

Solution: In many instances a circuit that appears complicated can be better understood and analyzed by being redrawn in a simplified form. For example, Fig. 7·7 is a simplified drawing of Fig. 7·6. To solve, find the equivalent resistance of the parallel combination R_2, R_3, and R_4. Add this resistance to R_6, and the result will be the resistance R_{cd} between points c and d. Combine R_{cd} with R_5, which is in parallel, and the result will be the equivalent resistance R_{ef} between points e and f. The circuit is now reduced to an equivalence of R_1, R_{ef}, and R_7 in series. Adding these will give the total resistance R_{ab} between points a and b.

The joint resistance of R_2, R_3, and R_4 is 1.67 ohms, which, when added to R_6, results in a resistance of 6.67 ohms between points c and d. The equivalent

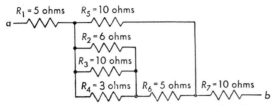

FIG. 7·6   Combination circuit for solving R_t.

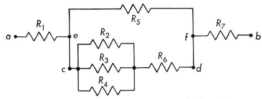

FIG. 7·7   Equivalent circuit of Fig. 7·6.

resistance between points e and f, formed by R_{ed} and R_5 in parallel, is 4 ohms. Therefore the total resistance between points a and b is

$$R_{ab} = R_1 + R_{ef} + R_7 = 19 \text{ ohms}$$

7·5 Bridge Circuits.   Figure 7·8 shows two groups of series resistors connected in parallel.   In Fig. 7·9 this same circuit is shown redrawn

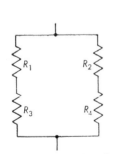

FIG. 7·8   Simple bridge circuit.

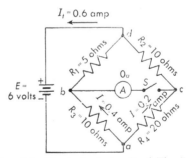

FIG. 7·9   Equivalent circuit of Fig. 7·8.

with the addition of a meter and source voltage.   This is known as a *Wheatstone-bridge* circuit, and it is used to measure unknown values of resistance.

Between R_1 and R_2 there exists a whole-number relationship, or ratio. A similar ratio exists between R_3 and R_4, even though the values of R_1 and R_3 are different as are the values of R_2 and R_4.   The direction of current is through the circuit from the negative terminal of the source to point a, where it branches into separate paths. One path is through R_4 and R_2 to point d; the other through R_3 and R_1 to point d, where both paths combine. Total current appears from d to the positive terminal of the battery. With 6 volts applied, current through the series combination of R_4 and R_2 will be 0.2 amp, while current through the other branch will be 0.4 amp. Therefore, voltage drops around the circuit are as follows: across R_1, 2 volts; R_3, 4 volts; R_2, 2 volts; and R_4, 4 volts.

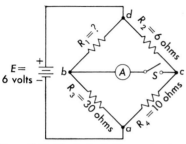

If the switch is closed and the ammeter is connected into the circuit as shown, there will be no current between points b and c, because they are at the same potential. Under these conditions the bridge is said to be *balanced*. This balanced condition exists only when the ratio between R_1 and R_2 is

Fig. 7·10 Typical bridge circuit used for measuring unknown resistances.

equal to that between R_3 and R_4. Expressed as an equation, the bridge is balanced when

$$\frac{R_1}{R_2} = \frac{R_3}{R_4}$$

The bridge shown in Fig. 7·10 is typical of the circuits used for measuring unknown resistances. R_2, R_3, and R_4 are known values, while the resistance to be measured is substituted for R_1. Since the ratio between R_3 and R_4 is known and the same ratio must exist between R_1 and R_2 when the bridge is balanced, determining the value of an unknown resistance (R_1 in this example) is a matter of substituting and transposing. Thus

$$R_1 = \frac{R_2 R_3}{R_4}$$

$$= \frac{6 \times 30}{10} = 18 \text{ ohms}$$

The bridge circuit is used in electronics to measure unknown resistances accurately. When the values of R_2, R_3, and R_4 and the ratio between R_3 and R_4 are known, it is possible to determine the value of any unknown resistor R_x.

7·6 Resistance Ratio. There are definite relationships that exist between two resistors in parallel. For example, two 10-ohm resistors would have an equivalent resistance of 5 ohms, or one-half that of either resistor. A 5-ohm and a 10-ohm resistor would have an equivalent resistance of 3.33 ohms, or one-third that of the larger resistor (R_L) and two-thirds the resistance of the smaller (R_S).   This relationship applies in all instances where there is a whole-number ratio between two parallel resistors.   As a time-saving aid, some of the ratios and equivalent resistances are shown in the following table.

R_S/R_L	Equivalent R
1:1	$\frac{1}{2}R_L$
1:2	$\frac{1}{3}R_L$
1:3	$\frac{1}{4}R_L$
1:4	$\frac{1}{5}R_L$
1:5	$\frac{1}{6}R_L$
1:6	$\frac{1}{7}R_L$
1:7	$\frac{1}{8}R_L$
1:8	$\frac{1}{9}R_L$
1:9	$\frac{1}{10}R_L$

REVIEW QUESTIONS

1. Using the table in Sec. 7.6, what is the joint resistance of a 5-ohm and a 35-ohm resistor in parallel?

2. What is the general procedure for solving values in a combination circuit?

3. Explain the ratio that must exist for a bridge circuit to be balanced.

4. In a balanced bridge circuit, $R_1 = 10$ ohms, $R_3 = 20$ ohms, and $R_4 = 120$ ohms. What is the value of R_2?

5. What is the equivalent resistance of the circuit in Question 4?

6. In the circuit of Fig. 7·11, $R_1 = 7.1$ ohms, $R_2 = 11.2$ ohms, $I_t = 19$ amp, and the voltage E across R_3 is 40 volts.   Find (a) I_2, (b) I_3, (c) R_3, (d) R_t, and (e) E_g.

7. In the circuit of Fig. 7·11, $R_1 = 10$ ohms, $R_2 = 20$ ohms, $R_3 = 250$ ohms, and $I_t = 10$ amp.   Find the voltage across R_1.

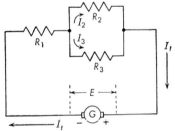   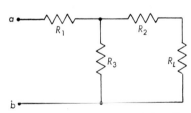

FIG. 7·11   Circuit for solving component values.

FIG. 7·12   Circuit for solving R_t.

8. In Question 7, if R_2 is open, how much power will be expended in R_3?

9. In Question 7, if R_3 is open, how much power will be expended in R_1?

10. In the circuit of Fig. 7·12, $R_1 = 250$ ohms, $R_2 = 200$ ohms, $R_3 = 200$ ohms, $E = 110$ volts, and $I_t = 0.3$ amp.   What is the resistance of R_L?

11. In Question 10, if R_1 is shorted, what will be the resistance between points a and b?

12. In the circuit of Fig. 7·13, $R_1 = 80$ ohms, $R_2 = 800$ ohms, $R_3 = 100$ ohms, $E = 100$ volts, and $I_t = 0.4$ amp.   What is the resistance of R_4?

13. In the circuit of Fig. 7·13, $R_1 = 250$ ohms, $R_2 = 200$ ohms, $R_3 = 400$ ohms, and $R_4 = 500$ ohms.   If 110 volts exists across R_4, what is the value of E?

14. How much power is being taken from the generator in Question 13?

15. In the circuit of Fig. 7·13 if the load resistor R_4 is shorted, what will be the current through R_3?

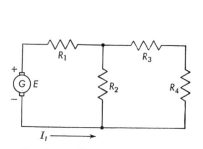

FIG. 7·13 Circuit for solving R_t.

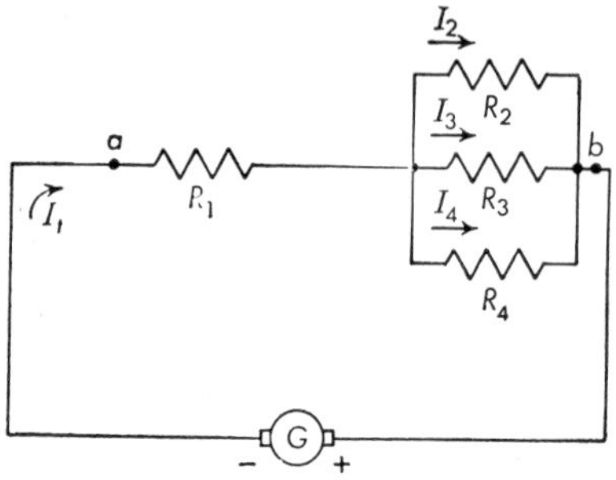

FIG. 7·14 Circuit for solving component values.

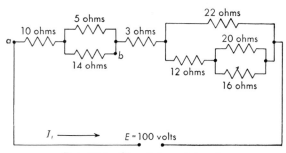

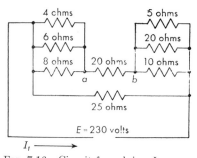

FIG. 7·15 Circuit for solving I_t.

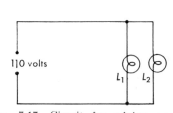

FIG. 7·16 Circuit for solving I_t.

FIG. 7·17 Circuit for solving current through L_1.

16. In the circuit of Fig. 7·14 the voltage across points a and b is 30 volts, $I_t = 4.5$ amp, $R_2 = 12$ ohms, $I_2 = 1.5$ amp, and $R_3 = 15$ ohms. Find (a) R_1, (b) R_4, (c) R_t, and (d) current through R_3.

17. What will be the current in the circuit of Fig. 7·15?

18. What will be the current in the circuit of Fig. 7·16?

19. How much power will be expended in the circuit of Fig. 7·16 if points a and b are shorted together?

20. In Fig. 7·17, if L_2 burns out, how will current through L_1 be affected?

CHAPTER 8

PRINCIPLES OF MAGNETISM

The principle of magnetism is utilized to perform many important functions in electronic equipment. Like electricity, magnetism is an invisible force; however, its effects are evident in the numerous devices whose operation is dependent upon magnetic action. Loud-speakers, telephones, transmitters, transformers, motors, generators, relays, antennas, television receivers, and record players are a few of those dependent upon magnets or magnetic fields.

Because electricity can produce a magnetic field around a conductor and magnetism can cause electrons to flow, the two properties work together in performing the numerous functions required by electronic circuits.

8·1   Magnets. Magnetism is one of the elementary forms of energy, generated by the motion of electrons through certain materials and characterized by the attraction it exerts on other materials. The property of magnetism is peculiar to materials such as nickel, iron, and cobalt, but is most pronounced in iron and some of its alloys.

The phenomenon of magnetism has been known since ancient times. Pieces of *lodestone* were found to attract each other and also to attract iron. Further, it was found that pieces of this mineral, if suspended by a string, would align themselves in a north-south direction with respect to the axis of the earth and return to that position if moved. Experiments proved that two points on the lodestone exerted the most attraction for iron and that these two points corresponded to the parts of the mineral that pointed to north and south. Thus, it was concluded that magnets also possess north and south *poles*.

The molecular theory of magnetism is that each molecule of a magnet is in itself a magnet. Before a magnetic material is magnetized, its molecules are arranged haphazardly as shown in Fig. 8·1a and neutralize the attraction the material would otherwise possess. After being magnetized, the molecules of a material align with their north poles pointing in one direction as shown in Fig. 8·1b. After being magnetized, either pole of the material will attract any unmagnetized magnetic substance,

ELEMENTS OF ELECTRONICS

although the north pole of one magnet will repel the north pole of another. This is in conformity with the law of charges.

Natural Magnets. A natural magnet is any material which, in its natural state, displays magnetic properties. The lodestone is the chemical compound magnetic oxide of iron, or *magnetite.* Natural magnets seldom have enough magnetic strength to be useful in electronics. Their

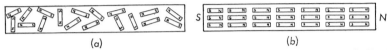

(a)   (b)

Fig. 8·1 Arrangement of molecules in magnetic material (a) before and (b) after magnetization.

use is generally limited to demonstrations, although a few are used in magnetic compasses. It has been proved that artificial magnets provide greater accuracy even in navigational instruments.

Natural magnets are also restricted in use, since they should be used in their natural shape. The application of force in an attempt to shape a natural magnet will quite often result in loss of its magnetism.

Artificial Magnets. Most magnets in current use are artificial. These may be made in several ways. For example, if a piece of hard steel is stroked continuously in the same direction by a piece of magnetite, the steel will become magnetized and possess a north and a south pole. Further, it will attract other unmagnetized magnetic materials and conform to the law of charges by attracting the unlike pole and repelling the like pole of another magnet.

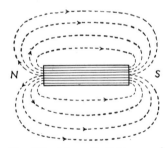

Fig. 8·2 Magnetic field around a bar magnet.

Because the molecular magnets within a magnetic material set up a magnetic force among themselves, the total force of the magnet is the sum of the forces of the molecular magnets, and a field exists around the magnet. This is shown in Fig. 8·2. If a piece of iron is placed within this field, parallel to the magnet, an artificial magnet will be produced. The part of the iron closest to the north pole of the magnet becomes the south pole of the new magnet. Conversely, the opposite end of the iron, which is nearest the south pole of the magnet, will become the north pole of the new magnet. This is known a producing a magnet through *induction.*

Artificial magnets can be made with many times the strength of natural magnets. Also, size and shape present no design problem, because the material can be first made in the size and shape desired, then magnetized. Another advantage of artificial magnets is their ability to retain magnetism either permanently or for long periods of time. Further, they can be designed to be magnetized and demagnetized as desired.

8·2 Types of Artificial Magnets. The ability of a magnetic material to retain its magnetism after the magnetizing force has been removed is called its *retentivity*. Generally, the harder the material, the greater its retentivity. For example, steel has great retentivity while soft iron has very little retentivity.

Temporary Magnets. A magnetic material having little retentivity is known as a temporary magnet. Generally, temporary magnets are those which remain magnetic only so long as the magnetizing force is present. Once the magnetizing force is removed, the material returns to approximately its normal state. Iron, nickel, and even soft steel are three of the magnetic materials that will lose practically all their magnetism when removed from the magnetizing force and are, therefore, temporary magnets.

Permanent Magnets. A magnetic material having high retentivity is known as a permanent magnet. Such a material will remain magnetic long after the magnetizing force has been removed. Hardened steel and some of its alloys are commonly used as permanent magnets for meters, loud-speakers, record-player pickups, and other equipment dependent on magnetic action.

When a magnetic material has been magnetized and the force causing the magnetism has been removed, the magnetism which the material retains is called the residue, or *residual magnetism*. When the magnetizing force has been removed from a temporary magnet, all the magnetism should disappear. However, there is no perfectly temporary magnet, and some residual magnetism will remain. Where only a small amount of residual magnetism will remain in a temporary magnet after the magnetizing force has been removed, in a permanent magnet the remaining magnetism almost equals that present while the magnetizing force was applied.

8·3 Magnetic Fields. Surrounding any magnet is a *field* of force, which is strongest in the immediate vicinity of the magnet and progressively weaker at greater distances. This is known as a *magnetic field* and is represented by a number of *lines of force* radiating out from the north pole and entering the south pole of a magnet. The lines of force are considered to be in a constant state of motion and are called *flux*. Although these flux lines are an invisible force, their strength can be measured in terms of their effects. Figure 8·2 shows the magnetic field in and about a bar magnet. The intensity of the magnetic field is measured in units called *oersteds*.

The term *flux density* refers to the number of flux lines per unit area. The total number of flux lines emanating from a magnet, divided by the area in which the flux exists, yields the flux density in lines per square centimeter, or gauss.   Figure 8·3 illustrates this concept of flux density.

A quantity that must be known in order to determine flux density, or gauss, is the magnetic force required to set up a given number of lines in a material having a given magnetic quality.   Similarly, in an electric circuit, the voltage required to produce a given current through a material of a given resistance must be known.

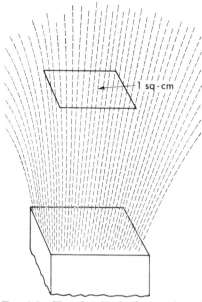

8·4   Characteristics of Magnetic Lines of Force.   There are certain definite patterns of behavior characteristic of lines of force around any magnet.   For example, each flux line follows the path of a closed circuit.   That is, each line leaves the magnet at its north pole and completes its closed course by entering at the south pole.   Also, one flux line will not cross another flux line.   Each line is approximately parallel to those adjacent.   Although the lines of force may describe various arcs, they will always form a complete path from one end of the magnet to the other.

FIG. 8·3   Flux density is the number of lines through a given area; here 1 sq cm.

Another characteristic of a magnet is that lines traveling in the same direction will repel one another.   This can also be seen in Fig. 8·2 where each flux line progressively increases in distance from the next as they leave the magnet.   Conversely, as later discussed, lines traveling in opposite directions will attract each other.   An example of both attraction and repulsion of flux lines is shown in Fig. 8·4.   Two bar magnets are placed close together with like poles together and a repelling action exists.   When unlike poles are placed together, an attraction exists.

Poles.   The two main parts of any magnetized material where the flux lines are concentrated are called its poles.   The pole that seeks the earth's north magnetic pole is called the north-seeking pole, or N pole. The other seeks the earth's south magnetic pole and is called the south-seeking pole, or S pole.   Every magnet has both a north and a south pole. Further, if a long, thin object such as a steel needle is magnetized and then broken in half, each half will become a magnet and possess both a north and a south pole.   If these halves are again broken and rebroken, each small piece is still a magnet and will possess poles. This demonstrates the molecular theory of magnetism, by which each molecule of a magnetic material is considered to be a magnet with a north and a south pole.

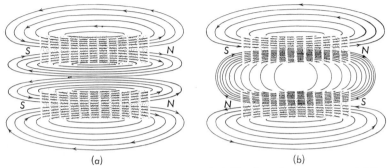

(a)   (b)

FIG. 8·4 Diagrams showing effects of magnetic fields of two bar magnets. (a) Repulsion. (b) Attraction.

8·5 Magnetization. The density and total number of lines of force surrounding a magnet are in direct proportion to the magnet's strength. The greatest portion of field strength is expended in forcing the lines from the north to the south pole through the air. Only a small portion is required to force the lines from south to north within the magnet. Since lines of force always follow the path of least resistance, the strength of a magnet can be preserved by providing an easier path for the flux lines when traveling outside the magnet. If a magnet is placed inside a soft iron ring as shown in Fig. 8·5, the lines will encounter a low-resistance path and the magnet will retain its strength longer than if surrounded by air.

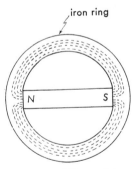

FIG. 8·5 Effect of iron on magnetic path.

Magnetization by Induction. If a magnetic material is placed within the magnetic field of a magnet, the material will become magnetized. This is known as magnetization by induction, since magnetism is induced into the magnetic material. The new magnet will then possess its own poles, positioned in such a direction as to create an attraction between the two magnets. In Fig. 8·6 the shaded member represents a magnet and the unshaded member a piece of soft iron. Lines of flux leave the north pole of the magnet and travel through the soft iron to the south pole of the magnet. This reorients the haphazard molecular arrangement within the soft iron, and it becomes a magnet. The molecules align themselves in the direction of the flux lines, and the new magnet forms its poles as shown.

Magnetic Shapes. Since most of a magnet's strength is expended in forcing flux lines through the air, the smaller the *air gap*, the longer a

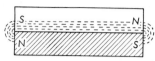

magnet's strength will last. A magnet in the shape of a horseshoe has a smaller air gap than a bar magnet and therefore retains its strength for a longer period. In addition,

Fig. 8·6 Magnetization by induction.

because the lines of force are concentrated at the ends of certain types of magnets, placing these ends close together will result in an increase in flux density. Therefore, the shape of a magnet has a decided effect upon both its strength and its life.

Magnetic Screens. Although there is no known material which will prevent the passage of flux lines, a magnetic material is often used as a

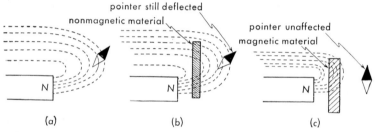

Fig. 8·7   Effect of magnetic and nonmagnetic materials on flux lines.

screen to alter the path of flux lines. Figure 8·7a shows an iron pointer placed in the vicinity of a magnet and being deflected because of the magnetic field. If a nonmagnetic material is placed between the pointer and the magnet, the magnetic lines will remain unaffected and the pointer will continue to deflect. However, if a magnetic material is placed between the pointer and magnet, as shown in Fig. 8·7c, a low-resistance path is offered for the flux lines. The path of the flux lines is altered and the pointer is *screened* from the magnet. Figure 8·8 is an example of the method used to shield nonmagnetic watch mechanisms from a magnetic field. The soft iron ring around the watch mechanism offers a path of low resistance to flux lines in case the watch should be subjected to the influence of a magnetic field.

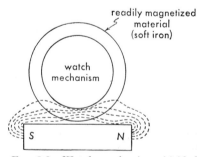

Fig. 8·8   Watch mechanism shielded against magnetic fields.

8·6 Constructing and Aging Magnets. A simple bar magnet is not very practical for use in electronic equipment. The horseshoe magnet, for example, has been found much more useful because of the stronger field caused by placing the poles closer together. It has also been found that a magnet constructed of *laminations*, or thin layers, of metal is more powerful than one of equal weight constructed of solid metal. This is mainly due to the even tempering possible with thin material but not possible with thicker material.

Because a permanent magnet becomes weaker with age, magnets are artificially aged by heating them to temperatures just below the point where the material would become soft. Because heat increases molecular activity within a material, the molecules of a magnet will often resume their haphazard arrangement if overheated. Aging the magnet through heat is a process of reducing the magnetic strength to a point of steady value that would ordinarily result from years of use. Thereafter, the magnet's strength remains constant and is not affected by temperature variations.

Physical shock can also reduce the strength of a magnet by causing some of its molecules to be literally knocked out of alignment. This reduces the contribution of their attraction to the total magnetism of the material. Magnets are therefore protected from physical shock as much as possible.

8·7 Permeability. The ratio of flux lines in a material to the flux lines that would exist if the material was replaced by air is called its *permeability* μ. The permeability of air is taken as 1. Nonmagnetic materials have a permeability of 1 or less, while magnetic materials have a permeability greater than 1. For example, the permeability of commercial iron and steel ranges from 50 to about 2,000. The permeability of a material can be determined by the formula

$$\mu = \frac{B}{H}$$

where B = flux density, lines per sq cm, or gauss

H = field intensity, oersteds

Diamagnetic Materials. A diamagnetic, or nonmagnetic, material when placed in a strong magnetic field will become only very weakly magnetized but in a direction opposite to that of the magnetizing field. Flux lines will tend to bypass the material; however, those that do pass through it will be a greater distance apart than when traveling through air. Diamagnetic materials have a permeability of less than 1.

Paramagnetic Materials. A paramagnetic material is one having a maximum permeability of less than 1 per cent more than air and will become weakly magnetized by a strong magnetic field in the same direction as the field.

Ferromagnetic Materials.   Any material that will become strongly magnetized by a weak field in the same direction as the field is called ferromagnetic.   Ferromagnetic materials have a high permeability and display few of the characteristics of the other two types.

8·8   Terrestrial Magnetism.   The phenomenon resulting from the fact that the earth is an enormous permanent magnet is called *terrestrial magnetism.*   The generally accepted theory is that the earth's core is iron

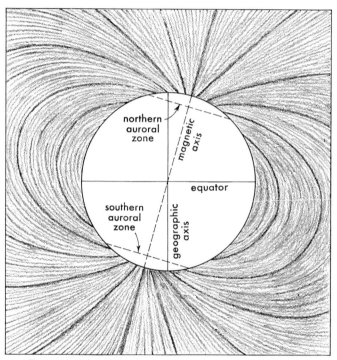

Fig. 8·9   Direction of magnetic forces around the earth.

which has become magnetized in some hitherto unexplained manner. Although this core is believed to be molten, which would suggest that it could not retain magnetism, the fact that the magnetic poles shift about is more consistent with the theory of a molten than with that favoring a solid core.   The average distance between the magnetic and geographic poles is approximately 1,350 miles at the north poles and 1,050 miles at the south poles.   Moreover, the shifting of the poles results in a change in the direction of the earth's magnetic field.   Magnetic storms also cause changes in both direction and intensity of the terrestrial magnetic fields.

Magnetic storms are the disturbances caused by *sunspot* activity. It is believed that sunspots are simply clouds of electrons or protons at or near the surface of the sun. Terrestrial magnetism could be caused by the magnetized core of the earth. It is also quite likely that it could be caused by the streams of electrons and protons in the sunspots. The latter theory is borne out by the fact that serious disturbances affect wire and radio communications during periods of severe sunspot activity. Currents near the earth's surface during these magnetic storms produce high voltages in telephone cables and lines which sometimes render the signals useless.

REVIEW QUESTIONS

1. List six practical applications of magnetism.
2. What is a lodestone?
3. What are three disadvantages of a natural magnet?
4. What is an artificial magnet?
5. What are sunspots thought to be?
6. What is a magnetic storm?
7. Explain the theory regarding the earth's magnetization.
8. In what way does sunspot activity affect wire communications?
9. Explain flux density.
10. Define residual magnetism.
11. List three advantages of an artificial magnet.
12. Define retentivity.
13. How does the residual magnetism of a temporary magnet compare with that of a permanent magnet?
14. List three characteristics of magnetic lines of force.
15. How does the law of charges apply to the poles of a magnet?
16. How are the poles of a magnet determined?
17. How is magnetic shielding accomplished?
18. What is a ferromagnetic material?
19. What kind of material would be called highly permeable?
20. Describe the process of aging magnets.
21. What is purpose of the aging process?
22. What is meant by magnetization by induction?
23. Explain the molecular theory of magnetism.
24. What kind of material would have a low retentivity?
25. A magnet has a permeability of 7 and a flux density of 500 gauss. What is its field intensity?

CHAPTER 9

ELECTROMAGNETISM AND MAGNETIC CIRCUITS

Although permanent magnets have many practical applications in electronic equipment, temporary magnetism produced by current through a conductor is used in almost every electronic device known.

It was long suspected that a definite relationship existed between magnetism and electricity, but it was not until 1819 that a Danish physicist, Hans Oersted, determined this relationship. He proved that all electric current is surrounded by a magnetic field. This later led to the belief that molecular magnets are created by the minute electric currents within the molecules.

The term *magnetic* applies to the theories and laws of magnetism alone, while *electromagnetic* applies to both electricity and magnetism.

9·1 Electromagnetic Field. There is at all times a continuous movement of free electrons within any conducting material. Each of these

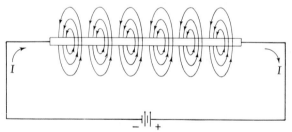

Fig. 9·1   Lines of force around a conductor.

electrons exerts a small force of attraction. However, there is no definite pattern of electron movement, and the over-all magnetic effect is near zero.

If a voltage is applied to a conductor as shown in Fig. 9·1, electron movement is no longer random. Electron flow through the conductor in one direction causes the molecules to align. The conductor becomes magnetized, and a magnetic field is set up around it. This magnetic field takes the form of concentric circles which diminish in intensity with progressive distance from the conductor.

Field Direction.   Current through a conductor will produce a *magnetic field whose direction is at right angles both to the conductor and to the direction of current.*   If the direction of the current through the conductor is reversed, the direction of the magnetic lines of force will also be reversed. If a small magnetized pointer is placed in the magnetic field caused by

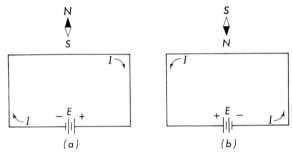

Fig. 9·2   Reversal of magnetic field around a conductor by reversal of current.

current through a conductor, as shown in Fig. 9·2*a*, it will take the position shown.   If the current through the conductor is reversed in direction, the pointer will also reverse its direction.   Therefore, it is logical to assume that the direction of the magnetic lines of force around the conductor has also reversed.

Polarity cannot be assigned in a single electromagnetic field, since there is physically no magnet to which such an assignment can be made.

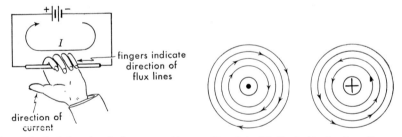

Fig. 9·3   Left-hand rule for magnetism.   Fig. 9·4   Method of indicating direction of current and flux lines.

However, if the direction of current is known, the *left-hand rule* can be used to determine the direction of lines of force around the conductor.

RULE: *Hold the left hand with the thumb pointing in the direction of current, and the curled fingers will indicate the direction of flux lines.*

An example of the left-hand rule is shown in Fig. 9·3.

Figure 9·4 is a pictorial method of expressing direction of flux lines around a conductor.   The $\oplus$ indicates that the direction of current is away from the observer, while the $\odot$ indicates that the current is directed toward the observer.

Field Strength.   Figure 9·5 shows the effect of voltage and current on the strength of an electromagnetic field.   In *a* the magnetized pointer is suspended outside the field caused by current through the conductor. Since a small source voltage is used, current is small and a weak magnetic field is produced around the conductor.   If the voltage is increased by the addition of another battery, as shown in *b*, current will increase. This increase in current causes a stronger magnetic field to exist around the conductor, and the pointer will align itself with this field.   This proves that current through a conductor governs the strength of the field around it.

RULE: *The strength of a magnetic field around a conductor is directly proportional to current through the conductor.*

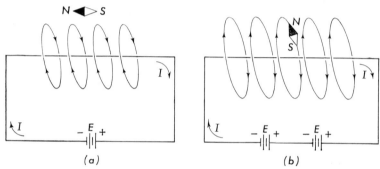

FIG. 9·5   Effect of voltage on magnetic field.

9·2   Field Produced by a Coil.   Since the direction of a magnetic field can be determined, it is possible to determine the effects of two fields upon each other.   Figure 9·6*a* shows two adjacent conductors carrying current in the same direction.   Although the current is in the same direction, the lines of force around the conductors are in opposite directions to each other at the point of tangency.   The flux lines between the two conductors will tend to neutralize each other while those on the outer side will combine with a result as shown.   This is in conformity with the law of charges, which states that lines traveling in opposite directions attract each other.   If either of the conductors were free to move, it would be attracted to the other.

In Fig. 9·6*b* there is current in opposite directions through adjacent conductors.   The lines between the two conductors are in the same direction at the point of tangency and oppose each other.   A resultant magnetic field will be produced at right angles to a plane between the two conductors, and if one conductor were free to move, it would be repelled by the other.   This also conforms to the law of charges, which states that lines of force traveling in the same direction repel each other.   The lines of force between the two conductors in a are traveling in opposite directions, although current through the two conductors is in the same direction. Further, those in b are traveling in the same direction, even though current is in opposite directions.

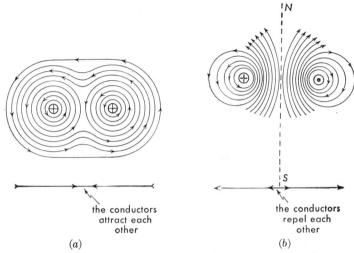

<table>
<tr><td style="text-align:center">the conductors
attract each
other
(a)</td><td style="text-align:center">the conductors
repel each
other
(b)</td></tr>
</table>

FIG. 9·6 (a) Attracting magnetic fields around two current-carrying conductors. (b) Opposing magnetic fields around two current-carrying conductors.

A wire coiled in the form of a spring is known as a *solenoid*. It will produce a magnetic field as shown in Fig. 9·7a when carrying current. If the solenoid is placed around a soft-iron bar, known as the *core*, the resultant field will cause the bar to become a temporary magnet. Figure

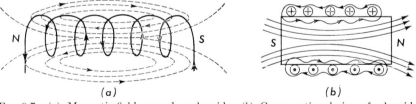

(a)   (b)

FIG. 9·7 (a) Magnetic field around a solenoid. (b) Cross-sectional view of solenoid.

9·7b represents a cross-sectional view of the solenoid and core with current entering the top conductors and leaving the bottom conductors. Since current is in the same direction in both the top and the bottom conductors, the lines about each conductor will combine with those of the others and the resultant field will be as shown. The direction of flux can be determined by application of the left-hand rule, which can also be used to determine the poles of the circuit. *With the curled fingers of the left hand pointing in the direction of current in a solenoid, the thumb will indicate the direction of the north pole of the magnetic field.*

Field Strength.   The strength of the magnetic field produced by a solenoid varies directly with current.   As current increases, field strength increases; conversely, a decrease in current will cause a decrease in field strength.

The number of turns also affects field strength.   As the number of turns is increased, field strength will also increase because of the greater concentration of flux lines.

The permeability of the iron core also directly governs field strength. Where a low-permeability core will retard the flux lines and prevent concentration, a high-permeability core will concentrate the lines.   The concentration of lines conserves power otherwise lost in making a complete magnetic path for the flux lines.

9·3   The Magnetic Circuit.   The main similarity between a magnetic circuit and an electric circuit is that a force of unit quantity is necessary to overcome a unit of opposition.   The force producing magnetizing action in a magnetic circuit is known as *magnetomotive force* (mmf).   In electricity there is an electron-moving force, or *electromotive force* (emf). One applies to magnetism and is measured in gilberts, while the other applies to electricity and is measured in volts.   The magnetic counterparts of voltage, current, and resistance are magnetomotive force, flux, and *reluctance*, respectively.   Ohm's law for magnetic circuits is

$$F = \Phi \mathfrak{R}$$

where F = magnetomotive force, gilberts
    Φ = flux, maxwells (the electromagnetic unit of magnetic flux)
    $\mathfrak{R}$ = reluctance

The reluctance of a material is its property which opposes the passage of flux lines through it.   Like resistance, reluctance varies directly with length and inversely with cross-sectional area.

The Gauss.   In referring to the strength of a magnet, the unit of flux density is usually used.   One gauss is equal to one maxwell per square centimeter.

The Oersted.   Magnetomotive force, which produces flux density, is expressed in gilberts per centimeter, or oersteds.

B-H Curves.   In order to reduce the labor ordinarily involved in computing magnetic-circuit values, tables and curves depicting magnetic characteristics have been made up for each of the most commonly used magnetic materials.   Of these the *B-H* curve, which shows the relationship between flux density and field intensity, is the most commonly used. Figure 9·8 shows a *B-H* curve for permalloy, an alloy of magnetic materials having a relatively high permeability. The following is an example of how *B-H* curves are used.

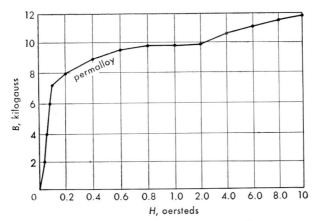

FIG. 9·8   Standard *B-H* curve for permalloy.

Example: A transformer is to be designed with a permalloy core of 4 sq cm cross-sectional area 23 cm long. A total flux of 32,000 lines is desired in the core. What will be the magnetomotive force in gilberts and the flux density in gauss?

Solution: Flux density may be determined by the following equation.

$$B = \frac{\Phi}{A}$$

where B = flux density, gauss
Φ = flux, maxwells
A = area, sq cm

$$B = \frac{32,000}{4} = 8,000 \text{ gauss}$$

By referring to the *B-H* curve of Fig. 9·8, it is found that in order to magnetize permalloy to a flux density of 8,000 gauss, a field intensity of 0.2 oersted is required. Since the magnetic path is 28 cm long and field intensity has been found to be 0.2 oersted, the magnetomotive force can be determined by the equation

$$F = HL$$

where F = magnetomotive force, gilberts
H = field intensity, oersteds
L = length of magnetic path, cm

$$F = 0.2 \times 28 = 5.6 \text{ gilberts}$$

Saturation. Magnetic saturation is that point in a magnetic circuit when further increase in field intensity produces little or no increase in flux density. When all the molecules of a magnetic material have been aligned with respect to the magnetizing force, the material is said to be saturated. As a material becomes saturated, its permeability decreases until at complete saturation its permeability is approximately that of air (unity).

Hysteresis. The ability of a magnetic material to maintain its own magnetic state is known as *hysteresis*. The power expended in changing the magnetic state of a material is known as *hysteresis loss*. It is a

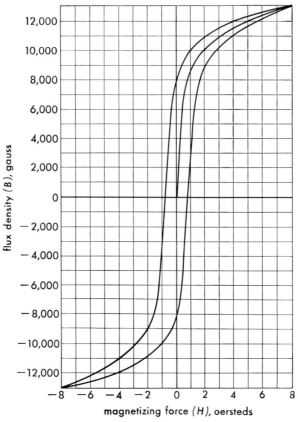

FIG. 9·9   Typical hysteresis curve.

magnetic friction effect which causes the magnetism produced (B) to lag behind the magnetizing force (H). When a magnetizing force is applied, magnetization is not immediately accomplished, and when the magnetizing force is removed, the material does not instantly or completely demagnetize. Therefore, residual magnetism is a form of hysteresis loss. Also, if a material is magnetized and demagnetized at regular intervals, the molecular action that occurs will dissipate some of the magnetizing power as heat. Figure 9·9 shows the hysteresis "loop" for a typical magnet.

Note that the hysteresis loss is present regardless of the polarity of magnetization.

9·4 Mathematics. Once the various equations governing the solving for values in magnetic circuits are known, the mathematics involved is similar to that involved in solving for values in electric circuits. The following examples are intended for purpose of familiarization with some of the more commonly used equations.

Example 1: Find the magnetomotive force required to produce a total flux of 18,000 maxwells through a material whose reluctance is 0.00333 units.

Solution: $F = \Phi\Re$
$$= 18{,}000 \times 0.00333 = 59.9 \text{ gilberts}$$

Example 2: How many ampere-turns would be required for a coil to supply a magnetic circuit of 6.3 gilberts?

Solution: The number of ampere-turns (NI) is found by multiplying the turns in the coil by the current through it. For example, 10 amp through 12 turns would result in 120 amp-turns. Further, magnetomotive force produces a flux proportional to the ampere-turns of a circuit. The proportionality constant has been found to be 1.26. Therefore

$$F = 1.26NI$$

Transposing,

$$NI = \frac{F}{1.26} = \frac{6.3}{1.26} = 5 \text{ amp-turns}$$

Example 3: When $NI = 62.2$ amp-turns and $N = 100$ turns, what is the current through the coil?

Solution: $NI = 62.2$

Transposing,

$$I = \frac{62.2}{N} = \frac{62.2}{100} = 0.622 \text{ amp}$$

Example 4: What is the reluctance of a magnetic material whose length is 10 cm and whose cross-sectional area is 2 sq cm if its permeability is 250?

Solution: The reluctance of a material may be found by the equation

$$\Re = \frac{L}{\mu A}$$

where L = length of magnetic path, cm
  μ = permeability
  A = cross-sectional area, sq cm

$$\Re = \frac{10}{250 \times 2} = \frac{10}{500} = 0.02$$

9·5   Simple Magnetic Circuit.   It has been proved that current in a coil produces a magnetic field around it.   It can also be proved that a changing magnetic field around a coil produces current in the coil.   Figure 9·10 shows a simple example of this phenomenon in which current produced by a magnetic field could be utilized to perform work.

Assume that a coil of wire is connected through a switch to a discharged battery.   With a permanent magnet placed around the coil as shown, magnetic lines of force will cut the turns of the coil.   While the switch is open, there will be no current in the circuit.   However, if the switch is closed with the magnet at right angles to the plane of the coil, there will be current in the circuit to the discharged battery.   During the time the switch is open, the open circuit will prevent the battery from discharging.   Because only a *moving* magnetic field can produce current in

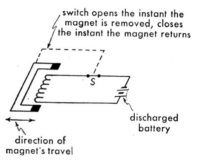

FIG.   9·10   Charging battery by means of magnetic action.

a conductor, assume that the magnet is moved quickly in and out of position and that the switch is operating in synchronization with its movement.   After a certain period of time it would be possible to recharge the battery completely.   The time required would depend upon the strength of the magnet and the rate at which it is brought into and out of position.   The stronger the magnet, the more flux lines and the larger the resultant current.   The greater the rate at which the magnet is moved, or rate at which its magnetic field "cuts" the turns of the coil, the greater the number of flux lines and current induced in the coil. This is the basic theory of motor and generator operation.

REVIEW QUESTIONS

1. What did Oersted prove?

2. Explain electromagnetism.

3. Why cannot polarity be assigned in a single electromagnetic field?

4. State the left-hand rule for determining poles and direction of current in a solenoid.

5. In what ways are electric and magnetic circuits similar?

6. What is the effect of adding turns to a solenoid?

7. How does permeability govern field strength in an electromagnet?

8. If a material has a high reluctance, does it have a high or low permeability?

9. Define the gauss.

10. How does the gauss relate to the maxwell?

11. Define the oersted.

12. How does the oersted relate to the gilbert?

13. What is the reason for plotting B-H curves for most magnetic materials?

14. List one type of hysteresis loss.

15. If a conductor is "cut" by a magnetic field, what occurs?

16. What is the relationship between magnetic field and current in a conductor?

17. How does the law of charges apply to magnetic fields around conductors?

18. What are ampere-turns?

19. Explain magnetic saturation.

20. Given $\mathcal{R} = 8.05$, $F = 200$ gilberts; find Φ.

21. Given $F = 400$ gilberts, $N = 20$; find I.

22. Given $B = 1,620$ gauss, $H = 12$ oersteds; find μ.

23. A magnet 5 cm in length has a reluctance of 0.5 and a cross-sectional area of 2 sq cm. What is the permeability of the material?

24. In Prob. 23, if $\Phi = 30,000$ maxwells, find the flux density.

25. What is gained in solenoid construction if a high-permeability core is used?

CHAPTER 10

AMMETERS

To all technicians and electricians, competence in the care, upkeep, and repair of measuring devices is important. All meters used in electronic applications can be considered *ammeters* since they operate on the principle of current. The deflection of the pointer or needle with respect to the scale is caused by the current through the meter movement. For measuring electrical quantities other than current, meters are calibrated in volts or ohms; however, the principle of operation is similar in all types. Meters employ the laws and characteristics of magnetism to accomplish their function.

10·1 D'Arsonval Meter Movement. When an object that can be magnetized is brought into the vicinity of a magnet, a force is exerted upon that object and it becomes a magnet.

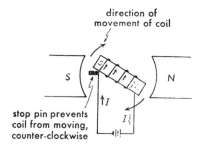

direction of movement of coil

S   N

stop pin prevents coil from moving, counter-clockwise

I

FIG. 10·1 Basic principles of D'Arsonval meter movement.

The new magnet will align itself so that its poles are attracted to unlike poles of the original magnet. Figure 10·1 shows a permanent magnet and an electromagnet. With current through the coil as shown, poles will be established in the core. It will turn on its axis and align itself so that the unlike poles between the two magnets will attract each other.

The magnetic action occurring in this example is that of the D'Arsonval meter movement. If the coil and its core are spring-loaded so that they will return to a horizontal position when the voltage is removed, the amount of *deflection* from the horizontal is an indication of the amount of current through the coil. The spring shown in Fig. 10·2 is mounted so that it tends to maintain the moving coil assembly in a horizontal position when there is no current. If current is passed through the coil, an electromagnetic field is set up and the south pole of the electromagnet repels the like pole of the permanent magnet. The other poles of the two magnets repel each other and the coil assembly will move clockwise away from its normal horizontal position. If current through the coil is increased, the magnetic action will increase and the assembly will move further away from the horizontal. Since spring tension increases with assembly movement, it can be seen that an appreciable amount of current would be necessary to effect complete alignment. However, the actual amount of deflection indicates the amount of current through the coil.

By mounting a pointer on the assembly as shown in Fig. 10·3, the amount of deflection resulting from known currents can be marked on a card mounted permanently behind the pointer. The result is a basic meter. Thereafter, unknown currents can be measured by comparing deflections with the known values as indicated on the card, or *scale*.

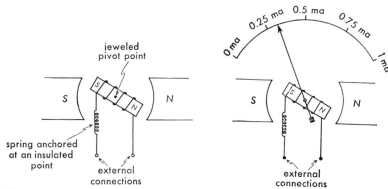

FIG. 10·2 D'Arsonval meter movement.

FIG. 10·3 Basic D'Arsonval meter.

10·2 Deflection Sensitivity. When a meter movement has been deflected by current to a point where a further increase in current will result in no further increase in deflection, it is considered to be in a state of *full-scale deflection*. The current required for this state is called the meter's *deflection sensitivity*. For example, a movement rated at 1 ma deflection sensitivity requires a current of 1 ma through the movement for full-scale deflection. A 50-μa movement requires 50 μa for full-scale deflection.

10·3 Meter Scales. The cards mounted behind the pointers on a meter are called *scales*. There are only a few general types of scales. The *linear* scale is one whose graduations or markings vary directly with the current through the movement. This type of scale shows uniform divisions for linear increases in current. *Square-law*, *logarithmic*, and *nonlinear* scales are usually employed in ohmmeters or meters used in special applications.

10·4 Ammeters. The movement of an ammeter is, basically, a coil of wire; therefore, there must be some resistance offered to current. If the resistance is known and is paralleled by an equal resistance, current

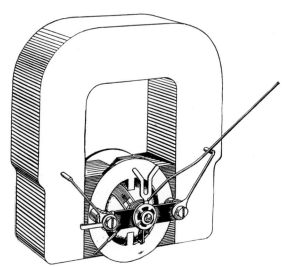

FIG. 10·4   Typical meter construction.

through the circuit will have two paths and the movement will deflect only half the distance it would deflect if not paralleled. Rather than use a meter with a different deflection sensitivity for each circuit being tested, it has been found more practical to parallel, or *shunt*, the meter with different values of resistance. Thus, current through the meter itself never exceeds that required for full-scale deflection regardless of the amount of current in the circuit. If the deflection sensitivity and the value of shunt resistance are known, the total current that the meter is capable of handling can be computed by solving as for any parallel circuit.

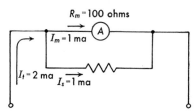

FIG. 10·5   Meter and shunt.

Figure 10·5 shows a meter and shunt resistor. To distinguish between them, "movement" refers to the coil assembly, while the term "meter" refers to both the movement and the shunt.

Example: Assume that the deflection sensitivity of the movement is 1 ma, the internal resistance of the movement is 100 ohms, and total current is 2 ma. What should be the value of the shunt resistor R_s?

Solution: $$I_s = I_t - I_m$$

where I_s = current through shunt
I_t = total current in circuit
I_m = current through movement

$$I_s = 2 - 1 = 1 \text{ ma}$$

Since there is 1 ma of current through both R_s and R_m, their resistances must be equal. Therefore

$$R_s = R_m = 100 \text{ ohms}$$

In the design of ammeters it is the practice to maintain only one deflection sensitivity while changing the value of shunts to enable the meter to be used over a wide range of current values. For example, a 1-ma movement can be used to measure 4 ma; however, the movement-and-shunt combination must offer a resistance of only one-fourth what it would offer without the shunt. Referring to the table of resistance ratios in Sec. 7·6, it is seen that a shunt resistor must be one-third the value of movement resistance in order for the combined resistance to be one-fourth of movement resistance.

10·5 Multirange Meters. The simplest and most economical means of designing meters for a wide range of currents is to use one movement, a selector switch, and a variety of shunts as shown in Fig. 10·6. This type of multirange meter is known as the *range-switching* type. It is simple to construct and easy to use. However, disadvantages include mechanical wear on the rotary switch, small errors introduced at high ranges because of the contact resistance of the switch, and the fact that a shorting switch must be used. When shifting from one shunt to another, the new shunt must be connected into the circuit before the contact is broken. This is necessary to prevent the current under test from going through the movement while the switch is being moved from one position to another. Since ammeters are delicate instruments, any slight *overload* might burn out the coil.

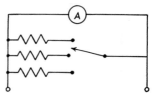

Fig. 10·6 Range-switching meter using three shunts.

Universal Shunt. The *universal,* or Ayrton, shunt meter differs from the range-switching type mainly in not having a switch. Also, in the universal-shunt type (Fig. 10·7) the shunt acts as both a current divider and a current limiter. Although the calculation of shunt values is rather complex, this is not important except in design considerations. This type has certain advantages. The absence of a switch eliminates mechanical wear. Since the entire resistance of the shunt is present as either a parallel or series resistance, the extremely small contact resistance between the test leads and test jacks has a negligible effect. One of the disadvantages is that the resistance of the shunt is at all times partially used as a current limiter; therefore, the movement itself must be very sensitive, and the meter is not as rugged as the range-switching type. Also, because of the use of greater values of resistance, temperature effects are at times more pronounced than with the range-switching type.

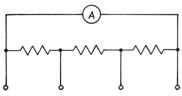

FIG. 10·7 Universal shunt meter.

10·6 Ammeter Construction. There are several standard parts of a basic ammeter movement that should be identified as to name and function.

Magnet. The magnet is a permanent type and is constructed of one of the better magnetic materials, such as Alnico. Its function is to produce the permanent magnetic field around the movement.

Pole pieces. These are integral parts of the magnet. They are usually polished, curved surfaces directed toward each other to provide a uniform flux density and minimum air gap between the coil assembly and the magnet.

Core. The core is sometimes referred to as the *armature* of the movement. It tends to rotate within the magnetic field. Its function is to concentrate the magnetic lines that are generated electrically within the coil. Cores are usually constructed of a highly permeable material, such as soft iron.

Bobbin. When flux lines cut a revolving material that has no external connections, small currents will be generated within the material. These are called *eddy currents.* The bobbin is a small aluminum form for the coil; it has no electrical connections. The core is inside the bobbin, and when the coil is energized, the meter tends to swing the flux lines of the permanent magnet. The eddy currents developed in the bobbin tend to demagnetize the core and slow down, or *damp*, the swing of the movement. With more current through the coil, the movement tends to swing faster. However, more eddy currents are developed, which result in additional damping. This is done to prevent "oscillations," or the swinging of the pointer back and forth before coming to rest at the correct reading. This system is known as *eddy-current damping.* Eddy currents and their effects will be discussed in greater detail in Chap. 19.

Restoring Springs. Springs are used to provide a counter force against the force of rotation of the movement on its axis. The springs are wound in such a way that temperature changes will not affect their length or strength. Also, they comprise part of the electric circuit between the coil and test jacks.

Zero Adjust. The zero adjust provides a means of mechanically adjusting the pointer to read zero when there is no current. It is also used to compensate for the fact that, as the springs and permanent magnet age, the pointer will not always return to zero when there is no current.

Meter Resistance. Figure 10·8 shows a schematic for calculating the value of R_m for any meter. The circuit consists of a variable resistor, a battery, and the movement under consideration. The resistor must be large enough to protect the movement from excessive current. If the variable resistor is adjusted until full-scale deflection is reached, connecting a small piece of Nichrome or resistance wire across the movement will help determine movement resistance. If sufficient wire is paralleled with the movement to reduce the deflection to mid-scale, the resistance of this length of wire is equal to the resistance of the movement. The length of the Nichrome wire can then be measured and its resistance determined by use of wire tables.

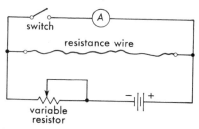

Fig. 10·8   Method of computing meter resistance.

The movement should never be placed directly across a measuring device for determining movement resistance. Since every ohmmeter has a built-in source of voltage, this voltage applied across the ammeter movement would probably result in a burned-out movement. To protect the movement, an ammeter is never connected *across* a circuit, but is always connected in *series* with the circuit under test.

10·7 Care of Meters. The most rugged meter is often rendered completely useless as a result of carelessness and rough handling. Most meters are delicate instruments and should be used with great care. Polarities must always be observed before connecting a meter in a circuit. Meters operate on magnetic principles and must not be brought near strong magnetic fields, or they will be rendered inaccurate. If the permanent magnet becomes demagnetized or even loses an appreciable amount of its magnetic properties, the meter becomes either inaccurate or totally useless. Further, the movements of most meters are mounted on jewel pivots and delicately balanced and counterbalanced to ensure uniform deflection. Any physical shock might upset that balance and produce inaccuracy. Meters should be kept in a clean, dry place, because moisture corrodes the pivot points and introduces friction that will contribute to inaccuracy. Current under test must be equal to or less than that required for full-scale deflection, because excessive current can burn out the coil. Also, the pointer is extremely fragile, and any deflection beyond full-scale could cause it to strike the stop pin with such force that the pointer might bend or break.

10·8 Mathematics. The mathematics of meters (particularly in their design) can become complex; however, very little mathematics is needed for the care and upkeep of meters.

There are seven basic components related to the ammeter and its shunt that should be considered: R_m, movement resistance in ohms; R_s, shunt resistance in ohms; I_t, total current in amperes; I_m, movement current in amperes; I_s, shunt current in amperes; E_m, voltage drop across movement in volts; and E_s, voltage drop across shunt in volts.

Although the voltage drop across the movement equals that across the shunt, for explanatory purposes they are both given consideration. Since

$$I_t = I_m + I_s$$

in agreement with Ohm's law, then

$$E_m = I_m R_m \quad \text{and} \quad E_s = I_s R_s$$

Further, since the two members are in parallel,

$$E_m = E_s$$

Therefore

$$I_m R_m = I_s R_s$$

Since the total current I_t is the sum of I_m and I_s and the value of I_s may be obtained by the equation

$$I_s = \frac{R_m}{R_s} I_m$$

then

$$I_t = I_m + I_s = \frac{R_m}{R_s} I_m + I_m$$

Dividing by I_m,

$$\frac{I_t}{I_m} = \frac{R_m}{R_s} + 1$$

The ratio I_t/I_m is actually the multiplying power of the shunt, or the whole-number increase in the range of the meter due to the shunt resistor. For simplicity the ratio is assigned a single letter designator n. Therefore

$$n = \frac{R_m}{R_s} + 1$$

where n = the multiplying factor of the shunt resistor. (No units are given since this is a ratio.)

Example 1: Find the multiplying power of a shunt for an ammeter when the resistance of the instrument is 2,000 ohms and the resistance of the shunt is 500 ohms.

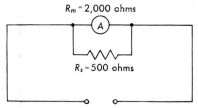

FIG. 10·9 Schematic for computing multiplying power of shunt.

Solution: These conditions are shown schematically in Fig. 10·9.

$$n = \frac{R_m}{R_s} + 1$$

$$= \frac{2,000}{500} + 1 = 4 + 1 = 5$$

This means that the readings are to be multiplied by 5 to obtain the value of total current.

Example 2: What must be the resistance of a shunt to provide a multiplying factor of 50 when used with an ammeter with a resistance of 200 ohms?

Solution:
$$n = \frac{R_m}{R_s} + 1$$

Transposing,

$$R_s = \frac{R_m}{n - 1}$$

$$= \frac{200}{50 - 1} = \frac{200}{49} = 4.08 \text{ ohms}$$

REVIEW QUESTIONS

1. Briefly explain the magnetic principle upon which the D'Arsonval meter movement operates.

2. Is a meter with a high deflection sensitivity used to measure large or small amounts of current? Explain.

3. What would be the effect on an ammeter if the restoring spring parted?

4. Why must meters be stored in dry places?

5. A 100-ohm movement with a deflection sensitivity of 100-μa is shunted such that it can measure 200-μa full-scale. What is the value of the shunt?

6. Explain the difference between "movement" and "meter."

7. Explain the action of a meter shunt.

8. List two disadvantages of the switching-type ammeter.

9. List one advantage of the switching-type ammeter.

10. Briefly explain eddy-current damping.

11. What special features have been incorporated in the design of the magnet used in meters?

12. What is the armature of the movement?

13. Name one disadvantage of the universal-shunt ammeter.

14. Name one advantage of the universal-shunt ammeter.

15. A 40-ohm movement is shunted with 30 ohms. What is its multiplying factor?

16. Explain the two functions of the zero adjust.

17. What is the source of meter resistance?

18. How is meter resistance determined?

19. How are meter movements mounted to ensure uniform deflection?

20. A multiplying factor of 50 is desired. Meter resistance is 200 ohms. What value of shunt should be employed?

21. One type of scale is the linear type. Name two other types.

22. Derive the equation for the multiplying factor *n*.

23. How should an ammeter be connected to the circuit under test?

24. What particular principle is common to all types of meters?

25. Why should the internal resistance of a meter never be measured with an ohmmeter?

CHAPTER 11

THE VOLTMETER

If the technician or electrician is not familiar with measuring devices and their construction, he may have to forgo their use when a problem could be more easily solved by their application. Although many circuit defects appear at first sight beyond solution, the proper employment of test equipment can quickly remedy the condition.

In any application where voltages are present, the *voltmeter* is one of the most important aids to trouble shooting known.

11·1 Theory of Operation. Figure 11·1 shows a 1-ma meter movement, a variable resistor, and a 10-volt source. Assume that the resistor is large enough to protect the movement and permit no more than full-scale deflection. If the resistor is set to allow only 1 ma of current, the movement will show full-scale deflection without being endangered. Further, assume that the setting of the resistor is unchanged but a 5-volt source is substituted for the 10-volt source. The only noticeable effect is in the movement itself; it deflects only half scale. A 10-volt source causes a deflection of 1 ma; a 5-volt source causes a deflection of 0.5 ma. Suppose that even though deflection is caused by current, the meter scale was marked 5 volts at mid-scale and 10 volts at full scale. It then becomes a *voltmeter*. Although the

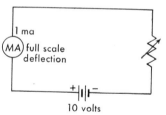

Fig. 11·1 Ammeter in basic circuit.

movement still deflects, owing to current through the coil, and the meter still actually measures current, it is *calibrated* in terms of the voltage producing the current and has become a voltmeter.

To expand this theory, assume that the variable resistor is adjusted so that the 10-volt source will cause only mid-scale instead of full-scale deflection. If a 20-volt source is then substituted for the 10-volt source, the meter will again show full-scale deflection. Therefore, the voltmeter could be *calibrated* to read 20 volts maximum range. This is the basic theory of *multirange voltmeters*.

11·2 Voltmeter Multiplier. A 1-ma movement with an internal resistance of 1,000 ohms could be placed across a 1-volt source and the resultant reading would be full-scale deflection, or 1 ma. If a 4,000-ohm resistor were placed in series with the movement, then the new maximum voltage would be 5 volts, and the range of the movement would have been multiplied by five. The resistor in series with the movement is called the *multiplier*. In Fig. 11·2 the multiplier is four times as large as the resistance of the movement, although the range of the meter has been made five times as large as it was without the multiplier. Therefore, an equation can be established for determining the multiplying factor of any multiplier. It is the ratio of the multiplier resistance to the movement resistance, plus 1. Or, as an equation,

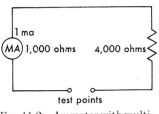

FIG. 11·2 Ammeter with multiplier.

$$n = \frac{R_M}{R_m} + 1$$

where n = multiplying factor
  R_M = multiplier resistance, ohms
  R_m = movement resistance, ohms

In this equation, current has not been taken into consideration, even though current is the basis of operation of all meters. This is in no way

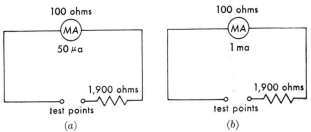

FIG. 11·3 Meters of different deflection sensitivity using same value of multiplier.

intended to suggest that current must not be considered. The equation is merely for convenience in determining multiplying factors. However, it must first be determined that the voltage under test is not so large that it will produce more current than that for which the meter is designed. Thus, current is a limiting factor; resistance is a multiplying factor.

Figure 11·3 shows an example of a multiplier with a resistance of 1,900 ohms being used in two different applications. Although the multiplying factor is the same in both cases, the current limits are different. The meter in *a* requires only one-twentieth as much current for full-scale deflection as the meter in b; therefore, it can read only one-twentieth as much voltage. This can be proved by applying Ohm's law. In each example, total current is that required for full-scale deflection, while total resistance is the sum of movement and multiplier resistances. The voltage that can be applied is the product of total current and total resistance. In a,

$$E = 2,000 \times 50 \times 10^{-6} = 0.1 \text{ volt}$$

In b,

$$E = 2,000 \times 0.001 = 2 \text{ volts}$$

The term *voltmeter* includes both the movement and the multiplier. Voltmeters are usually rated by their range and identified as having zero volts minimum reading, for example, a 0- to 10-volt meter.

11·3 Voltmeter Sensitivity. Voltmeters are also rated as to their ohms-per-volt *sensitivity*. The sensitivity is usually expressed in terms of ohms in the multiplier for each volt of range. Although the movement itself has some resistance, which should be considered in any precision application, for rating purposes alone the movement resistance is incorporated into that of the multiplier.

The ohms-per-volt sensitivity of a voltmeter is determined by dividing the current required for full-scale deflection into 1. Actually, this is computing the reciprocal of maximum current.

Example: A 1-ma movement has a voltmeter sensitivity of how many ohms per volt?

Solution: Sensitivity is the reciprocal of the current required for full-scale deflection. Therefore, since a 1-ma movement requires 1 ma for full-scale deflection,

$$\text{Sensitivity} = \frac{1}{1 \text{ ma}} = \frac{1}{0.001 \text{ amp}} = 1,000 \text{ ohms per volt}$$

In the above example the range of the meter times the sensitivity equals the maximum resistance. It also equals the multiplier resistance for that particular range. The exact multiplier resistance would be the total resistance for that particular range less the small movement resistance.

As will be subsequently shown, sensitivity is a direct indication of the quality of a voltmeter. Meter accuracy increases with an increase in ohms-per-volt sensitivity.

Shunting Effect. The ohms-per-volt sensitivity of a meter can have a definite effect upon the circuit under test. For example, Fig. 11·4 shows a 12-volt source with two 10,000-ohm resistors in series. Placing a 1,000-ohms-per-volt meter with a range of 0 to 10 volts across one of the resistors is the same as paralleling it with another 10,000-ohm resistor.

The joint resistance of the combination would then be 5,000 ohms.   With
the meter disconnected, there will be 6 volts across R_2 and 6 volts across
R_1.   The connected meter combines with R_2 to offer an equivalent resistance of 5,000 ohms.   Therefore, by Ohm's law it can be proved that
8 volts will be read across R_1 and the remaining 4 volts across R_2.   Thus
the meter has introduced an error into the circuit because of its low ohms-
per-volt sensitivity.

Figure 11·5 shows a circuit identical except for the meter, which has a
sensitivity of 5,000 ohms per volt.   With a range of 0 to 10 volts the total
resistance of the meter is 50,000 ohms.   With the meter disconnected

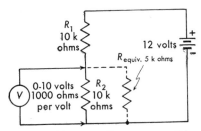

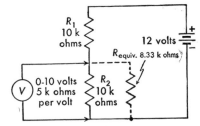

FIG. 11·4   Meter-reading error resulting
from low ohms-per-volt rating.

FIG. 11·5   High ohms-per-volt rating
meter used to reduce error in voltage
reading.

6 volts appears across each resistor.   Connecting the meter across R_2 will
produce a joint resistance of 8,333 ohms.   By equation,

$$I_t = \frac{E}{R_t}$$

where R_t = sum of R_1 and R_2.   Therefore,

$$I_t = \frac{12}{10,000 + 8,333} = \frac{12}{18,333} = 0.65 \text{ ma}$$

Since current is the same in all parts of a series circuit, 0.65 ma appears
across both R_1 and R_2.   Therefore, 6.5 volts will appear across R_1, and
the meter will read 5.5 volts across R_2.   The meter has again introduced
an error; however, due to its higher ohms-per-volt sensitivity, the error
is much smaller.

This shunting effect of a voltmeter on circuits under test has long presented a problem, but these errors have been reduced by using meters with
high ohms-per-volt sensitivity.   A good meter is one having at least
20,000-ohms-per-volt sensitivity on all ranges.   Meters with such sensitivity have a very slight shunting effect on the circuits under test.

11·4   Multirange Voltmeters.   Because of aging springs and weakened magnets in meters, errors are often encountered in reading voltages

near full-scale deflection or small voltages near the low end of the scale. To minimize these errors, multirange meters are employed. If a voltage reading would appear at the extreme end of one scale, another scale is provided upon which the reading would appear at approximately mid-scale. For example, on a 0- to 500-volt range 500 volts would deflect full scale; however, on a 0- to 1,000-volt range, the same 500 volts would deflect only half scale, where the error is smaller. In a critical voltage circuit the 0- to 1,000-volt range is used when voltages in the vicinity of 500 volts are measured. Further, if both ranges had the same ohms-per-volt sensitivity, the higher ranges would introduce the least shunting effect on the circuit under test.

Another obvious argument for the multirange meter is versatility. Rather than employ a separate movement for each voltage reading, it is

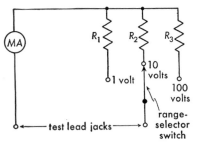

FIG. 11·6   Multirange meter.

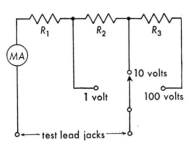

FIG. 11·7   Multirange meter with series multipliers.

more practical to use the same basic movement with a switching arrangement and a variety of multipliers. One of the more common types of multirange voltmeters is like that shown in Fig. 11·6. One side of the circuit to be tested is applied to the meter, while the other is applied through the range-selector switch and appropriate multiplier. In this type of meter a separate multiplier is used for each range, while all other multipliers are out of the circuit.

The example shown in Fig. 11·7 is a more practical type of multirange meter in which series multipliers are used. On the 1-volt range the total resistance is that of the movement and the multiplier R_1. On the 10-volt range, R_2 and R_1 comprise the multiplier, while on the 50-volt range, the necessary multiplier resistance is provided by the combination of R_3, R_2, and R_1.

11·5   Voltmeter Construction.   There are several minor considerations in the construction and physical make-up of the average voltmeter. First, since voltages are under test, safety must be a governing factor. Where large enough resistors are used and polarities observed, the meter itself is in no great danger of being damaged.   However, in dealing with high values of voltage, the technician is involved with an element that should be given the utmost respect at all times.

Polarity.   Most meters either have the *test lead jacks* marked PLUS and MINUS or have the abbreviation POS and NEG to denote proper circuit connections.   Other types have their negative side marked COMMON and use one of the other accepted markings for the positive side.   All multirange meters are connected internally so that the range switch and multipliers are in the positive side of the circuit.   This is done to protect the technician.   In most servicing work voltage readings are taken between some

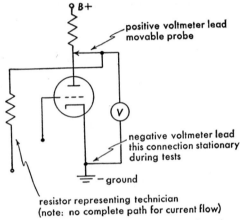

FIG. 11·8   Schematic representation of correct procedure for testing voltage.

positive point and ground, since ground is a common point for most voltages in electronic equipment.   The practice is to make the negative connection with the voltmeter test lead by clamping the lead to ground, usually the chassis of the equipment.   This requires that only one of the technician's hands be used in obtaining the voltage readings by touching the positive lead, or probe, to the point within the circuit to be tested. Thus, with only one hand in the vicinity of the voltage to be tested and no contact with the negative side of the circuit, the technician runs less risk of coming into contact with live circuits.   This situation is shown schematically in Fig. 11·8, in which the technician is represented by a resistor.   There can be no current through this resistor unless the circuit is completed to the negative side of the circuit under test.   Therefore, the voltage present at the positive test point will have no effect on the technician.

Restoring springs, counterbalances, bobbins, and the other various ammeter components are also present in the voltmeter.

REVIEW QUESTIONS

1. What is meant by ohms-per-volt sensitivity?

2. Explain the shunting effect.

3. What is actually being measured in a voltmeter?

4. What is one advantage of the multirange meter shown in Fig. 11·6?

5. Why are multipliers so named?

6. Why are multirange meters generally the most desirable?

7. A movement having an internal resistance of 150 ohms is to have its range multiplied 6 times. What size multiplier must be used?

8. A movement has its range multiplied 10 times. The multiplier is 1,800 ohms. What is the movement resistance R_m?

9. What is the ohms-per-volt sensitivity of a 50-μa movement?

10. A 50,000-ohms-per-volt meter requires how much current for full-scale deflection?

11. Find the multiplying resistance if a 1-ma movement with an internal resistance of 225 ohms is to read 100 volts full scale.

12. A multiplier of 49,500 ohms is used with a 50-μa movement. Movement resistance is 500 ohms. What is the maximum voltage that can be read?

13. What sensitivity rating would be characteristic of a good voltmeter?

14. Why are the higher voltage ranges used even though a lower range could indicate the voltage under test?

15. List three considerations in the construction and physical make-up of the average voltmeter.

16. How should a voltmeter be connected to the circuit under test?

17. A 100-μa meter has a resistance of 400 ohms. What value of multiplier resistance should be used if the meter is to be used as a 0- to 10-volt voltmeter? (Hint: What total resistance is necessary to limit current to 100μa with 10 volts applied?)

18. What will be the ohms-per-volt sensitivity of the voltmeter in Prob. 17?

19. What minimum voltage range is obtainable with the meter of Prob. 17? (Hint: What is the range without the multiplier?)

20. A 5-ma ammeter with an internal resistance of 25 ohms is to be used as a 0- to 50-volt voltmeter. How much resistance must be added to that of the meter?

CHAPTER 12

THE OHMMETER

The *ohmmeter* is one of the most often used of the measuring devices. In any application where high voltages are present, it is generally safer and more practical to remove power from the equipment to be tested and perform what is referred to as "cold servicing." Most circuit components have an assigned ohmic value, in addition to current and voltage ratings. Therefore, if the resistance of a component is other than what a particular circuit requires, the current and voltage values will also be in error.

12·1 Ohm's Law in Ohmmeters. Figure 12·1 shows a voltage source, a 1-ma movement, and a 1,500-ohm resistor connected in a series circuit.

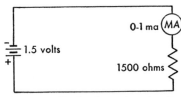

FIG. 12·1   Basic ohmmeter circuit.

Assuming that the movement itself has no resistance, by Ohm's law it is seen that the movement will show full-scale deflection. Thus, a 1.5-volt source will produce 1 ma of current through the 1,500-ohm resistor. As in any meter, voltage and resistance will govern the current through the meter movement. If the voltage is a constant value, the only variable is the resistance. If resistance is doubled for a constant voltage, current will be halved. If the resistance is tripled, current will be reduced to one-third.

Although the movement in an ohmmeter is deflecting as a result of current, the amount of deflection is controlled by a known resistance. Therefore, like any other meter, the ohmmeter operates on the principle of current. If unknown values under test give the same indication as known values previously tested, then they equal the known values. For example, if a resistor of unknown value was substituted for the 1,500-ohm resistor in Fig. 12·1 and the movement again showed full-scale deflection, then the value of the unknown resistor is also 1,500 ohms. Further, if an unknown value of resistance was substituted and half-scale deflection resulted, then the value of unknown resistance would be 3,000 ohms.

108

Ohmmeter scales are calibrated in ohms, or in terms of the resistance which controls the current.

12·2 The Series Ohmmeter. The principle of operation of the circuit in Fig. 12·1 is utilized in the construction of the series ohmmeter shown in Fig. 12·2. As shown, there is no current through the movement when the ohmmeter is not being used because of the open circuit that exists. When there is no current, resistance can be assumed to equal infinity, because any number divided by zero equals infinity. Therefore, infinite resistance is the value marked at the zero-current end on the ohmmeter scale.

If the pin jacks, or points for test leads, are shorted together, full-scale current will appear because 3 volts across 3,000 ohms will produce 1 ma of current. However, this is because of the resistance of the *internal* circuit. Since the resistance of the *external* circuit is zero, the ohmmeter scale is marked to indicate 0 ohms. If a 3,000-ohm resistor to be measured were placed across the test points, the current would be only ½ ma and the meter would deflect to half scale.

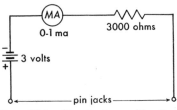

FIG. 12·2 Circuit for calibrating ohmmeter.

Therefore, the mid-scale point on the ohmmeter scale would be marked to indicate 3,000 ohms.

Any other intermediate values can be marked accordingly on the meter scale. As the resistance nears infinity, current decreases but the resistance reading will increase. Conversely, as the resistance approaches zero, current will increase but resistance readings will decrease. Ohmmeters of this type are usually accurate to 10 times the center reading on the high-resistance side and to one-tenth the center reading on the low-resistance side. The ohmmeter in this example would have a usable range of approximately 300 to 30,000 ohms.

Limiting Resistor. The voltage source in ohmmeters is usually in the form of cells within the meter. As long as no other voltages are introduced, the meter will not be damaged. Even while the test leads are shorted together, only full-scale deflection results, while any resistance greater than zero will permit something less than full-scale deflection. Therefore, the series resistor has the twofold purpose of establishing a center-scale value and limiting current, so that the meter will be protected.

Variable-resistance Ohmmeter. The ohmmeter shown in Fig. 12·3 is another series ohmmeter with the same resistance in the circuit as those previously shown. However, part of the resistance is variable to provide a means of compensating for aging of the battery. As batteries age, their output voltage decreases and an error will be introduced into resistance measurements unless compensated for.   For example, with a full 3-volt output from the battery in Fig. 12·3, there will be 1 ma of current through the full 3,000 ohms resistance when the pin jacks are shorted together.   If the battery voltage decreased to 2.9 volts after a period of use, the total meter resistance would have to be reduced to 2,900 ohms in order for the meter to deflect to full scale.   As battery voltage becomes progressively lower, additional resistance must be removed from the circuit in order for the movement to deflect to full scale.

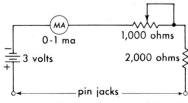

FIG. 12·3   Basic ohmmeter with variable resistor.

Unless compensation is provided, a decrease in voltage from 3 volts to 2.9 volts would cause the center-scale reading to be 2,900 ohms although the scale was marked to indicate 3,000 ohms.   While such a small error would be of little importance in general servicing and could be neglected, a considerable decrease in battery voltage would introduce errors beyond the *tolerance* rating of the resistor being measured.

Pin Jacks.   These are the connection points for test leads.   Usually, they are of insulated low-resistance wire and enable the technician to leave the meter in one place while using the leads to make measurements at some remote point.

12·3   Scale Calibration.   Theoretically, an ohmmeter should read resistances ranging from zero ohms to infinity.   However, due to the extremely small amount of deflection changes at the extreme ends, the average ohmmeter is limited in use from one-tenth to 10 times center scale.   Although the meter can be used beyond these limits, the results are inaccurate.

Original scale calibration is accomplished by means of numerous precision resistors.   After making the scale according to the deflection resulting from these known resistors, any unknown resistor within this range may be measured by comparing the deflection with those marked on the scale during calibration.   Figure 13·2 shows a meter whose top scale is in ohms.

12·4   Multirange Series Ohmmeters.   An ohmmeter cannot be made versatile unless some means is provided for changing the mid-scale values. A simple multirange series ohmmeter is shown in Fig. 12·4.   The movement resistance is 30 ohms, shown here as a milliampere movement because it operates on the principle of current.   Although the internal resistance of a meter movement is never neglected, a meter schematic usually includes movement resistance with a fixed meter-range resistor, rather than showing them as two separate resistances.   Since they are in series, it is of little importance whether they are shown singly or together.

In designing multirange meters, it is considered best to multiply the ranges by some practical, easily remembered value and to use as many values as possible which cause deflection near center scale on one of the ranges. In the circuit of Fig. 12·4 as the value of meter resistance increases, the applied voltage must increase proportionately. However, the current required for full-scale deflection is the same regardless of range. On the R range, total resistance is 1,500 ohms; on the $R \times 2$ range, total resistance is 3,000 ohms; and on the $R \times 3$ range, total resistance is 4,500 ohms. Therefore, 1 ma of current will cause full-scale deflection on all three ranges. Further, a resistor equal in value to the total resistance of any one range will result in mid-scale deflection when measured on that particular range. The 100-ohm variable resistor compensates for aging of the batteries.

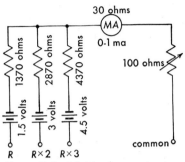

FIG. 12·4   Multirange series-type ohmmeter.

12·5   Shunt-type Ohmmeter. The series-type ohmmeter is primarily used for measuring relatively large values of resistance. At low resistance values, battery voltage required would necessarily be smaller than that produced by most types manufactured. For measuring low values of resistance, the shunt type shown in Fig. 12·5 is more commonly used. Although this type is similar to other meters in that current is the principle of operation, the shunt-type ohmmeter differs from the series type in several respects.

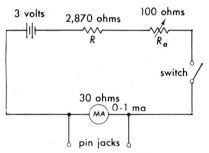

FIG. 12·5   Shunt-type ohmmeter.

There is current continually in the meter, series resistor, and the meter-adjusting resistor, R_a. With 3 volts applied as shown and the variable resistor adjusted to 100 ohms, 3,000 ohms resistance is offered to current and the meter will show full-scale deflection. If a 30-ohm resistor were placed between the pin jacks, current through the meter would be halved because of the two paths provided, and deflection would be only to half scale. If the pin jacks were shorted together, current would follow the path of least resistance and bypass the meter. Therefore, the movement would not deflect.

The method of calibrating the shunt-type ohmmeter is similar to that used for calibrating the series type, although the sequence is reversed.

With infinite resistance between the test points of a shunt type, there is maximum current; with zero resistance between the test points, zero current.

Compensation for aging of batteries is made by adjusting for full-scale deflection with the test points open-circuited. This is different from the method used for adjusting the series type.

A disadvantage of the shunt type is the fact that the battery is connected into the circuit at all times. However, this is compensated for by the addition of a normally open, spring-loaded switch which is momentarily closed only when the meter is being adjusted or measuring a resistance. An advantage over the series type is the ability of the shunt type to read lower values of resistance. Since the 30-ohm movement resistance parallels the resistance being measured, another 30-ohm resistance across the pin jacks would show only mid-scale deflection. Also, the movement has a built-in shunt which reduces the equivalent resistance to an even smaller value when measuring extremely low values. Basically, this is one of the methods used in converting a shunt-type to a multirange meter. However, because of the difficulties and expense involved in supplying shunt resistors of small and uncommon values, the shunt-type ohmmeter is not often designed with more than two or three ranges. Range limitations are the same as for the series type, namely, from one-tenth to ten times mid-scale reading.

Precautions. The usual meter precautions apply to all types of ohmmeters. They should be protected at all times from physical shock and kept away from strong magnets. Further, there is one specific precaution that applies only to ohmmeters. They should never be connected into any circuit containing voltage. Therefore, a circuit must be deenergized before using an ohmmeter to make resistance measurements.

12·6 Mathematics. The mathematics involved in the study of ohmmeters is quite simple, since there are only two equations for calculating unknown resistance. In the series-type ohmmeter, by equation,

$$R_x = R_m \frac{I_1 - I_2}{I_2}$$

where R_x = unknown resistance, ohms
R_m = meter resistance, ohms
I_1 = current with test points shorted, amp
I_2 = current with R_x in the circuit, amp

Although this is basically a calibrating equation, it can also be used to compute meter current or meter resistance.

Example 1: With the test points shorted, meter current is 1 ma; with R_x in the circuit, I_2 is ⅓ ma. If the meter resistance is 4,000 ohms, what is the value of R_x?

Solution: $R_x = R_m \dfrac{I_1 - I_2}{I_2}$

$$= 4,000 \times \frac{0.001 - 0.000333}{0.000333} = 8,000 \text{ ohms}$$

The unknown resistance of a shunt-type ohmmeter can be found by the equation

$$R_x = R_m \frac{I_2}{I_1 - I_2}$$

where R_m = meter resistance, ohms
   I_1 = current without R_x across meter, amp
   I_2 = current with R_x across meter, amp

Example 2: There is current of 1 ma in a shunt-type meter reading infinite resistance. Meter resistance is 50 ohms. When R_x is connected across the meter, current through the movement is reduced to 0.25 ma. What is the value of R_x?

Solution: $R_x = R_m \dfrac{I_2}{I_1 - I_2}$

$$= 50 \times \frac{0.00025}{0.001 - 0.00025} = 16.67 \text{ ohms}$$

REVIEW QUESTIONS

1. Explain the calibration technique for a series-type ohmmeter.

2. Explain the calibration technique for a shunt-type ohmmeter.

3. How is compensation for aging batteries provided in series-type ohmmeters?

4. Why is it safer to service electronic equipment with an ohmmeter?

5. Even though an ohmmeter operates on a current principle, what factor controls deflection?

6. Explain the function of the variable resistance shown in Fig. 12-3.

7. Explain the function of the limiting resistor in Fig. 12-2.

8. If the movement shown in Fig. 12-2 were a 50-μa movement, what value of limiting resistor would be needed?

9. In a series-type ohmmeter, how does the meter current vary with respect to the resistance being measured?

10. What is the theoretical range of an ohmmeter?

11. Why cannot the entire theoretical range of an ohmmeter be read?

12. Why is the series-type ohmmeter usually unsuitable at very low resistance ranges?

13. What would be the mid-scale error of an ohmmeter with a meter resistance of 4,500 ohms if battery voltage decreased from 6 volts to 5 volts?

14. In a multirange ohmmeter, what two circuit components are varied?

15. What is the main advantage of the shunt-type ohmmeter.

16. State one disadvantage of a shunt-type ohmmeter.

17. How is this disadvantage usually overcome?

18. Why are the ranges usually limited in number in the shunt-type ohmmeter?

19. $R_m = 8,000$ ohms, $I_1 = 1$ ma, $I_2 = 0.2$ ma; find R_x. (Series-type)

20. $R_x = 1,500$ ohms, $I_2 = 500\mu$a, $I_1 = 1$ ma; find R_m. (Shunt-type)

CHAPTER 13

MULTIMETERS, WHEATSTONE BRIDGE
AND MEGOHMMETERS

The preceding three chapters have been devoted to a discussion of the ammeter, voltmeter, and ohmmeter. This chapter will primarily deal with a combination of the three known as the *multimeter*. For most electronic servicing encountered outside a laboratory, a meter that combines the ranges and functions of all three is the most desirable. Other considerations such as portability and working space make a multimeter almost essential.

The *Wheatstone bridge* will also be discussed in greater detail in this chapter, in addition to an instrument used only for measuring extremely high resistances—the *megohmmeter*.

13·1 Multimeter Theory. A multimeter is, as its name implies, a combination of several meters in a single case. Any meter that performs several functions and has several ranges of those functions is considered a multimeter.

In Fig. 13·1 there is a simplified schematic of a typical multimeter in which polarity problems have been simplified by making the negative side of the meter common for all functions and ranges. The ammeter section is capable of reading currents on four ranges and up to 1 amp. The shunt employed is the universal type. The movement itself is rather sensitive, 500 μa being slightly above average for the usual multimeter.

Two series-type ohmmeter ranges are available with this type of multimeter, $R \times 100$ and $R \times 1,000$. Although there are many multimeters that employ both series type for large values of resistance and shunt type for low values, only the series type is shown here. In this example low values are read on the LOW range.

The voltmeter section is a standard multirange voltmeter. All ranges are connected by means of pin jacks to which the test leads are connected. In other meters provisions are made to switch from one range or one function to another while using the same pin-jack connections. However, the switching type is usually more expensive and subject to failures that are not common with this type.

Figure 13·2 shows the scale used with a typical multimeter of the commercial type. While it is not practical for all ranges to be calibrated on the meter scale, some multiple is employed between ranges and the same scale used. Thus, on a higher range it is a matter of adding a zero to the

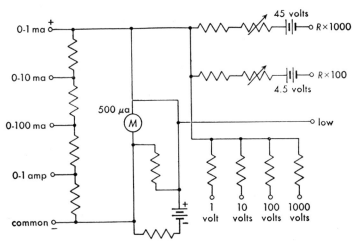

FIG. 13·1 Schematic of simple multimeter.

FIG. 13·2 Multimeter scale. (*Electronic Instrument Company, Inc.*)

reading obtained. For example, when using the 50-volt d-c range, 25 volts would cause mid-scale deflection; on the 5-volt range, 2.5 volts would deflect to mid-scale.

Although the sensitivity of the movement in Fig. 13·1 is 500 μa, the universal shunt is across the movement at all times.

The mid-scale reading of the ohmmeter section on the $R \times 100$ range is 4,500 ohms, since the source voltage on this range is 4.5 volts. If 4.5 volts produce 1 ma of current through the meter, then its internal resistance must be 4,500 ohms. According to calibration procedures for ohmmeters, this is established as the mid-scale reading. On the $R \times 1,000$ range mid-scale reading would be 45,000 ohms.

In a series-type ohmmeter, scale readings decrease in value from left to right; in a shunt-type ohmmeter, values decrease from right to left. Therefore, the direction of pointer movement is a means of determining the type of ohmmeter employed inside the case without circuit tracing.

13·2   Wheatstone Bridge.   Figure 13·3 shows a schematic of an elementary Wheatstone bridge. The circuit consists of two fixed resistors, one variable resistor, a *galvanometer*, a source voltage, and an unknown resistor R_x. Briefly, a galvanometer can be considered as a meter whose movement deflects as a result of current through it. However, this type of meter is designed so that its zero-current position is at mid-scale and current in either direction will cause a deflection in that direction. For example, current in a direction from point B to point C would cause the pointer to deflect to the right of mid-scale, while current in a direction C to B would result in deflection to the left of mid-scale. The movement itself is extremely sensitive and any excess currents are likely to damage the movement. Therefore, a normally open, spring-loaded switch is inserted in series with the galvanometer. When an unknown resistance is measured, the switch is momentarily closed long enough for the amount of deflection to be observed. If the deflection is excessive, the switch is immediately released and the galvanometer circuit opened.

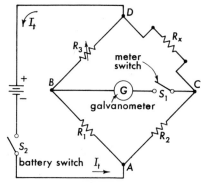

FIG. 13·3   Basic Wheatstone bridge circuit.

Bridge Theory.   The bridge in Fig. 13·3, with switch S_2 closed and S_1 open, can be considered as two series resistors, R_1 and R_3, in parallel with two more series resistors, R_2 and R_x. Current exists from the negative side of the source to point A, where it divides through two paths. Part of I_t goes through R_1 and R_3 while the remainder goes through R_2 and R_x. The sum of the voltages across R_1 and R_3, and across R_2 and R_x equals the source voltage. Therefore, individual voltages can be computed across each resistor by application of Ohm's law.

With S_1 closed, if the voltage developed across R_1 equals that across R_2, the relative voltage difference between points B and C is zero. Therefore, the galvanometer does not deflect. Further, if the resistance values of

R_1, R_2, and R_3 are known, the source voltage and various currents known, then the value of R_x can be solved.

This is explained in terms of ratios existing between the various resistors. By expressing voltage in terms of IR, if the IR across R_1 equals the IR across R_2, the bridge is balanced and there will be no current through the galvanometer. Further, if the IR's across R_1 and R_2 are equal, then the IR's across R_3 and R_x are equal to each other—although not necessarily equal to the other two IR's. With a 6-volt source, if it is assumed that 4 volts are across R_1, then 2 volts will be across R_3. If the bridge is balanced, there will also be 4 volts across R_2 and 2 volts across R_x. Hence, there exists an IR ratio between R_1 and R_3 that is the same as the ratio between R_2 and R_x when the bridge is balanced. Or, by equation,

$$\frac{IR_1}{IR_3} = \frac{IR_2}{IR_x}$$

This comparison of ratios is the key to the principle of operation of the Wheatstone bridge. One current exists through the series combination of R_1 and R_3; another through R_2 and R_x. By basic arithmetic, equal values in both numerator and denominator may be canceled. Thus canceling I,

$$\frac{R_1}{R_3} = \frac{R_2}{R_x}$$

Transposing,

$$R_x = \frac{R_2 R_3}{R_1}$$

Further transposing,

$$R_1 R_x = R_2 R_3$$

Cross dividing,

$$\frac{R_1}{R_2} = \frac{R_3}{R_x}$$

This is the ratio most often used in bridge applications and from which some conclusions can be drawn. First, if the ratio existing between R_1 and R_2 is known, even though their actual ohmic value is unknown, then R_3 is the only value that must be known in order to solve for R_x. If the bridge is balanced and the ratio between R_1 and R_2 is 10:1, for example, then this same ratio exists between R_3 and R_x. Thus, if R_3 were a 10-ohm resistor, R_x would be a 1-ohm resistor; if R_3 were a 100-ohm resistor, R_x would be 10 ohms.

The average Wheatstone bridge has an error of 1 per cent, or less, of the resistance being measured. The secret behind this accuracy lies in the extremely sensitive galvanometer and the requirement that the ratio be exactly equal in order for the bridge to balance. Usually, the variable resistor R_3 is the most accurate of the resistors used in the bridge. Since only the ratio between R_1 and R_2 is known, the resistor whose actual value is known must of necessity be a precision one.

13·3 Megohmmeter. There are numerous instances where an approximate measurement must be made of materials and circuits having extremely large values of resistance. While insulators offer almost infinite resistance, there is no perfect insulator and some current will exist through them. If enough voltage can be applied across an insulator to produce a measurable amount of current through it, the quality of the insulating material can be determined. For example, if one insulator requires 1,000 volts before it will carry 1 μa of current and another insulator will allow the same amount of current with only 500 volts across it, then the former possesses the better insulation resistance.

The instrument designed to apply high values of voltage and measure the resultant currents is called the *megohmmeter*. More commonly known by the trade name *Megger*, derived from the fact that the scale is calibrated in megohms, it is a device that measures the approximate value of extremely high resistances.

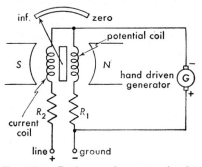

Fig. 13·4 Basic megohmmeter circuit.

13·4 Megohmmeter Construction. Figure 13·4 is a combination drawing and schematic of a basic megohmmeter. The hand-driven generator is the source that supplies a voltage when the crank is turned. The meter movement is a special type having two moving coils and mounted on jewel pivot points. Since there are no restoring springs in a megohmmeter, with no voltage applied the movement will come to rest along the scale at some point not necessarily zero or infinity.

The need for two moving coils can be explained by considering first the potential coil. With the test points not connected, resistance is infinite. The only path for current is through the potential coil, through the limiting resistor R_1, and back to the other side of the source. The potential coil is wound in such a way that the pointer deflects to the left as shown. The amount of deflection is limited by R_1 so that with maximum voltage from the generator, the pointer will come to a stop at the point marked INFINITY. If the two test points are shorted together, there will be two paths for current. From the negative side of the generator, current divides at the junction of the two coils. Part goes through the potential coil, through R_1, and back to the source. The remainder goes through the current coil, through R_2, and back to the source. The current coil is wound in such a way that it causes deflection from left to right in opposition to that caused by the potential coil.   The number of turns in the current coil and the turn spacing are such that with the test points shorted the deflection caused by the potential coil is overcome and the pointer deflects to zero. R_2 limits the deflection so that the pointer will not go beyond the zero point.   Mechanical stops prevent pointer travel beyond either zero or infinity, should R_1 or R_2 decrease in resistance.   The values between zero and infinity are marked on the meter scale as a result of measuring known resistances.

13-5 Megohmmeter Applications.   To maintain as high a resistance as practicable, insulators used with antenna systems may be tested with a

megohmmeter.   Normally, antenna resistance to ground is upwards of 100 megohms.   If the resistance decreases appreciably because of dirty or cracked insulators, much of the antenna's ability to receive or radiate energy will be lost.   By use of the megohmmeter, the resistance can be measured and corrective measures taken to maintain the resistance at a proper value.

Another very common application of the megohmmeter is in the testing of insulation resistance of a multi-conductor cable.   If the insulating material between two or more conductors partially *breaks down*, its insulation resistance will decrease and render the cable unsafe for power-handling applications.

Since maximum current never exceeds a fraction of a milliampere, delicate circuit components are not

Fig. 13-5   Typical commercial multimeter.   (*Electronic Instrument Company, Inc.*)

necessarily in danger from the megohmmeter; however, its lack of accuracy makes it impractical for low values of resistance.

Most megohmmeters employ a ratchet arrangement that will allow the generator to rotate only when the hand crank is rotated in one direction. This eliminates the possibility of a reversal in polarity of output voltage. A similar ratchet or slip-clutch arrangement is used as a speed control. Most megohmmeters are designed to deliver maximum voltage at approximately 150 rpm.   Any speed of the hand crank in excess of 150 rpm will merely actuate the slip clutch without any increase in output voltage.

Utmost care should be exercised in the use of a megohmmeter because high voltages generated at the test points can be highly dangerous. Proper procedure for measuring is first to make the necessary connections while making certain that the component or material under test has no voltage applied.   Then the hand crank is turned at some speed approaching maximum as specified for the megohmmeter.   While maintaining this speed constant, the resistance value of the material under test can be read from the meter scale.

One common disadvantage of the megohmmeter is its lack of ranges. Because readings can be observed only at some point between zero and infinity, it is at best only an approximating device.

REVIEW QUESTIONS

1. What is one main advantage of the multimeter?

2. How are polarity problems simplified in multimeter construction?

3. What type of meter is used for measuring the higher ranges of resistance in the multimeter shown in Fig. 13·1?

4. What type of meter is used for measuring the lower values of resistance?

5. What type of voltmeter is incorporated in the multimeter of Fig. 13·1?

6. Why is such a type used?

7. How is the problem of several ranges being shown on one scale handled?

8. What is a galvanometer?

9. What is one main advantage of the Wheatstone bridge?

10. What is the principle of operation of the Wheatstone bridge?

11. State the Wheatstone bridge resistance ratio.

12. What is the equation for R_x on the Wheatstone bridge?

13. How is the galvanometer protected in a Wheatstone bridge?

14. The ratio between R_1 and R_2 is 50, $R_3 = 250$ ohms; find R_x.

15. For what purposes is the megohmmeter used?

16. What is the purpose of the potential coil in the megohmmeter?

17. What is the purpose of the current coil?

18. Explain the operation of the ratchet and slip-clutch arrangement in the megohmmeter.

19. What is the trade name for the megohmmeter?

20. $R_1 = 350$ ohms, $R_2 = 70$ ohms, $R_x = 500$ ohms; what must be the value of R_3 to balance the Wheatstone bridge?

21. With respect to scale calibration, how does a series-type ohmmeter differ from a shunt-type ohmmeter?

22. The R_1 to R_2 ratio is 1:15, $R_3 = 15$ ohms; find R_x.

23. What is the position of the pointer when the megohmmeter is not in use?   Why?

24. What is the proper procedure for measuring resistance with a megohmmeter?

25. List one disadvantage of the megohmmeter.

CHAPTER 14

VACUUM-TUBE VOLTMETER

The last measuring device to be discussed is the *vacuum-tube voltmeter* (VTVM), often called the *electronic* voltmeter. Although self-contained meters are usually desirable, there are many instances where consistently accurate measurements are required. Because of temperature changes and other factors causing resistance variations in the multipliers, many of the portable, self-contained types are unsatisfactory for precision use. The vacuum-tube voltmeter, which is in reality a combination of vacuum-tube and bridge principles, is one of the most accurate voltmeters in general use.

14·1 VTVM Operation. The VTVM employs the advantages of the Wheatstone bridge in conjunction with the characteristics of the electron tube.

Figure 14·1 is a schematic of a basic VTVM. This is typical of a basic type for purpose of explanation only and must not be construed as the average type actually employed in electronics use. However, the principles that apply in this example are equally applicable in almost all VTVM's now in use.

With no voltage across the test points, the source voltage is across the voltage dividing network comprised of R_1 and R_2. While this voltage may be obtained from batteries, as in other measuring devices, it has been found more practical to use an ordinary source of alternating voltage and a *power supply*, which is a means of converting a-c volts to the desired value of direct voltage. With current through R_1 and R_2 as shown, one side of R_1 is positive with respect to the other side. With no voltage being measured, there is no current through R_7 and R_8, and the voltage at the control grid of the tube is the same as at the negative side of R_1. Since the cathode of the tube is connected to the positive side of R_1, the cathode is positive with respect to the grid and the tube is biased. Since a triode has some value of plate resistance R_p, if the tube's emission is being controlled by biasing, then its plate resistance is constant enough to be considered as a fixed resistor under static conditions. In order to achieve a condition of balance in the bridge, R_3 must be adjusted to equal the value of plate resistance of the tube. When these two resistances are equal, the voltage difference between points B and C will be zero and there will be no current through the meter movement. The movement in a VTVM is not that of a galvanometer but is a moving-coil type with zero deflection at the left side rather than at mid-scale.

The values of R_4 and R_5 are not important as long as they satisfy the requirements of a balanced bridge and as long as R_4 does not limit current through V_1 to such an extent that the tube cannot conduct.

Therefore, with no voltage between the positive and negative probes, the variable resistor R_3 is set for zero deflection on the movement and the bridge is balanced. Paths for current are as follows: from point A through V_1, to point B, through R_4, and to the positive side of the source.

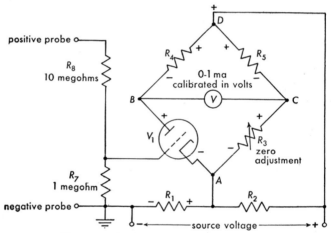

Fig. 14·1   Basic vacuum-tube voltmeter.

The other path is from point A through R_3 to point C, through R_5 and back to the positive side of the source.

If a voltage is placed under test, this voltage will appear across both R_7 and R_8. Since R_8 is 10 times as large as R_7, only a small part of this voltage will be applied across R_7, while the major part will be across R_8. The grid side of R_7 will become more positive than the cathode side; therefore, the bias on the tube will be reduced and conduction will increase. If V_1 increases conduction, R_4 must pass more current and the voltage across it must also increase. This increase in voltage will cause point B to be less negative than point C and there will be some amount of current through the meter movement from left to right.

Thus, with voltage between the test probes, the bridge becomes unbalanced and there is current through the meter movement. Like all other meters discussed, the movement is deflecting as a result of current. However, the movement is calibrated in terms of what is being measured

rather than the amount of current.   A VTVM is calibrated much like a
standard   voltmeter   or   ohmmeter.   Known   voltages   are   connected
between the probes, and the deflection resulting from these known voltages is marked on the scale.   Thereafter, by comparison, unknown voltages can be measured.

14·2   Multirange VTVM.   The method employed in making a VTVM
usable over a wide range of voltages can be understood by reference to
Fig. 14·2.   This is a typical VTVM circuit which includes a rotary switch
and a tapped resistor substituted for R_7 as shown in Fig. 14·1.   Assume
that the meter is adjusted to read 10 volts and that 10 volts is connected
between the test probes.   Circuit conditions are the same as in the example previously shown.

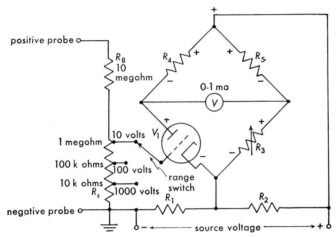

Fig. 14·2   Typical vacuum-tube-voltmeter circuit.

Total resistance between the probes is 11 megohms, 10 megohms of
which is not tapped.   The 1-megohm resistor R_s, although tapped, is in
the circuit at all times between the probes.   By application of Ohm's law,
current through the resistors with 10 volts applied is

$$I = \frac{E}{R} = \frac{10}{11 \times 10^6} = 0.91 \ \mu a$$

Since this is a series circuit, voltage across R_s can be computed by

$$E = IR_s$$
$$= 0.91 \times 10^{-6} \times 1 \times 10^6 = 0.91 \ \text{volt}$$

Therefore, when 0.91 volt is present at the control grid of the tube, the
meter movement is showing full-scale deflection.

The 100-volt range operates on much the same principle.   Between the
two probes 11 megohms resistance is present; however, because 100 volts

is applied at full scale, the current will be 10 times as great as on the 10-volt range.   Therefore, if R_s were not tapped, 9.1 volts would be present at the top of R_s and applied to the grid of the tube.   Since this value is obviously too much for the meter movement, R_s is tapped at a point where only 0.91 volt is applied when using the 100-volt range.   This point is at 0.1 megohm.   Thus, on the 10-volt range grid resistance to ground is 1 megohm, while on the 100-volt range it is 0.1 megohm. When the 1,000-volt range is used, this 10:1 relation is maintained by tapping R_s at 10,000 ohms, which is the 0.91-volt point.

On each range, full-scale deflection will result when the grid is made 0.91 volt less negative with respect to the cathode.   Therefore, the degree of unbalance reaches a point where there will be 1 ma of current when the bias on V_1 is reduced by 0.91 volt.

The variable resistor R_3 is used in the multirange VTVM to compensate for both contact resistance changes in the rotary switch and aging of the tube.   Another important use of R_3 is to compensate for voltage fluctuations in the power supply.   If the source voltage should change, then the bias on the tube will change.   This results in a change in current and plate voltage that effectively compensates for the fluctuation in power supply and maintains the condition of balance.

Although a 10:1 ratio of voltage and resistance was used in Fig. 14·2, this was merely for purpose of explanation.   Many VTVM's have ranges starting at approximately 3 volts with higher ranges in multiples of 3.

14·3   VTVM Sensitivity.   In the examples shown, there is at all times 11 megohms between the probes, regardless of the range being used.   If 10 volts is being measured, this 11-megohm resistance across the voltage under test will have an almost negligible shunting effect.   At higher values of voltage, the shunting effect will be correspondingly smaller. By comparison, an ordinary voltmeter having a sensitivity rating of 1,000 ohms per volt would offer a total of only 10,000 ohms on the 10-volt range.

The procedure for computing the ohms-per-volt sensitivity of a vacuum-tube voltmeter is to divide the resistance between the probes by the maximum voltage of any particular range.   For example, the sensitivity for the 10-volt range of the VTVM in Fig. 14·2 is

$$\frac{11 \times 10^6}{10} = 1.1 \text{ megohms per volt}$$

For the 100-volt range, the sensitivity is

$$\frac{11 \times 10^6}{100} = 110,000 \text{ ohms per volt}$$

For the 1,000-volt range, the sensitivity is

$$\frac{11 \times 10^6}{1,000} = 11,000 \text{ ohms per volt}$$

The sensitivity of a vacuum-tube voltmeter, even on its highest range, is often better than that of the average voltmeter. Also, even though only a 1-ma movement is used, the result is a more rugged measuring device. The shunting effect which is considerable in most other voltmeters because of insensitive movements, is not a consideration with a VTVM. Since the meter input of a VTVM is electrically isolated from the movement input, changes present at the meter input are independent of the movement itself.

14·4 VTVM Advantages. The uses of the VTVM and its advantages over other types of voltage measuring devices are numerous. The VTVM can be used in any application where shunting effect would otherwise cause an erroneous reading. It is ordinarily as portable as other types and can be used with equal accuracy in both laboratory and field. The main advantage, however, is that a VTVM can be made electrically more rugged than other voltmeters, yet provide greater accuracy. This is because the movement can be less sensitive without sacrificing accuracy. It is therefore often advantageous to use the vacuum-tube voltmeter in preference to any of the ordinary types discussed. The only outstanding disadvantage is the requirement of an a-c source. This is minimized, however, by the fact that most electronic equipment is energized from sources of voltage that may also be used for energizing the VTVM while servicing the equipment.

Fig. 14·3   Typical commercial VTVM. (*Electronic Instrument Company, Inc.*)

Precautions. Normal precautions apply to vacuum-tube voltmeters as to all meters. Polarities must be observed, and the meter should be set for the highest range, then reduced to the proper range that will give a readable deflection. A VTVM should be protected against physical shock. Also, sufficient warmup time should be allowed so that the electron tube will be conducting normally prior to making any measurements.

14·5   Tube Testers.   While it is not essential to this text that measuring devices other than those already mentioned should be discussed in great detail, one additional measuring device that merits mentioning is the *tube tester*.   This is an instrument that also operates on the principle of the vacuum tube and is used to measure the characteristics of a vacuum tube in determining its suitability for a particular circuit.   The tube to be tested is connected into a socket that is further connected to the various voltages required by the tube under normal operating conditions.   The

Fɪɢ. 14·4   Typical commercial tube tester.   (*Electronic Instrument Company, Inc.*)

tube tester then gives indications as to the ability of the tube to perform its design function.

REVIEW QUESTIONS

1. If a vacuum-tube voltmeter has a rating of 3.67 megohms per volt on its 3-volt range, what would be its rating on its 30-volt range if the 10:1 relation was maintained?

2. In Question 1 what is the resistance between the probes of the VTVM?

3. In Question 1 what is the current through the input resistor at full-scale deflection on the 30-volt range?

4. Explain how the bridge is balanced in a VTVM.

5. Trace the paths for current through the VTVM bridge.

6. Under normal conditions when no voltage is being measured, how does the bridge become unbalanced?

7. Explain the principle of operation of multirange VTVM's.

8. In Question 7 how is the same bias-reducing voltage arrived at for each range?

9. What are two purposes of the variable resistor R_3?

10. In Fig. 14·1, what is the function of R_1 and R_2?

11. In Fig. 14·1, what is the function of R_7 and R_8?

12. What requirements must be met when selecting values for R_4 and R_5?

13. List two advantages of the VTVM.

14. List one disadvantage of the VTVM.

15. Explain how a bias is developed on the tube in Fig. 14·1.

16. Explain why the shunting effect of the VTVM is negligible.

17. How does the plate resistance of the tube affect the balance of the bridge in a VTVM?

18. Why is a warmup time necessary when using a VTVM?

19. What precautions are necessary when using a VTVM?

20. Upon what principle does a tube tester operate?

CHAPTER 15

ALTERNATING-CURRENT FUNDAMENTALS

Thus far, alternating current has only been mentioned, while direct voltages and currents have been considered in detail. While electric current is a movement of electrons through a conductor, the effect of this movement is changed once movement ceases to be in one direction and of one magnitude. Over 90 per cent of all electrical energy produced is in the form of alternating current, which is one that alternates, or changes its direction periodically. A direct voltage does not change in polarity nor does a direct current change its direction. Once direction and polarity is changed, as in alternating currents, there is a change in the constants and characteristics of an electric circuit.

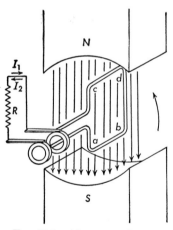

Fig. 15·1   Alternator theory.

The volume of energy produced for commercial applications makes the study of alternating current of importance to the electrician, while the electronics technician is even more concerned, because practically all electronic circuits are based upon alternating-current phenomena.

15·1 Alternator Theory. The simplest type of machine for generating an alternating voltage, or electromotive force, is called the *alternator*. An emf that periodically reverses its direction, or polarity, is known as an alternating electromotive force and the resulting current is known as alternating current (a-c).

The principle of simple alternator operation is shown in Fig. 15·1. A conducting loop of wire *abdc*, with its ends connected to *slip rings*, is rotated on its horizontal axis in the air space between the north and south poles of a magnet. The principle of operation is that of an emf being induced in a conductor due to its movement through a magnetic field.

128

The slip rings are for the purpose of transferring the emf and current generated for use in external circuits.

From previous study of magnetic circuits, it is apparent that an emf will be generated. For purpose of illustration, consider the coil to be rotated in a counterclockwise direction. When side ab moves from its present position away from the S pole of the magnet, it will cut some of the lines of force that comprise the magnetic field between N and S and an emf will be generated in the coil. The direction of current resulting from this generated emf will be from b to a; that is, b will be negative with respect to a. At the same time ab is cutting the lines of force in one direction, side cd is moving away from the N pole and cuts through the magnetic field in the opposite direction. Therefore, the direction of current in the cd side will be from c to d, adding to that from b to a and sending a current I_1 through the load resistor R.

Current from point c will continue in the direction $cdba$ as long as the magnetic lines of force are being cut in the same direction; that is, until the coil has rotated through 90° from the position shown. When it has rotated by this amount, the plane of the coil is perpendicular to the lines of force and cuts none of them. At this instant, emf generated is zero, and therefore current is zero.

As the side ab begins to move further toward the N pole of the magnet, the emf generated in it will now be in the direction from a to b. This reversal of direction is due to the change in direction of motion with respect to the lines of force. Similarly, because side cd is now moving down toward the S pole, the emf in it will be from d to c which adds to that in side ab. Current through R is represented by I_2 and is in the direction indicated by the arrow.

Current through the coil will be in the direction $abdc$ for 180°, or until the plane of the coil is again perpendicular to the magnetic lines of force. At the instant this point is reached, which is 270° from that shown in Fig. 15·1, emf and current are again zero, since none of the lines of force are being cut. Rotation beyond this point, however, causes an electromotive force to be generated that will result in current in the original direction I_1.

15·2 Variation of Alternating Emf. In addition to changing direction, or polarity, alternating emf and current vary in amplitude as a *sine wave*. A sine wave is a graphical representation of an induced emf or current in a conductor rotating in a uniform magnetic field. Explanation of this action is shown in Fig. 15·2, which represents a cross-sectional view of the alternator of Fig. 15·1. Although it must be understood that the coil is in continuous movement, for purpose of explanation it will be considered stopped at successive instants during rotation as represented by the numbers 0 to 11.

In order for an emf to be generated in a conductor, there must be a component of its velocity at right angles to the lines of force. For example, a conductor must actually cut the lines of force through which it passes. The amount of emf generated will be proportional to the number of lines cut and the rate of cutting. For a given magnetic field, an increase in the speed of cutting will result in an increase in generated emf; likewise, for a given speed, an increase in magnetic field strength will cause an increase in emf.

From Fig. 15·2 it is evident that the amount of emf generated will be proportional to the angle of rotation of the conductor to the magnetic lines of force. Because the component of horizontal velocity is perpendicular to the magnetic field, it is this component that develops an emf. For example, when the conductor is at position 0-6, it is moving parallel to the

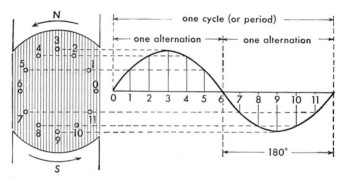

Fig. 15·2   One cycle of alternator voltage varying as a sine wave.

field, where the angle of rotation is zero, and there is no voltage generated. As it moves toward position 1-7, the component of horizontal velocity becomes greater due to increased angular velocity with respect to the lines of force being cut, and the generated emf increases from point 0 to point 1 on the sine wave. As it continues to move in a counterclockwise direction and arrives at point 2-8, the increased angle of rotation results in greater cutting effect and an increase in emf shown at point 2 on the sine wave. At point 3-9 the component of horizontal velocity is maximum due to the conductor's being at right angles to the magnetic field. At this instant, cutting effect is maximum and emf is maximum as shown at point 3 on the sine wave. Continued rotation to point 4-10 within the alternator field reduces the angle of cutting, and emf decreases to point 4. As the conductor continues to rotate, the component of horizontal velocity becomes less until the conductor is moving parallel to the field and the angle of rotation is again zero. When this condition is reached, voltage is again zero as shown at point 6 on the sine wave. Further movement to point 7-1 results in an emf generated in the opposite direction but of the same magnitude as that shown at point 1 on the sine wave. The remaining rotation through the full 360° follows the same pattern as that through the first 180° but with a change in polarity.

Therefore, the sine curve of Fig. 15·2 is a graphical representation of the induced emf. The voltage starts from zero, increases in a positive direction to a maximum positive value at 90° of rotation, decreases to zero at 180°, increases in the opposite direction until it attains maximum negative value at 270°, then again decreases to zero at 360°. Thus, the emf is said to vary as a *sine wave*. The induced emf in a coil rotating in a magnetic field can be expressed by the relation

$$e = E_{max} \sin \theta$$

where e = instantaneous value of emf at any angle θ

E_{max} = maximum value of emf

θ = angular position of coil

sin = function of an angle, the ratio of side opposite to hypotenuse in a right triangle (see Sec. 16·7 and Appendix XII)

15·3 Frequency Spectrum. From the previous discussions, it is evident that during the 360° of conductor rotation, two *alternations* have taken place, each equal to 180° of rotation. Two alternations constitute one *cycle;* that is, when the alternator has gone through 360° it is said to have completed one cycle, as shown in Fig. 15·2. The *frequency f* of the induced emf is the number of cycles completed in one second.

Frequency is best defined as *rapidity of occurrence* and has many important aspects in the study of electronics. While the electrician knows that most of the electrical energy supplied for commercial use is of the 60-cycle variety, the technician is more concerned with what is known as the *radio-frequency* (r-f) *spectrum*. A 60-cycle current transmitted through power lines is one which rises to maximum in both directions 60 times a second, or has a frequency of 60 cycles per second (cps). In transmitting electrical impulses, or *waves*, through the air over great distances the frequency is of the order of millions of cycles per second.

An example of audible frequency change and its effect upon the human ear is in the variation in *pitch* of a siren. Pitch is defined as the number of air waves per second either produced by a vibrating source or received by the ear. The low pitch of a siren is comprised of vibrations that are low in frequency, while the high pitch means an increase in the number of vibrations per second, or frequency. The ear is most sensitive to vibrations, or frequencies, between 400 and 4,000 cps. Although the range to which the human ear will respond varies, it has been found to be from approximately 20 to 20,000 cps. This is known as the *audio-frequency* (a-f) *range*.

While the number of cycles per second of a radio wave is called its frequency, the distance that a radio wave travels in one cycle is called its *wavelength*. Expressed in meters, it is the space occupied in air by one cycle. Since all electromagnetic energy propagated through space travels at the speed of light, or 186,000 miles per sec (3×10^8 meters per sec), wavelength is inversely proportional to frequency. As the frequency of the vibration increases, the wavelength will decrease. Likewise, as wavelength is increased, frequency is decreased. This relation can be expressed as follows:

$$\lambda = \frac{300,000,000}{f}$$

where λ = wavelength, meters
f = frequency, cps

The audio-frequency range is used in commercial power applications, telephony, and public address systems, to mention a few of its uses. However, for transmission of electromagnetic energy through space over great distances, higher order frequencies are used. To eliminate interference and for best results, the Federal Communications Commission (FCC) allocates frequencies within certain ranges for various uses. This is called the radio-frequency spectrum and is classified in decades, with a name given to each, ranging from the low-frequency decade to that of the super-high frequency. For example, the very low-frequency band, or decade, is in the range from 10,000 to 30,000 cps; the high-frequency band from 3,000 to 30,000 kc; and the ultra-high frequency band from 300 to 3,000 Mc, etc.

15·4 A-C Values. For purposes of computing power or the amount of work performed by an alternating current or voltage, the effect must be considered as different from that produced by direct currents or voltages. Since the magnitude of an alternating current is varying at each instant, for any given instant the effect on a resistor would be the same as that produced by a corresponding d-c value but the effect of one complete cycle would not be comparable.

Instantaneous Value. The instantaneous value e of a pure sine wave of voltage or current is the value at any instant during the cycle. In Fig. 15·3 any point on the sine wave could be considered as an *instantaneous* value for determining voltage or current at that particular point.

Maximum Value. The maximum voltage and current values reached during one cycle are known as *maximum* values and are represented by the notations E_{max} and I_{max}. The maximum value attained by the sine wave of voltage in Fig. 15·3 is as indicated.

Average Value. Since an alternating current or voltage is of sine-wave form, the average voltage or current through one cycle is zero due to the reversal of direction on each half-cycle.   However, average value is used to mean the average value of one half-cycle, disregarding positive or negative signs.   This value may be computed fairly accurately by taking the average of many instantaneous values, separated by equal values of angle. The *average* value of a sine wave is equal to its average height and will be

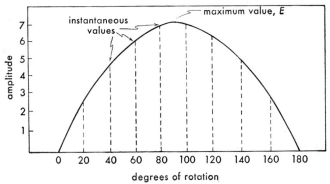

Fɪɢ. 15·3   One-half of sine wave showing instantaneous and maximum values.   Average value can be computed by averaging dotted ordinates.

found to be 0.637 times the maximum value, represented by the notations E_{av} and I_{av}.   Thus

$$E_{av} = 0.637E_{max} \quad \text{and} \quad I_{av} = 0.637I_{max}$$

Also

$$E_{max} = \frac{E_{av}}{0.637} = 1.57E_{av} \quad \text{and} \quad I_{max} = \frac{I_{av}}{0.637} = 1.57I_{av}$$

Effective Value.   The *effective* value of alternating current or voltage is that which will produce the same heating effect in a given resistor as the same value of direct current or voltage.   Since an alternating current or voltage is varying in magnitude at each instant, an alternating current with a maximum value of 1 amp could not be expected to produce as much heat in a resistor as a direct current of 1 amp.   Thus, alternating current is not so effective as direct current for the same maximum value.   In order to determine the effective value of an alternating current, it has to be rated in terms of direct current.

The effective value of a sine wave may be computed to a fair degree of accuracy by taking equally spaced instantaneous values and extracting the square root of their average, or mean, squared values.   Because of the sequence in which effective values are found, they are often called *root-mean-square* (rms) values.   The effective or rms value E of a pure sine wave has been found to be about 0.707 of the maximum value. Thus

$$E = 0.707 E_{max} \quad \text{and} \quad I = 0.707 I_{max}$$

Also

$$E_{max} = \frac{E}{0.707} = 1.414E \quad \text{and} \quad I_{max} = \frac{I}{0.707} = 1.414I$$

15·5 Measuring Alternating Current. A common type of meter used for measuring small values of alternating currents and voltages is the *copper-oxide* type. By combining copper and copper oxide, current is produced through a meter in one direction only, a phenomenon known as *rectification*. By proper scale calibration, effective values are measured.

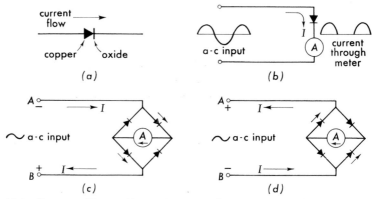

FIG. 15·4   Copper-oxide rectifier action. (*a*) Circuit symbol of copper-oxide unit showing direction of current. (*b*) Action of copper-oxide rectifier on full-wave a-c input. Only one half-cycle flows through meter. (*c*) Current through meter and rectifier on one-half of a-c input cycle. (*d*) Current through meter and rectifier on opposite half of a-c input cycle.

The copper-oxide rectifier is made by causing a layer of cuprous oxide to form on the face of a pure copper washer, or disk, by a special heat treatment. Due to orientation, or polarization, of the molecules at the junction between copper and oxide, the transfer of electrons will encounter less opposition in one direction than in the other. In this particular application, electrons will flow from the copper to the oxide but will find a high resistance to their flow from the oxide to the copper. If a meter is connected as shown in Fig. 15·4*b*, on one half of the cycle, there will be current through the meter. On the opposite half-cycle the high resistance offered by the oxide-to-copper action will reduce current to practically zero. Therefore, current indicated on the meter, if calibrated in effective values, is the effective value of one half-cycle.

In order to indicate the effective value of alternating current on both halves of the cycle, four of the copper-oxide disks are connected in an arrangement known as a bridge circuit, as shown in Fig. 15·4c and d. When point A of the input circuit is negative, current exists through the bridge circuit and meter as shown in c.   On the opposite half-cycle when point A is positive, current exists through the bridge circuit as shown in d. However, current through the meter is in the same direction as before. The resultant current that the meter "sees" is a form of direct current through rectification, in which both halves of the a-c cycle are utilized for measurement.   This is known as *full-wave* rectification, in which both halves of the a-c cycle are rectified, that is, changed from alternating to direct current.   If only one half-cycle was rectified, it would be known as *half-wave* rectification.

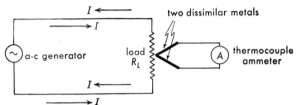

FIG. 15·5   Thermocouple ammeter circuit.

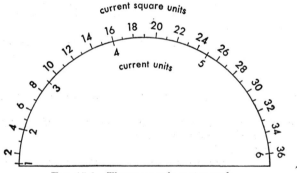

FIG. 15·6   Thermocouple meter scale.

Thermocouple Ammeter.   Another means of measuring alternating currents is the *thermocouple ammeter* which utilizes the thermal principle of producing an emf.   As previously stated, certain dissimilar metals will produce a difference of potential if heated at their junction point.   The emf indicated on a measuring device connected across the thermocouple can be measured by the amount of heat causing it.

In the thermocouple ammeter an alternating current heats the junction of the dissimilar metals, as shown in Fig. 15·5.   Since heat produced as a result of current through resistance varies as the square of the current $(P = I^2R)$, it follows that the meter deflection will roughly follow a square law pattern, and so this type of meter usually has a nonlinear scale.

Some of the metals from which thermocouple-ammeter units are made are bismuth, antimony, and steel. A meter using this principle may be calibrated in evenly spaced units called *current-square* units or in units which read current directly. Figure 15·6 shows a typical thermocouple meter scale calibrated by both methods.

REVIEW QUESTIONS

1. Explain the major differences between direct and alternating currents.

2. Explain the basic principle upon which an alternator operates.

3. What factors are necessary in order for an emf to be generated in a conductor?

4. Explain the difference between alternations, cycles, and frequency.

5. What is the difference between low and high pitch?

6. What is wavelength and how is it determined?

7. Explain the relation between wavelength and frequency.

8. Explain radio-frequency spectrum and the different decades of which it is comprised.

9. How is the instantaneous value of a sine-wave voltage determined?

10. Explain the difference between average and maximum values of an alternating current or voltage.

11. How are effective (rms) values of alternating current or voltage determined?

12. Explain the principle of operation of a copper-oxide rectifying device.

13. How is it possible for copper-oxide-type meters to measure alternating currents and voltages?

14. Explain the principle of operation of the thermocouple ammeter.

15. What is the difference between half-wave and full-wave rectification?

16. Explain in detail why the effects of alternating currents differ from those of direct currents.

17. What causes the change in direction of current in a coil rotating in a magnetic field?

18. Explain the relation between amount of emf generated, strength of magnetic field, rate of cutting, and number of lines cut.

19. What is a sine wave?

20. Explain why the human ear is more sensitive to frequencies within a certain range.

21. Why is the technician mostly concerned with the r-f spectrum?

22. Explain the difference in effect between 1 ampere of alternating current and 1 ampere of direct current.

CHAPTER 16

INTRODUCTION TO TRIGONOMETRY

A clear understanding of alternating-current theory and circuits is based upon the knowledge of trigonometry. The word "trigonometry" is derived from two Greek words and means *measurement* or *solution of triangles*. It is both algebraic and geometric in nature. And while it forms a basis for more advanced study in mathematics, in this text the study of trigonometry will be confined to the solution of triangles.

One of the most important applications of trigonometry is the solution of *right* triangles, the most universally used of all geometric figures. Most of the problems relating to the analysis of alternating-current circuits involve the solution of right triangles in one form or another.

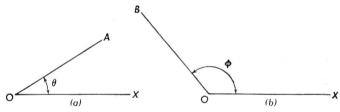

Fig. 16·1   Angular relationships.

16·1   Angles.   In order to understand the meaning and measurement of angles, it is necessary to study the relations that exist among the angles and sides of triangles.

An angle is formed when two straight lines meet at a point. In Fig. 16·1a, lines OA and OX meet at point O to form the angle AOX. Also, in Fig. 16·1b, the angle BOX is formed by lines OB and OX meeting at point O. The point where the lines meet is called the *vertex* of the angle, and the two lines are called the *sides* of the angle. The lengths of the sides of an angle have no bearing on its size. The *size*, or magnitude, is determined by the measure of the difference in *directions* of the sides.

It is customary to denote an angle by the symbol $\angle$. If this notation is used, angle AOX would be written $\angle AOX$. An angle can also be denoted by a letter at its vertex or by a supplementary letter placed inside the angle.   Thus, angle AOX can be correctly denoted by $\angle AOX$, $\angle O$, or $\angle\theta$.

If four equal angles are formed by the intersection of two straight lines,

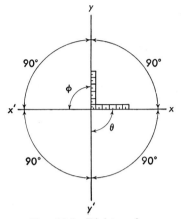

the angles are called *right angles*.   In Fig. 16·2 all four of the angles are right angles.

An *acute* angle is an angle that is less than a right angle.   In Fig. 16·3a $\angle\alpha$ is an acute angle.

An *obtuse* angle is an angle that is greater than a right angle.   In Fig. 16·3b $\angle\beta$ is an obtuse angle.

Two angles whose sum is equal to one right angle are called *complementary* angles.   Either one is said to be the complement of the other.   In Fig. 16·3c angles ϕ and θ are complementary angles.

Fig. 16·2   Right angles.

Two angles whose sum is equal to two right angles (a straight line) are called *supplementary* angles.   Either one is said to be the supplement of the other.   Thus, in Fig. 16·3d angles b and a are supplementary angles; b is the supplement of a, and a is the supplement of b.

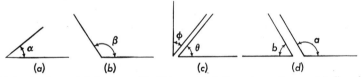

Fig. 16·3   Angles.   (*a*) Acute.   (*b*) Obtuse.   (*c*) Complementary.   (*d*) Supplementary.

16·2   Generation of Angles.   In the study of trigonometry as applied to alternating-current theory, an angle should be thought of as being generated by a line segment that starts in a certain initial position and rotates about a point called the vertex.   The original position of the rotating line is called the *initial side* of the angle and the final position is called the *terminal side*.

An angle is called a *positive* angle if it is generated by a line revolving around its vertex in a counterclockwise direction.   If the line revolves clockwise, it generates a *negative* angle.   In Fig. 16·4 θ is a positive angle that was generated by the line OP moving counterclockwise from OX; ϕ is a negative angle generated by the line OM moving clockwise from OX.

16·3   Angular Measurement.   Although there are several systems of angular measurement, of primary concern in this text is the *degree*.   The degree is defined as the angle formed by $\frac{1}{360}$ of a revolution of the angle-generating line; 90° is one-fourth of a circle. The degree is divided into 60 equal parts called *minutes*, and the minute into 60 equal parts called *seconds.* This system of measurement is called the "sexagesimal" system, a derivative of a Latin word pertaining to the number 60.

For convenience, however, fractions of degrees will be divided into decimals rather than minutes and seconds in future portions of this text. Thus, in expressing an angle of 38 degrees 24 minutes, instead of 38°24′ it will be written 38.4°. Likewise, 47°30′ will be written 47.5°. (0.5 × 60° = 30°.)

The angle formed by a generating line can be found in any of four standard positions on the circular plane of reference and is measured to the nearest X axis. In Fig. 16·4 angle YOX is known as the first quadrant, angle YOX' as the second quadrant, $X'OY'$ as the third quadrant, and $Y'OX$ as the fourth quadrant. If the terminal side of an angle lies in the first quadrant, then that angle is said to be *an angle in the first quadrant.* Thus, angle θ is in the first quadrant and angle ϕ is in the third quadrant.

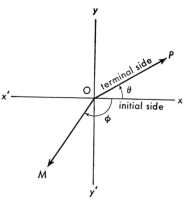

Fig. 16·4 Positive angle θ. Negative angle ϕ.

Angles of Any Magnitude. Thinking of an angle as being generated, as previously explained, permits consideration of angles of any size. The generating line may rotate from its original position in a positive or negative direction to produce an angle even in excess of 360°. However, for purposes of ordinary computation, such an angle is considered to be in the same quadrant as its terminal side with a magnitude equal to the remainder after the largest multiple of 360° it will contain has been subtracted from it. Thus, in Fig. 16·5 the angle is in the first quadrant and is equal to 750° − 720° = 30°.

Fig. 16·5 Angular measurement.

16·4 Similar Triangles. Two triangles are said to be *similar* when their corresponding angles are equal; that is, when they are identical in shape although not necessarily of the same size. The important characteristic is that a direct proportionality exists between corresponding sides. The three triangles of Fig. 16·6 have been constructed so that their corresponding angles are equal. Therefore, they are similar and lead to several proportions, for example:

$$\frac{AB}{AC} = \frac{DE}{DF} = \frac{GH}{GI} \quad \text{and} \quad \frac{BC}{AB} = \frac{EF}{DE} = \frac{HI}{GH}$$

Then, if side AB was equal to 1 in., DE equal to 2 in., and GH equal to 3 in., it would follow that DF is twice as long as AC and GI is three times as long as AC. Also, HI is three times as long as BC, and EF is twice as long as BC.

Since the sum of the three angles of *any* triangle is 180°, then if two angles of a triangle are equal to two angles of another triangle, the third angle of one has to be equal to the third angle of the other. Therefore,

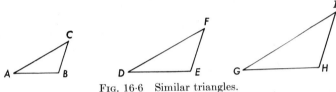

Fig. 16·6   Similar triangles.

two triangles are similar if *two angles of one are equal to two angles of the other.*

16·5   The Right Triangle.   If one of the angles of a triangle is a right angle, or 90°, the triangle is called a *right triangle.* Then, since the sum of the angles of any triangle is 180°, a right triangle contains one right angle and two acute angles. Also, as previously learned, the sum of the acute angles must be 90°. This relation enables the finding of one acute angle when the other is given. For example, if one acute angle of a right triangle is 35°, then the other acute angle must be 90° − 35° = 55°.

Since all right angles are equal, if an acute angle of one right triangle is equal to an acute angle of another right triangle, the two triangles are similar.

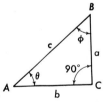

Fig. 16·7   Right triangle.

The side of a right triangle opposite the right angle is called the *hypotenuse*. Thus, in Fig. 16·7 the side c is the hypotenuse, side a is called the *altitude*, and side b is called the *base*. Another important property of any right triangle is that the *square of the hypotenuse is equal to the sum of the squares of the remaining two sides*. This relation provides a means of computing any one of the three sides if two sides are given and is expressed algebraically

$$c^2 = a^2 + b^2$$

16·6   Facts about Triangles.   In summary, it will be useful to remember the following facts about triangles.

a. All triangles have six elements; three sides and three angles.

b. The sum of the three angles enclosed in a triangle is always 180°.

c. The sum of the two acute angles in a right triangle is equal to 90°.

d. The largest side of a triangle always lies opposite the largest angle.

e. Two triangles are said to be similar when their corresponding angles are equal.

f. Corresponding sides of similar triangles are directly proportional.

g. If one of the angles of a triangle is equal to 90°, the triangle is called a right triangle.

16·7 Trigonometric Ratios. The correlation that exists between the sides and angles of a right triangle is expressed in terms of ratios. These ratios are as follows and have been assigned the following names.

$\dfrac{a}{c}$ is called the *sine* of the angle θ and written sin θ.

$\dfrac{b}{c}$ is called the *cosine* of the angle θ and written cos θ.

$\dfrac{a}{b}$ is called the *tangent* of the angle θ and written tan θ.

$\dfrac{b}{a}$ is called the *cotangent* of the angle θ and written cot θ.

$\dfrac{c}{b}$ is called the *secant* of the angle θ and written sec θ.

$\dfrac{c}{a}$ is called the *cosecant* of the angle θ and written csc θ.

These definitions can be remembered better if the position of the sides of the triangle is taken into consideration with respect to the acute angle being computed.   For example, in Fig. 16·8, b is called the *adjacent side* of θ, and a is called the *opposite side*.   Defined in terms of sides, these trigonometric functions are as follows:

$$\sin \theta = \frac{\text{opposite side}}{\text{hypotenuse}} = \frac{a}{c}$$

$$\tan \theta = \frac{\text{opposite side}}{\text{adjacent side}} = \frac{a}{b}$$

$$\sec \theta = \frac{\text{hypotenuse}}{\text{adjacent side}} = \frac{c}{b}$$

$$\cos \theta = \frac{\text{adjacent side}}{\text{hypotenuse}} = \frac{b}{c}$$

$$\cot \theta = \frac{\text{adjacent side}}{\text{opposite side}} = \frac{b}{a}$$

$$\csc \theta = \frac{\text{hypotenuse}}{\text{opposite side}} = \frac{c}{a}$$

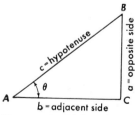

FIG.   16·8   Right-triangle nomenclature.

The sine, cosine, and tangent are the ratios most frequently used in practical work, and they should be memorized. If this is done, the others can be remembered because they are reciprocals. For example,

$$\sin \theta = \frac{a}{c} = \frac{1}{\dfrac{c}{a}} = \frac{1}{\csc \theta} \quad \text{and} \quad \csc \theta = \frac{c}{a} = \frac{1}{\dfrac{a}{c}} = \frac{1}{\sin \theta}$$

16·8　Solving Right Triangles.

In alternating-current problems a different form of notating the various elements of right triangles is employed. The opposite side is lettered X, adjacent side R, and hypotenuse Z. This change has no effect on the fundamental relations existing between the elements of a right triangle, nor are any new ideas involved in connection with the trigonometric functions.

The following examples illustrate all the possible conditions encountered in the solution of right triangles.

Given an Acute Angle and a Side Not the Hypotenuse.

Example 1: In Fig. 16·9 if $R = 30.0$ and $\theta = 25.0°$, solve for Z, X, and ϕ.

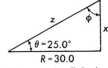

Solution:
$$\phi = 90° - \theta$$
$$= 90° - 25° = 65°$$

$$\tan \theta = \frac{X}{R}$$

FIG. 16·9 Solution of right triangle with one angle and one side known (side adjacent).

Solving for X,

$$X = R \tan \theta$$

Substituting the values of R and $\tan \theta$,

$$X = 30 \times 0.466 \text{ (Appendix XII)}$$
$$= 14.0$$

$$\sin \theta = \frac{X}{Z}$$

Solving for Z,

$$Z = \frac{X}{\sin \theta}$$

Substituting the values of X and $\sin \theta$,

$$Z = \frac{14.0}{0.423} = 33.1$$

Example 2: Given $X = 106$, and $\theta = 36.4°$, solve for Z, R, and ϕ.

Solution: The construction is shown in Fig. 16·10.

$$\sin \theta = \frac{X}{Z}$$

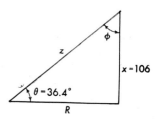

FIG. 16·10 Solution of right triangle with one angle and one side known (side opposite).

Solving for Z,

$$Z = \frac{X}{\sin \theta}$$

Substituting the values of X and $\sin \theta$,

$$Z = \frac{106}{0.593} = 179$$

$$\cos \theta = \frac{R}{Z}$$

Solving for R,

$$R = Z \cos \theta$$

Substituting the values of Z and $\cos \theta$,

$$R = 179 \times 0.805 = 144$$
$$\phi = 90° - \theta$$
$$= 90° - 36.4° = 53.6°$$

Given an Acute Angle and the Hypotenuse.

Example 1: In Fig. 16·11 if $Z = 45.3$ and $\theta = 20.3°$, find R, X, and ϕ.

Solution:
$$\phi = 90° - \theta$$
$$= 90° - 20.3° = 69.7°$$
$$\cos \theta = \frac{R}{Z}$$

Solving for R,

$$R = Z \cos \theta$$

Substituting the values of Z and $\cos \theta$,

$$R = 45.3 \times 0.938 = 42.5$$
$$\sin \theta = \frac{X}{Z}$$

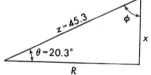

Fig. 16·11 Solution of right triangle with one angle and hypotenuse known (θ).

Solving for X,

$$X = Z \sin \theta$$

Substituting the values of Z and $\sin \theta$,

$$X = 45.3 \times 0.347 = 15.7$$

Example 2: Given $Z = 265$ and $\phi = 22.4°$, find R, X, and θ.
Solution: The construction is shown in Fig. 16·12.

$$\theta = 90° - \phi$$
$$= 90° - 22.4° = 67.6°$$

When θ is found, this triangle is solved by methods used in Example 1. Hence

$$R = Z \cos \theta = 265 \cos 67.6 = 265 \times 0.381 = 101$$
$$X = Z \sin \theta = 265 \sin 67.6 = 265 \times 0.924 = 245$$

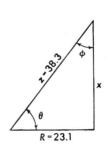

FIG. 16·12 Solution of right triangle with one angle and hypotenuse known (ϕ).

FIG. 16·13 Solution of right triangle with hypotenuse and side R known.

Given the Hypotenuse and One Other Side.

Example 1: In Fig. 16·13, $Z = 38.3$ and $R = 23.1$. Find X, θ, and ϕ.
Solution:

$$\cos \theta = \frac{R}{Z}$$

Substituting the values of R and Z,

$$\cos \theta = \frac{23.1}{38.3} = 0.603$$

Therefore

$$\theta = 52.9° \text{ (cosine table)}$$
$$\phi = 90° - \theta$$
$$= 90° - 52.9° = 37.1°$$
$$\sin \theta = \frac{X}{Z}$$

Solving for X,

$$X = Z \sin \theta$$

Substituting the values of Z and $\sin \theta$,

$$X = 38.3 \times 0.798 = 30.5$$

Example 2: Given $Z = 10.7$ and $X = 8.10$, find R, θ, and ϕ.
Solution: The construction is shown in Fig. 16·14.

$$\sin \theta = \frac{X}{Z}$$

Substituting the values of X and Z,

$$\sin \theta = \frac{8.10}{10.7} = 0.757$$

Therefore

$$\theta = 49.2° \text{ (sine table)}$$
$$\phi = 90° - \theta$$
$$= 90° - 49.2° = 40.8°$$
$$\cos \theta = \frac{R}{Z}$$

Solving for R,

$$R = Z \cos \theta$$

Substituting the values of Z and $\cos \theta$

$$R = 10.7 \times 0.653 = 6.99$$

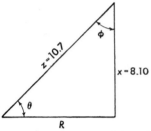

FIG. 16·14 Solution of right triangle with hypotenuse and side X known.

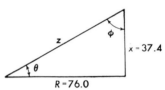

FIG. 16·15 Solution of right triangle with sides X and R known.

Given Two Sides Not the Hypotenuse.

Example: Given $R = 76.0$ and $X = 37.4$, find Z, θ, and ϕ.
Solution: The construction is shown in Fig. 16·15.

$$\tan \theta = \frac{X}{R}$$

Substituting the values of X and R,

$$\tan \theta = \frac{37.4}{76.0} = 0.492$$

Therefore

$$\theta = 26.2 \text{ (tangent table)}$$
$$\phi = 90° - \theta$$
$$= 90° - 26.2° = 63.8°$$

Z may be found equal to 84.7 by any one of the methods explained in preceding examples.

16·9   Sine Function.   The most important curve or graph encountered in alternating-current circuits is that of the *sine function*.   In order to develop the sine curve it is necessary to arrange the plane of reference as shown in Fig. 16·16.   The point of origin is at O, and angular displacement, or time, is measured along the horizontal axis.   The X axis may be laid off in any desired units such as seconds, degrees, or *radians* (57.3°).

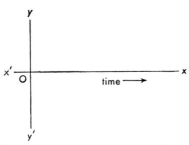

Fɪɢ. 16·16   Plane of reference for a sine curve

Figure 16·17 shows the projection of a point having uniform circular motion.   The radius vector r rotates about a point in a counterclockwise direction with a uniform angular velocity of 1 rps.   If the radius vector starts at 0°, at the end of $\frac{1}{12}$ sec it will have rotated 30° to point P_1. At the end of $\frac{1}{6}$ sec it will have rotated to P_2 and generated an angle of 60°.   The projection of the end point P of the radius vector may be plotted as a curve.   This can be done by extending the horizontal diameter of the circle to the right for use as an X axis along which time is to be plotted.   By the choice of a convenient length along the X axis, it can be

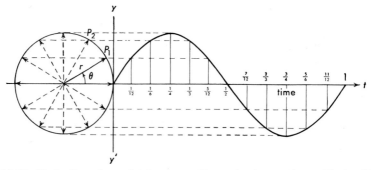

Fɪɢ. 16·17   Projection of a point having uniform circular motion.   (*Cooke, "Basic Mathematics for Electronics," McGraw-Hill Book Company, Inc.*, 1960.)

divided into as many intervals as there are angle values to be plotted. In Fig. 16·17 it is divided into 12 divisions, or every 30°.   Therefore, since one complete revolution occurs in 1 sec, each division of the X axis represents $\frac{1}{12}$ sec.

Vertical lines are drawn through the points of division on the time axis and intersected with horizontal lines made by the end point P of the radius vector at corresponding points.   The resulting curve drawn through the points of intersection is called a sine curve, or sine wave, and represents the sine value for any angle generated by the radius vector r.

From geometry it is known that the circumference of a circle is given by the relation

$$C = 2\pi r$$

where r = the radius of the circle

π = 3.14

The y value of the curve is proportional to the sine of the generated angle θ and the length of the radius vector r. Therefore, it can be expressed mathematically as

$$y = r \sin \theta$$

The generated angle θ is proportional to the number of cycles per second (f) of the radius vector and the amount of elapsed time t. Thus the number of revolutions is equal to ft, and since there are 2π radians $(6.28 \times 57.3° = 360°)$ in one revolution, the generated angle θ, measured in radians, can be expressed as

$$\theta = 2\pi ft$$

and, therefore,

$$y = r \sin 2\pi ft$$

In Fig. 16·17, since the radius vector r completes 1 revolution in 1 sec $(f = 1)$, the y value of the curve at any time t can be represented as

$$y = r \sin 2\pi t$$

In electrical work it is common practice to call the quantity $2\pi f$ the *angular velocity*, represented by the Greek letter ω (omega). Using this notation, the value of y can then be represented by the equation

$$y = r \sin \omega t$$

Any motion that can be described by this equation, that is, if the motion or variation may be represented as a sine curve, is said to be *sinusoidal* or to vary *sinusoidally*. A function that repeats itself in exactly the same order at regular intervals, or periodically, is called a *periodic function*. Figure 16·17 represents a periodic curve.

16·10 Amplitude. The value of the radius vector r determines the amplitude of a general curve, and for this reason the factor r in the general equation

$$y = r \sin \omega t$$

is called the *amplitude factor*. Thus, the amplitude of a periodic curve is taken as the maximum displacement, or value, of the curve. It is also apparent, then, that if the length of the radius vector which generates a sine wave is varied, the amplitude of the sine wave will vary accordingly. This is illustrated in Fig. 16·18.

16·11   Frequency.   When the radius vector makes one complete revolution, it has generated one complete sine wave, or completed one cycle.   The number of cycles occurring in a periodic curve in a unit of time is called the *frequency*.   For example, if the radius vector rotated 5 rps, the curve describing its motion would go through 5 cycles in 1 sec.   The frequency *f*, in cycles per second, is obtained by dividing the angular

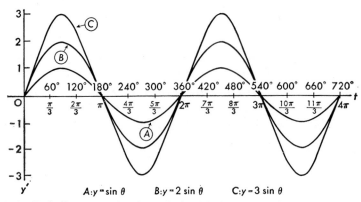

Fɪɢ. 16·18   Periodic curves showing relationship between radius vector and amplitude.   (*Cooke, "Basic Mathematics for Electronics," McGraw-Hill Book Company, Inc.,* 1960.)

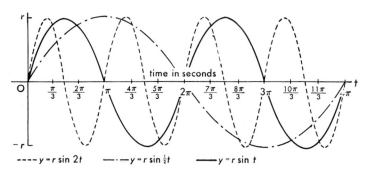

Fɪɢ. 16·19   Curves of different frequencies.   (*Cooke, "Basic Mathematics for Electronics," McGraw-Hill Book Company, Inc.,* 1960.)

velocity ω by 360° when the latter is measured in degrees or by 2π when measured in radians.   Curves for different frequencies are shown in Fig. 16·19.

In the equation $y = r \sin \frac{1}{2}t$, since $\omega t = \frac{1}{2}t$, the angular velocity ω is $\frac{1}{2}$ radian per sec.   That is, at the end of 2π, or 6.28, sec the curve has gone through one half-cycle, or 3.14 radians (180°) of angle as shown.

In the equation $y = r \sin t$, since $\omega t = t$, the angular velocity ω is 1 radian per sec.   Thus at the end of 2π sec the curve has gone through one complete cycle (360°), or 2π radians of angle.

Similarly, in the equation $y = r \sin 2t$, the angular velocity ω is 2 radians per sec. Then at the end of 2π sec the curve has completed two cycles (720°), or 4π radians of angle.

16·12 Period. The time t required for a periodic function, or curve, to complete one cycle is called the *period*. It is expressed by the equation

$$t = \frac{1}{f} \sec$$

For example, if a curve repeats itself 60 times in 1 sec, it has a frequency of 60 cps and a period of

$$t = \tfrac{1}{60} = 0.0167 \sec$$

In Fig. 16·19 the curve represented by $y = r \sin \tfrac{1}{2}t$ has a frequency of $0.5/2\pi = 0.0796$ cps and a period of 12.6 sec. The curve $y = r \sin t$ has a frequency of $1/2\pi = 0.159$ cps and a period of 6.28 sec. The curve $y = r \sin 2t$, has a frequency of 0.318 cps and a period of 3.14 sec.

16·13 Phase. In Fig. 16·20 two radius vectors are rotating about a point with equal angular velocities ω and separated by the constant

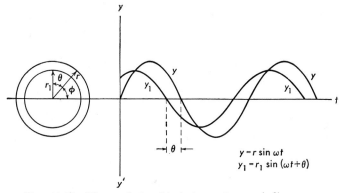

FIG. 16·20   Phase relationship between two periodic curves.

angle θ. That is, if r starts from the horizontal axis, then r_1 starts ahead of r by the angle θ and maintains this angular difference. When $t = 0$, r starts from the horizontal axis to generate the curve $y = r \sin \omega t$. At the same time, r_1 is ahead of r by an angle θ; hence, r_1 generates the curve $y_1 = r_1 \sin (\omega t + \theta)$. It will be noted that this displaces the y_1 curve along the horizontal by an angle θ as shown in the figure.

The angular difference between the two curves is called the *phase angle*, and since y_1 is ahead of y, it is said that y_1 leads y. Thus, in the equation $y_1 = r_1 \sin (\omega t + \theta)$, θ is called the *angle of lead*. In Fig. 16·20 y_1 leads y by 30°; therefore, the equation for y_1 becomes

$$y_1 = r_1 \sin (\omega t + 30°)$$

If y_1 lagged behind y by 30°, θ would be called the *angle of lag* and the equation for y_1 would become

$$y_1 = r_1 \sin (\omega t - 30°)$$

PROBLEMS

1. What is the complement of (a) 32°? (b) 98°? (c) −60°? (d) 66°?

2. What is the supplement of (a) 210°? (b) −85°? (c) 96°? (d) 133°?

3. Through how many right angles does the minute hand of a clock turn from 11:45 A.M. to 2:30 P.M. of the same day?

4. A motor has a speed of 3,600 rpm. What is the angular velocity (speed) in degrees per second?

5. How many degrees per minute does the minute hand of a clock rotate?

6. How many degrees per minute does the hour hand of a clock rotate?

7. An 1,800-rpm motor has its shaft connected directly to a pulley 18 in. in diameter. What is the pulley rim speed in feet per second?

8. What is the approximate angular velocity of the earth in degrees per minute?

9. Express in terms of π the number of radians in the following angles: (a) 360°. (b) 60°. (c) 90°. (d) 45°. (e) 180°.

10. A pole 80 ft in height is to be guyed 6 ft from its top to a point on the ground 50 ft from the base of the pole. What is the length of the guy?

11. An antenna tower casts a shadow 225 ft long at a time during the day when a yardstick, held upright with one end touching the ground, casts a shadow 2 ft 3 in. long. What is the height of the tower?

12. A vessel steams east at the rate of 20 knots and another south at 14 knots. If both start from the same place at the same time, how far apart will they be in 5 hr?

13. From the table of functions, find (a) sine of 42.5°, (b) cosine of 12.8°, (c) tangent of 81.6°, (d) sine of 34.3°, (e) cosine of 66.6°, (f) tangent of 89.9°.

14. Find the angles having the following as tangents. (a) 1.2938, (b) 0.0017, (c) 0.5774, (d) 14.67, (e) 1.0000.

15. Solve the following right triangles for the unknown elements: (a) $R = 175$, $\theta = 12.3°$, (b) $R = 525$, $\theta = 37.4°$, (c) $X = 9.21$, $\theta = 5.2°$, (d) $X = 1250$, $\theta = 25.7°$, (e) $R = 0.423$, $\theta = 64.9°$, (f) $X = 48.4$, $\theta = 84.1°$, (g) $X = 867$, $\theta = 57.6°$, (h) $R = 1750$, $\phi = 69.3°$.

16. Solve for the third side of the following right triangles: (a) $Z = 15.3$, $R = 2.84$, (b) $Z = 13.9$, $X = 8.50$, (c) $Z = 500$, $X = 43.3$, (d) $Z = 22.6$, $R = 8.10$, (e) $R = 65.2$, $X = 14.1$, (f) $R = 10.9$, $X = 4.65$.

17. A road rises 350 ft in a distance of 2,500 ft. What is the percentage of grade? What is the angle of inclination of the roadbed with the horizontal?

18. A building 600 ft high cast a shadow 262 ft long. What was the angle of elevation of the sun at this time?

19. A flywheel has a velocity of 300 rpm. How much time is required for the wheel to generate 628 radians?

20. Express the angular velocity of 6 rps in radians per second.

In Probs. 21–25 of periodic curve equations, express: (*a*) amplitude, (*b*) angular velocity, (*c*) frequency, (*d*) period, and (*e*) angle of lead or lag with respect to a curve of the same frequency but having no displacement angle.

21. $y = 25 \sin (2t + 30°)$

22. $y = 32 \sin (37.7t - 10°)$

23. $e = 325 \sin (314t - 18°)$

24. $e = E_{max} \sin (157t + 17°)$

25. $i = I_{max} \sin (6.28t \times 10^3 - 90°)$

CHAPTER 17

VECTORS AND PHASE RELATIONSHIPS

Many physical quantities having only magnitude can be expressed by specifying a certain number of units, such as feet, degrees, miles per hour, or feet per second. Such quantities are *scalar* quantities. There are other types of physical quantities that cannot be expressed by specifying magnitude alone. For example, the entire system of electric-circuit analysis is built around the idea of expressing both magnitude and direction of voltages and currents. These quantities having both magnitude and direction are called *vector* quantities. A vector quantity is conveniently represented by a directed straight-line segment called a vector, the length of which is proportional to the magnitude and the head of which points in the direction of the vector quantity.

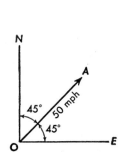

FIG. 17·1   A typical vector.

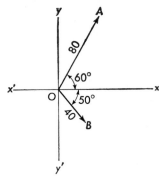

FIG. 17·2   Two   vectors   in   different directions.

17·1   Vector Examples.   A typical example of a vector showing both magnitude and direction is that shown in Fig. 17·1. If an automobile is traveling northeast at a speed of 50 mph, its speed can be represented by a line whose length represents 50 mph, to some convenient scale as shown. The direction of the line represents the direction in which the automobile is traveling. Thus the line OA is a vector that completely describes the velocity of the vehicle.

Another vector example is that shown in Fig. 17·2. The vector OA

represents a force of 80 lb pulling on a body at O in the direction of 60°. The vector OB represents another force of 40 lb acting on the same body but in a direction of 310°, or $-50°$.

17·2 Addition of Vectors. Scalar quantities are added algebraically. Thus 10 cents + 12 cents = 22 cents, and 4 resistors − 3 resistors = 1 resistor.

Since vector quantities involve direction as well as magnitude, they cannot be added algebraically unless their directions are parallel. In Fig. 17·3 vector OA may be considered as motion from O to A, and vector AB as motion from A to B. Then the sum of the vectors represents the sum of the motions from O to A and from A to B, which is the motion from O to B. This sum is the vector OB, that is, the *vector sum* of OA and AB is OB. Thus, if the initial point of the second vector is joined to the terminal point of the first, the sum of the two vectors is the vector joining the initial point of the first to the terminal point of the second.

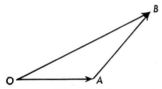

FIG. 17·3 The sum of two vectors.

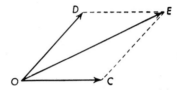

FIG. 17·4 Parallelogram composition of vectors.

In Fig. 17·4 vectors OC and OD are equal to vectors OA and AB, respectively, of Fig. 17·3. However, in Fig. 17·4 the vectors start from the same origin. By comparing Figs. 17·3 and 17·4, it is evident that the sum of the vectors in Fig. 17·4 can be represented by the diagonal of a parallelogram of which the vectors are adjacent sides. This is known as the *parallelogram law* for the composition of forces and holds for the composition or addition of all vector quantities.

From this it can be seen that two forces acting simultaneously on a point or an object may be replaced by a single force called the *resultant*. That is, the resultant force will produce the same effect on the point or object as the joint action of the two forces. In Fig. 17·3 the vector OB is the resultant of forces OA and AB. Similarly, in Fig. 17·4 the vector OE is the resultant force of vectors OC and OD.

Example: Three forces, A, B, and C are acting on point O as shown in Fig. 17·5. Force A exerts 150 lb at an angle of 60°, B exerts 100 lb at an angle of 135°, and C exerts 150 lb at an angle of 260°. Find the resultant force.

Solution: The resultant of vectors OA, OB, and OC can be found graphically by two methods.

a. First draw the vectors to scale. Find the resultant of any two vectors, such as OA and OC, by constructing a parallelogram with OA and OC as adjacent sides.   Then the resultant of OA and OC will be the diagonal OD of the parallelo-gram $OADC$, as shown in Fig. 17·6.   Now, there are but two forces, OB and OD,

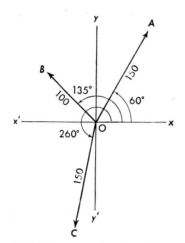

FIG. 17·5   Three vectors in different directions.

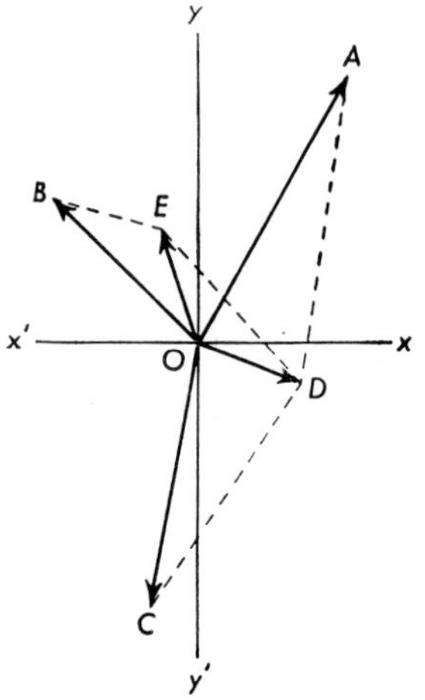

FIG. 17·6   Parallelogram addition of three vectors.

acting on point O.   The resultant of these two forces is found as before by con-structing a parallelogram with OB and OD as adjacent sides.   The resultant force on point O is then the diagonal OE of the parallelo-gram $OBED$.   Upon measuring with scale and pro-tractor, OE will be found to be 57 lb acting at an angle of 112°.

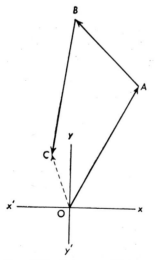

b. Draw the vectors to scale as shown in Fig. 17·7, joining the initial point of OB to the terminal point of OA, then joining the initial point of OC to the terminal point of OB.   The vector drawn from the point O to the terminal point of OC is the resultant force.

A figure such as $OABCO$, in Fig. 17·7, is called a *polygon* of forces.   The vectors may be joined in any order, as long as the initial point of one vector joins the terminal point of another vector and the vectors are drawn with the proper magnitude and direction.

FIG. 17·7   Polygon addition of three vectors.

The length and direction of the line necessary to close the polygon, that is, the line from the original initial point to the terminal point of the last vector drawn, constitutes a vector that represents the magnitude and the direction of the resultant.

17·3   Vector Components.   From what has been considered regarding combining or adding vectors, it follows that a vector may be resolved into components along any two specified directions.   For example, in Fig. 17·3 the vectors OA and AB are components of the vector OB.   If the directions of the components are chosen so that they are at right angles to each other, the components are called *rectangular components*.

By placing the initial point of a vector at the origin of the X and Y axes, the rectangular components are readily obtained either graphically or mathematically.

Example 1: A vector with a magnitude of 10 makes an angle of 53.1° with the horizontal.   What are the vertical and horizontal components?

Solution: The vector is illustrated in Fig. 17·8 as the directed line segment OA, whose length drawn to scale represents the magnitude of 10, making an angle of 53.1° with the X axis.

The *horizontal component* of OA is the horizontal distance from O to A and is found graphically by projecting the vector OA upon the X axis.   Thus the vector OB is the horizontal component of OA.

The *vertical component* of OA is the vertical distance from O to A and is found graphically by projecting the vector OA upon the Y axis. Similarly, the vector OC is the vertical component of OA.

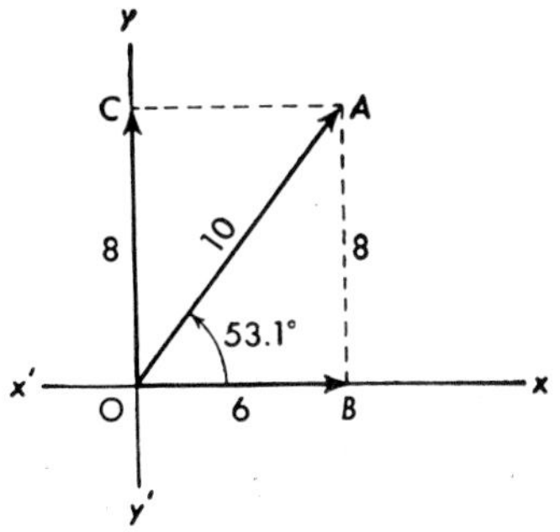

FIG. 17·8   Rectangular components.

Finding the horizontal and vertical components of OA by mathematical means is now simply a problem in solving a right triangle, with OA as the hypotenuse, AB as side opposite, and OB as the adjacent side.   Hence

$$OB = 10 \cos 53.1° = 6$$
and
$$OC = AB = 10 \sin 53.1° = 8$$
Check:

$$10^2 = 6^2 + 8^2 = 36 + 64 = 100$$

The foregoing may be summarized by the following rules.

RULE 1: *The horizontal component of a vector is the projection of the vector on a horizontal line and equals the magnitude of the vector multiplied by the cosine of the angle made by the vector with the horizontal.*

RULE 2: *The vertical component of a vector is the projection of the vector on a vertical line and equals the magnitude of the vector multiplied by the sine of the angle made by the vector with the horizontal.*

Example 2: An airplane is flying on a course of 40° at a speed of 250 mph. How many miles per hour is the plane advancing in a due eastward direction? In a direction due north?

Solution: Draw the vector diagram as shown in Fig. 17·9 (courses are measured from the north). The vector OB, which is the horizontal component of OA, represents the velocity of the airplane in an eastward direction. The vector OC, which is the vertical component of OA, represents the velocity of the airplane in a northward direction.

Again the process of finding the magnitude of OB and OC resolves into a problem in solving the right triangle of OBA. Hence

$$OB = 250 \cos 50° = 161 \text{ mph eastward}$$
and $\qquad OC = BA = 250 \sin 50° = 192 \text{ mph northward}$

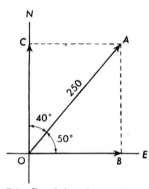

Fig. 17·9   Resolving the resultant vector into its horizontal and vertical components.

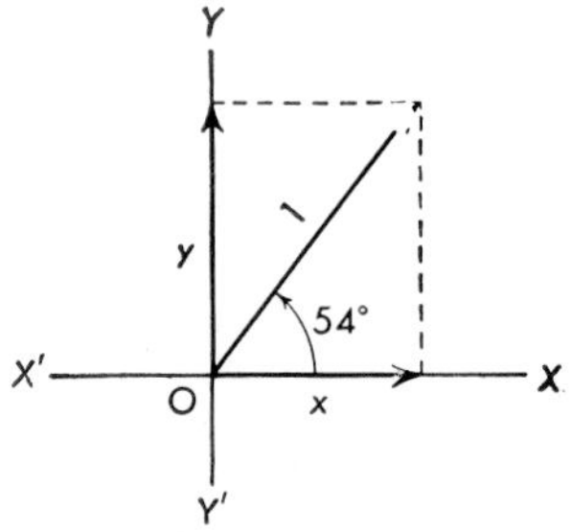

Fig. 17·10   Instantaneous resolution of a radius vector and its horizontal and vertical components (after 0.15 sec).

Example 3: A radius vector of unit length is rotating about a point with a velocity of 2π radians per sec. What are its horizontal and vertical components

(a) At the end of 0.15 sec?
(b) At the end of 0.35 sec?
(c) At the end of 0.75 sec?

Solution:

(a) At the end of 0.15 sec the rotating vector will have generated $2\pi \times 0.15$ $= 0.942 \times 57.3° = 54°$ as shown in Fig. 17·10. The horizontal component, measured along the X axis, is

$$x = 1 \cos 54° = 0.588$$

The vertical component, measured along the vertical axis, is

$$y = 1 \sin 54° = 0.809$$

(b) At the end of 0.35 sec the rotating vector will have generated an angle of $2\pi \times 0.35 = 2.20$ radians, or $2.20 \times 57.3° = 126°$, as shown in Fig. 17·11.

The horizontal component, measured along the X axis, is

$$x = 1 \cos 126° = 0.588$$

The vertical component, measured along the Y axis, is

$$y = 1 \sin 126° = 0.809$$

(c) At the end of 0.75 sec the rotating vector will have generated $2\pi \times$ 0.75 = 4.71 radians, or $4.71 \times 57.3° = 270°$, as shown in Fig. 17·12.

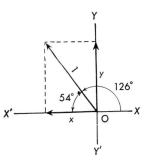

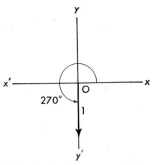

FIG. 17·11   Instantaneous resolution of a radius vector and its horizontal and vertical components (after 0.35 sec).

FIG. 17·12   Instantaneous resolution of a radius vector and its horizontal and vertical components (after 0.75 sec).

The horizontal component is

$$x = 1 \cos 270° = 0$$

The vertical component is

$$y = 1 \sin 270° = 1$$

17·4   Vector Addition of Rectangular Components.

If two forces are at right angles to each other and acting on a body, their resultant may be found by the usual methods of vector addition as previously explained. However, the resultant may be obtained by geometric or trigonometric methods since the problem is that of solving for the hypotenuse of a right triangle when the other two sides are given.

Example: Two vectors are acting on a point. One with a magnitude of 6 is directed along the horizontal to the right of the point, and the other with a magnitude of 8 is directed vertically above the point. Find the resultant.

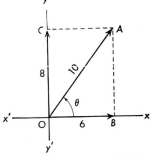

FIG. 17·13   Vector addition of rectangular components.

Solution 1: In Fig. 17·13 the horizontal vector is shown as OB and the vertical vector as OC. The resultant may be obtained graphically by completing the parallelogram of forces $OCAB$, with OA representing its length and the angle determined by measurement with a protractor.

Solution 2: Since $BA = OC$, then OBA is a right triangle, the hypotenuse of which is the resultant OA. Therefore the magnitude of the resultant is

$$OA = \sqrt{6^2 + 8^2} = 10$$

Solution 3: Since OBA is a right triangle for which OB and BA are given, the hypotenuse (resultant) can be computed by using the fundamental relations that exist among the elements of a right triangle.

$$\tan \theta = \frac{\text{opposite side}}{\text{adjacent side}} = \frac{BA}{OB} = 1.33$$

Therefore

$$\theta = 53.1°$$

Then

$$OA = \frac{OB}{\cos 53.1°} = \frac{6}{0.6} = 10$$

or

$$OA = \frac{BA}{\sin 53.1°} = \frac{8}{0.8} = 10$$

17·5 Vector Representation of Sine Curves.

Since the sine wave, or curve, of an alternating electromotive force is a periodic function, a simpler method of representing the amount of electromotive force induced to the angle of rotation is available through use of vectors. For example, the rotating conductor in an alternator may be represented by a rotating radius vector whose length corresponds to the magnitude of the maximum generated voltage E_{max}. Then the instantaneous value for any position of the conductor may be represented by the vertical component of the vector. In Fig. 17·14 the vector represents the conductor of an alternator whose maximum generated voltage E_{max} equals 100 volts. In the position shown, vector E_{max} is at 0° and therefore has no vertical component. Thus, the value of the electromotive force in this position is zero. Or, since

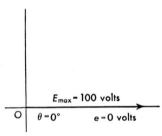

$E_{max} = 100$ volts

O $\theta = 0°$ $e = 0$ volts

FIG. 17·14   Vector representation of a voltage at 0°.

$$e = E_{max} \sin \theta$$

by substituting the values of E_{max} and θ,

$$e = 100 \sin 0° = 0$$

In Fig. 17.15 the vector represents the coil after it has moved 60° from the zero position. It is therefore at an angle of 60° from the reference axis, and the instantaneous value of the induced electromotive force is represented by the vertical component of E_{max}. Then, since

$$e = E_{max} \sin \theta$$

by substituting the values of E_{max} and θ,

$$e = 100 \sin 60° = 86.6 \text{ volts}$$

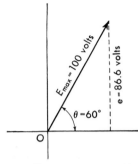

FIG. 17·15 Vector representation of a voltage at 60°.

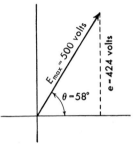

FIG. 17·16 Vector solution for an instantaneous value of voltage (first quadrant).

Example 1: What is the instantaneous value of an alternating electromotive force when it has reached 58° of its cycle? The maximum value is 500 volts.

Solution: Draw the vector diagram to scale as shown in Fig. 17·16. The instantaneous value is the vertical compo nent of the vector E_{max}. Then, since

$$e = E_{max} \sin \theta$$

by substituting the values of E_{max} and θ,

$$e = 500 \sin 58° = 424 \text{ volts}$$

Example 2: What is the instantaneous value of an alternating electromotive force when it has reached 216° of its cycle if the maximum value is 163 volts?

Solution: Draw the vector diagram to scale as shown in Fig. 17·17. The instan-

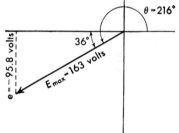

FIG. 17·17 Vector solution for an instantaneous value of voltage (third quadrant).

taneous value is the vertical component of the vector E_{max}. Then, since

$$e = E_{max} \sin \theta$$

by substituting the values of E_{max} and θ,

$$e = 163 \sin 216 = 163 \sin (216° - 180°)$$
$$= 163 \sin 36° = 95.8 \text{ volts}$$

NOTE: A vector diagram drawn to scale should be made for every alternating-current problem. This not only provides a better insight into the functioning of alternating currents but serves as a good check on the mathematical solution.

Since the current in a circuit is proportional to the applied voltage, it follows that an alternating electromotive force which varies periodically will produce a current of similar variation. Hence the instantaneous current of a sine wave of alternating current is given by

$$i = I_{max} \sin \theta$$

where i = instantaneous value of current
   I_{max} = maximum value of current
   θ = angular position of coil

17·6   Cycles, Frequency, and Poles.   Each revolution of a coil in a magnetic field results in one complete *cycle* which consists of one positive and one negative loop of the sine wave. The number of cycles generated in 1 sec is called the *frequency* of the alternating voltage or current, and the *period* is the time required to complete one cycle. One half-cycle is called an *alternation*. Thus, by a 60-cycle alternating current is meant that the current passes through 60 cycles each second, resulting in a period of 0.0167 sec. Also, a 60-cycle current completes 120 alternations per sec.

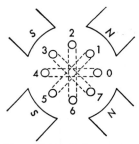

Figure 17·18 represents a coil rotating in a *four*-pole machine, that is, between the N and S poles of *two* magnets. When one side of the coil has rotated from position 0 to position 4, it has passed under the influence of an N and an S pole, thus generating one complete sine wave, or electrical cycle. This corresponds to 2π electrical radians, or 360 electrical degrees, although the coil has rotated only 180 space degrees. Therefore, in one complete revolution in space the coil will generate two complete cycles, or 720 electrical degrees, so that for every *space degree* there result two *electrical time degrees*.

Fig. 17·18   Coil rotating in a four-pole machine.

In any alternator the armature, or field, must move an angular distance equal to the angle formed by two consecutive like poles in order to complete one cycle. It is evident, then, that a two-pole machine must rotate at twice the speed of a four-pole machine to produce the same frequency. Therefore, to find the frequency of an alternator in cycles per second, the number of pairs of poles is multiplied by the speed of the armature in revolutions per second. That is,

$$f = \frac{PS}{60}$$

where f = frequency, cps

P = number of *pairs* of poles

S = speed of armature or field, rpm

Example: What is the frequency of an alternator having four poles with a speed of 1,800 rpm?

Solution:
$$f = \frac{2 \times 1,800}{60} = 60 \text{ cps}$$

17·7 Equations of Voltages and Currents. Since each cycle consists of 360 electrical degrees, or 2π electrical radians, the variation of an alternating electromotive force can be expressed in terms of time. Thus, a frequency of f cps results in $2\pi f$ radians per sec, denoted by ω. Hence, the instantaneous electromotive force at any time t is given by the relation

$$e = E_{\max} \sin \omega t$$

The instantaneous current is

$$i = I_{\max} \sin \omega t$$

Example 1: Write the equation of a 60-cycle alternating voltage that has a maximum value of 156 volts.

Solution: The angular velocity ω is 2π times the frequency, or $2\pi \times 60 = 377$ radians per sec. Substituting 156 volts for $E_{\max}$ and 377 for ω,

$$e = 156 \sin 377t$$

Example 2: Write the equation of a current of 700 kc that has a maximum value of 2.12 amp.

Solution: $I_{\max} = 2.12$ amp and $f = 700 \text{ kc} = 7 \times 10^5$ cycles. Then $\omega = 2\pi \times 7 \times 10^5 = 4.4 \times 10^6$. Substituting these values

$$i = 2.12 \sin (4.4 \times 10^6)t$$

Example 3: If the time $t = 0$ when the voltage of Example 1 is zero and increasing in a positive direction, what is the instantaneous value of the voltage at the end of 0.002 sec?

Solution: Substituting 0.002 for t in the equation for the voltage,

$$e = 156 \sin (377 \times 0.002)$$
$$= 156 \sin 0.754$$

where 0.754 is the time-angle in radians. Then, since 1 radian = 57.3°,

$$e = 156 \sin (0.754 \times 57.3°)$$
$$= 156 \sin 43.2° = 107 \text{ volts}$$

17·8 Phase Relations and Phase Angles. Nearly all alternating-current circuits contain circuit elements, or components, that cause the voltage and current to pass through their corresponding zero values at different times. If both alternating voltage and current are of the same frequency and pass through corresponding zero values at the same instant, they are said to be *in phase*.

If the current passes through a zero value before the corresponding zero value of the voltage, they are *out of phase* and the current is said to *lead* the voltage.

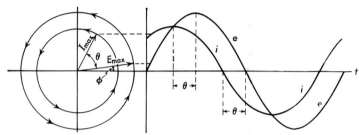

FIG. 17·19   Vector relationship between *I* and *E* shown as a phase relationship (*I* leading *E*).   (*Cooke, "Basic Mathematics for Electronics," McGraw-Hill Book Company, Inc.,* 1960.)

Figure 17·19 illustrates a vector diagram and the corresponding sine wave of current of *i* amp leading a voltage of *e* volts by a *phase angle θ*. Hence, if the voltage is taken as reference, the general equation of the voltage is

$$e = E_{\text{max}} \sin \omega t$$

and the current is given by

$$i = I_{\text{max}} \sin (\omega t + \theta)$$

The instantaneous values of the voltage and current for any angle ϕ of the voltage are

$$e = E_{\text{max}} \sin \phi$$
and
$$i = I_{\text{max}} \sin (\phi + \theta)$$

Example 1: In Fig. 17·19 the maximum values of the voltage and the current are 156 volts and 113 amp. The frequency is 60 cps and the current leads the voltage by 40°.

(*a*) Write the equation for the voltage at any time *t*.

(*b*) Write the equation for the current at any time *t*.

(*c*) What is the instantaneous value of the current when the voltage has reached 10° of its cycle?

Solution:

Given: Maximum voltage $E_{\text{max}} = 156$ volts
    Maximum current $I_{\text{max}} = 113$ amp
    Frequency $f = 60$ cps
    Phase angle $\theta = 40°$ lead
    Voltage angle $\phi = 10°$

Draw a vector diagram as shown in Fig. 17·19.
(a) Substituting given values,

$$e = 156 \sin 2\pi \times 60t$$
$$e = 156 \sin 377t$$

(b) Substituting given values,

$$i = 113 \sin (377t + 40°)$$

(c)

$$i = 113 \sin (10° + 40°)$$
$$i = 113 \sin 50° = 86.6 \text{ amp}$$

Figure 17·20 illustrates a vector diagram and the corresponding sine waves for a current of i amp lagging a voltage of e volts by a *phase angle* θ.

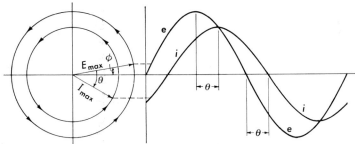

FIG. 17·20   Vector relationship between I and E shown as a phase relationship (I lagging E). (*Cooke, "Basic Mathematics for Electronics," McGraw-Hill Book Company, Inc.,* 1960.)

Therefore, if the voltage is taken as reference, the general equation of the voltage will be given as

$$e = E_{max} \sin \omega t$$

and the current will be

$$i = I_{max} \sin (\omega t - \theta)$$

The instantaneous value of the current for any angle ϕ of the voltage is

$$i = I_{max} \sin (\phi - \theta)$$

Example 2: In Fig. 17·20 the maximum values of the voltage and the current are 170 volts and 14.1 amp. The frequency is 800 cps, and the current lags the voltage by 40°.

(a) Write the equation for the voltage at any time t.
(b) Write the equation for the current at any time t.
(c) What is the instantaneous value of the current when the voltage has reached 10° of its cycle?

Solution:

Given: Maximum voltage E_{max} = 170 volts
Maximum current I_{max} = 14.1 amp
Frequency f = 800 cps
Phase angle θ = 40° lag
Voltage angle ϕ = 10°

Draw a vector diagram as shown in Fig. 17·20.
(a) Substituting given values,

$$e = 170 \sin 2\pi \times 800t$$
$$e = 170 \sin 5,030t$$

(b) Substituting given values,

$$i = 14.1 \sin (5,030t - 40°)$$

(c)

$$i = 14.1 \sin (10° - 40°)$$
$$i = 14.1 \sin 30° = 7.05 \text{ amp}$$

Example 3: In a certain alternating-current circuit a current of 14 amp lags a voltage of 220 volts by an angle of 60°. What is the instantaneous value of voltage when the current has completed 245° of its cycle?

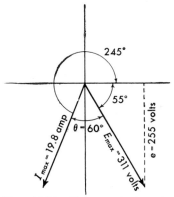

NOTE: Unless otherwise specified, all voltages and currents will be considered to be *effective* values.

Solution: Draw the vector diagram as shown in Fig. 17·21.

$$E_{max} = \sqrt{2} \times E = \sqrt{2} \times 220 = 311 \text{ volts}$$
$$\phi = 245° + \theta = 245° + 60° = 305° = 55°$$

Fig. 17·21 Vector solution for instantaneous voltage with out-of-phase current.

Then, by substituting the values of E_{max} and θ,

$$e = 311 \sin 55° = 255 \text{ volts}$$

17·9 Summary. The following facts about vectors and phase relations should be remembered.

a. A vector is a line drawn to represent a quantity having both direction and magnitude.

b. Vectors are always rotated in a counterclockwise direction.

c. The vector sum of a combination of forces is known as the resultant.

d. If only two forces act on a point, the resultant may be found graphically by measuring the diagonal of a parallelogram.

e. If more than two forces act on a point, the resultant may be found graphically by adding vectors, two at a time, to find their combined sum.

f. Vectors at right angles to one another are most easily added by trigonometric methods.

g. Alternating voltages and currents are said to be in phase when they reach maximum and zero values at the same instant in the same direction.

h. The resultant of two inphase sine waves of voltages or currents may be found by arithmetical addition of their effective values.

i. The time difference between two out-of-phase components is expressed in degrees by the angle θ.

j. When a phase difference exists, alternating currents or voltages must be added vectorially.

PROBLEMS

1. A shell is fired at an angle of 45° with a velocity of 2,000 ft per second. What is its initial horizontal velocity?

2. The resultant of two forces acting at right angles is a force of 810 lb that makes an angle of 22.5° with one of the forces. Find the two component forces.

3. A ship sails 53 miles northwest. How far west has it moved?

4. Resolve a force of 48 lb into two rectangular components, one of which is 23.2 lb.

Find the horizontal and vertical components, denoted by H and V respectively, of the following vectors:

5. 7.15 at 69.1°.   **6.** 80.7 at 270°.
7. 105 at 25.8°.   **8.** 61.2 at 221.4°.
9. 9.78 at 340.6°.   **10.** 508 at 180°.

Find the resultant forces of the following vectors:

11. 201 at 90° and 117 at 180°.   **12.** 46.2 at 0°, 71.4 at 90° and 38 at 0°.
13. 50 at 0° and 42.1 at 270°.   **14.** 92.6 at 90° and 108 at 270°.
15. 110 at 270° and 32 at 180°.   **16.** 30.6 at 90° and 13.4 at 90°.
17. 16.3 at 0° and 8.2 at 0°.   **18.** 80.2 at 180° and 21.5 at 90°.

19. Two forces of 42.1 and 22.5 lb are acting at right angles to each other. Find the resultant force and the angle between the resultant and the 22.5-lb force.

20. An 800-cycle alternator generates a maximum voltage of 170 volts at 4,000 rpm. (a) How many poles has it? (b) Write the equation for the voltage. (c) What is the value of the voltage when the time t is equal to 0.000796 sec?

21. At what speed must a 24-pole 50-cycle generator be driven in order to develop its rated frequency?

22. The equation for a certain alternating voltage is $e = 707 \sin 314t$. What is its frequency?

23. A broadcasting station operating on 710 kc develops a maximum potential of 0.155 mv across a listener's antenna. Write the equation for this voltage.

24. What is the average value of an alternating voltage whose maximum value is 600 volts?

25. What is the effective value of an alternating voltage whose maximum value is 311 volts?

26. A meter reads 440 volts of alternating voltage. What is the maximum value of the voltage?

27. A 25-cycle alternator is generating 6,600 volts at 700 amp. The current lags the voltage by an angle of 22°. (a) Write the equation for the current at any time t. (b) What is the instantaneous value of the current when the voltage has completed 50° of its cycle?

28. In the alternator of Prob 27, what will be the instantaneous value of the current when the voltage has completed 184° of its cycle?

29. A 50-cycle alternator generates 2,300 volts with a current of 200 amp. The phase angle is 25° lagging. (a) Write the equation for the current at any time t. (b) What is the instantaneous value of the current when the voltage has completed 70° of its cycle?

30. In the alternator of Prob. 29, what is the instantaneous value of the voltage when the current has completed 230° of its cycle?

31. A 60-cycle current has a value of 30 amp at 230 volts. If the instantaneous value of the voltage is −67.6 volts when the instantaneous value of the current is 26.1 amp, what is the phase angle between current and voltage?

CHAPTER 18

LAWS AND PROPERTIES OF INDUCTANCE

Almost all electronic circuits involving alternating currents and voltages consist of two components in addition to vacuum tubes and resistors. These added components are known as *capacitors* and *inductors* and are for the purpose of introducing into circuits the elements of *capacitance* and *inductance*. Each contributes toward making the circuit more versatile but also creates effects that must be compensated for.

This portion of the text will be devoted to the construction, properties, and principles of inductors. Any component purposely introducing inductance into a circuit is called an inductor. In subsequent portions they will be known more specifically as choke coils, inductance coils, inductances, reactances, etc., but all fall into the category of inductor.

18-1 Definitions. Before proceeding to the study of inductors it might be well to define a few of the more common terms connected with this particular component.

Inductor. An inductor is a coil of wire, usually in the form of a solenoid, possessing the property of inductance in proportion to physical arrangement, such as shape, number of turns, and permeability of its core.

Inductance. A change in current through a conductor will cause a change in the magnetic flux around it. When these flux lines cut across a conductor, the change in flux causes a voltage to be generated in the conductor and in circuits nearby. If more than one turn of wire is used, the flux around one turn will cut across adjacent turns and induce voltage in them that is of opposite polarity to the original voltage causing current. Therefore, the gener-

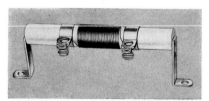

FIG. 18-1   An inductor.   (*J. W. Miller Company.*)

ated voltage opposes current and is known as *back emf*, or *counter emf*.

Inductance is the property of a coil that causes voltages to be induced in a direction such that the resulting currents oppose the force that produces them.

Counter emf. This is the emf induced in a coil because of its property of inductance. It is in opposition to the applied emf. Counter emf, abbreviated cemf, will oppose any change in current regardless of whether the current is increasing or decreasing.

Henry. The henry is the unit of inductance. A circuit is said to have *a self-inductance of one henry when a cemf of one volt is generated by a current changing at the rate of one ampere per second.*

18·2 Theory of Inductance. As previously stated, a magnetic field will be set up around a current-carrying wire, and the direction of this

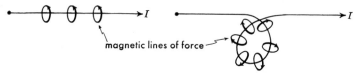

Fig. 18·2 Magnetic lines of force resulting from current through a wire.

field can be found by application of the left-hand rule (see Fig. 18·2). Ordinarily, the inductance resulting from current through a straight wire is of negligible value. However, if the wire is coiled in the form of a solenoid as shown in Fig. 18·3, the flux from one turn links the others and the inductive effect can become quite pronounced.

Inductive effect in an electric circuit can be considered analogous to power and inertia with respect to an automobile. While additional power must be expended to overcome the inertia of rest before getting the auto-

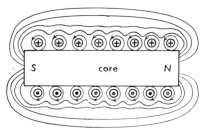

Fig. 18·3 Magnetic field around coil, showing how lines of force link the coil.

mobile into motion, less power is then required to maintain that motion. In order to terminate motion, additional power must be expended to overcome momentum. Similarly, in producing current through an inductive circuit, not only must the normal amount of resistance be overcome but additional power must be expended in building up the magnetic field. When this magnetic field builds up, or expands, around a coil it cuts across the turns of the coil and induces an emf in them. This induced, or counter, emf is of such polarity that it opposes the current being built up through the coil.

Once the current reaches a steady level, the magnetic field becomes stationary and no longer cuts across the turns of the coil. Therefore, the counter emf falls to zero and there is no opposition to current other than the normal resistance of the circuit.

If the amount of current through the coil is decreased in value, the flux lines comprising the magnetic field around the coil will contract. As the field reduces in size the flux lines again cut across the turns of the coil and generate a counter emf of a polarity that opposes the decrease in current.

The opposition offered by an inductor to any change of current through it is known as *inductive reactance*. This reactance opposes any increase or decrease of current through an electric circuit much as reactance due to inertia opposes any increase or decrease in the speed of a rotating object.

18·3 Physical Aspects. Although there is some inductance in d-c circuits, its effect is of minor importance because inductance offers opposition only to *changes* in current. Since the current in any d-c circuit is usually of a steady value, the effect of inductance would be evident only at those instants when current is starting or stopping. However, in a-c circuits, where the current is varying in amplitude and changing in polarity many times per second, inductance is more pronounced and therefore of greater importance. For this reason, only a-c circuits will be considered.

Inductance is considered to be a constant property of a circuit and is thought of in terms of the "lumped" inductance of some form of coil or transformer. The inductance (also known as self-inductance) of such a device is determined by various factors, some of which are dimensions, number of turns, nature of winding, type of core material on which coil is wound, etc. While the calculation of inductance by physical formula is a laborious process, it is essential that the student understand the general factors that determine the inductance of a coil. For example, the formula for determining the inductance of an ordinary solenoid using a core of magnetic material is

$$L = \frac{1.26N^2\mu A}{10^8 l}$$

where L = inductance of the coil, henrys
   N = number of turns of wire on the coil
   μ = permeability of core material
   A = cross-sectional area of the coil
   l = length of core, cm

While the many formulas used in determining the inductances of the various types of coils are of little consequence, it is important to show how inductance varies with change in physical features. For example, in the foregoing formula it is shown that the inductance will vary directly as the square of the number of turns on the coil if the other dimensions are held constant. If a coil having 100 turns was unwound and then rewound with 200 turns in the same space, the inductance would increase to four times the original value.

It is also shown that inductance will increase directly with an increase in permeability. This means that iron-core coils will have more inductance than those wound on air cores. Further, the better the magnetic qualities of the iron, the higher the coil inductance. In proof of this, it was found that by substituting a soft-iron core for an air core in a solenoid, the magnetic flux was increased by 300.

The third factor in the formula shown is that inductance increases with an increase in cross-sectional area. A coil of a given number of turns would have a greater amount of inductance if wound on a form of large diameter than if wound on a form of small diameter.

While inductance varies directly with all other factors in the formula, it varies inversely with the length of core. With all other dimensions and factors held constant, an increase in the length of core would cause a decrease in the inductance of the coil.

18·4 Series and Parallel Combinations. Inductances in series are computed like resistances in series, as shown in Fig. 18·4. If they are so

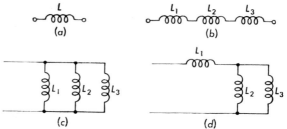

FIG. 18·4 Inductor arrangements. (*a*) Circuit symbol for inductance. (*b*) Inductors in series. (*c*) Inductors in parallel. (*d*) Inductors in series parallel.

spaced as to eliminate any magnetic coupling between them, each inductance of the series branch helps to oppose any change of current through the circuit. Therefore, if three inductances L_1, L_2, and L_3 were placed in series, the total inductance L_t could be computed as

$$L_t = L_1 + L_2 + L_3$$

Example: What is the total inductance of three coils having inductances of 50, 75, and 200 μh if connected in series in a circuit?

Solution: $L_t = L_1 + L_2 + L_3$
                 $= 50 + 75 + 200 = 325 \ \mu$h

When inductors are connected in parallel, the combined inductance is always less than that of any one of the coils and is computed in the same manner as for resistors in parallel. And, as in series combinations, they must be spaced so that no magnetic coupling exists between them. Then, inductances in parallel can be computed by the following formula:

$$\frac{1}{L_t} = \frac{1}{L_1} + \frac{1}{L_2} + \frac{1}{L_3}$$

Example: What is the joint inductance of three inductors of 5, 10, and 12.5 μh if connected in parallel in a circuit?

Solution:

$$\frac{1}{L_t} = \frac{1}{5} + \frac{1}{10} + \frac{1}{12.5}$$
$$= 0.2 + 0.1 + 0.08 = 0.38$$
$$L_t = 2.63 \ \mu h$$

NOTE: Except in some instances, the henry is a unit of inductance too large for practical use. Therefore, most inductances are expressed in either millihenrys (10^{-3}) or microhenrys (10^{-6}).

Inductors connected in series-parallel combinations are computed like resistors similarly connected and can be determined by the following formula.

$$L_t = L_1 + \frac{1}{\dfrac{1}{L_2} + \dfrac{1}{L_3}}$$

18-5 Inductive Reactance. Since the effect of inductance is to set up a counter emf that opposes any change in current, this opposition can be considered as an additional resistance to electron flow. To distinguish from ohmic resistance, this additional resistance is known as *inductive reactance* and can be expressed in ohms because it, too, constitutes an opposition to current. However, unlike resistance, it does not result in any power loss because its presence is due to a counter, or back, pressure rather than an effect comparable to friction. Actually, the effect of reactance is to necessitate the application of a higher emf to a circuit in order to pass a given current than would be required if only resistance were present.

The inductive reactance, in ohms, in a circuit depends upon both the inductance of the circuit and the frequency of the voltage. Since the amount of inductance is partially determined by the change in amplitude and direction of current, it follows that an increase in frequency would result in an increase in the inductive reactance of the circuit. This may be expressed by the following formula:

$$X_L = 2\pi f L$$

where X_L = inductive reactance, ohms
f = frequency, cps
L = inductance, henrys
2π = 6.28

This means that a voltage must overcome the inductive reactance $2\pi fL$. Therefore

$$\frac{E}{I} = 2\pi fL$$

and

$$E = 2\pi fLI$$

A similarity between the relations of voltage, current, resistance, and inductive reactance will be noted. Both resistance and inductive react-

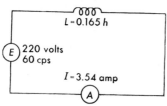

ance offer an opposition to an alternating current; both are expressed in ohms and both are equal to the voltage divided by the current. However, here the similarity ends, since there is no inductive reactance to direct current, because there is no change in amplitude and direction of current.

FIG. 18·5   Inductive circuit.

Figure 18·5 represents a 60-cycle alternator delivering 220 volts to a coil having an inductance of 0.165 henry. The opposition, or inductive reactance, to the current is

$$X_L = 2\pi fL$$
$$= 2\pi \times 60 \times 0.165 = 62.2 \text{ ohms}$$

Although it is impossible to construct an inductance containing no resistance, in examples like this the coil will be considered as having negligible resistance. Then, current can be computed as

$$I = \frac{E}{X_L} = \frac{220}{62.2} = 3.54 \text{ amp}$$

Example 1: What is the inductive reactance of an inductance of 17 μh at a frequency of 2,500 kc?

Solution: $f = 2,500 \text{ kc} = 2.5 \times 10^6 \text{ cps}$
$L = 17 \ \mu\text{h} = 1.7 \times 10^{-5} \text{ henry}$
$X_L = 2\pi fL$
$= 2\pi \times 2.5 \times 10^6 \times 1.7 \times 10^{-5} = 267 \text{ ohms}$

Example 2: What is the inductance of a coil connected to 115 volts, 60 cycles, if an ammeter connected in series with the coil reads 0.714 amp?

Solution: $X_L = \frac{E}{I} = \frac{115}{0.714} = 161 \text{ ohms}$

$$L = \frac{X_L}{2\pi f} = \frac{161}{2\pi \times 60} = 0.427 \text{ henry}$$

The effect of inductance in a circuit prevents the current from reaching its maximum value the instant voltage is applied. A voltage and current in phase will reach maximum value and return to zero at the same instant.

However, the effect of inductance is to cause the maximum and minimum values of current to lag behind corresponding values of the voltage causing current. Because an alternating current is constantly changing, in an inductive circuit there is always present a reactance that opposes this change.

RULE: *In a purely inductive circuit, the current lags the voltage by* 90°.

This is illustrated by the vector diagram in Fig. 18·6, which shows the voltage to be at maximum positive value while the current is passing

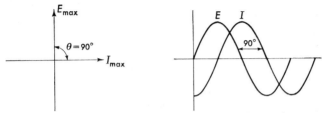

FIG. 18·6   Current lagging voltage by 90° in purely inductive circuit.

through zero. The instantaneous voltage across an inductance is given by

$$e = E_{max} \sin \omega t$$

where $\omega = 2\pi f$. And since the current lags the voltage by a phase angle θ of 90°, the current through the inductance is given by

$$i = I_{max} \sin (\omega t - \theta)$$

or

$$i = I_{max} \sin (\omega t - 90°)$$

If the voltage has completed ϕ degrees of its cycle, then the instantaneous current is given by

$$i = I_{max} \sin (\phi - 90°)$$

Example: What is the instantaneous value of a current of 5 amp I_{max} when the voltage has completed 120° of its cycle?

Solution: Draw a vector diagram of the current and voltage relations as shown in Fig. 18·7.

$$i = I_{max} \sin (\phi - 90°)$$
$$= 5 \sin (120° - 90°)$$
$$= 5 \sin 30° = 2.5 \text{ amp}$$

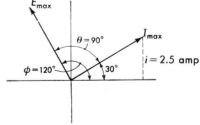

FIG. 18·7   Vector solution for an instantaneous value of I_{max}.

Although in a purely inductive circuit the current lags the voltage by a phase angle of 90°, in an actual circuit the angle of lag will be less than 90°.

This is because all inductors, by the nature of their physical construction, contain some amount of resistance. The exact angle (time) by which current lags the voltage will be determined by the ratio of inductive reactance to resistance.

While the opposition offered to d-c circuits is called resistance, the added reactance offered in a-c circuits brings up a new term. *Impedance* is the *total* opposition offered to current in alternating-current circuits. It is comprised of resistance, inductive reactance, and—to be discussed later—*capacitive reactance*.

18·6 Inductance and Resistance. As previously explained, the voltage and current through a pure resistance are in phase, while a current

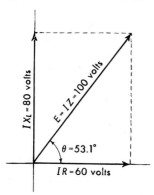

through a pure inductance lags the voltage by 90°. However, most practical circuits contain both resistance and inductance. As in their d-c counterparts, the sum of all voltage drops around an a-c circuit must equal the applied emf. In considering the resistance and reactances of the circuit, arithmetical addition or subtraction no longer applies, because of the phase difference of current and voltage between them. Impedance is the vector sum of resistance and reactance and can be calculated by employing trigonometric methods for solving angles. Impedance is represented by the symbol Z. By Ohm's law, $Z = E/I$.

Fig. 18·8   Vector showing resultant voltage in a series inductance-resistance circuit.

Because the current is the same in all parts of any series circuit, it may be used as a reference and voltage plotted across both resistance and inductance as shown in Fig. 18·8. The resultant of two voltages, treated here as rectangular components, must equal the applied emf. Hence, if IR and IX_L are the potential differences across the resistance and inductive reactance, respectively, then

$$E = \sqrt{(IR)^2 + (IX_L)^2}$$
$$= \sqrt{60^2 + 80^2} = 100 \text{ volts}$$

The phase angles between voltage and current can be found by using any of the trigonometric functions. For example,

$$\tan \theta = \frac{IX_L}{IR} = \frac{80}{60} = 1.33$$

Therefore

$$\theta = 53.1 \text{ degrees}$$

and it is apparent from the vector diagram that the current through the circuit lags the applied voltage by this amount.

Because the current is the same in all parts of a series circuit, resistance and reactance may be plotted as rectangular components and solved by any of the trigonometric methods for solving right triangles. *Inductive reactance is plotted as the side opposite, resistance as the side adjacent, and impedance as the hypotenuse.* Plotting the phase angle of the lagging current then evolves into a continuation of the same process.

Example: A circuit consisting of 120 ohms resistance in series with an inductance of 0.35 henry is connected across a 440-volt 60-cycle alternator.

(a) What is the phase angle between current and voltage?

(b) What is the impedance of the circuit?

(c) What is the current in the circuit?

Solution: Draw the vector diagram as shown in Fig. 18·9.

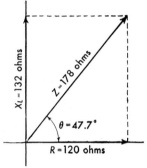

$$X_L = 2\pi fL$$
$$= 2\pi \times 60 \times 0.35 = 132 \text{ ohms}$$
$$\tan \theta = \frac{X_L}{R} = \frac{132}{120} = 1.10$$

Therefore

(a) $$\theta = 47.7°$$

FIG. 18·9 Vector solution for phase angle, impedance, and current in a series *LR* circuit.

NOTE: The phase angle denotes the position of the applied voltage with respect to the current, which is taken as a reference.

(b) $$Z = \frac{R}{\cos \theta} = \frac{120}{\cos 47.7°} = 178 \text{ ohms}$$

(c) $$I = \frac{E}{Z} = \frac{440}{178} = 2.47 \text{ amp}$$

PROBLEMS

1. Assuming negligible resistance, what current would flow through an inductance of 0.0326 henry at a potential of 120 volts, 800 cps?

2. What happens to the inductive reactance of a circuit when (a) the inductance is held constant and the frequency is varied? (b) The frequency is held constant and the inductance is varied?

3. If there are 110 volts, 25 cps across an inductance and a current of 215 ma flows, what is the inductance of the coil?

4. A current of 425 ma, 50 cps flows through an inductance of 1.65 henrys. (a) What is the potential difference across it? (b) What is the instantaneous value of the current when the voltage has completed 26° of its cycle?

5. A circuit consisting of 120 ohms resistance in series with an inductance of 0.35 henry is connected across a 440-volt, 60-cycle alternator. (a) What is the phase angle between voltage and current? (b) What is the impedance of the circuit? (c) How much current flows through the circuit?

6. A circuit consists of 800 ohms resistance in series with an inductance of 360 μh. If there are 2000 volts, 1000 kc across the circuit, find (a) the impedance of the circuit, (b) the current flowing through the circuit, (c) the potential across the resistor, (d) the potential across the inductance.

7. In the circuit of Prob. 6, the applied voltage is held constant while the frequency is decreased until the current is twice the value found in Prob. 6. Under this condition, find (a) the impedance, (b) the frequency.

REVIEW QUESTIONS

1. Explain the theory of inductance.
2. Explain how counter emf is induced in a coil.
3. Why does current lag the voltage in an inductive circuit?
4. What is the difference between inductance and resistance?
5. What are the various factors that determine the inductance of a coil.
6. Explain inductive reactance.
7. What is the net effect of inductance in a circuit?
8. Explain impedance.
9. What is the unit of inductance? Explain.
10. How can inductances in series be computed like resistances in series?
11. Why cannot resistance and inductance in a circuit be added arithmetically?
12. What is the relation between inductance, frequency, and inductive reactance?
13. What is the relation between voltage, current, resistance, and inductive reactance?
14. Why is inductive reactance more pronounced in a-c than in d-c circuits?
15. Explain the relation between inductive reactance and inertia.
16. Why do iron-core coils have more inductance than air-core coils?

CHAPTER 19

INDUCTOR CHARACTERISTICS AND APPLICATIONS

The inductance and inductive effects in a circuit are the direct result of the magnetic field produced by current through a coil of wire. These effects have many uses in electronic equipment, and the inductors designed to produce them take many forms, depending upon their particular application. Some have inductances of a few microhenrys and are wound on insulating forms having air cores, while others may have inductances as high as 100 henrys and contain thousands of turns of wire. In all cases the size of the wire of which the inductor is wound will be determined by the amount of current it is designed to carry.

To fully understand this important circuit phenomenon it is necessary to study some of its characteristics and uses.

19·1 Effective Resistance. The energy stored in the magnetic field of an inductance is due to the current through it. As the current decreases, the magnetic field collapses and this energy is returned to the circuit. For this reason it can be understood that, in a purely inductive circuit, there is no loss or expenditure of electrical energy. However, since all substances contain some amount of resistance, there is a loss or dissipation of energy through heat. Resistance, therefore, may be defined as that property of a substance by virtue of which electrical energy is converted to thermal energy. With a given value of current, it has been proved that the losses in a circuit may be greater with alternating current than with direct current. Under these conditions it is indicated that the apparent resistance of a circuit is greater with alternating current than with direct current. This apparent resistance with alternating current is called

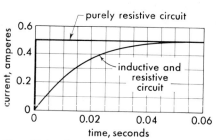

Fig. 19·1 Comparison between resistive and resistive-inductive circuits as to time required for current to reach maximum.

effective resistance and can be found by dividing the power by the square of the current.

$$R_{\text{eff}} = \frac{P}{I^2}$$

Of the several important factors contributing to this difference between d-c and a-c resistance, the following will be briefly explained.

Ohmic Resistance. The ohmic resistance of a coil or conductor, for all practical purposes, is its d-c resistance, which is determined by the nature of the material, dimensions, and operating temperature to which it is subjected.

Skin Effect. While the flow of electrons in a d-c circuit is distributed evenly throughout the conductor, this is not true in an a-c circuit. Since the current is constantly changing in value or amplitude, the *distributed inductance* of the conductor has to be considered. As the current varies in amplitude, the flux lines around the conductor are correspondingly contracting and expanding from its center. While this is occurring, the inner portions of the conductor are being cut by more flux lines than the outer portions. Since the inductance of any coil is mainly dependent upon the number of flux lines encircling it, the inductance of the wire will be somewhat greater at the center than at the surface. Thus, the impedance will be maximum at the center and minimum at the surface. Therefore, alternating current in a conductor will follow the path of least resistance and concentrate near the surface. This is called *skin effect* and, so far as the circuit is concerned, acts like a decrease in cross-sectional area of the conductor. Since inductive reactance is proportional to frequency, it follows that skin effect will become pronounced with higher frequencies.

Eddy-current Loss. This loss will occur in any conductor when placed in a varying magnetic field. As a conductor is being cut by flux lines at varying rates, small values of voltage will be induced at many points along the conductor. Since these voltages are of different values, they will create a difference of potential between these points and produce current. Therefore, additional currents are set up within the conductor, known as *eddy currents*. Since these currents only exist between the various points

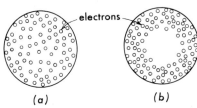

(a)   (b)

Fig. 19·2 Electron distribution in a current-carrying conductor. (*a*) Even distribution in a d-c circuit. (*b*) Skin effect in an a-c circuit.

of potential difference within the small areas of the conductor itself, they perform no useful work. Instead, they are a loss in the conductor in the form of additional heating and produce the same effect as an increase in resistance. The effect is that, due to eddy currents, the resistance of the circuit is increased and the applied emf must supply the energy lost because of them.

Dielectric Loss. While this type of loss is more aptly applied to capacitors, it is a factor that should be included in explaining the difference between a-c and d-c resistance. Dielectric loss is defined as the loss of energy which occurs when an insulating material or device is placed in an electrostatic field, that is, when an emf is placed across it. For example, leakage current is a form of dielectric loss.

Corona Loss. Electric corona loss occurs when the potential between any two points is raised to such a value that the air between the two points becomes ionized. This loss represents the energy expended by the circuit in ionizing the air.

Radiation Loss. This type of loss is the result of energy radiated in the form of electromagnetic waves from any alternating-current circuit. While this loss may be negligible at lower frequencies, it can become serious at the high-order frequencies.

19·2 Figure of Merit. An important consideration of any inductor is its *figure of merit Q*. The inductive reactance of a coil may be considered as a measure of its ability to store energy in a magnetic field, while the effective resistance is a measure of the energy lost in the coil. Then, the ratio between these two factors is called the figure of merit, or *storage factor*, of the coil and can be found by

$$Q = \frac{\text{coil reactance}}{\text{coil resistance}} = \frac{X_L}{R} = \frac{2\pi f L}{R}$$

In most electric circuits the Q of the coil is taken to be the Q of the circuit, since, in most cases, the coil is the device which contains the major amount of circuit resistance.

19·3 Mutual Inductance. Thus far, only the effects of an inductance in a single circuit element have been considered. However, when two or more coils are brought close enough together so that one magnetic field will link the other, an effect known as *mutual inductance* will result. This is shown in Fig. 19·3. Mutual inductance is a term used to describe the relationship that exists between coils when a current change in one induces an emf in another. When this condition exists, the coils, or circuits, are said to be coupled together by mutual inductance. *Two circuits have a mutual inductance of one henry when an average rate of change of one ampere per second in one circuit induces an average of one volt in the other circuit.*

19·4 Degree of Coupling. In order to calculate mutual inductance between coils, the *degree of coupling* has to be considered. When two coils are so coupled that all the flux lines from one cut across all the turns of the other, a condition of 100 per cent, or maximum, coupling has been realized. This condition is also known as *unity coupling*.

The degree to which two coils are mutually coupled is expressed as a percentage of unity (100 per cent) coupling. This is called the *coefficient of coupling k*. As an example, if the coefficient of coupling between two coils was 0.01, it would mean that only 1 per cent of the lines of force from one coil were cutting across the other.

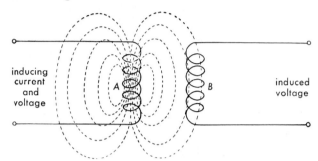

inducing current and voltage

induced voltage

FIG. 19·3   Mutual inductance of two coils.

The mutual inductance of two coils depends upon the coefficient of coupling and can be determined by the following equation.

$$L_m = k \sqrt{L_p L_s}$$

where L_m = mutual inductance, henrys

  k = coefficient of coupling

  L_p = inductance of *primary*, or energized coil, henrys

  L_s = inductance of *secondary* coil, henrys

19·5 Coil Arrangements. The mutual inductance effect between coils may be used for a variety of purposes in practical circuit applications,

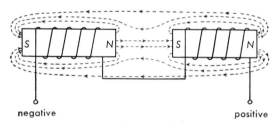

negative

positive

FIG. 19·4   Series aiding coils.

depending upon the total amount of inductance desired. There are several methods in which coils may be coupled, each requiring a different method for calculating total inductance.

For example, when two coils are connected *series aiding*, as shown in Fig. 19·4, it means that the flux produced by each coil combines to provide a total flux greater than that produced by either coil alone. In this arrangement both coils are wound in the same direction so that their resultant magnetic fields are of such polarity as to be additive. The total inductance is found by

$$L_t = L_1 + L_2 + 2L_m$$

where L_t = total inductance of the combination, henrys
L_1 = inductance of first coil, henrys
L_2 = inductance of second coil, henrys
L_m = mutual inductance of combination

When these two coils are wound in opposite directions, as shown in Fig. 19·5, they are in an arrangement known as *series opposing*. They would also be series opposing if they were wound in the same direction but current through one were reversed in direction. In this arrangement

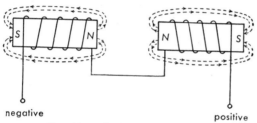

negative   positive

FIG. 19·5   Series opposing coils.

the fields are of opposite polarity. This reduces total flux and produces a total inductance less than that of either coil. The total inductance is found by

$$L_t = L_1 + L_2 - 2L_m$$

Two or more inductors may also be connected in parallel, either aiding or opposing. In an arrangement for parallel aiding, total inductance may be found by

$$L_t = \frac{1}{\dfrac{1}{L_1 + L_m} + \dfrac{1}{L_2 + L_m}}$$

In a parallel arrangement where the fields oppose, the inductance may be found by

$$L_t = \frac{1}{\dfrac{1}{L_1 - L_m} + \dfrac{1}{L_2 - L_m}}$$

19·6   Low-frequency Inductance Coils.   The values of inductors used in electronic equipment vary over a wide range and are designed for various frequency bands. Those inductors used in circuits operating at audio frequencies or lower will be discussed as low-frequency inductance coils. Generally, the lower the frequency, the more inductance required for a given application. Most low-frequency applications, such as power-supply filters and audio-frequency transformers, require large inductances. To obtain these relatively high values it is necessary to use coils of many turns of wire wound on iron cores of high permeability.

Power-supply Filters. Possibly the most common type of low-frequency inductance coil is that used in the filter circuits of rectifier power supplies. The usual purpose of this type of power supply is to convert alternating to direct current for use at the plates of vacuum tubes. The coils in this particular circuit have a current of the order of 60 or 120 cps through them. In conjunction with other circuit components, it is the purpose of the coil to smooth out the *pulsations* and effectively convert the alternating to direct current. Since the cemf of the coil offers opposition to the constantly changing current through it, some of the pulsating *ripple* is choked out and the output current closely approaches a d-c value. While inductances of 20 to 30 henrys are commonly used, similar applications sometime require inductance up to 100 henrys. These coils are appropriately referred to as *chokes.* Filter chokes are rated as to their inductance at normal load, current-handling capabilities, d-c resistance, and test voltage of their insulation.

Audio-frequency Transformers. A *transformer* can be defined as a device for coupling energy from one circuit to another. Figure 19·6 shows a basic transformer circuit. An alternating current in the *primary* sets up a varying magnetic field around it. This varying flux cuts across the turns of a *secondary* winding and induces an emf which produces current in the secondary.

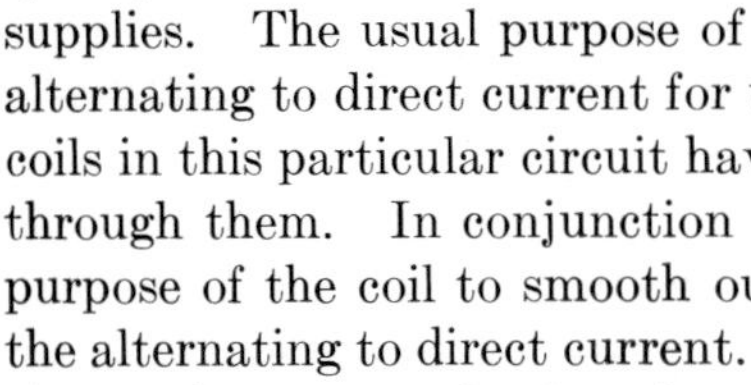

FIG. 19·6   Simple transformer.

Transformers may have either a step-up or step-down ratio, depending upon their purpose. If the secondary has more turns than the primary, it is called a *step-up* transformer; if less turns, a *step-down* transformer.

Inductance coils are used in audio-frequency circuits for coupling energy from one circuit to another. In this application they also serve as impedance-coupling devices for maximum transfer of energy between stages, audio-frequency filters, and feed-supply of the rectified voltage to the plates of vacuum tubes. Coils thus used are usually known as *interstage* transformers and operate at frequencies of approximately 100 to 5,000 cycles. They are ordinarily of the step-up type in order to increase the a-f voltage being transferred. Both primary and secondary are wound on laminated iron or steel cores, and these transformers have inductances of about 100 henrys.

Output Transformers. Another application of low-frequency inductance coils is in coupling the output stage in a radio receiver to the loudspeaker. For this use they must be capable of handling considerable amounts of power and able to match a high-impedance source to a low-impedance load. Output transformers usually have a very high step-down ratio, with primary impedance ranging from about 2,000 to 20,000 ohms and secondary impedance of 2 to 30 ohms.

Although many other transformers are used in a-f applications, their principle of operation is basically the same as for those previously considered and, therefore, will not be discussed in detail here.

19·7 High-frequency Inductance Coils. In radio-frequency circuits the inductance required for any given application is usually less than that for lower-frequency use. Although some r-f coils may be wound on special iron cores, most are of the air-core type. Also, in most high-frequency uses it is desirable to maintain the Q of the circuit at the highest possible value. For this reason, great care must be taken in both design and construction to keep effective resistance at the lowest possible value.

Radio-frequency Chokes. As the name implies, this type of coil is designed to offer high impedance to radio-frequency currents and little opposition to direct current. To accomplish this, the inductors must offer high reactance at the operating frequency but have little ohmic resistance. Inductance ratings of r-f chokes vary from about 2.5 to 125 mh, with resistance varying from about 20 to 250 ohms. Other r-f coils used at higher frequencies have inductances as low as a fraction of a microhenry.

Radio-frequency Transformers. Of the many forms of transformers used in both receiving and transmitting equipment, those most often used have the primary and secondary windings wound on an insulating sleeve. They are usually of the step-up type and are wound on either an air core or one of powdered iron. The powdered iron provides fairly high permeability without introducing serious losses for frequencies up to about 100 Mc. This type of transformer is used to couple two stages of a tuning circuit. It is designed to operate at the frequency range of the device in which it is to be used.

The *intermediate-frequency* transformer is a form of r-f transformer designed to operate over only a small band of frequencies.

Variable Inductors. For numerous purposes, inductors are designed so that the amount of inductance obtainable can be varied. Probably the simplest form of variable inductor is that from which different amounts of inductance may be obtained from several taps along the windings. Another form is the variometer, which consists of two windings,

closely coupled and arranged one within the other. This arrangement
provides for a change from a mutually aiding condition to a mutually
opposing condition by rotating one coil with respect to the other and
changing the physical alignment of its magnetic field.

A more common method in use is to change the inductance by varying
the permeability of the core. This is accomplished by the use of either
a powdered-iron or a copper core. Where the powdered iron increases

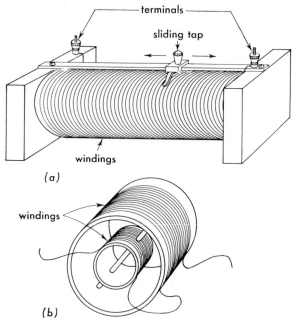

FIG. 19·7   (a) Variable inductor with sliding tap.   (b) Variometer.

the permeability and inductance, the copper has the opposite effect. It
introduces eddy currents which oppose the inducing flux and therefore
decrease the value of inductance.

19·8   Inductance Summary.   The following important points are given
as a summary of the subject of inductance.

a. Inductive reactance is the opposition an inductance offers to the passage of alternating current and is expressed as $X_L = 2\pi fL$ and measured in ohms.

b. In addition to offering opposition to current, inductance causes the
current to lag the voltage; the angle of lag depends upon the relative
values of inductance and resistance.

c. The opposition offered to alternating current is known as impedance
and is expressed as $Z = E/I$.

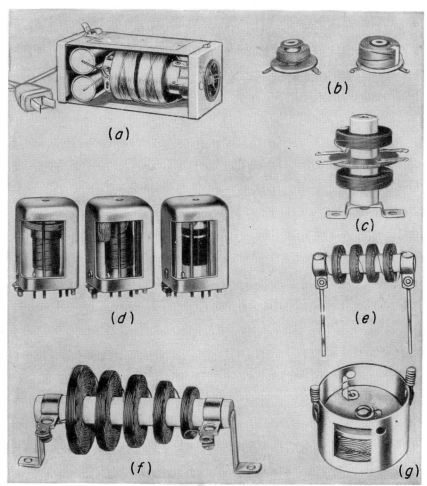

FIG. 19·8 Typical commercial inductances. (*a*) Radio interference filter. (*b*) Unshielded air-core chokes. (*c*) Twin rectifier filter choke. (*d*) Permeability-tuned coils. (*e*) Multiple π-wound choke. (*f*) Heavy-duty transmitter choke. (*g*) Shielded iron-core choke. (*J. W. Miller Company.*)

d. The figure of merit, or storage factor, of a coil is called its Q and is found by dividing coil reactance by coil resistance.

e. Mutual inductance is the term used to describe the relationship that exists when a current change in one circuit induces an emf in another circuit. It depends upon the coefficient of coupling and the relative value of the two inductances.

f. The coefficient of coupling is unity when all the flux lines of one coil cut across all the turns of the other.

g. Coils may be connected, either series or parallel, in such a manner that their fields will either aid or oppose each other.

h. Inductors are found in numerous sizes, shapes, and forms. They may be broadly classified as either low-frequency or high-frequency coils.

i. Low-frequency coils are those that operate at audio frequencies or lower and possess inductance of the order of henrys. They are normally built with laminated cores.

j. High-frequency coils are used at radio frequencies and are of much lower inductance ratings, usually of the order of microhenrys or millihenrys. They usually are wound on either powdered iron or air cores.

k. A variable inductor most often consists of a fixed coil with some means of varying its permeability.

REVIEW QUESTIONS

1. Explain how effective resistance is determined.

2. What are the various factors that comprise the difference between a-c and d-c resistance?

3. Explain skin effect.

4. Explain the effects of eddy currents.

5. How do corona losses add to the resistance of a circuit?

6. What determines the figure of merit of an inductor?

7. Explain mutual inductance.

8. How is the degree of coupling between two coils determined?

9. Explain the difference in effects of series aiding and series opposing coils.

10. Explain the principle of operation of a transformer.

11. What relationship exists between the Q of a coil and the frequency for which it is designed?

12. What is the purpose of a power-supply filter?

13. Explain the principle of operation of a variable inductor.

14. Name one use of a step-down transformer.

15. What is meant by coefficient of coupling?

16. How are inductors usually classified?

17. What determines the difference between a step-up and a step-down transformer?

18. Explain the difference between high- and low-frequency inductance coils.

19. What is the purpose of an r-f transformer?

20. Explain some of the advantages of the resistive-inductive circuit over the purely resistive circuit.

CHAPTER 20

LAWS AND PROPERTIES OF CAPACITANCE

Both the property of inductance and the property of *capacitance* can be compared to inertia. When a voltage is first applied across a coil, the inductance of the coil opposes the initial current; if a voltage is removed from a coil, the inductance will oppose the decrease in current. This constitutes a type of electrical inertia.

When a voltage is applied across a *capacitor*, the capacitor will initially offer practically no resistance, thus permitting instantly a large amount of current. In effect, then, the capacitor opposes the voltage which is causing the current. Moreover, when the voltage is removed from a capacitor, the current will tend to sustain that voltage. Therefore, inductive effect opposes current while capacitive effect opposes voltage. This, too, is an inertia of a sort.

20·1 Capacitor Theory. In electrostatic theory it was learned that if two oppositely charged objects are brought into contact with each other, they will neutralize each other in order to reach a state of balance. However, if the two objects are brought close together but do not actually touch, each object will retain its charge. Further, if a conductor is connected between them, their charges will be neutralized, but not quite as rapidly as if they had been brought into actual contact. Also, if the length of the conductor is increased, the charges will be neutralized more slowly.

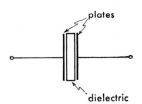

Fig. 20·1   Simple capacitor.

If two oppositely charged objects are brought close together but are kept from actually touching by an insulating material, theoretically the charges will remain indefinitely. However, since there is no perfect insulator, the charges will *neutralize* (return to normal) after a period of time. The time required for neutralization will depend upon the distance between the objects, the type of insulating material, and the amount of surface area exposed between them. A basic capacitor is shown in Fig. 20·1, in which the plates correspond to the two objects discussed.   The insulating material between the two plates is called the *dielectric*, or nonconductor.

A *capacitor* may be defined as any two conductors across which a difference of potential might exist, separated by a dielectric.   Examples of capacitors range from two power lines suspended in air, to a pair of extremely thin metal plates separated by a thin wafer of ceramic material. In the case of the power lines, the dielectric is the air itself.

Capacitance may best be defined as that property of a capacitor which enables it to *store* a charge.   The capacitor is said to have a *capacitance of one farad when a change of one volt per second produces a current of one amp.*

20·2   Simple Capacitor.   Capacitor action is shown in Fig. 20·2, in which a capacitor is connected to a battery through a switch S_1 and a meter.

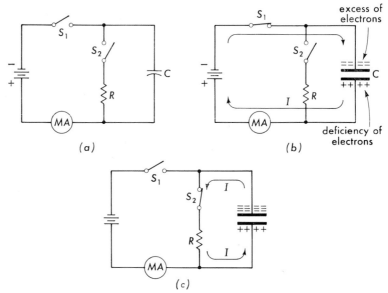

Fig. 20·2   Action of a capacitor during charge and discharge, showing current paths. (a) S_1, S_2 open, no charging action.   (b) S_1 closed, S_2 open, capacitor charging.   (c) S_1 open, S_2 closed, capacitor discharging.

In any instance where a difference of potential exists across a closed circuit, electrons will travel around the circuit in one direction.   If the circuit is broken and a capacitor inserted, the action will be somewhat similar in that electrons will leave one plate and flow through the external circuit to the other plate.   However, after a period of time, electron flow will cease and the capacitor will be charged.   The *amount of charge* is determined by the number of electrons in excess at the negative terminal of the capacitor as compared to the number deficient at the positive terminal.

The dielectric of a capacitor may be air, mica, ceramic or any of several other types of insulating material. The plates of the capacitor act as storage points for the electrons, while the difference of potential that exists across the plates acts upon the dielectric to set up what is known as an *electrostatic field*.

If the switch S_1 in Fig. 20·2b is closed, electrons at the plate nearest the positive side of the battery will flow away from the capacitor, while the plate nearest the negative side of the battery will receive additional electrons. This movement of electrons will be indicated by the meter; however, electron flow will only exist for a fraction of a second until the capacitor is fully charged. The electrons at the negatively charged plate will repel the electrons in the dielectric, while the positively charged plate will attract dielectric electrons. The result is that the dielectric electrons are strained out of their normal orbital paths, and an electrostatic field exists between the capacitor plates. Although the dielectric electrons do not normally become separated from their parent atoms, their orbital *distortion* sets up an additional electrostatic field within the dielectric that is in opposition to that caused by the charge on the capacitor. This further increases the flow of electrons around the circuit, thereby increasing the charge on the capacitor.

This action is referred to as *charging* the capacitor because one plate has become negatively charged while the other has become positively charged. The electrostatic fields resulting from charging act in straight lines and are sometimes called *electrostatic lines of force*. The quantity of charge on the plates will be determined by the value of emf and surface area of the plates. Unless a discharge path were provided, a perfect capacitor would retain its charge indefinitely. However, since there is no perfect insulator, some of the charge will leak off through the dielectric after a period of time. Therefore, once the capacitor is charged, opening S_1 will have no immediate effect. If, however, after opening S_1, switch S_2 is closed, the capacitor will commence its discharge immediately.

With the capacitor charged and a resistor inserted into the circuit, as shown in Fig. 20·2c, the capacitor will discharge at a rate determined by the value of resistance of the resistor. As resistance is increased and additional opposition is offered to the discharging electron movement, the discharge time becomes longer. Moreover, if the circuit of Fig. 20·2a had contained a resistor, the charging time would have been correspondingly longer. There is a direct relationship here that bears emphasizing. The initial, or charging, current is indicative of the time required for charging a capacitor. As resistance increases, charging time also increases.

Farad. The unit of capacitance is the farad, which defines a capacitor arrangement that will *hold a charge of one coulomb* (6.28 × 10^{18} electrons) *when one volt is applied across the plates.* Because the farad is too large a unit to be practical, capacitance is usually expressed in microfarads or micromicrofarads. By formula,

$$C = \frac{Q}{E}$$

where C = capacitance, farads

Q = charge, coulombs

E = emf, volts

For example, if a capacitor is charged to 10 coulombs at 100 volts, the capacitance is 0.1 farad.

20·3 Capacitive Action in D-C Circuits. Figure 20·3 shows a capacitor in a simple d-c circuit. The resistance is in the circuit for the purpose of opposing the rate of charge and, for explanatory purposes, can be of any value.

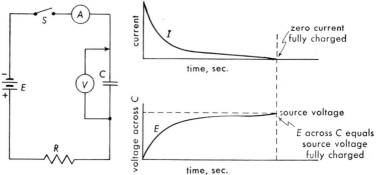

Fig. 20·3 Capacitor-resistor charge circuit with curves depicting rate of charge.

The charging current is maximum at the instant the switch is closed, because the maximum number of electrons will leave one plate and move to the other. At the instant the current starts, there is no voltage across the capacitor because the voltage of the battery must appear across the resistor. Therefore, initial current is equal to the battery voltage divided by the resistance of R. Thus, at zero time, or the instant when the switch is closed, there will be maximum current and zero voltage across the capacitor, as shown in Fig. 20·3.

As the current in the circuit soon partially charges the capacitor, a small voltage will also appear across the capacitor proportional to its charge. Since this voltage is in opposition to the battery voltage, it will subtract from the battery voltage. Also, since the capacitor will now contain some quantity of charge, current will be reduced. Therefore, at some instant after the switch is closed, current will decrease and the voltage across C will increase.

When C is fully charged, the full battery voltage will appear across it. At the same time, there is no current in the circuit, the voltage across the resistor is zero, and the current across the capacitor is zero, as shown.

An ampere of current has been defined as a coulomb of electrons per second, or

$$I = \frac{Q}{t}$$

where I = current, amp

Q = charge, coulombs

t = time, sec

If voltage across the capacitor rises uniformly from zero to a point where it equals source voltage, the rate of voltage change across the capacitor is equal to E/t where E = voltage across the capacitor and t = time in seconds.

Since

$$C = \frac{Q}{E}$$

the current in amperes can be computed by

$$I = \frac{CE}{t}$$

From the foregoing, some definite conclusions can be drawn. For a given resistance and voltage, a small capacitor (less capacitance) will charge in less time than a large capacitor. A decrease in C will result in a decrease in Q. If Q is decreased, then the charging time t will also decrease. Also, if the series resistor is increased in value, the time required for charging is also increased.

For all practical purposes, a capacitor, once charged, offers an open circuit to the voltage that brought about the charge. For example, there are often instances when it is desired to allow an alternating voltage to pass while blocking a direct voltage. A capacitor of the proper value can do this.

20·4 Factors Affecting Capacitance. The capacitance of any capacitor is governed by the type of dielectric, the area of the plates, and the distance between them.

Dielectric. The medium separating the plates of a capacitor is called the dielectric, which is a material that is nonconducting. Air itself is a dielectric, and many capacitors in electronic applications are of the air-dielectric variety. Different dielectrics produce different capacitances. For example, a capacitor will show a marked increase in capacitance if the dielectric is changed from air to mica. The ability of a dielectric material to increase capacitance is called its *dielectric constant*, or *strength*. As dielectric constant increases, so does capacitance.

Because the atoms of different materials have different orbital electron arrangements, the nature of the dielectric is an important factor in determining capacitance. In most tables of dielectric constants (k), air is assigned a constant of 1, and other materials assigned a value that corresponds to the amount by which they multiply capacitance when substituted for air. For example, mica has a dielectric constant of 5.5 since it provides 5.5 times as much capacitance as air, while aluminum oxide has a k of 10 since it provides 10 times as much.

The voltage to which a capacitor can safely charge without breaking down the dielectric also affects dielectric strength. Often called the direct working voltage, this voltage varies directly as the dielectric strength of the material.

Distance. The dielectric offers a certain amount of opposition to the setting up of electrostatic lines of force between the plates. Work is done in charging a capacitor, because the dielectric opposes the setting up of these lines, or the displacement of the normal electric field within the dielectric. The energy of the charging source is stored as electrostatic energy in the dielectric and returned to the circuit when the capacitor is discharged. However, since force is required to distort the pattern of the orbital electrons in the dielectric, it follows that a reduction in dielectric thickness will result in a reduction in opposition to the electrostatic flux. Therefore, if the spacing between plates is reduced by using a thinner dielectric, an increase in capacitance will result.

Area of Plates. Since large plates provide more area over which electrons can be distributed than small ones, it follows that additional plate area will increase the charge for a given voltage and therefore increase capacitance. From the definition of capacitance, it is evident that the number of electrons flowing from one plate to another will be directly proportional to plate area. Therefore, the capacitance of any capacitor is directly proportional to the active area of its plates, and the larger the area, the larger the capacitance.

In view of the preceding factors, it is obvious that some concession must be made to the size of a capacitor with a large value of capacitance and capable of operating with a large direct working voltage. It would appear that these two objectives are diametrically opposed, since a thicker dielectric permits a larger working voltage, but increasing the distance between the plates decreases the capacitance. Although this can be compensated for to some extent by increasing plate area, the solution appears to lie in the type of dielectric material used. Recently it has been found that some of the *titanates* (combinations of titanium with other elements) have produced dielectric constants in hundreds.   Capacitors using this type of dielectric material have been used extensively in some of the electronic applications where it is desired to conserve both weight and space.   Examples of these applications are guided missiles, ballistics missiles, and satellites.

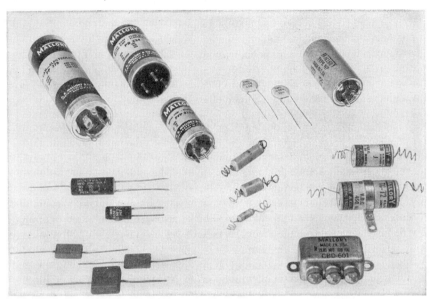

Fig. 20·4   Typical commercial capacitors.   (*P. R. Mallory & Company, Inc.*)

20·5   Capacitive Losses.   Theoretically, any type of insulating material could be used as a capacitor dielectric.   However, certain other factors which contribute to losses in capacitors make the selection of dielectric material an important consideration.

Leakage.   If the insulation resistance of the dielectric material is low, leakage between the plates through the dielectric will result.   This not only reduces the charge on a capacitor but also produces a detrimental heating effect in the dielectric.

Dielectric Hysteresis.   When a capacitor is charged, there is a stress upon the dielectric.   The orbital electrons within the material are attracted to the positive plate.   Although these electrons seldom leave their orbits completely, their movement is distorted.   When a capacitor is discharged, the energy consumed in returning these electrons to their normal orbits is called *hysteresis loss*.   Not too pronounced in d-c applications, dielectric hysteresis loss becomes a limiting factor in high-frequency a-c applications.

Capacitor losses combine and result in an equivalent resistance which retards both charge and discharge time.

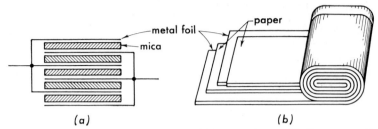

FIG. 20·5   Capacitor construction.   (a) Mica capacitor.   (b) Paper capacitor.

20·6   Capacitance Summary. The following important points are given as a summary of the subject of capacitance.

a. Capacitance is the property of an electric circuit that opposes any change in the amount of voltage across the circuit.

b. A capacitor is a device especially designed to offer a *lumped* value of capacitance in an electric circuit. It usually consists of two plates of conducting material separated by a suitable insulating material.

c. A capacitor and resistor in series are referred to as an *RC* circuit and can be used as a timing device. The operation of many parts of electronic circuits depends upon the rate at which a capacitor charges and discharges through a resistor.

d. The capacitance of a capacitor is directly proportional to plate area and dielectric constant, and inversely proportional to plate spacing.

e. Electrons move from the positive to the negative plates of a capacitor during charging and in the opposite direction during discharging.

f. Capacitive action in an a-c circuit is approximately opposite to that of inductive action.

REVIEW QUESTIONS

1. What is capacitance?

2. What is a capacitor?

3. Explain why there is normally no current within a capacitor.

4. What is orbital distortion?

5. What parts comprise a simple capacitor?

6. Define the farad.

7. What is the relationship between charge time and circuit resistance?

8. Given the charging voltage and the amount of charge, how is capacitance computed?

9. A 10-$\mu\mu$f capacitor is storing a charge of 20×10^{-9} coulomb. What must be the charging voltage?

10. In Question 9, neglecting any circuit resistance, if the charging time is 12 μsec, what must be the charging current?

11. What value of charge does a 0.01-μf capacitor attain when 100 volts are applied to it?

12. In Question 11, $t = 2.5$ sec. What is the charging current?

13. A capacitor develops a charge of 3.5 coulombs in 1.5 sec.   What is the charging current?

14. What is the main advantage of a titanate dielectric?

15. What is a dielectric material and how is its strength determined?

16. How does capacitance vary with plate separation?   Why?

17. How does capacitance vary with plate area?   Why?

18. How does capacitance vary with dielectric constant?   Why?

19. What technique might well be employed to increase capacitance while at the same time possibly reducing the physical size of the capacitor?

20. Describe the direction of motion of electrons while a capacitor is charging. While discharging.

CHAPTER 21

CAPACITOR CHARACTERISTICS AND APPLICATIONS

With few exceptions, electronic circuits consist of resistors, inductors, capacitors, and vacuum tubes or transistors working together to perform a certain function. If the patterns of behavior and limitations of these five components are recognized and understood, the technician will be capable of analyzing almost any electronic circuit and remedying abnormalities within the circuit.

The capacitor, though useful in some d-c applications, is almost exclusively utilized where frequency is a contributing factor; therefore, this portion of the text will be devoted to capacitors in a-c circuits.

21·1   RC Time.   It was shown that a capacitor does not arrive at a state of full charge instantaneously.   However, if a capacitor alone is connected across a given voltage it will assume its maximum charge in less time than if connected in series with a resistor across that voltage.   Also, the larger the value of the series resistor, the more time consumed in charging the capacitor.   Capacitance was defined as the ability of a capacitor to assume and hold a charge.   Since this charge is actually the number of electrons in excess on the negative plate as compared to the number deficient on the positive plate, the charge varies directly as capacitance.   And because a condition of charge cannot exist without some amount of time elapsing, a capacitor's charging time also varies directly as its capacitance.

Mathematically and experimentally it has been proved that a capacitor will have arrived at 63 per cent of the full-charge state when the time elapsed in seconds is equal to the product of the capacitance in farads and the resistance in ohms.   Or, by formula,

$$t = RC$$

where t = time elapsed, sec
R = resistance, ohms
C = capacitance, farads

Usually referred to as the "RC time" of a resistor-capacitor network, such a time constant has been invaluable in design work and will also prove useful to the technician in servicing.

When five RC times have elapsed, the capacitor is considered to be fully charged and, for all practical purposes, there is no current in the circuit. Further, since voltage and charging current vary inversely across the capacitor, at one RC time the charging current will decrease by 63 per cent from its initial or maximum value.

21·2 Imperfect Capacitors. As was pointed out in the preceding chapter, there is no perfect insulator; and a leakage current exists in the dielectric material of the capacitor. The fact that even an extremely small amount of current exists implies that the resistance of the dielectric is, though very large, some finite value. An imperfect capacitor can be represented as shown in Fig. 21·1, in which C is the capacitance of the capacitor and R_P represents the resistance of the dielectric. For high-quality capacitors the value of R_P is extremely high—several megohms. For certain electrolytic capacitors the value of R_P might be as low as one-tenth of a megohm.

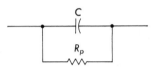

Fig. 21·1   Representation of an imperfect capacitor.

21·3 Capacitance in the A-C Circuit. The total amount of charge any given capacitor will hold is equal to the product of the capacitance in farads and the voltage appearing across the capacitor in volts.

$$Q = CE$$

It must be remembered that Q (charge in coulombs) is a quantity, the number of electrons; while the *rate* at which a capacitor receives this quantity is current in the circuit, or coulombs per second. In an a-c circuit

$$I_{\mathrm{av}} = \frac{CE_{\mathrm{max}}}{t}$$

This means that the current (I_{av}) when a capacitor is charging is equal to the product of the capacitance and the rate of change in volts. Thus current in a capacitive circuit is dependent upon three main factors.

1. Size of the capacitor (as C increases, I increases).
2. Voltage applied across the capacitor (as E increases, I increases).
3. Charging time (as t increases, I decreases).

Voltage and Current Relationships. When a capacitor is connected across an alternating voltage, the plates of that capacitor will alternately charge and discharge in step with the applied voltage. The sine wave of voltage at the plates is essentially the same as that of the source voltage, except for a difference in phase. The charging and discharging cycles of the plates bring about a continuous shift of electrons which constitutes an alternating current that can be measured by a meter placed in series with the capacitor. As the rate of charge and discharge increases, the shift of electrons and resultant current increases. Therefore, current has a direct relationship to the frequency of charge and discharge. As the frequency of the applied voltage increases, the current in the circuit also increases.

Phase Relationships. There will be current in a capacitive circuit only when the voltage across the capacitor is changing. With alternating voltages a continuous change is taking place, and current is always present. Maximum current exists at the time when the rate of change of voltage is greatest, which is when the voltage is passing through 0 or 180°.

As a capacitor nears its charged state, current is reduced because the polarity of charge is in opposition to the voltage being applied. When

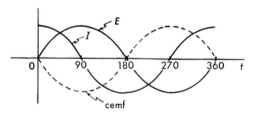

Fig. 21·2   *E* and *I* phase relationships across a capacitor.

the capacitor is fully charged, the applied voltage and the charge on it are equal in amplitude but opposite in polarity, so current ceases. Because of this cemf in a capacitor and because maximum current exists at the instant of maximum voltage change, the current leads the voltage by 90° in a purely capacitive circuit. Figure 21·2 is an illustration of this relationship. Since there is no perfect dielectric, the phase relation between current and voltage will always be less than 90°. In most of the better capacitors, however, this condition is approached so closely that the difference may be disregarded for purposes of computation.

21·4 Capacitive Reactance. As a capacitor is reaching a state of charge, an opposition to current, or cemf, is being set up. This opposition to current limits the current just as resistance does. It is known as *capacitive reactance* and, like resistance, is a ratio of voltage to current.

$$X_C = \frac{E_C}{I_C}$$

where X_C = capacitive reactance, ohms
E_C = cemf (capacitor's charge)
I_C = charging current

E_C must be considered as a maximum value, as explained by Fig. 21·3. Note that there are four distinct changes during one cycle of an alternating voltage or current, each change equal to the time of one-fourth cycle: (1) from zero to maximum positive, (2) from maximum positive to zero, (3) from zero to maximum negative, and (4) from maximum negative to zero. Since the frequency of any alternating voltage is the reciprocal of the time required, then the time of one voltage change is one-fourth of the time for one cycle.

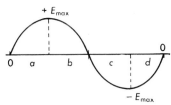

FIG. 21·3 Maximum voltage across a capacitor.

$$t = \frac{1}{4f}$$

By formula

$$I_{av} = \frac{CE_{max}}{t}$$

Substituting for t,

$$I_{av} = \frac{CE_{max}}{\dfrac{1}{4f}} = 4fCE_{max}$$

Since the above equation contains an average term and a maximum term, then (Sec. 15·4)

$$I_{av} = \frac{2}{\pi} I_{max} = 0.637 I_{max}$$

Substituting for this value of I_{av},

$$\frac{2}{\pi} I_{max} = 4fCE_{max}$$

which then becomes

$$I_{max} = 2\pi fCE_{max}$$

Because both voltage and current are now in terms of the same values effective values may be used. Thus

$$I = 2\pi fCE$$

The factors $2\pi fC$ represent a reaction due to the frequency of the alternating voltage and the amount of capacitance in the circuit. As in the case of purely resistive circuits, the opposition to current can be obtained by dividing the voltage by the current. Therefore,

$$\frac{E}{I} = \frac{1}{2\pi fC}$$

The right member in the above equation represents the opposition to current in a capacitive circuit and is denoted by X_C and expressed in ohms. Thus,

$$X_C = \frac{1}{2\pi f C}$$

where X_C = capacitive reactance, ohms
 f = frequency, cps
 C = capacitance, farads

Example 1: What is the capacitive reactance of a circuit in which a 60-cycle alternator is delivering 220 volts to a capacitor of 14.5 μf?

Solution: $X_C = \dfrac{1}{2\pi f C} = \dfrac{1}{2\pi \times 60 \times 14.5 \times 10^{-6}} = 183$ ohms

Example 2: What is the capacitive reactance of a 350-$\mu\mu$f capacitor at a frequency of 1,200 kc?

Solution: f = 1,200 kc = 1.2×10^6 cps
 C = 350 $\mu\mu$f = 3.5×10^{-10} farad

$$X_C = \frac{1}{2\pi f C}$$

$$= \frac{1}{2\pi \times 1.2 \times 10^6 \times 3.5 \times 10^{-10}} = 379 \text{ ohms}$$

21·5 Impedance in a Capacitive Circuit. Since every circuit contains some resistance, the angle between current and voltage will be less than 90°. The exact angle will depend upon the relative amounts of resistance and capacitive reactance. As the amount of resistance is decreased, the angle approaches 90°. The total opposition offered to an alternating current is the impedance. In a capacitive circuit the impedance is found by solving for the reactance of the capacitor and adding, vectorially, to the resistance in the circuit.

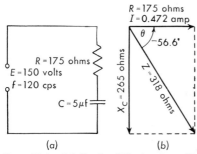

(a)   (b)

FIG. 21·4 (a) Basic RC circuit. (b) Impedance vector for a basic RC circuit.

Example 1: Figure 21·4a represents a circuit consisting of 175 ohms resistance in series with a capacitor of 5.0 μf connected across a source of 150 volts, 120 cycles. Figure 21·4b is the vector equivalent.

(a) Find the phase angle between voltage and current.
(b) Find the impedance of the circuit.
(c) Find the current through the circuit.

Solution:
$$X_C = \frac{1}{2\pi \times 120 \times 5 \times 10^{-6}} = 265 \text{ ohms}$$

$$\tan \theta = \frac{X_C}{R} = \frac{265}{175}$$

$$= 1.51$$

Therefore

(a)
$$\theta = -56.6°$$

Thus the current leads the voltage by 56.6°.

(b)
$$Z = \frac{R}{\cos \theta}$$

$$= \frac{175}{\cos 56.6°} = 318 \text{ ohms}$$

(c)
$$I = \frac{E}{Z} = \frac{150}{318}$$

$$= 0.472 \text{ amp}$$

As was shown in Sec. 21·2, the imperfection within a capacitor can be represented as a capacitor in parallel with a large value of resistance. In

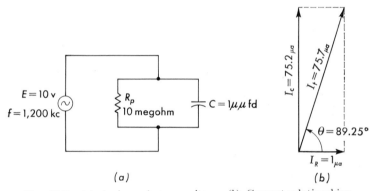

(a)

(b)

Fig. 21·5 (a) An imperfect capacitor. (b) Current relationships.

Fig. 21·5a is shown a capacitor whose dielectric offers a resistance of 10 megohm. A frequency of 1,200 kc is associated with the 10-volt source applied to the capacitor. Since the resistance of the dielectric is essentially independent of the frequency, the current I_R through the left-hand branch is

$$I_R = \frac{E}{R} = \frac{10}{1 \times 10^7} = 1 \times 10^{-6} \text{ amp}$$

It is noted that I_R is in phase with the voltage applied. The current I_C associated with the capacitor alone is a ratio of the voltage applied to the capacitive reactance.   The capacitive reactance

$$X_C = \frac{1}{2\pi fC} = \frac{1}{2\pi \times 1.2 \times 10^6 \times 1 \times 10^{-12}}$$
$$= 0.133 \text{ megohm}$$

and $\qquad I_C = \dfrac{E}{X_C} = \dfrac{10}{0.133 \times 10^6} = 75.2 \times 10^{-6} \text{ amp}$

As shown in Fig. 21·5b, the total current I_t is found by

$$I_t = \sqrt{I_R{}^2 + I_C{}^2} = \sqrt{(1 \times 10^{-6})^2 + (75.2 \times 10^{-6})^2}$$
$$= 75.7 \times 10^{-6} \text{ amp}$$

The angle θ which exists between I_C and I_R can be determined as in the previous example:

$$\tan \theta = \frac{I_C}{I_R} = \frac{75.2 \times 10^{-6}}{1 \times 10^{-6}}$$
$$= 75.2$$

therefore, $\qquad \theta = 89.25°$

The degree of imperfection of the capacitor, then, is indicated by the amount by which the total current differs from 90°.   In this case, θ differs from 90° by 0.75°.   The cosine of this small angle, while approaching one (0.999), is nevertheless less than one.   By definition, the cosine of the angle by which a capacitor fails to arrive at the 90° angular relationship associated with a perfect capacitor is called the *power factor* of the capacitor.   In Chap. 26 a *power factor* will be determined in a slightly different manner.   However, it will be essentially the same power factor as the one just considered.

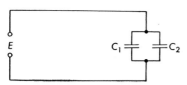

Fig. 21·6   Capacitors in parallel.

21·6   Capacitors in Series and Parallel.   Figure 21·6 represents two capacitors C_1 and C_2 paralleled across a voltage E.   The charge on C_1 will be

$$Q_1 = C_1 E$$

and that on C_2 is

$$Q_2 = C_2 E$$

The total quantity on both capacitors is $Q_1 + Q_2$.   Then

$$Q_1 + Q_2 = C_t E$$

where C_t is the total capacity of the combination.   Adding,

$$Q_1 + Q_2 = C_1 E + C_2 E$$

Then, by substituting the value of $Q_1 + Q_2$,

$$C_t E = (C_1 + C_2)E$$

and
$$C_t = C_1 + C_2$$

Thus, it is apparent that capacitors in parallel combine like resistors in series; that is, the capacitance of parallel combinations is equal to the sum of individual capacitances.

Figure 21·7 represents two capacitors in series with a voltage E across the combination. Because they are in series, the same quantity of electricity must be sent across them. Then, if E_1 and E_2 represent the voltages across C_1 and C_2, Q represents the quantity of electricity in each capacitor and C_t is the capacity of the combination. Hence,

FIG. 21·7 Capacitors in series.

$$E = \frac{Q}{C_t} \qquad E_1 = \frac{Q}{C_1} \qquad E_2 = \frac{Q}{C_2}$$

Since
$$E = E_1 + E_2$$

by substituting the values for all voltages,

$$\frac{Q}{C_t} = \frac{Q}{C_1} + \frac{Q}{C_2}$$

or
$$\frac{1}{C_t} = \frac{1}{C_1} + \frac{1}{C_2}$$

which resolves to

$$C_t = \frac{C_1 C_2}{C_1 + C_2}$$

The foregoing illustrates the fact that capacitors in series combine like resistances in parallel; that is, the reciprocal of the combination is equal to the sum of the reciprocals of the capacitances of the individual capacitors. Two capacitors in series have the same effect as one capacitor with the same plate area but twice the dielectric thickness. For a constant plate area, doubling the dielectric thickness doubles the breakdown voltage and reduces the capacitance by one-half.

21·7 Types of Capacitors. There are numerous types of capacitors. The difference lies mainly in the type of dielectric between the plates and the physical construction of the plates themselves. Other considerations are economy, space available, and, in many cases, frequency.

Mica Capacitors. Constructed with the plates separated by a sheet of mica, this type is usually housed in a molded Bakelite case. Small, or postage-stamp-size, mica capacitors are restricted mostly to use in receivers and other low-power applications. Larger sizes are used in medium- and high-power applications. Direct voltage ratings, or the voltage the capacitor can handle without breaking down the dielectric, range from 500 to several thousand volts. The mica capacitor is generally used in circuits containing high voltages.

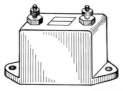  

Fig. 21·8   Three types of mica capacitors.

Paper Capacitors. The dielectric in this type is usually a thin sheet of paper. The plates are either tin or aluminum foil. After the strips of foil have been separated by the dielectric, the combination is rolled into tubular form. Thus, a greater plate area can be obtained in a minimum of space. Figure 21·9 shows several sizes of paper capacitors. Paper capacitors are generally used in low-power applications.

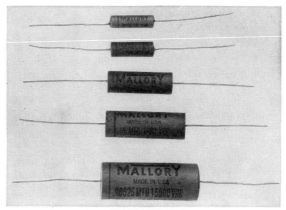

FIG. 21·9   Several sizes of paper capacitors.   (*P. R. Mallory & Company, Inc.*)

Electrolytic Capacitors. Figure 21·10a illustrates a cutaway view of a typical electrolytic capacitor. This type usually consists of two pieces of aluminum separated by a dielectric. To construct these capacitors, direct voltage is applied to the aluminum, and there is current between the outer plate, or container, and the inner plate. After some time elapses, the current causes an aluminum oxide film to form on the inner plate. The film acts as a dielectric and cuts off the current. Removal of the voltage will not change this condition; the inner plate remains coated with the dielectric. Once the coating is formed, no further applications of voltage will produce current. The aluminum oxide coating has the property of stopping current, but it will emit electrons if the outer plate is made positive. In electrolytic capacitors, polarity must always be observed.

Since the oxide coating is very thin, it is possible to obtain extremely high values of capacitance in comparatively small spaces. This type of capacitor is used almost exclusively in filter applications. Figure 21·10b

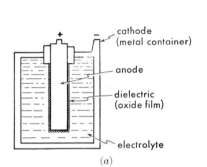
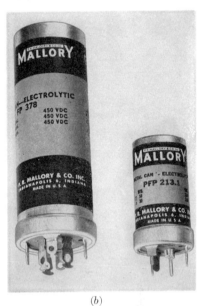

(a)   (b)

FIG. 21·10   (a) Wet electrolyte capacitor.   (b) Multisection electrolytic capacitors. (P. R. Mallory & Company, Inc.)

shows two sizes of multisection electrolytic capacitors. Actually, these are three or four capacitors of different capacitance contained in the same case.

Variable Air Capacitors. Consisting of a set of rotating (rotor) plates and a set of stationary (stator) plates, this type uses air as a dielectric. Since capacitance varies directly as the effective surface area of the plates, maximum capacitance is obtained when the plates are fully meshed. Figure 21·11a shows one section of this type of capacitor. Variable air capacitors are practically the only tuning capacitors in use.

This type of capacitor is constructed in various shapes and sizes, depending upon its tuning function, but basically consists of a rotor, a stator, and a shaft. Since the shaft is connected to the rotor, capacitance will vary in proportion to the degree of rotation. As the rotor's position is varied with respect to the stator, effective plate area is varied. There are no polarity requirements with this type of capacitor, although it is generally considered safer to have the shaft and rotors at ground or at a very low voltage. Two types are shown in Fig. 21·11b.

Ceramic Capacitors. There are two types of ceramic capacitors in general use. One consists of a small ceramic disk with silver coatings, one on each side, which act as the plates. The ceramic forms the dielectric. The other, more common, type is the tubular ceramic capacitor. Constructed physically like a resistor, it consists of a hollow ceramic tube

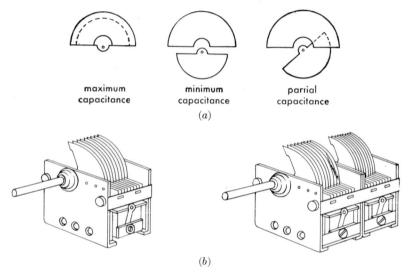

<table>
<tr><td>maximum
capacitance</td><td>minimum
capacitance</td><td>partial
capacitance</td></tr>
</table>

(a)

(b)

Fig. 21·11   (a) Variable air-dielectric capacitor section.   (b) Single and double-section variable capacitors.

with silver coatings on the inside and outside that act as the plates. Advantages of ceramic capacitors lie mainly in the high dielectric resistance of the ceramic. Unusually high values of capacitance can be obtained with relatively small capacitors.

REVIEW QUESTIONS

1. In an RC circuit what is the relationship between resistance and time?

2. What is the relationship between capacitance and charge time?

3. Define capacitance.

4. At one RC time how close to fully charged is a capacitor?

5. At five RC times how close to fully charged is a capacitor?

6. At what points on a sine wave does the greatest rate of change occur?

7. Where does the smallest rate of change exist?

8. What three factors is current dependent upon in a capacitive circuit?

9. In a purely capacitive circuit what would be the phase relationship between voltage and current?

10. State the equation for capacitive reactance.

11. What is the capacitive reactance of a capacitor of 12 μf at a frequency of 60 cps?

12. With capacitance constant, if frequency is increased, what will happen to capacitive reactance?

13. Two capacitors of 8 and 4 μf, are connected in series across 180 volts, 120 cps. (*a*) What is the current through the capacitors? (*b*) Which capacitor has the greater voltage across it?

14. The equation for capacitors in series is _____.

15. The equation for capacitors in parallel is _____.

16. In Fig. 21·12, compute the total capacitance.

17. In Fig. 21·12, what is the magnitude of the current?

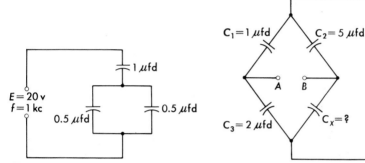

FIG. 21·12   For Questions 16 and 17.   FIG. 21·13   For Questions 18 and 19.

18. In Fig. 21·13, if no potential exists between points A and B (balanced bridge), what must be the value of C_X?

19. What magnitude of current flows in Fig. 21·13?

20. Define the power factor of a capacitor.

CHAPTER 22

SERIES LCR CIRCUITS

Thus far, the resistor, inductor, and capacitor have each been discussed individually. The three components are used in various combinations in most electronic circuits for a variety of purposes. In this portion of the text, all three will be discussed with respect to their relation to each other in series with an alternating voltage.

22·1 Voltage and Current Relationships. It was shown that the inductive reactance of an inductor causes the current to lag the applied

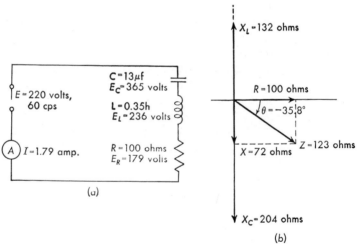

(a)

(b)

FIG. 22·1   (*a*) Series *LCR* circuit.   (*b*) Impedance vector of a series *LCR* circuit.

voltage and that capacitive reactance causes the current to lead the applied voltage. The two effects, then, are exactly opposite. Resistance differs from both capacitive and inductive reactance in that the current through a resistor is in phase at all times with the voltage across that resistor. The relationships between the three reactances are best shown vectorially. Figure 22·1a represents a series circuit consisting of resistance, inductance, and capacitance connected in series across a 220-volt, 60-cycle source. Figure 22·1b is a vector diagram of the relationships between the different reactances. Since X_L and X_C are oppositely directed vectors, it is evident that the resultant reactance will have a magnitude equal to their algebraic sum and with the direction of the greater. Therefore, the net reactance of the two is a capacitive reactance of 72 ohms as illustrated. Thus the entire load circuit could be replaced with an equivalent series circuit of 100 ohms resistance and 72 ohms capacitive reactance. The effective resistance, called the impedance Z, may be obtained by the hypotenuse relation in a right triangle.

$$Z = \sqrt{R^2 + X^2}$$
$$= \sqrt{100^2 + 72^2} = 123 \text{ ohms}$$

where Z = impedance, ohms
R = resistance, ohms
X = net reactance (algebraic sum of X_C and X_L), ohms

Since the current is the same throughout a series circuit, it may be found by applying Ohm's law.

$$I = \frac{E}{Z} = \frac{220}{123}$$
$$= 1.79 \text{ amp}$$

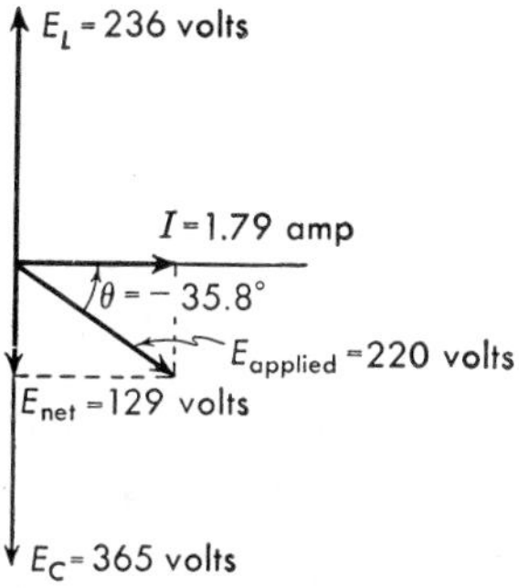

Further, since the current through an inductor lags the voltage across that inductor and the current through a capacitor leads the voltage across that capacitor, the two voltages then are also vectorially opposite. The diagram in Fig. 22·2 shows the vector relationships of the voltages in the circuit of Fig. 22·1a. Given the series current and the individual reactances, Ohm's law will again serve the purpose in solving for the voltages around the circuit.

Fig. 22·2 Voltage vector of a series LCR circuit.

$$E_C = IX_C = 1.79 \times 204 = 365 \text{ volts}$$
$$E_L = IX_L = 1.79 \times 132 = 236 \text{ volts}$$
$$E_R = IR = 1.79 \times 100 = 179 \text{ volts}$$

Note that the voltage across the reactances is greater than the voltage impressed across the entire circuit. This is reasonable, for the applied voltage is across the impedance, which has a smaller ohmic value than the reactances. Because the current is common to all circuit components, the greatest potential difference will exist across the component offering the greatest opposition. Note also, however, that the net voltage (the algebraic sum of E_C and E_L) is smaller than the applied voltage. Observe in Fig. 22·2 that the hypotenuse of the right triangle formed by the voltage across the resistor and the net reactive voltage is equal to the source.

The impedance of the circuit in Fig. 22·1a and the applied voltage, if not known, may be found by trigonometric means. By equation,

$$\tan \theta = \frac{X}{R} = \frac{72}{100}$$
$$= 0.72$$
$$\theta = 35.8°$$

Therefore

$$Z = \frac{x}{\sin \theta}$$
$$= \frac{72}{0.585} = 123 \text{ ohms}$$

It is a common practice to express the angle at which the impedance lies with respect to the zero or resistance reference level of the vector diagram. For example, the impedance in Fig. 22·1 is expressed as

$$Z = 123\underline{/-35.8°} \text{ ohms}$$

The angle is prefixed in this case with a minus sign because it falls below the zero level on the vertical axis. This is known as the *polar form* of expressing impedance. Another, and even more convenient method of notation is called the *rectangular form*. For example, instead of "A series circuit consisting of 100 ohms resistance and 72 ohms capacitive reactance," the statement in rectangular form would be "A series circuit of $100 - j72$ ohms." If the reactance to be noted is inductive, then the statement in rectangular form would be "A series circuit of $100 + j72$ ohms." The letter j is used to show that the value immediately following is to be plotted on the vertical, or y, axis of the vector. The sign of the j, either positive or negative, denotes whether the value is above or below the zero reference level.

NOTE: The sign of the phase angle in the polar form is the same as that of j in the rectangular form.

It must be understood that neither the rectangular form nor the polar form is a method for solving series circuits. They are simply convenient forms of notation that completely describe circuit conditions from both electrical and mathematical viewpoints. In converting from rectangular to polar form, the usual trigonometric methods of solution are employed. The technician should always remember that the resistance and the net reactance of any series LCR circuit form the two sides of a right triangle and the impedance is the hypotenuse of that triangle.

If two or more series LCR circuits are themselves connected in series across a common source voltage, their effects and impedances are also considered in series. The best and simplest approach to finding a combined impedance is to change each LCR circuit into its rectangular form and then add the rectangular forms algebraically.

Example: Combine a series circuit of 235 + j130 ohms and a series circuit of 183 − j70 ohms.

Solution:

$$\begin{array}{r}
235 + j130 \text{ ohms} \\
183 - j70 \ \text{ ohms} \\
\hline
418 + j60 \ \text{ ohms}
\end{array}$$

Observe that the reactive components were combined by prefixing the sign of the larger to j and subtracting. If the signs were the same, it would be simple addition as with the resistive component. Often termed *adding vectors* rather than *adding rectangular forms*, this system of solution will prove extremely valuable in parallel LCR circuits.

22·2 The General Series Circuit. In a series circuit consisting of several resistances and reactances, the total resistance is the sum of all the series resistances, and the total reactance is the algebraic sum of the series reactances. Hence, the impedance is

$$Z = R_t \pm jX$$

As an alternate method, such a circuit can always be reduced to an equivalent series circuit by combining inductances and capacitances before computing reactances. Thus the total inductance is

$$L_t = L_1 + L_2 + L_3 + \cdots$$

and the capacitance of the circuit is

$$\frac{1}{C_t} = \frac{1}{C_1} + \frac{1}{C_2} + \frac{1}{C_3} + \cdots$$

However, when voltages developed across individual reactances are desired, it is best to find the equivalent circuit by combining reactances.

When solving alternating-current problems, it is often convenient to substitute the Greek letter ω (omega) for the factor $2\pi f$. It is generally convenient to solve for the value of this factor in all reactance problems, since it is common to all reactance equations.

Example: Given the circuit of Fig. 22·3, supplied by 220 volts, 60 cycles, find:
(a) The equivalent series circuit.
(b) The impedance of the circuit.
(c) Current.
(d) Voltage across C_1.

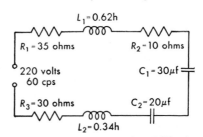

Fig. 22·3 Complex series LCR circuit.

Solution:

(a)
$$R_t = R_1 + R_2 + R_3 = 35 + 10 + 30 = 75 \text{ ohms}$$
$$\omega = 2\pi f = 2 \times 3.14 \times 60 = 377$$
$$L_t = L_1 + L_2 = 0.62 + 0.34 = 0.96 \text{ henry}$$
$$X_L = \omega L_t = 377 \times 0.96 = 362 \text{ ohms}$$

$$X_{C1} = \frac{1}{\omega C_1} = \frac{1}{377 \times 30 \times 10^{-6}} = 88.4 \text{ ohms}$$

$$X_{C2} = \frac{1}{\omega C_2} = \frac{1}{377 \times 20 \times 10^{-6}} = 132.6 \text{ ohms}$$

$$X_C = X_{C1} + X_{C2} = 88.4 + 132.6 = 221 \text{ ohms}$$
$$X = X_L - X_C = 362 - 221 = 141 \text{ ohms}$$

The equivalent series circuit consists of a resistance of 75 ohms and an inductive reactance of 141 ohms. That is,

$$Z = 75 + j141 \text{ ohms}$$

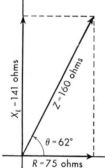

The vector diagram for the equivalent circuit is shown in Fig. 22·4.

(b) $$\tan \theta = \frac{X}{R_t} = \frac{141}{75} = 1.88$$

$$\theta = 62°$$

$$Z = \frac{R}{\cos \theta} = \frac{75}{\cos 62°} = 160 \text{ ohms}$$

$$Z = 160\underline{/62°} \text{ ohms}$$

FIG. 22·4 Equivalent impedance vector of circuit of Fig. 22·3.

(c) $$I = \frac{E}{Z} = \frac{220}{160} = 1.38 \text{ amp}$$

(d) $$E_{C1} = I X_{C1} = 1.38 \times 88.4 = 122 \text{ volts}$$

22·3   Series Resonance.   It has been shown that the inductive reactance of any circuit varies directly as the frequency of the applied voltage and that the capacitive reactance varies inversely as the frequency. That is, the inductive reactance will increase and the capacitive reactance will decrease as the frequency is increased, and vice versa. Therefore, for any given value of inductance and capacitance in a circuit, there is one frequency at which the two reactances are equal. This condition is called *resonance*, and the frequency at which it occurs is called the *resonant frequency* (f_0). Since these two reactances are vectorially opposite, their algebraic sum, or net reactance, will be zero. Such a circuit condition expressed in rectangular form would be

$$Z = R + jX$$

and since $X = 0$,

$$Z = R \pm j0,$$
or
$$Z = R$$

Thus, in a series-resonant LCR circuit the impedance is equal to the resistance of the circuit. In any condition other than resonance the impedance is always greater than the resistance.

In polar form, resonance is expressed as

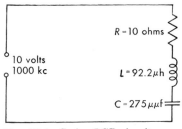

FIG. 22·5 Series LCR circuit operating at resonance.

$$Z = R\underline{/0°}$$

Example: In the circuit of Fig. 22·5, find:
(a) The impedance of the circuit.
(b) The current.
(c) The voltage across the reactances.

Solution:

(a)
$$\omega = 2\pi f = 6.28 \times 10^6$$

$$X_L = \omega L = 6.28 \times 10^6 \times 92.2 \times 10^{-6} = 579 \text{ ohms}$$

$$X_C = \frac{1}{\omega C} = \frac{1}{6.28 \times 10^6 \times 275 \times 10^{-12}} = 579 \text{ ohms}$$

Since $X_L = X_C$, then

$$Z = R = 10 \text{ ohms}$$

(b)
$$I = \frac{E}{Z} = \frac{10}{10} = 1 \text{ amp}$$

(c)
$$E_C = IX_C = 1 \times 579 = 579 \text{ volts}$$
$$E_L = IX_L = 1 \times 579 = 579 \text{ volts}$$

Note that the voltages across the inductance and capacitance are much greater than the applied voltage.

In most series LCR circuits the only resistance is the inherent resistance of the turns of the inductor. Schematically and for the sake of simplicity, the circuit is drawn as three separate components, disregarding the resistive element of the capacitor.

The *figure of merit* of an inductance, usually denoted by Q, is defined as the ratio of its inductive reactance to its resistance.

$$Q = \frac{X_L}{R} = \frac{\omega L}{R}$$

If at resonance

$$E_C = E_L = I\omega L$$

then substituting for I,

$$E_C = E_L = \frac{E\omega L}{R}$$

and substituting for $\frac{\omega L}{R}$,

$$E_C = E_L = EQ$$

It can be said then that the voltage across either reactance at *resonance* is the product of the source voltage and the Q of the inductance. Because the usual electronic circuit has been purposely designed for high Q values, it is seen that very high voltages may be developed in series-resonance circuits. The Q of the circuit of Fig. 22·5 is

$$E_C = EQ$$
$$Q = \frac{E_C}{E} = \frac{579}{10}$$
$$= 57.9$$

The frequency at which a circuit will resonate may be determined by simple manipulation of the equation stating the relationship between the reactances. Thus

$$X_L = X_C$$

or

$$2\pi f L = \frac{1}{2\pi f C}$$

and transposing,

$$f = \frac{1}{2\pi \sqrt{LC}}$$

where f, L, and C are in the usual units, cycles per second, henrys, and farads.

Example: At what frequency will the circuit of Fig. 22·6 resonate?

Solution:

$$L = 500 \ \mu h = 5 \times 10^{-4} \text{ henry}$$
$$C = 400 \ \mu\mu f = 4 \times 10^{-10} \text{ farad}$$
$$f_0 = \frac{1}{2\pi \sqrt{LC}}$$
$$= \frac{1}{6.28 \times \sqrt{5 \times 4 \times 10^{-14}}} = \frac{10^7}{6.28 \times \sqrt{20}}$$
$$= 356{,}000 \text{ cycles} = 356 \text{ kc}$$

It should be noted that the only variables in the equation for resonant frequency are the values of L and C. Note also that their combination can be varied an infinite number of ways and still yield the same product. For example, in the problem shown, if L were doubled and C halved, the reactive product and the resonant frequency f_0 would remain the same.

Figure 22·7 is a representation of the variation of reactances resulting from frequency variations of the voltage applied. The horizontal axis denotes frequency, the vertical axis above zero represents inductive reactance, and the vertical axis below zero denotes capacitive reactance. Note that there is one point at which the two reactances are equal. At

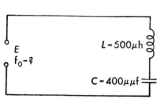

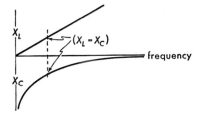

Fig. 22·6 Solving a series LC circuit for resonant frequency.

Fig. 22·7 Reactance curves.

this point the circuit is resonant, and the frequency at which this occurs is the resonant frequency.

22·4 Summary. From the foregoing section on series LCR circuits there are several salient points which can be tabulated as conclusions on resonant and nonresonant LCR circuits.

a. The voltage across the inductor is algebraically opposite to that across the capacitor.

b. The reactance of an inductor is algebraically opposite to that of a capacitor.

c. The current is the same throughout a series LCR circuit, and in vectors showing voltage relationships should be considered as the zero reference level.

d. The voltage across one of the reactances is often much greater than the source voltage. In resonant LCR circuits the voltage across either reactance is the product of the source voltage and the Q of the coil.

e. There are countless numbers of LC products for any one given resonant frequency.

f. In a series-resonant LCR circuit current is maximum, impedance is minimum, and the only impedance that affects current is the resistance of the circuit.

REVIEW QUESTIONS

1. What is the vector relationship between capacitive and inductive reactance?

2. (*a*) What is the phase relationship between capacitive reactance and current? (*b*) Between inductive reactance and current?

3. What is the relationship between capacitive and inductive voltages?

4. In a series LCR circuit, why is the voltage across one of the reactances often greater than the source voltage?

5. Explain the rectangular form of noting impedance.

6. Explain the polar form of noting impedance.

7. Explain the conditions that exist within a circuit when at resonance.

8. What is meant by resonant frequency?

9. What is the relationship between the Q of a circuit and resonance?

10. With all other factors constant, what will be the effect upon a resonant circuit of tripling the inductance and halving the capacitance?

11. Explain how the right-triangle method can be applied to solving for values in series LCR circuits.

12. How is total resistance, reactance, and impedance computed in a series LCR circuit?

PROBLEMS

1. 25 volts, 600 kc is present across a series circuit consisting of 350 $\mu\mu$f and 201 μh. At this frequency the effective resistance of the coil is 13 ohms. (*a*) How much current flows through the circuit? (*b*) How much power is expended in the circuit? (*c*) What are the values of the voltages across the inductive and capacitive reactances? (*d*) What is the Q of the coil?

2. A tuning capacitor can be varied from 100 $\mu\mu$f to 10 $\mu\mu$f. What value of inductance must be used with this capacitor if the lowest resonant frequency is to be 3,750 kc? What will be the highest resonant frequency?

3. A circuit consists of a series combination of capacitor, inductance of 8 μh, and an effective resistance of 5 ohms. If a current of 0.5 amp flows through the circuit at resonance (7,500 kc), find: (*a*) Q of the coil, (*b*) capacitance of the capacitor, (*c*) total voltage across the circuit, (*d*) voltage across the capacitor.

CHAPTER 23

PARALLEL-RESONANT CIRCUITS

The state of being resonant is by no means limited to series LCR circuits. In *any* a-c application, regardless of type of circuit connections, when the inductive and capacitive reactances are equal the circuit is at resonance. When resonance occurs, the frequency of the applied voltage is the resonant frequency.

This chapter will deal with the properties and characteristics of parallel-resonant circuits and their similarity to series LCR circuits.

23·1 Inductance-Resistance Circuit. Figure 23·1 shows a basic parallel LR circuit with curves depicting variations of current and inductive reactance with variations in frequency. Since inductive reactance is

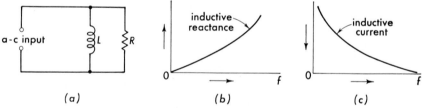

$$(a) \qquad\qquad (b) \qquad\qquad (c)$$

Fig. 23·1 (a) Basic LR circuit. (b) Inductive reactance increases with an increase in frequency. (c) Inductive current decreases as frequency and inductive reactance increase.

directly proportional to frequency ($X_L = 2\pi fL$), at zero cps the inductive reactance of the circuit will be zero. Since there is no inductive reactance, inductive current will be infinity and no current will appear through the resistor at this instant. As the frequency is increased, inductive reactance will increase and inductive current will decrease. As inductive current decreases, current through the resistor increases until, at infinity, inductive current will be zero and the only current in the circuit will be that through the resistor. Therefore, inductive reactance in a parallel-resonant circuit can be considered in terms of current.

23·2 Capacitance-Resistance Circuit. In the circuit of Fig. 23·2, when the frequency of the applied voltage is zero cps, capacitive reactance will be infinity. Therefore, at this instant the capacitive current will be zero and the only current in the circuit will be that through the resistor. Because capacitive reactance is inversely proportional to frequency, an increase in frequency will result in a decrease in the capacitive reactance of the circuit. As frequency is further increased, capacitive reactance decreases and the capacitive current increases. At infinity cps, capacitive reactance will be zero and current across the capacitor will be infinite.

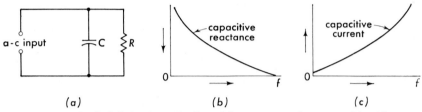

FIG. 23·2 (a) Basic RC circuit. (b) Capacitive reactance decreases with an increase in frequency. (c) Capacitive current increases with an increase in frequency and decrease in capacitive reactance.

Therefore, there will be a frequency at which the parallel impedance of an RC circuit will be zero with only resistance offered to the flow of current. This occurs at infinity cps in an RC circuit and at zero cps in an LR circuit. Moreover, capacitive reactance in a parallel resonant circuit can be considered in terms of current.

It should be noted in both Figs. 23·1 and 23·2 that an infinite amount of current is purely a hypothetical condition. Current cannot arrive at infinity because there is no perfect capacitor or inductor. However, for purposes of discussion it is merely assumed that both are perfect.

23·3 Inductance-Capacitance Circuit. Since inductance and capacitance are algebraically and vectorially opposite, capacitive and inductive

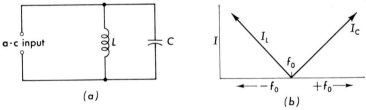

FIG. 23·3 (a) Parallel-resonant LC circuit. (b) Inductive and capacitive currents below, at, and above resonance.

currents will be as shown in Fig. 23·3b. At resonance, X_L and X_C are equal and cancel. At this point there is no inductive or capacitive current. If the voltage is decreased below the resonant frequency, inductive reactance will decrease and the inductive current will increase. Conversely, if the frequency is increased above resonance, capacitive reactance will decrease and the capacitive current will increase. Therefore, below resonance the current is inductive in nature and above resonance it is capacitive in nature. This means the inductive current will lag the applied voltage while the capacitive current will lead the applied voltage.

In a parallel-resonant LC circuit, if current is zero, the impedance of the circuit must be infinite. Figure 23·4 represents the impedance of such a circuit at, above, and below resonance. At resonance the two reactances cancel, while above resonance X_C decreases, yielding a parallel impedance less than infinity. Below resonance the effect is the same, with X_L being the controlling factor.

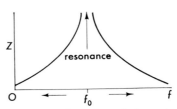

23·4   Effect of Resistance in the Circuit.
Although resistance was purposely omitted in the previous example of an LC circuit, there is always some resistance present in the practical LC circuit. While the

FIG. 23·4   Impedance below, at, and above resonance in an LC circuit.

resistance of the capacitor is generally so small as to be disregarded, inductor resistance must always be considered. An inductor is made up of many turns of wire which always involve some value of resistance. This resistance is drawn separately in the schematic of a parallel LCR circuit (Fig. 23·5) and is always considered as a third component, in series with the inductance. In this circuit the resonant frequency will be that frequency at which X_L equals X_C. However, unlike the circuit of Fig.

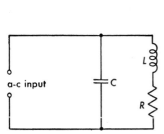

FIG. 23·5   Parallel LCR circuit showing resistive component.

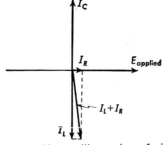

FIG. 23·6   Vector illustration of circuit in Fig. 23·5.

23·3a where I_C is equal and opposite to I_L, the inductive current will be slightly less than the capacitive current. This is because the impedance of the LR portion is slightly greater than the reactance of the C portion due to the presence of R.

Current through the LR portion will not lag the applied voltage by exactly 90° and therefore will not be canceled by the capacitive current. This is illustrated vectorially in Fig. 23·6. I_C is shown leading the applied voltage by 90°, while the resultant current of L and R does not arrive at a

90° lag. It should be noted that I_R, if considered separately, is in phase with the applied voltage. Although the circuit of Fig. 23·5 is still considered resonant, the current can no longer be considered zero as in Fig. 23·3b. Therefore, the impedance cannot be considered infinite as in Fig. 23·4. However, for all practical purposes, if I_R is less than one-tenth as great as I_L, then I_L is considered to be equal and opposite to I_C.

23·5 Impedance of a Parallel-resonant Circuit. With parallel resistances, total resistance may be found by

$$R_t = \frac{R_1 R_2}{R_1 + R_2}$$

The formula for a combined reactance or impedance, denoted by Z, is

$$Z = \frac{X_L X_C}{X_L + X_C}$$

where Z = total impedance, ohms
X_L = inductive reactance, ohms
X_C = capacitive reactance, ohms
In the normal high-Q circuit the impedance of the LR branch is for all practical purposes equal to X_L. This being true, then with X_L and X_C equal the formula for Z could be rewritten as

$$Z = \frac{X_L{}^2}{X_L + X_C}$$

However, since the sum of X_L and X_C would be zero, the two being 180° apart, the R of the LR branch cannot be neglected when adding the reactances. Now the formula can be rewritten as

$$Z = \frac{X_L{}^2}{X_L + X_C + R}$$

Since X_L and X_C cancel each other at resonance,

$$Z = \frac{X_L{}^2}{R}$$

Since Q is defined as the ratio of an inductor's reactance to its resistance, by substituting Q for $\frac{X_L}{R}$, the formula may be further rewritten as

$$Z = Q X_L$$

Again, since by transposition it can be shown that $X_L = QR$,

$$Z = Q^2 R$$

If the values of inductance, capacitance, and resistance are all known, the impedance may also be calculated from the formula

$$Z = \frac{L}{CR}$$

where L, C, and R are all in basic units.

In summary then, it is seen that impedance can be solved for by any one of at least six different formulas. It must be remembered that the foregoing formulas are applicable only when the circuit is operating at resonance. It cannot be denied that an error is introduced into each of the formulas by ignoring the value of R in the numerator of the basic formula; however, in the normal high-Q circuit the error is so small as to be wholly negligible. For example, in a circuit with a Q of 100, the error is only about 0.005 per cent.

Example: In the resonant circuit of Fig. 23·7 solve for

(a) Impedance in terms of Q and X_L.
(b) Impedance in terms of Q and R.
(c) Impedance in terms of X_L and R.
(d) Capacitance in terms of Z, L, and R.
(e) Capacitance on the premise that X_C equals X_L.

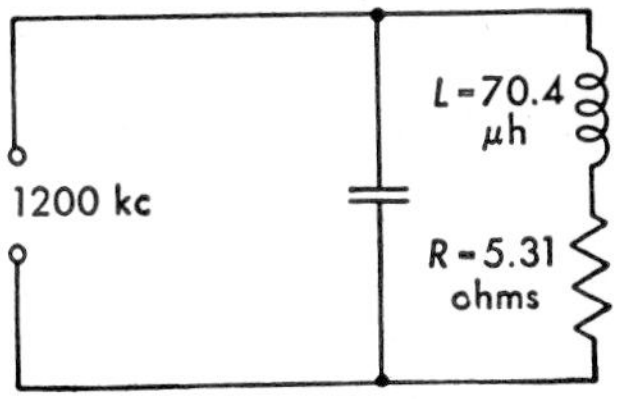

Fig. 23·7 Solution of a parallel-resonant LCR network.

Solution:

(a)
$$\omega = 2\pi f = 6.28 \times 1{,}200 \times 10^3 = 7.536 \times 10^6$$
$$Q = \frac{X_L}{R} = \frac{\omega L}{R}$$
$$= \frac{7.536 \times 10^6 \times 70.4 \times 10^{-6}}{5.31} = \frac{531}{5.31} = 100$$
$$Z = QX_L$$
$$= 100 \times 531 = 53{,}100 \text{ ohms}$$

(b)
$$Z = Q^2 R$$
$$= 100 \times 100 \times 5.31 = 53{,}100 \text{ ohms}$$

(c)
$$Z = \frac{X_L^2}{R}$$
$$= \frac{5.31 \times 10^2 \times 5.31 \times 10^2}{5.31} = 5.31 \times 10^4 = 53{,}100 \text{ ohms}$$

(d)
$$Z = \frac{L}{CR}$$

and
$$C = \frac{L}{ZR}$$
$$= \frac{70.4 \times 10^{-6}}{5.31 \times 10^4 \times 5.31} = \frac{70.4 \times 10^{-10}}{28.19} = 250 \ \mu\mu f$$

(e)
$$X_C = X_L = 531 \text{ ohms}$$

Since $X_C = \dfrac{1}{\omega C}$,

$$C = \frac{1}{\omega X_C}$$

$$= \frac{1}{7.536 \times 5.31 \times 10^{10}} = \frac{1 \times 10^{-10}}{39.02} = 250 \ \mu\mu\text{f}$$

23·6   Currents in a Parallel-resonant Circuit.

Thus far, the current in a parallel-resonant circuit has been shown to be that current taken from the source voltage. There is, however, another current present that must be considered. Figure 23·8 shows a direct-voltage source, switch, and parallel LC circuit. When the switch is closed, the capacitor will charge to the source voltage and remain charged to that value for as long as the switch is closed. The inductor, after its initial opposition to the start of current, will stabilize and allow a constant amount of current through it. If the switch is opened, the capacitor will immediately start discharging through L, causing a flux field to build up around it. When the capacitor is completely discharged, the collapsing flux lines around L will tend to maintain the current in the same direction until the lines have completely collapsed. This electronic inertia on the part of L will cause C to charge again with a polarity opposite to the original charge. When the field around L has completely collapsed, C will discharge in a new direction and produce current through L in this new direction, again building up a field around L. When C has completely discharged, L and its field will recharge C to its original polarity. This oscillatory effect, most commonly termed the *flywheel effect*, will continue in a perfect LC circuit indefinitely. Unfortunately, however, there is some resistance in the circuit, and with each cycle of this flywheel action some of the power is dissipated in the resistance. It should be pointed out here that the higher the Q of the circuit, the longer the flywheel action will exist.

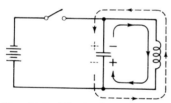

FIG. 23·8   Flywheel action in a parallel-resonant circuit after source voltage has been removed.

The LC circuit of Fig. 23·8 can be considered as a parallel arrangement; however, when the switch is opened and there are no external connections, the combination of L and C is actually in series. This is more easily visualized if the capacitor, after the switch is opened, is considered to be a voltage source.

The frequency of these oscillations is the resonant frequency of the LC combination. This is reasonable since, in a perfect LC network, the capacitor completely discharges and then completely charges during each cycle. In order for this to occur, X_L and X_C must be equal.

Examining Fig. 23·8 further, assume that after two or three cycles of flywheel action the switch is closed, allowing C to charge to its original maximum value, and then the switch is opened. If this operation is repeated every few cycles, the circuit will continue to oscillate and the amplitude of oscillations will be relatively constant. Any circuit characterized by flywheel action is often termed a *tank circuit* rather than an LC or LCR resonant circuit.

The current just described is generally called *circulating current* and can be calculated by applying Ohm's law, where

$$I_{circ} = \frac{E}{X_L}$$

or, since $X_L = X_C$,

$$I_{circ} = \frac{E}{X_C}$$

The magnitude of this current is dependent upon the reactance of either member of the circuit, while the reactance itself is dependent upon the ratio of L to C. It was stated that so long as the LC product remains the same f_0 also remains the same. However, in any given situation if C is doubled for a given frequency, X_C is halved. Conversely, to maintain a constant LC product, if C is doubled, then L must be halved. Further, if L is halved, then X_L is also halved. Therefore, the greater the C/L ratio with the LC product remaining constant, the less the individual reactance and the greater the circulating current. It is generally desirable to develop as much circulating current as practicable. The small amount of resistance inherent in the tank circuit does not materially affect I_{circ} so long as the Q is fairly high.

Current other than circulating current is called *line current*. By Ohm's law

$$I_{line} = \frac{E}{Z}$$

Line current is an essential part of the flywheel effect in that it serves to replace losses in the tank circuit due to the inherent resistance. Here again, Q plays a role in LCR resonant circuits. If Q is large, R must be small. Therefore, only a small amount of current is required to replace the I_{circ} losses through R. This can be further demonstrated by the formula

$$Z = QX_L$$

Since

$$I_{\text{line}} = \frac{E}{Z} \quad \text{and} \quad Z = \frac{E}{I_{\text{line}}}$$

then

$$\frac{E}{I_{\text{line}}} = QX_L$$

Also, since

$$I_{\text{circ}} = \frac{E}{X_L} \quad \text{and} \quad X_L = \frac{E}{I_{\text{circ}}}$$

then

$$\frac{E}{I_{\text{line}}} = Q\frac{E}{I_{\text{circ}}} \quad \text{and} \quad I_{\text{circ}} = QI_{\text{line}}$$

23·7 Selectivity and Bandwidth. The *selectivity* of any *tuned*, or resonant, circuit is defined as its ability to select one desired frequency and discriminate against all others. In a parallel LCR circuit, selectivity is measured and evaluated by the sharpness of the curve obtained by plotting the impedance of the circuit as the applied frequency is varied from below to above resonance. The higher the Q of the circuit, the greater the impedance at resonance and the higher the selectivity. It should be noted here that the selectivity of a series-resonant circuit is measured by the sharpness of the curve depicting current as the frequency is varied from below to above resonance. In a series-resonant circuit, the higher the Q, the larger the current; therefore, selectivity is a direct variable of Q.

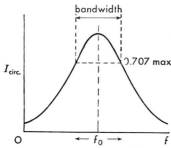

Fig. 23·9 Curve evolving bandwidth in terms of circulating current, resonant frequency, and Q.

Bandwidth. In a parallel circuit *bandwidth* is considered as the range of frequencies lying between the points where the circulating current is 0.707 of maximum, as shown in Fig. 23·9. In a series-resonant circuit bandwidth is determined in the same manner; however, the series line current is considered. In both series- and parallel-resonant circuits, as selectivity increases, bandwidth is decreased. Further, since Q and selectivity vary directly, Q and bandwidth vary inversely.

Bandwidth is approximately equal to the resonant frequency divided by Q. For example, in the circuit of Fig. 23·7 with a Q of 100 and resonant at 1,200 kc,

$$\text{Bandwidth} = \frac{f_0}{Q}$$

$$= \frac{1,200 \times 10^3}{100} = 12 \times 10^3 = 12 \text{ kc}$$

This means that the bandwidth of the circuit would be from 1,194 to 1,206 kc, or 6 kc on either side of resonance. These points would represent the half-power points (0.707 of maximum) on the I_{circ} curve below and above resonance.

23·8 Summary. The following table is a combination summary and tabulation of relationships existing between all the components and characteristics of a parallel-resonant circuit.

STARTING FROM RESONANCE

$f\uparrow$	$X_L\uparrow$	$X_C\downarrow$	$Z\downarrow$	$R\rightarrow$	$I_{line}\uparrow$	$I_{circ}\downarrow$	$L\rightarrow$	$C\rightarrow$	$Q\uparrow$
$f\downarrow$	$X_L\downarrow$	$X_C\uparrow$	$Z\downarrow$	$R\rightarrow$	$I_{line}\uparrow$	$I_{circ}\downarrow$	$L\rightarrow$	$C\rightarrow$	$Q\downarrow$

AT RESONANCE

Selectivity$\uparrow$	$Q\uparrow$	B.W.$\downarrow$	$Z\uparrow$	$I_{line}\downarrow$	$I_{circ}\uparrow$
Selectivity$\downarrow$	$Q\downarrow$	B.W.$\uparrow$	$Z\downarrow$	$I_{line}\uparrow$	$I_{circ}\downarrow$

The arrow pointing upward denotes increase, while downward denotes decrease. Arrow pointing to the right means "remains the same." It should be understood that the relationships are not necessarily in the order of cause and effect.

The following is a summary of certain of the more pertinent conditions in a parallel LCR circuit.

At resonance:

a.
$$X_L = X_C$$
b.
$$Z = QX_L \quad \text{or} \quad Z = QX_C$$

c. Line current is minimum; circulating current is maximum; net current and voltage applied are in phase.

d.
$$I_{circ} = QI_{line}$$

e. Above resonance, the circuit is capacitive and resistive.

f. Below resonance, the circuit is inductive and resistive. The magnitude of the currents determines the nature of the parallel circuit.

PROBLEMS

1. In a parallel resonant circuit, $R = 5$ ohms, $L = 5\mu h$, and $C = 4\mu f$. Find (*a*) the resonant frequency, (*b*) circuit Q, and (*c*) impedance of the circuit.

2. In a parallel resonant circuit, $Q = 15$, $C = 30\mu f$, $L = 10\mu h$. Find (*a*) the resonant frequency, (*b*) the impedance of the circuit, and (*c*) the resistance, R.

3. $F_0 = 500$ kc, $C = 25\mu\mu f$, $Q = 15$. Find (a) the inductance, L, (b) the impedance, Z and (c) the resistance, R.

4. An inductor of 24 μh and a capacitor of 75 $\mu\mu f$ are connected in parallel. What is the resonant frequency of the circuit if the effective resistance of the coil is 113 ohms?

5. What is the Q of the inductor in Prob. 4?

6. In Prob. 4, what is the impedance of the circuit?

7. An inductance of 14 μh with a Q of 100 is connected in parallel with a capacitor of 32.2 $\mu\mu f$. What is the resonant frequency of the circuit?

8. In Prob. 7, what is the effective resistance of the inductor?

9. A tank circuit's bandwidth is rated as ranging from 1,300 to 1,450 kc. What is the resonant frequency?

10. In an LC circuit the value of capacitance is 500 $\mu\mu f$ and the resonant frequency is 356 kc. If the impedance at resonance is 64,000 ohms, what is the Q of the inductance?

REVIEW QUESTIONS

1. Explain the relationships between current, inductance, inductive reactance and frequency in an inductive-resistive circuit.

2. In a capacitive-resistive circuit, explain the effects of an increase in frequency on capacitive reactance and capacitive current.

3. In terms of inductive and capacitive reactances, and inductive and capacitive current, explain the conditions that exist in a capacitive-inductive circuit at resonance.

4. What effect does coil resistance have on inductive current in an inductive-capacitive circuit?

5. Explain how the impedance of a parallel-resonant circuit is determined.

6. Explain flywheel effect.

7. What is circulating current?

8. Explain the difference between circulating and line currents.

9. How is the selectivity of a circuit determined?

10. What is meant by bandwidth? How is bandwidth determined?

11. With respect to the frequency of an inductive-resistive circuit, at what point will current flow only through the resistor?

12. List four formulas that can be used for solving the impedance of a parallel-resonant circuit.

13. What is a tank circuit?

14. What is a tuned circuit?

15. Why is selectivity a desirable feature of a circuit?

16. List several practical applications of a tuned circuit.

17. Why is the bandwidth of a circuit important?

18. How is circulating current produced?

CHAPTER 24

APPLICATION OF LCR CIRCUITS

The components of an LCR circuit have been individually considered in detail, while their specific purposes and applications have only been mentioned. Circuits comprised of these components occupy an important position in a major portion of electronic equipment. Actually, they can be considered as second only to vacuum tubes in the successful operation of most equipment in current use.

Although they may often be referred to in different terminology, circuits functioning upon the relationship that exists between resistance, inductance, and capacitance are broadly classified into two categories, namely, *tuning circuits* and *filters*. In both applications it is their purpose in an electric circuit to separate voltages and currents of different characteristics.

24·1 Resonant Circuits. One use to which a series or parallel LCR circuit is often put is to produce a specific condition for one frequency or a band of frequencies.

In the antenna of any radio or television receiver a multitude of signals is present within the radio-frequency spectrum. These signals represent many different services, such as broadcast-band entertainment, essential communications, television, and many others. In order to utilize only one of these signals while rejecting the others, it is necessary to design an antenna circuit that will select a signal of one frequency from all the others. This is referred to as *tuning* and is accomplished by designing inductance and capacitance in variable amounts within the circuit to provide resonance at the frequency of the desired signal. If a series-resonant circuit produces an increased reactive voltage and large line current at the resonant frequency, it can be seen that one frequency is being selected from among many others and that the circuit has *selectivity*.

24·2 Series Resonance. Figure 24·1 shows a typical series-resonant circuit and its action in selecting a signal at its resonant frequency. This is a simple antenna tuning circuit in which the primary of the antenna transformer acts as the inductance, the tuning capacitor provides the capacitance, and the resistance is that furnished by the conductors and the inductor.

The source voltage is the radio wave cutting across the circuit between antenna and ground. This will produce a current through the primary of the antenna transformer in an amount determined by the impedance offered to the frequency of the source voltage. In this example, with a

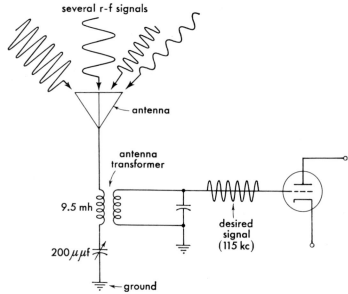

FIG. 24·1   Series-resonant circuit selecting one desired frequency from several present at antenna.

fixed value of inductance of 9.5 mh and the tuning capacitor tuned to 200 μμf, from the formula

$$f_0 = \frac{1}{2\pi\sqrt{LC}}$$

it can be determined that the resonant frequency is 115 kc. As previously shown in a series-resonant circuit, current will be high at the resonant frequency and very low with signals of other frequencies. Therefore, signals other than 115 kc cutting across the antenna will encounter a high impedance, and very little current will be induced in the primary of the antenna transformer. Moreover, the magnetic flux will be of negligible value and only a negligible amount of voltage will be induced in the transformer secondary.

When a 115-kc signal cuts across the antenna, it will encounter low impedance. Therefore, there will be a high current through the primary of the antenna transformer and a magnetic flux will be created around it.

This flux will cut across the secondary windings and induce in it a voltage at the same frequency. By selecting one frequency from among many, the series-resonant circuit is said to be *tuned*, or *selective*.

Secondary Circuit. When a voltage is induced into the secondary of the antenna transformer shown in Fig. 24·1, it is considered as being induced into each turn of the coil and is, therefore, additive. Since this induced voltage is in series with the primary LCR circuit (see Fig. 24·2), both primary and secondary circuits are considered as one series combination. Then the secondary circuit is also acting as series-resonant. When a voltage is induced in this secondary circuit, resonant at the frequency of the induced voltage, there will be a high current in the secondary.

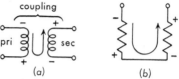

(a) (b)

Fig. 24·2 Series effect between primary and secondary of transformer. (a) 180° phase shift between transformer primary and secondary. (b) Similar equivalent-series circuit.

The amount of voltage present across a capacitor and inductor in a series-resonant circuit is equal to the applied voltage times the Q of the circuit. Thus, the voltage in the secondary circuit is Q times the applied voltage. This voltage is then applied to the control grid of an electron tube for further amplification.

24·3 Parallel Resonance. Figure 24·3 shows a typical example of parallel-resonant-circuit action. In this application the output from the plate of one electron tube is coupled through an *interstage* transformer to the control grid of another tube. The source voltage is therefore furnished by the tube across the parallel combination of C_1 and the transformer primary. If C_1 is tuned so that the LC combination offers resonance to the applied *signal*, then there will be a high circulating current within the circuit. This circulating current through the primary of the transformer will set up a magnetic field around it. This magnetic field cuts the turns of the transformer secondary and induces a voltage in it at the frequency of the voltage in the primary. However, the secondary circuit must be tuned to the resonant frequency of the applied voltage, or the voltage induced in it will be less than the applied voltage

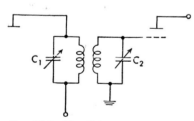

Fig. 24·3 Parallel-resonant circuit.

times Q. For example, at exact resonance the induced voltage will be Q times the applied voltage, but it will decrease as the secondary circuit is tuned from resonance. This is due to the amount of impedance offered by the secondary. At resonance the impedance is lowest, but any deviation from resonance will bring about a corresponding increase in impedance.

24·4 General. A series LCR circuit is one in which the source voltage is connected in series with the inductor and capacitor. In a parallel circuit the source voltage is connected across the combination. However, the secondary of any transformer is usually considered as a series-resonant circuit, regardless of the manner in which it is connected. This is because the voltage induced in the secondary is induced in each turn of the coil and is therefore additive.

Tuning. Circuits for tuning purposes are necessary to select one desired frequency and reject all others. If there were no means of changing the resonant frequency of a circuit, only one frequency could be received. Examination of the formula for resonant frequency will show that varying either L or C will vary the resonant frequency of any circuit. This method is used where it is desired to select only one frequency from among many others. In some circuit schematics it will be noted that both L and C are of fixed values. This is appropriate for circuits through which only one frequency is to be passed. Therefore, the amount of inductance and capacitance is designed to provide fixed resonance at that particular frequency.

In tuning circuits the most common method of changing frequency is by varying the capacitance. This may be accomplished by varying the number of plates, the material of the dielectric, the active area of plates, or the distance between plates. The inductance could also be varied by any means previously discussed, but this is not often done.

24·5 Filters. A *filter* can be generally considered as a device used to separate different currents or voltages. Its basic principle of operation

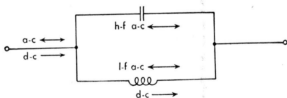

Fig. 24·4 Paths of various types of current through inductor and capacitor.

depends upon several factors. Of these, seven are relatively important in the study of filter action.

1. An inductor offers less opposition to direct current than to alternating current.

2. A capacitor blocks direct current completely and offers more opposition to low-frequency current than to high-frequency current.

3. A series-resonant circuit offers a low impedance at resonance with impedance increasing as deviation from resonance is increased.

4. A parallel-resonant circuit offers a high impedance at resonance, with impedance decreasing as deviation from resonance is increased.

5. In a purely inductive circuit the opposition offered to alternating current will increase as frequency increases.

6. In a purely capacitive circuit the opposition offered to alternating current will decrease as frequency increases.

7. Resistors alone provide no filter action because they oppose the flow of both alternating and direct current. However, the amount of resistance in the circuit affects the sharpness of the filter action. As the resistance is increased, impedance is increased and a wider band of frequencies will be passed. Conversely, decreasing resistance causes a decrease in impedance and results in a sharper filter action.

Low-pass Filter. This is a filter designed to pass all direct current, but to pass alternating-current signals only below the "cutoff" frequency, while attenuating all those above the cutoff frequency. As in the case of most filters, it is comprised of a combination of capacitors, inductors,

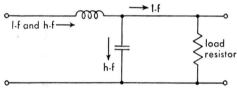

FIG. 24·5   Low-pass filter showing paths of low-frequency and high-frequency currents.

and resistors. These can be connected either series-resonant or parallel-resonant, or both. A simple *low-pass filter* is shown in Fig. 24·5. The inductance inserted in the line will offer little opposition to low-frequency currents and an increasingly large amount of opposition to currents of higher frequencies. Since $X_L = 2\pi fL$, inductive reactance is reduced as frequency is decreased. The capacitor is inserted across the applied voltage as a bypass to divert the unwanted high frequencies back to the source. The value of the capacitor is so chosen that it will offer little opposition to current for all frequencies above cutoff while greatly opposing those below cutoff. As current always follows the path of least resistance, the high-frequency currents will appear through the capacitor. Although currents of both frequencies are present in the source, the net effect of the low-pass filter is to offer little impedance or opposition to low-frequency currents while offering high impedance to high-frequency currents and partially short-circuiting them across the line.

High-pass Filter. This type of filter is one which allows all currents having a frequency above a certain value to pass through the circuit while rejecting or attenuating those below the predetermined cutoff frequency. A simple type of *high-pass filter* is that shown in Fig. 24·6. The capacitor in the line offers little opposition to high-frequency currents but increases the opposition as the frequency is decreased. It will also block direct current. When a high-pass filter is designed, the capacitor should be chosen of a value that will allow the passage of currents above cutoff while rejecting those below this value. The inductor inserted across the source voltage is used to bypass the unwanted low-frequency currents. Since inductive reactance decreases with frequency, low-frequency currents will find little or no opposition through the inductor; however, high-frequency currents will encounter a high impedance and be forced to continue through the load resistor.

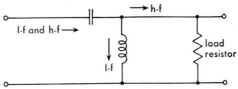

FIG. 24·6   High-pass filter showing paths of low-frequency and high-frequency currents.

Band-pass Filter.   A filter designed to allow currents of a narrow band of frequencies to pass through a circuit and reject all frequencies above and below this band is called a *band-pass filter.*   It has been shown that a series-resonant circuit will offer a low impedance to currents of frequencies at or near its resonant frequency and a high impedance to all others. Also, a parallel-resonant circuit will offer a high impedance to currents of frequencies at or near its resonant frequency and a low impedance to all others.   By connecting these two circuits together as shown in Fig. 24·7

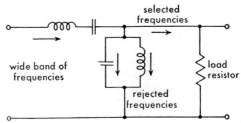

FIG. 24·7   Band-pass filter showing paths of unwanted frequencies and band of desired frequencies.

a simple band-pass filter is formed.   Both circuits are designed so that they will be resonant to the middle frequency of the band desired to be passed.   The series circuit, offering lowest impedance at resonance, will pass all frequencies within the band; the parallel-resonant circuit will offer a high impedance to these frequencies and thus force them to continue through the series circuit.   Any current whose frequency is outside this band will encounter a high impedance offered by the series-resonant circuit and a low impedance offered by the parallel-resonant circuit.   Thus, frequencies other than those of the desired band will be bypassed through the latter circuit.

Band-reject Filter. This type of filter is often referred to as *band-stop*, *band-suppression*, and *band-exclusion*. Its function is opposite to that of the band-pass filter. Its principle of operation is the same in that both series-resonant and parallel-resonant circuits are used; however, their relative position in the circuit is reversed. The series-resonant circuit is inserted across the applied voltage, while the parallel-resonant circuit occupies a position in series with the line. Both circuits are designed to be resonant at the middle frequency of the band to be rejected. Since the parallel circuit offers highest impedance at or near resonance, these frequencies will be rejected and thus bypassed through the path of least opposition offered by the series circuit. A simple form of *band-reject filter* is shown in Fig. 24·8.

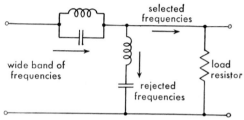

Fig. 24·8   Band-reject filter showing paths of frequencies passed and band of rejected frequencies.

24·6   Filter Characteristics. For purposes of explanation, each of the filters previously considered was shown as consisting of only one section. While it is possible to obtain filter action through the use of only one section, the addition of inductors, capacitors, and resonant circuits will increase the sharpness of the action. When these components have been added, filters often look like various letters when observed in a circuit schematic. For example, by adding an inductor to a simple low-pass filter, its appearance in a schematic would be like the letter T. A filter comprised of an inductor and a capacitor would appear like the letter L, while an additional inductor or capacitor across the line would cause it to look like the Greek letter π. For obvious reasons, then, filters are referred to by their appearance in a circuit as well as by their purpose. Several examples of the different types of multisection filters are shown in Fig. 24·9.

24·7   *LCR* Summary. In summarizing the action of inductance, capacitance, and resistance combined in a circuit, the following points should be remembered.

a. Although their basic principle of operation is sometimes identical, circuits comprised of *L*, *C*, and *R* are broadly classified as either tuning circuits or filters, depending upon their design function and position in an electric circuit.

b. Tuning circuits are necessary to select one frequency from among many others. Filters may select and pass one frequency or a band of frequencies, reject a certain band of frequencies, pass low frequencies and reject high frequencies, or pass high frequencies and reject low frequencies.

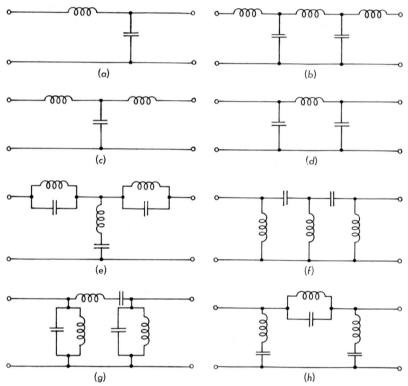

FIG. 24·9   Typical filter circuits.   (a) Basic L-type low-pass filter.   (b) Two-section low-pass filter.   (c) Basic T-type low-pass filter.   (d) Basic π-type low-pass filter. (e) Single-section T-band-reject filter.   (f) Two-section high-pass filter.   (g) π-type band-pass filter.   (h) π-type band-reject filter.

c. The source frequency is that of the current applied to the filter from the applied voltage. The output frequency is that passed by the filter to the load impedance.

d. Filters are classified as to their appearance in a circuit schematic and design purpose.

e. All LCR circuits operate on the principle of impedance offered to currents of different frequencies. Inductive reactance increases and capacitive reactance decreases with an increase in frequency. Series

LCR circuits offer low impedance at resonance, while parallel LCR circuits offer high impedance at resonance.

f. Increasing the number of filter components results in an increase in the sharpness of filter action. Also, reducing the ratio of resistance to reactance causes an increase in the Q of the circuit and sharper band-pass characteristics. Conversely, increasing resistance will allow a wider band of frequencies to be passed, as shown in Fig. 24·10.

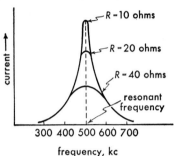

300 400 500 600 700

frequency, kc

Fig. 24·10   Effect of resistance on current at or near resonance.

24·8   Filter Derivations. *Low-pass Filter.* A simple low-pass filter may be designed by using the following equation for determining value of components:

$$L = \frac{R}{\pi f_c} \quad \text{and} \quad C = \frac{1}{\pi f_c R}$$

where L = inductance, henrys

C = capacitance, farads

f_c = cutoff frequency, cps

R = terminating, or load, resistance, ohms

The cutoff frequency in cycles per second may be found by the equation

$$f_c = \frac{1}{\pi \sqrt{LC}}$$

NOTE: The terminating resistor should be of approximately the same value as the source, or input, resistor.

High-pass Filter. For a high-pass filter the values of L and C may be determined as follows, with the same rule applying for R as in the case of low-pass filters.

$$L = \frac{R}{4\pi f_c} \quad \text{and} \quad C = \frac{1}{4\pi f_c R}$$

The cutoff frequency in cycles per second may be found by the equation

$$f_c = \frac{1}{4\pi \sqrt{LC}}$$

Band-pass and Band-reject Filters.   The process of solving for values of components in these types of filters resolves itself into a problem of tuned circuits and resonance.   Any of the previously discussed methods may be employed to determine L and C components so that tuned circuits will offer resonance to the middle frequency of the band.

24·9   Circuit Stage.   Combinations of LCR circuits and vacuum tubes are essential portions of electric circuits.   When used together they are called a *stage.*   Common terms used in referring to a stage usually indicate its purpose, such as audio stage, oscillator stage, radio-frequency

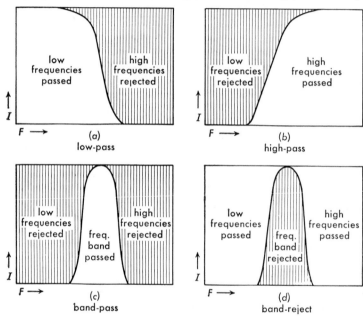

Fig. 24·11   Typical characteristics curves for simple filters.

amplifier stage, etc.   For example, a radio-frequency amplifier stage would indicate a circuit comprised of a vacuum tube and LCR components designed to receive only currents within the radio-frequency spectrum and amplify them prior to being passed on to another stage.

Although any number of methods may be used for connecting the combination, the two most often used are connecting the output of an LCR circuit to the input of a vacuum tube or the output of a vacuum tube to the input of an LCR circuit.

REVIEW QUESTIONS

1. Explain the differences between tuning circuits and filters.

2. Explain how a tuning circuit may select one frequency from among many others.

3. What impedances do series-resonant and parallel-resonant circuits offer to currents at their resonant frequency? Why?

4. Why are *LCR* circuits so important to the successful operation of electric circuits?

5. Explain the action of a series-resonant circuit in coupling energy from the primary of a transformer to the grid of an electron tube.

6. Explain the action of a parallel-resonant circuit in coupling energy from the plate of one electron tube to the grid of another.

7. Explain the action of a low-pass filter.

8. Explain the action of a high-pass filter.

9. Explain the difference between a band-pass and a band-reject filter.

10. What effect does resistance have upon filter operation? Explain.

11. How does the addition of components affect filter action?

12. In band-pass and band-reject filters, to what frequency are both series-resonant and parallel-resonant circuits tuned?

13. What effect will increasing the *Q* of a circuit have upon filter action?

14. Why is the secondary circuit of an interstage transformer considered as series-resonant?

15. What is a circuit stage? Explain an audio stage.

16. List some of the methods commonly used for varying the frequency of tuning circuits.

17. Merely by looking at a circuit schematic, how is it possible to distinguish between tuning circuits and filters?

18. Design a simple low-pass filter that will pass only frequencies below 1,000 kc.

19. Design a simple high-pass filter that will pass only frequencies above 20 mc.

20. Name one practical application of a band-pass filter.

CHAPTER 25

SOURCES OF DIRECT CURRENT

A *dynamo* is a machine for converting mechanical into electrical energy or electrical into mechanical energy. When used for producing electrical energy it is known as a *generator*, and when used for producing mechanical energy it is known as a *motor*.

Generators require some type of power plant for rotation such as water turbines, steam turbines, or gasoline or diesel engines, while motors are rotated by electrical energy. Both machines are similar in outward appearance. Generators are reversible; that is, electrical energy can be applied to a generator from the external circuit to cause the generator to act as a motor and drive a mechanical load.

25·1 Simple D-C Generator. Any generator, whether a-c or d-c, operates on the principle of an electromotive force being induced into a conductor that is moving through a magnetic field.

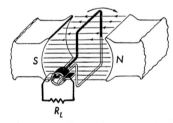

Fig. 25·1 Loop in magnetic field connected to commutator.

A method of producing an emf in a conductor moving through a magnetic field was discussed in Chap. 15. With a single conductor rotating in the field, a sine wave of alternating current was generated and transferred to an external circuit by means of slip rings.

In order to produce a d-c value of emf there must be some means of rectifying the alternating emf. This is accomplished by connecting both ends of the conductor to opposite sides of one metal ring as shown in Fig. 25·1. The ring is then split into two sections; it is then called a *commutator*. Each half of the ring is called a commutator *segment*. Brushes made of carbon are placed so that they press against opposite segments of the commutator and transfer the electrical energy from the conductor to the external circuit. As the loop conductor is rotated and polarity reversed, the connections to the external circuit are also reversed. This causes the polarity of the emf in the external circuit to remain the same through 360° of rotation. This is called mechanical rectification or *commutation.* This type of rectification does not produce an emf of constant amplitude, as can be seen by the graph in Fig. 25·2; however, by increasing the number of loops and correspondingly increasing the number of commutator segments, a voltage of near-constant amplitude can be produced at the brushes. Figure 25·3 shows a two-loop generator and resultant emf for one revolution.

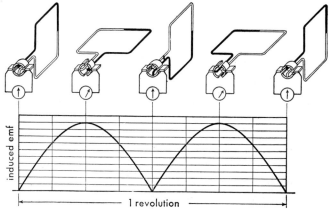

FIG. 25·2 Amplitude of rectified output for one rotation of loop.

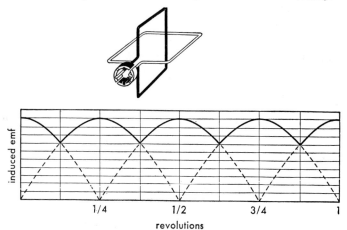

FIG. 25·3 Two loops and resultant output.

25·2 Armature. Generators use many loops, instead of only one or two, wound on a soft-iron core known as an *armature.* The induced emf is connected to the external circuit through brushes and commutator segments, as previously discussed. In the simplest types of generators the field is stationary while the armature rotates. However, in many cases a fixed armature (stator) is used while the field (rotor) rotates. The emf is drawn directly from the armature by fixed contacts.

Multicoil Armatures. Figure 25·4 shows a *ring*-wound armature with 20 coils connected in series so as to make a completely closed circuit. A connection is made from each coil to a segment on the commutator, and a pair of brushes is placed on the commutator at the point where no voltage is produced in the coil connected to that particular segment. As the armature rotates, the coils are shorted by the brushes. By starting at one brush and tracing the path of current to the other, it will be found that

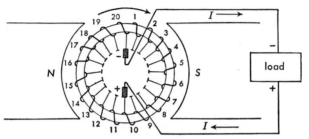

FIG. 25·4   Ring-wound armature.

there are two paths in parallel. The voltage induced in the coils of each path is of the same polarity and is thus additive. The greatest voltage will be induced in the two coils directly in front of the poles of the magnet. Voltage induced in the coils on either side will be less, with minimum voltage induced in the coils directly under the brushes. If each coil was represented as a battery cell, the equivalent circuit would show two banks of cells in parallel, as in Fig. 25·5. The output voltage would be equal to

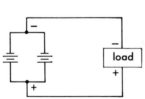

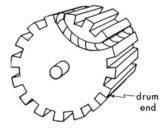

FIG. 25·5   Equivalent circuit of ring-wound armature.

FIG. 25·6   Drum-type armature.

the sum of voltages produced across each coil. Output current would be twice that of the current in one path.

Another type of multicoil armature is the *drum* type, in which the coils are located in slots extending along the length of the armature as shown in Fig. 25·6. The two types of windings used with the drum-type armature are the *lap* winding and *wave* winding.

The lap winding is used where the generator is required to supply large amounts of current at relatively low voltage. This type of winding provides as many parallel paths for current through the armature as there are poles and brushes. Thus, no one winding is carrying a large amount of current. This allows smaller wire to be used without causing the internal resistance to be too great. A lap winding is shown in Fig. 25·7.

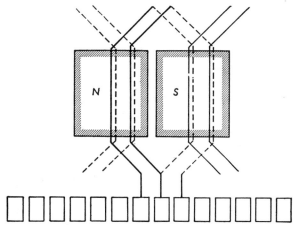

FIG. 25·7   Lap winding on d-c generator.

The wave winding, shown in Fig. 25·8, is used only where there will be a high voltage output at relatively low current. In this type of winding only two brushes are required, and only two parallel paths for current exist, regardless of the number of poles.

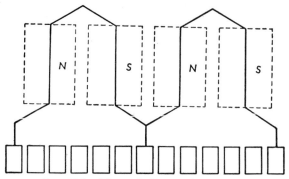

FIG. 25·8   Wave winding on d-c generator.

25·3   Field Excitation.   In the practical generator permanent magnets are replaced by coils of wire wound on alloy-steel blocks. These blocks are made of laminated sheet steel and are called *pole pieces*. The face of the pole is constructed larger than the portion on which the coil is wound, in order to reduce the reluctance of the air gap between the pole pieces and the armature. When a direct current is passed through the coils, a magnetic field is set up around the pole pieces.   If this direct current is supplied by some outside source, such as an external battery or another d-c generator, the generator is said to be *separately excited*.   This is shown in Fig. 25·9, where the generator field is excited from a battery through a rheostat.   If the generator uses its own output for field excitation, it is said to be *self-excited*, as shown in Fig. 25·10.

Residual Magnetism.   Ordinarily, a self-excited d-c generator retains some of its magnetic field after rotation is terminated.   Even though

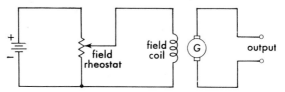

Fig. 25·9   Separately excited generator.

there is no voltage present at the brushes and field current is zero, some of the magnetic field remains.   This is known as *residual magnetism* and makes it possible to restart the generator without external field excitation.

Self-excited Generator.   The self-excited generator depends upon a small amount of permanent magnetism in the pole pieces to start the generator action.   In Fig. 25·10 there are two paths for current, through the external load or through the shunt field.   Residual magnetism in the pole pieces causes a small voltage to be induced into the armature when it is

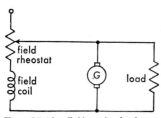

Fig. 25·10   Self-excited shunt generator.

rotated.   The voltage induced is applied to the field windings and produces a current which builds up a field that aids the field of the residual magnetism.   This larger field then induces a larger voltage that is applied to the field coils, the action continuing until the generator arrives at normal operating voltage.   Current through the field of this type of generator is limited by the resistance of the field rheostat.

Flashing the Field.   Occasionally a generator will lose some of its residual magnetism and will not build up an output voltage although rotated at its proper speed.   In order to overcome this condition, the field windings must be disconnected from the armature and connected momentarily to an external d-c source, carefully observing polarity.   This procedure, known as *flashing the field*, restores to the pole pieces their residual magnetism, and the generator will then build up to its normal operating voltage.

25·4   Field Connections.   The three types of generators are named to indicate the method by which the field circuit is connected to the armature circuit.

Series-connected Generator. In this type of generator the armature, field coils, and external circuit are connected in series. Since the current in the field coils is relatively large, a comparatively small number of turns will produce the required flux. When the external circuit is open, there is no field current and the induced voltage in the armature is low; when the external circuit is closed, there is current through the generator, strengthening the field and increasing the output voltage. This increase in voltage will continue with an increase in load until saturation of the pole pieces is reached. Figure 25·11a shows the schematic of a series-connected generator.

Shunt-connected Generator. In this type the fields are placed directly across the full output voltage of the armature, as shown in Fig. 25·11b. The shunt-connected generator will build up a voltage with no external load connected. The field coils are wound with many turns of fine wire so that a very small current through them will produce the necessary flux.

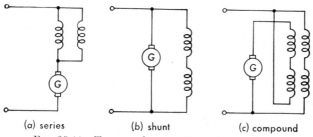

| (a) series | (b) shunt | (c) compound |

Fɪɢ. 25·11   Types and connections of generators.

Flux intensity may be regulated by placing a rheostat in series with the field coil, which will control both the current through the coil and the voltage at the output.

Compound-connected Generator. This generator employs both the series and shunt fields. The shunt field provides the main magnetic field for the generator, while the series field acts as a controlling device that determines the characteristic of the output voltage under load conditions. In the series generator the output voltage increases as the load increases; in the shunt type, the voltage decreases as the load increases. Compounding these two actions results in a more nearly constant voltage output regardless of load.

25·5 D-C Motors. The operation of a d-c motor depends upon the principle that *a current-carrying conductor in a magnetic field tends to move at right angles to the field.* Since a current-carrying conductor has a magnetic field around it, placing the conductor within a magnetic field will cause the two fields to react on each other. If a conductor is placed in a magnetic field as shown in Fig. 25·12, and the direction of current is away from the observer (left-hand rule), the resultant magnetic field is as shown in *a*. The field above the conductor is weakened because the two fields are opposite in direction, while those below the conductor are in the same direction and combine to produce a stronger field. This exerts a force that tends to push the conductor upward. Conversely, current through the conductor in the opposite direction would tend to push the conductor downward. This is the basic principle of operation of a motor.

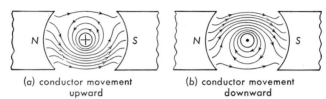

(a) conductor movement
upward

(b) conductor movement
downward

FIG. 25·12   Effects of field reactions upon conductor movement.

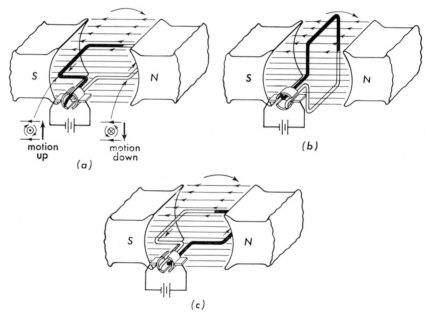

FIG. 25·13   Loop rotation as result of reaction between two fields.

The relation that exists between the direction of current in the conductor, the direction of the lines in the magnetic field, and the direction in which the conductor tends to move can be found by applying the *right-hand rule for motors*. Extend the thumb, first finger, and second finger of the right hand at right angles to each other.

RULE: *The first finger denotes the direction of flux, the second finger denotes direction of current in the conductor, and the thumb denotes direction of conductor movement.*

Figure 25·13 shows the reaction between the two magnetic fields in a motor for one cycle. In *a* current supplied by the battery is so directed through the loop that the side nearest the south pole of the magnet, or field, is forced upward. Since the current through the other side of the loop is in the opposite direction, the reaction will tend to push it downward. In *b* the loop has rotated in a clockwise direction to where the brushes rest on the insulated portion of the commutator. However, since the loop has gained momentum, it will continue until it reaches the position shown in *c*, where the magnetic field reaction causes the side nearest the south pole to be repelled upward and the side nearest the north pole to be repelled downward. This is the same effect that resulted from the position shown in *a*, because the direction of current through the conductor has reversed. Thus, due to the reaction between the two fields, the motor will continue to rotate and convert electrical into mechanical energy.

25·6 Armature Reaction. When the field windings of a two-pole generator are energized and there is no load across the armature, lines of

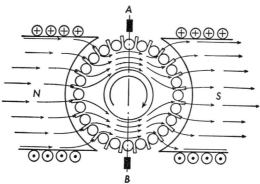

Fig. 25·14 Flux distribution, with current in field winding only.

flux will be distributed evenly across the faces of the pole pieces, as shown in Fig. 25·14. The line *AB* at right angles to the lines of force is known as the neutral plane. Those coils directly under this line will have no voltage induced in them and may be shorted out by the brushes as they rotate between the commutator segments. When the armature is rotated and a voltage is induced in it, there will be current through the windings. This armature current sets up a magnetic field which is at right angles to that set up by the field windings and is called *armature reaction* (Fig. 25·15). The greater the current, the greater the armature reaction. Polarity of this field may be determined by the left-hand rule for solenoids. Figure 25·16 shows the distortion of the main field caused by the reaction due to armature current. Lines of flux are crowded into the trailing tip of both the north and south poles, causing the neutral plane to shift to the position indicated by line *A'B'*. Movement of the neutral plane is in the same direction that the armature is rotating. If the neutral plane is shifted, then the brushes must be shifted or sparking will result, which not only causes the brushes and commutator segments to be pitted but produces interference that affects other electronic equipment. When the brushes are along line *AB*, the coils under them are cutting

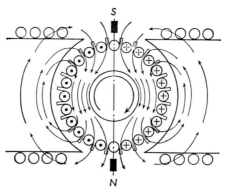

Fig. 25·15   Flux distribution, with current in armature only.

sufficient lines of force at an angle that will cause voltage to be induced in them. It is this voltage which produces the arcing. If the armature current varies, then the neutral plane will continue shifting and the brushes must move back and forth. Since this is not practical, some other means must be devised.

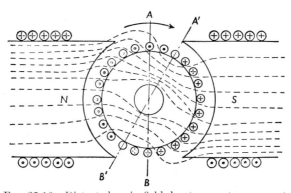

Fig. 25·16   Distorted main field due to armature current.

Interpoles. To counteract the continuous shifting of the neutral plane, smaller auxiliary poles are placed between the poles of the generator, as shown in Fig. 25·17. These are called commutating poles, or *interpoles*, of which there must be one pair for each pair of main poles. The polarity of each interpole is always the same as the main pole following it in the direction of rotation. Since like poles repel, the field of the interpole opposes the field of the armature and cancels its effect on the main field of the generator. Therefore, the main magnetic field is no longer distorted. Since the strength of the magnetic field produced by the armature current is proportional to the current through the armature, the strength of the field of the interpoles should also be dependent upon armature current. The interpole windings are connected in series with the armature so that there will always be complete cancellation of the field set up by the armature. Therefore, with the use of interpoles it is not necessary to shift the brushes, since the neutral plane remains fixed.

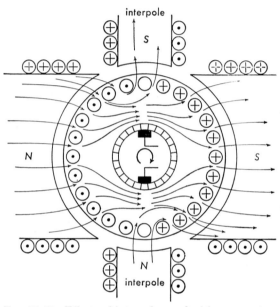

Fig. 25·17   Effects of interpoles used with a generator.

Types of D-C Motors.   D-c motors are of the same principal types as d-c generators. These are shown in Fig. 25·11. The series motor has its field connected in series with the armature, like the series generator. The shunt motor is connected so that the field is connected directly across the line in parallel with the armature, while the compound motor has both a shunt and a series field. These two fields are usually connected so that the series winding aids the shunt winding.

The shunt motor is a constant-speed motor, while the series motor is a variable-speed motor. The latter adjusts itself automatically to run slower under heavy loads and faster under light loads. Therefore, a series motor must always be connected to a load when energized to prevent excessive speed.

Motor field windings may be connected in series, parallel, or series-parallel with respect to each other; however, field connections do not determine the type of motor.

REVIEW QUESTIONS

1. What is a dynamo? A generator? A motor?
2. Explain the right-hand rule for motors.
3. In a simple d-c generator how is the alternating current rectified?
4. What is meant by mechanical rectification?
5. With a single d-c generator, how is a voltage of near-constant amplitude produced?
6. What are the two most common types of armatures?
7. What is one advantage of using lap windings? Wave windings?
8. What are pole pieces?
9. List the two methods of supplying field excitation for a d-c generator.
10. What causes the initial build-up of voltage in a self-excited generator?
11. What is meant by flashing the field? Why is it necessary?
12. What are the three types of field connections used in a d-c generator or motor?
13. Explain the operation of a d-c motor.
14. What causes armature reaction, and how is it compensated for?
15. Explain the function of interpoles.
16. What is an armature?
17. What is meant by the neutral plane, and what causes it to shift?
18. Why must a series motor always be connected to a load?
19. What would be one advantage of the ring-wound armature?
20. Draw a set of curves similar to that in Fig. 25·3 for a basic three-loop situation.

CHAPTER 26

ALTERNATING-CURRENT GENERATORS

Most of the electrical energy in use today is in the form of alternating current and voltage. The types of equipment that develop and deliver alternating current are all based upon the same principle of operation. A-c equipment is not only used to produce large values of current and voltage for commercial use, but also on occasions where only a small value of current is desired. For example, rotating television antennas are among the many devices utilizing a-c machinery principles.

Ordinarily, the technician requires only a general knowledge of the theory of alternating-current machinery. It is therefore essential to this text that only the fundamentals be discussed.

26·1 Types of A-C Generators. Like almost all dynamos operating on the principle of a conductor in a magnetic field, the alternator is one of two basic types.

Rotating Armature. In this type the armature rotates within a stationary magnetic field causing an emf to be generated that is brought out to the external circuit by means of slip rings and brushes. Due to the difficulty of insulating the slip rings and brushes for high voltage and the large number of brushes required for heavy currents, this type of alternator is used only where low voltages and small currents are required.

Rotating Field. In all but very low-voltage a-c generators the armature remains fixed and the field coils rotate as shown in Fig. 26·1. Since there is a relative motion between conductor and field flux, the same effect results as from a rotating armature. The fields and the drum on which they rotate is called the *rotor*, while the fixed armature winding is called the *stator*. The armature winding is placed around the inside of the stationary housing, and the fields rotate within these windings. The number of field coils is limited only by the circumference of the rotor. The field coils are fitted into slots running lengthwise on the face of the rotor. Figures 26·2 and 26·3 show placement of armature windings around the inside of the housing, and connection of the rotating field coils used on the type of alternator shown in Fig. 26·1. With this arrangement it is easier to insulate the armature windings. Field excitation comes from

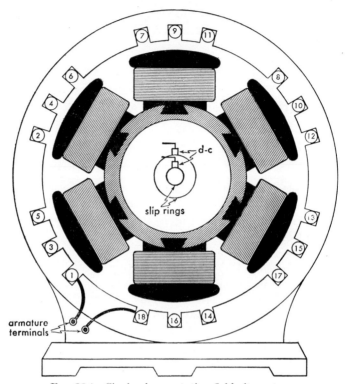

FIG. 26·1   Single-phase rotating-field alternator.

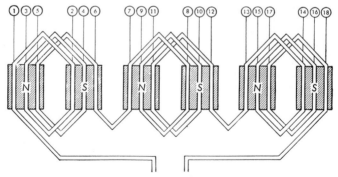

FIG. 26·2   Placement of armature windings in single-phase alternator.

some low-voltage d-c source, such as a shunt generator mounted on the same shaft as the a-c generator fields.   Where field-excitation voltage may be approximately 250 volts, output from the armature winding can be as high as 30,000 volts.   Slip rings and brushes are used for connecting the fields to the d-c excitation source.   Output voltage is taken directly from the stationary armature winding.

26·2 Three-phase Alternator. Most alternating current generated is of the *three-phase* type. With only a slight increase in physical size, a much greater voltage output may be realized with a three-phase alternator. In three-phase systems three armature windings are placed around the inside of the housing approximately 120° apart. As the field

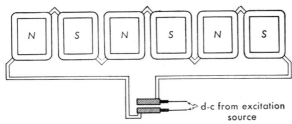

FIG. 26·3 D-c excited alternator field.

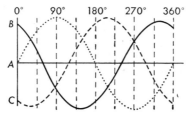

FIG. 26·4 Phase relations of three-phase alternator voltages.

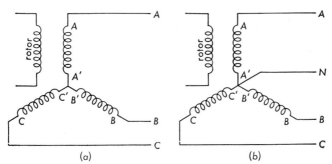

FIG. 26·5 (a) Three-wire Y connection for three-phase alternator. (b) Four-wire Y connection for three-phase alternator.

coil rotates past each armature a voltage is induced in the winding. Since the windings are 120° out of phase with each other, three separate voltages will be induced that are also 120° out of phase with each other (Fig. 26·4). It would appear that six leads were necessary for external connections. However, by connecting the coils internally as shown in Fig. 26·5a it is possible to use only three leads. If four leads are used, the fourth is referred to as neutral (Fig. 26·5b).

Coil Connections. The coils of an alternator may be connected in one of two ways. When connected as shown in Fig. 26·5*a* and *b* they are said to be *wye*-connected (Y-connected), and when connected as shown in Fig. 26·6 they are said to be *delta*-connected (Δ-connected).

Each type of connection has certain advantages. In a Δ-connected alternator there is more than one internal path for current toward the load. This results in a higher current-carrying capacity for the generator, line current being approximately 1.73 times as great as coil current. With the Y-connected alternator there are two coils in series across any two of the output leads. The induced voltages of the two coils are additive, and the resultant output voltage is larger than the voltage of any one coil. Therefore, the Y connection is used where high voltage outputs are desired. With this arrangement, output voltage is approximately 1.73 times as great as coil voltage.

Where it is necessary to supply both single- and three-phase voltages, the Y connection is used. By connecting the neutral lead to the common

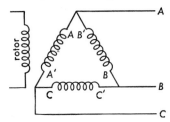

FIG. 26·6   Delta connection for three-phase alternator.

junction it is possible to obtain three single-phase voltages and one three-phase voltage. For example, from a generator designed to produce a 208-volt, three-phase, 60-cycle output, it would be possible to obtain three additional single-phase voltages of 120 volts each by using the four-wire Y connection. To prevent overheating of this type of alternator, it is important that the load be distributed evenly across the three coils. Figure 26·7 shows the actual arrangement of fields and armature windings of a three-phase alternator.

26·3   Regulation. In a single-phase alternator having one pair of poles the armature must complete one revolution in order to produce one cycle of alternating current. If the number of pairs of poles is increased, the frequency will increase.

$$f = \frac{SP}{60}$$

where f = frequency, cps
     S = speed of alternator, rpm
     P = number of pairs of poles
     60 = conversion factor (f in cps and S in rpm)

If additional *pairs* of poles are added, the frequency will increase in steps, whereas any increase in speed will result in a comparatively smooth increase in frequency. For this reason, the number of pairs of poles is determined by the frequency for which the alternator is designed, and day-by-day corrections in frequency are made by varying the speed.

The value of alternator output voltage is governed by the speed of rotation, number of conductors, and strength of field flux being cut. Since the speed of rotation will also affect the frequency of output, it is

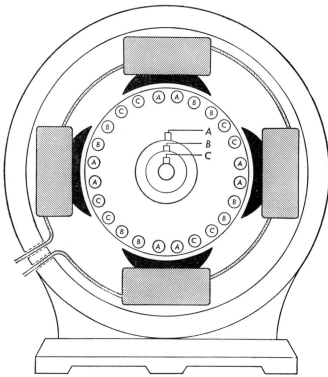

Fig. 26·7   Three-phase rotating-armature alternator.

not practical to regulate the amplitude by varying speed. The number of conductors used is a design consideration and cannot be varied. Since the current in the field of the d-c exciter is comparatively small, it is easier to regulate output voltage by varying the field flux of the exciter unit. As the *voltage regulator* varies the field current of the exciter unit, the number of flux lines is varied.

26·4 Connections. In applications requiring considerable power, it may sometimes be necessary to operate two alternators in parallel to supply the desired output. It is also desirable sometimes to shift a single load from one alternator to another without interruption. This can be done only where two or more alternators are connected in parallel, an arrangement that must meet certain requirements. Before connecting two alternators in parallel, their voltages must be in phase, output voltages must be equal, and there must be no frequency difference. When these conditions are realized, the alternators are said to be *synchronized*.

Where it is desired to produce an output voltage beyond the capabilities of a single alternator, without an increase in current, alternators may be connected in series. With this arrangement, the current will be of the same value as that produced by a single alternator, while output voltage will be the sum voltage of the combination.

26·5   Some A-C Power Considerations.   The power consumed in a d-c circuit is the product of the voltage applied and the current through the circuit. The voltage and current are directly related. In a purely resistive a-c circuit, the power being consumed at any given time is the

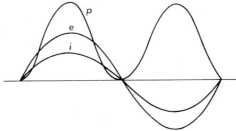

Fig. 26·8   Purely resistive voltage, current, and power relationships.

product of the instantaneous value of the voltage applied and the instantaneous current. As shown in Fig. 26·8, the voltage and current in the purely resistive circuit are always in phase. The curve P, representing the instantaneous power, has twice the frequency of the voltage and current curves. Moreover, the power curve is never negative. This is best understood by remembering the basic arithmetic law that the product of two positive numbers is positive, as is also the product of two negative numbers.

Figure 26·9 represents the voltage, current, and power relationships that exist in a purely reactive circuit. As shown, in a purely reactive a-c circuit the voltage and current are 90° out of phase. Thus, the instantaneous power, being the product of the instantaneous voltage and instantaneous current, while doubling in frequency, is now alternately positive and negative. The positive portion of the curve P is power being taken from the source. The negative portion indicates power that has been supplied to the source. Since the size of the negative portions of curve P is equal to that of the positive portions, no net power is taken from the source.

In a capacitive-resistive situation such as that depicted by Fig. 26·10, the positive portions of curve P are greater than the negative portions, and some power is taken from the source. The voltage and current in Fig. 26·10 are not quite 90° out of phase. Some of the power supplied by the source is returned to the source as indicated by the shaded portions of curve P.

The ability of a reactance to return instantaneous power to the generator arises from the fact that a reactance can store energy or charge. The charge stored by a capacitor depends upon the voltage applied. Thus the maximum storage of energy in a capacitor occurs when the applied voltage is at a maximum. At this time the current is zero, or

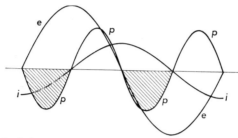

Fig. 26·9   A purely inductive reactance with voltage, current, and power relationships.

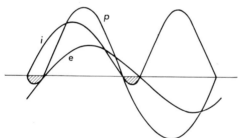

Fig. 26·10   Resistive-capacitive voltage, current, and power relationships.

nearly zero, and immediately thereafter starts to increase in the opposite direction.

The instantaneous power taken by a circuit is constantly undergoing change even though a net positive quantity of power is being used. The average power that is consumed by the load (resistive-reactive) is important, since it is this power that determines the size of the generator to be used and the amount of useful work that can be done in the load.

$$P = I^2 R$$

where P = effective power, watts
I = effective current, amp
R = resistive part of the load, ohms

The product of the voltage and the current is a quantity called the *apparent power*. Its relation to the average power depends upon the ratio of the resistance to the reactance of the load.

$$P_A = EI$$

where P_A = apparent power, volt-amp

E = applied voltage (effective), volts

I = effective current, amp

The ratio of the average power to the apparent power is defined as the *power factor* of the load circuit.

$$\text{p.f.} = \frac{P}{P_A}$$

$$= \frac{I^2 R}{EI} = \frac{IR}{E}$$

Since $\qquad\qquad E = IZ$

$$\text{p.f.} = \frac{IR}{IZ} = \frac{R}{Z} = \frac{R}{\sqrt{R^2 + Z^2}}$$

It can be said then that the power factor of a circuit is the ratio of its resistance to its impedance. Since a pure reactance, capacitive or inductive, contains no resistive component, the power factor of such a circuit is precisely zero. Conversely, the power factor of a purely resistive circuit equals one.

Another often-used expression for the power factor can be derived as follows:

$$\text{p.f.} = \frac{P}{P_A}$$

and $\qquad\qquad P = P_A \times \text{p.f.} = P_A \times \dfrac{R}{Z}$

also $\qquad\qquad \dfrac{R}{Z} = \cos \theta$

and $\qquad\qquad P_A = EI$

Therefore $\qquad\qquad P = EI \times \cos \theta$

where E and I are the effective values of voltage and current and θ is the angle between voltage and current. The cosine expression is in fact the power factor and can have values from zero to one. The power factor is often expressed as a per cent. For example 80 per cent power factor is the equivalent of 0.8 p.f., a cosine value of 0.8, or a resistance-impedance ratio of 0.8.

26·6 Synchro Systems. A special application of the generator-motor combination is that of the *synchro* systems. The name is derived from the system's ability to synchronize itself. The generator, often termed the transmitter, and motor, or receiver, comprise the two basic units of a system.   In Fig. 26·11a it can be seen that the two rotors are connected in parallel to a common source voltage.   Also, it can be seen that the stator leads on the generator (S_1, S_2, and S_3) are connected to the same stator leads on the motor.   In appearance, the generator and the motor are identical.   The only difference between the two is the addition of a brake on the rotor shaft of the motor.

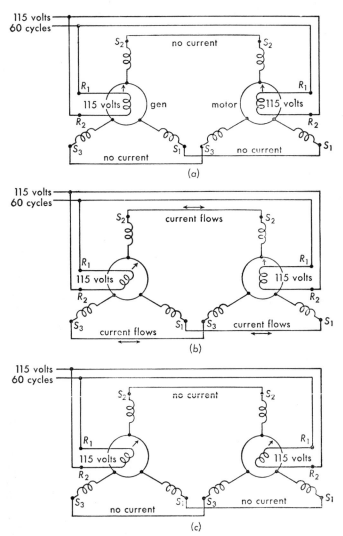

FIG. 26·11   (a) A basic synchro system at "rest."   (b) The synchro-generator rotor has been moved 30°.   (c) The motor rotor has followed the generator rotor, and the system is again at "rest."

Theory of Operation. At a position of "rest," both the generator and the motor are at *electrical zero.* There is current through both rotors, setting up a flux field around both. A voltage is induced in the generator stators, but the same value of voltage is induced in the motor stators. Electrical zero occurs any time the system is balanced.

If the generator rotor is turned 30° clockwise as shown in Fig. 26·11*b*, the field surrounding the rotor will also move 30° in a clockwise direction. The voltages induced in the stator windings will now be of different values. More voltage will be induced in S_3, while less voltage will be induced in S_2 and practically no voltage in S_1. The relative position of rotor and stator determines the amount of voltage induced in the stator or secondary winding. The only connections between the generator and the motor are electrical. Since the voltages induced in the generator stator windings are now of different values, there will be a voltage difference between generator stator and motor stator. There will be current

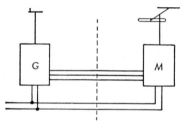

FIG. 26·12 Typical application of a simple synchro system.

in the stator windings, which will each set up a magnetic field that will act upon the magnetic field surrounding the motor rotor. It will be remembered that magnetic lines of force always tend to remain parallel to each other and do not cross. The action of the fields of the motor stator windings is to cause the motor rotor to reposition itself by moving 30° in a clockwise direction. When the motor rotor has traveled 30°, the rotor field will induce voltages in the motor stator windings that are the same as those that were induced in the generator stators. Current will stop between generator and motor stators, as shown in Fig. 26·11*c*. Once again, the system is at electrical zero.

Figure 26·12 shows a synchro generator equipped with a hand crank. The generator is located at some remote point of control, while the motor is located at the base, in this case, of a television antenna. The rotor shaft of the motor is connected directly to the antenna. If the crank on the generator rotor is shifted a number of degrees, the electrical balancing action just described will take place and the result will be that the antenna will move the same distance as did the crank at the remote control point.

The advantages of the synchro system are many. In addition to eliminating the use of extensive mechanical equipment, the system is highly accurate. Frictional losses are at a minimum, maintenance problems are practically nonexistent, and the installation of a system is normally not complicated.

REVIEW QUESTIONS

1. What factors determine the output frequency of an alternator?

2. What is the frequency of an alternator revolving at 1,800 rpm, and having four poles?

3. How many pairs of poles does an alternator have which revolves at 30 rpm and whose output frequency is 60 cps?

4. Why are the fields in some alternators mounted on the rotor instead of on the inside of the housing?

5. How are alternator fields usually excited?

6. Why is it advantageous to use a three-phase alternator rather than a single-phase type?

7. What is the phase relationship between the three voltages produced by a three-phase alternator?

8. What is the purpose of the fourth lead on a three-phase alternator?

9. Explain the advantage of a Δ connection.

10. Explain the advantage of a Y connection.

11. What precautions should be observed when using the four-wire connection with a three-phase generator?

12. What is the purpose of a voltage regulator?

13. What is a practical method of varying alternator frequency?

14. Why is it practical to vary the exciter field current when regulating the output voltage of an alternator?

15. Describe the action of the rotating-field alternator.

16. What precautions must be taken when connecting alternators in parallel?

17. Describe briefly the operation of a basic synchro system.

18. What is the difference between a synchro generator and a synchro motor?

19. Define the power factor.

20. Given: p.f. = 0.95; P_A = 100 watts. Find P.

CHAPTER 27

POWER TRANSFORMERS

The transformer is a stationary device used to raise or lower a-c voltages to desired values. If used to raise voltages, they are called *step-up* transformers. If used to lower voltages, they are called *step-down* transformers. A properly designed transformer is a very efficient device that makes the use of alternating voltages very flexible. Most electronic equipment, such as radio receivers, television receivers, and transmitters, employs some type of transformer.

27·1 Magnetic Induction. It was shown that when electrons move along a conductor, a magnetic field is built up around the conductor. If current is reversed in direction, the magnetic field will also reverse. With alternating current through a conductor, the field builds up to maximum, reduces to zero, builds up to maximum of opposite polarity, then reduces to zero in step with the current. If another conductor is placed in this expanding and collapsing field, an emf will be induced into it and current will exist. The process of inducing this emf is known as *magnetic induction*.

27·2 Transformer Action. In transformers, as in generators, it is necessary to have a magnetic field, a conductor, and motion. However, with transformers the magnetic field is in motion, while the conductor is always stationary.

When two conductors are placed parallel to each other, as shown in Fig. 27·1, current through conductor A causes an expanding magnetic field which cuts conductor B. This field induces a voltage in B that will in turn produce a current. Current in conductor B is opposite in direction to that through conductor A. The left-hand rule indicates that current in A is directed toward the observer, while current in B is directed away from the observer.

If two coils were substituted for the two conductors, current in coil A of Fig. 27·2 would induce a voltage in coil B that would produce current in the opposite direction to that of A. This is the principle of operation of all transformers. The coil which carries current to set up the magnetic

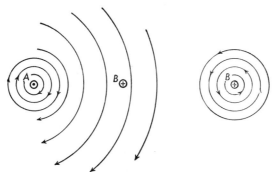

FIG. 27·1 Current in one conductor induces a current in another conductor. Direction of induced current is opposite in direction to current causing it.

field is called the *primary*. The coil in which the voltage is induced is called the *secondary*.

27·3 Power in Transformer Circuits. In the course of accomplishing its purpose of transforming or changing the voltage in an electronic circuit, the transformer leaves the power unaffected. That is,

$$P_p = P_s$$

where P_p = primary power, watts
P_s = secondary power, watts
Inserting the voltage-current products for both the primary and secondary,

$$E_p I_p = E_s I_s$$

transposing, and cross multiplying,

$$\frac{E_p}{E_s} = \frac{I_s}{I_p}$$

From the foregoing, some obvious conclusions can be drawn. For example,

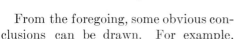
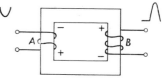

FIG. 27·2 A simple transformer showing instantaneous polarities for one alteration of primary voltage.

if the primary voltage is greater than the secondary voltage, then the secondary current will be larger than the primary current in order to maintain the equality shown. Another conclusion is that there must be no power loss in the transformer action. For all practical purposes, this is true; however, there are some minor power losses. These are discussed in Sec. 27.5.

If the number of turns in the secondary exceeds the number in the primary, the arrangement is that of a step-up transformer. If the primary has the greater number of turns, the transformer steps the voltage down. *The value of the voltage induced in the secondary is directly proportional to the ratio of turns between primary and secondary.* There is a voltage drop across each turn of wire in the primary. For most practical purposes, the voltage induced into each turn of the secondary is assumed to be equal to the voltage drop across each turn in the primary. For example, if 10 volts are applied to a transformer with 10 turns in the primary, 1 volt will appear across each turn. If there are 100 turns in the secondary, there will be 1 volt across each turn, or a total of 100 volts across the entire secondary. The ratio of primary to secondary voltage for transformers is, by equation,

$$\frac{E_p}{E_s} = \frac{N_p}{N_s}$$

where E_p = voltage of primary, volts
E_s = voltage of secondary, volts
N_p = number of turns in primary
N_s = number of turns in secondary

Example: With a transformer whose primary has 220 turns, and is connected to 110 volts, it is desired to step up the secondary voltage to 900 volts. How many secondary turns are required?

Solution: $$\frac{E_p}{E_s} = \frac{N_p}{N_s}$$

Transposing,

$$N_s = \frac{N_p E_s}{E_p}$$

$$= \frac{220 \times 900}{110} = 1{,}800 \text{ turns}$$

The current ratio in a transformer is inversely proportional to the turns ratio.

$$\frac{I_p}{I_s} = \frac{N_s}{N_p}$$

Example: A transformer whose primary is connected to 110 volts is delivering 550 volts at 0.25 amp to the load. What is the current in the primary?

Solution: It is obvious that the turns ratio is a 1:5 step-up. If the ratio is known, it is not necessary to know the exact number of turns in both primary and secondary.

$$\frac{I_p}{I_s} = \frac{N_s}{N_p}$$

Transposing,

$$I_p = \frac{N_s I_s}{N_p}$$

$$= \frac{5 \times 0.25}{1} = 1.25 \text{ amp}$$

27·4 Transformer Construction. The physical construction of transformers consists of two or more windings insulated from each other and

wound on a common form called a *core*. To ascertain that as many lines
of force as possible cut the secondary, the core is made of *laminations*.
These are thin strips of a high-grade steel, designed to magnetize easily
and demagnetize completely.

Shell Core. Figure 27·3a depicts a basic transformer with the primary
and secondary on a common core and a continuous path for both primary
and secondary flux lines. This type is one of the most efficient cores for
transformers.

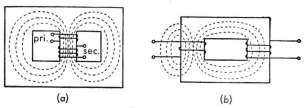

(a)   (b)

Fig. 27·3   Basic transformer construction showing flux paths for (*a*) shell-core and (*b*)
closed-core types.

Closed Core. The closed-core type of transformer forms a closed magnetic path through the core area. This type of transformer is often
found to be less efficient than others because a small number of the
flux lines leave the primary as shown in Fig. 27·3b and travel through
the air back to the other side of the primary. These lines are not
inducing any voltage in the secondary.

Autotransformer. It is not necessary that the primary and secondary
windings be completely separate and distinct. Figure 27·4 shows what is
known as an *autotransformer* in which the secondary winding is in reality
a part of the primary winding. The
voltage across the secondary, however, bears the same relation to that
of the primary as it would if there
were two distinct windings. The
ratio of voltages still corresponds to
the ratio of turns associated with
primary and secondary exactly as it
does in the more conventional type
of transformer. The obvious advan-

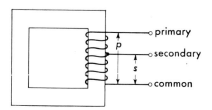

Fig. 27·4   The autotransformer.

tage of this type is the use of three, rather than four, terminals. One
disadvantage of such a transformer would be the increased interaction
between primary and secondary. In higher power applications, once a
voltage has been induced in the secondary, it in turn induces a voltage
back in the primary. If the two windings are physically separated, this
reinduction is usually a negligible consideration. It can be seen that
reinduction is more often a factor to contend with in the case of the auto-

transformer.   Another disadvantage is the lack of conductive isolation between primary and secondary.

27·5 Transformer Losses. Often the flux field from the primary induces a voltage in the core itself.   This sets up currents that manifest themselves as heat or power losses, often called *eddy currents*.   Eddy currents are minimized by constructing the core of laminations which are electrically insulated from each other.

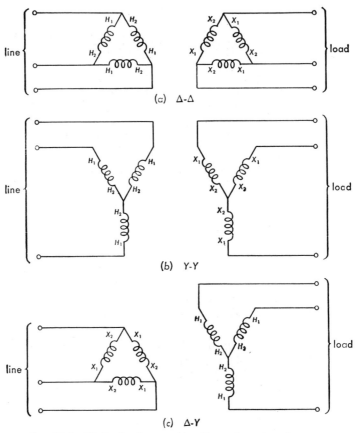

Fig. 27·5   Methods of connecting three-phase transformers.

Hysteresis losses are heat or power losses resulting from molecular friction within the core material when subjected to an alternating voltage. These losses are reduced by constructing the core of special types of metal such as silicon steel or permalloy.

The size wire that must be used in winding both primary and secondary is determined by the amount of current the transformer is designed to handle.   If the proper size wire is used, the transformer will not overheat and the wire resistance will be kept to a minimum.

27·6 Considerations. As previously stated, most of the voltage generated for use in electronic equipment is of the three-phase type. Across any three-phase a-c source, it is possible to use either a three-phase transformer or three single-phase transformers. The advantage of the latter is ease of replacement should one fail. Should one winding of a three-phase transformer fail, replacement of the entire unit would be required.

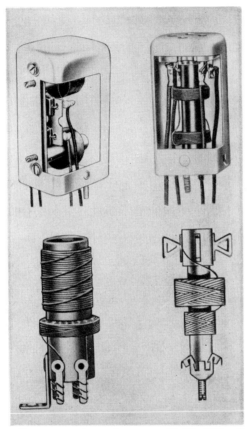

Fig. 27·6   Four types of transformers.   (*J. W. Miller Company.*)

Three common methods of connecting primaries and secondaries of three-phase transformers are shown in Fig. 27·5. With the Y-Y and Δ-Δ connections, output voltage is equal to line voltage times turns ratio. The Δ-Y connection provides a higher output voltage but a corresponding reduction in output current. The Δ-Δ connection is used with relatively low voltages and its main advantage lies in its ability to retain the load with the two remaining windings should one winding open.

For purpose of identifying leads, most transformers are marked in accordance with the Radio Manufacturers Association (RMA) set of standards. Either a color code or identifying numbers and symbols are used. In some instances high-voltage leads are marked H_1, H_2, while low-voltage leads are marked X_1, X_2, etc. With transformers used in rectifier power supplies, color coding is used to identify both primary and secondary windings. In this portion of the text, transformer schematics are shown as using the H and X markings. These indicate relative polarity of the windings. Those having the same subscripts are of the same instant polarity.

Rating. Like most other a-c machinery, power transformers are rated in terms of the maximum amount of current the windings can carry. The name plate of a power transformer usually lists data as to input and output voltages, frequency limits, and current rating.

Shielding. Sometimes it is necessary to prevent interaction between power lines connected to the transformer primary and electron-tube circuits that are supplied by the secondary. This interaction is often manifested in the form of high-frequency interference that is transferred from line to load or from load back to line. An effective means of eliminating this condition is arrived at by placing an electrostatic shield, usually constructed of copper, brass, or aluminum, between primary and secondary. This shielding prevents transfer of interference voltage from one winding to the other or to associated circuits.

REVIEW QUESTIONS

1. How does the manner in which the voltage is induced in the primary of a transformer differ from the manner in which it is induced in the secondary?

2. A transformer has 100 primary turns and 665 secondary turns. If 220 volts is applied to the primary, what is the value of voltage induced in the secondary?

3. A transformer has 120 volts applied to the primary and 60 volts induced in the secondary. If the primary has 200 turns, what is the turns ratio?

4. If the secondary current of a transformer with a turns ratio of 8:1 is 30 amp, what is the value of primary current?

5. A transformer has 130 primary turns and 910 secondary turns. Primary current is 1 amp with 115 volts applied. What is the value of secondary voltage and current?

6. What purpose is served by the core in a transformer?

7. Explain the advantage of a shell-core transformer.

8. What causes eddy currents?

9. How are eddy currents minimized?

10. What causes hysteresis losses?

11. How are hysteresis losses minimized?

12. How are transformer leads marked?

13. How are transformers rated?

14. What is the purpose of shielding in transformers?

15. What is the phase relationship between primary voltage and that induced in the secondary?

16. List the different types of three-phase connections possible with transformers.

17. In three-phase connections, how is secondary voltage computed?

18. What condition makes shielding necessary in a transformer?

19. Explain the principle of operation of the autotransformer.

20. List one disadvantage of the autotransformer.   One advantage.

21. Given an autotransformer with a step-up turns ratio of 6 and a primary voltage of 110 volts, what is the secondary voltage?

CHAPTER 28

BATTERIES

One of the three methods of producing an emf is by chemical means. Devices which convert chemical energy into electrical energy are called *cells*. When two or more cells are electrically connected, they form a *battery*. Although not used as extensively as other means of generating an emf, batteries find many applications in electronic equipment. They play an important role in the supplying of d-c power. In many rural areas, where there is no other source of electric power, batteries alone provide electrical energy. Because of their compactness and their ability to generate electricity within themselves, batteries often provide the power required to operate portable electronic equipment such as transmitters and receivers.

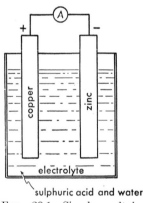

Fig. 28·1 Simple voltaic cell.

sulphuric acid and water

28·1 The Cell. All cells are basically the same. In order to produce an emf, two dissimilar metals must be placed in a solution called the *electrolyte*. Due to the greater chemical action by the electrolyte on one metal than on the other, electrons will be removed from one metal and deposited on the other. This causes a difference of potential to exist between the two metals.

One of the simplest forms of cell is that shown in Fig. 28·1. A strip of copper and a strip of zinc are immersed in an electrolyte composed of about 1 part sulfuric acid to 20 parts water.

There are two general types of cells, namely, *primary* and *secondary* cells. A typical primary cell is shown in Fig. 28·2. The chemical action of the electrolyte causes one of the electrodes to be "eaten away" after a period of use, necessitating replacement of the entire cell. In a secondary cell both the electrolyte and electrodes are altered in characteristics as the cell delivers current to an external circuit. However, they may be restored to their original condition by passing current through the cell in a direction opposite to that during delivery. When a cell is delivering current to an external circuit, it is said to be *discharging*. When the external circuit has been removed and reverse current is sent through the cell, restoring the electrodes and the electrolyte to their original conditions, the cell is said to be *charging*. During discharge time current will be supplied to an external circuit as long as the chemical action within the cell continues to provide a voltage difference between the electrodes.

A further classification of cells deals with the electrolyte used. A *dry* cell, which is usually a primary cell, contains an electrolyte with the consistency of paste. A *wet* cell, which might be either a primary or a secondary cell, uses a liquid electrolyte. Dry cells are usually smaller, low-current types that may be thrown away after discharge.

Dry-cell Ratings. The capacity of a cell is usually measured in ampere-hours, or the total number of hours a cell will deliver a specified amount of current to a load. Since dry cells are not required to deliver a large amount of current, they are not specifically rated but can be depended upon to deliver between ⅛ and ¼ amp of current for several hours at a time. Since they are adapted only to intermittent operation, they should be given a chance to recuperate after any prolonged period of use. However, a dry cell is no longer useful after the electrolyte has become dry and inactive. This can also result from prolonged inactivity.

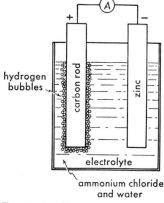

Fig. 28·2 Chemical action in a simple cell similar to that in a dry cell.

Smaller sizes of cells have a shorter "shelf life" than larger sizes; thus their usefulness is proportionate to size.

28·2 Cell Applications. Although not used so frequently today as in the past, certain types of batteries still find usefulness in electronic equipment. For example, the A battery is used in some filament supplies where low voltage and relatively high current are required. This type supplies up to 5 volts, but since the current drain is rather high, replacement is often necessary.

The B battery is made up of several individual cells and is used to supply higher voltage at lower current, such as that required by electron-tube plates. Usually manufactured in 22½- and 45-volt sizes, they can be connected in series for additional voltage such as 67½, 90, 135, and 180 volts.

For medium voltage at very low current the C battery is used. It can be used to supply voltage from 4½ to 22 volts for use as bias on the control grid of electron tubes. Since current drain is exceptionally low, the life of a C battery is longer than that of other types.

28·3 Secondary Cell. The operation of a secondary cell is similar to that of a primary cell except for the chemical action that takes place within the cell. In the primary cell it is not possible to reverse the action and change the materials back to their original form. Once the electrolyte and electrodes have been changed into some other form, replacing them is the only way the cell can be made useful. Since this is impractical in most applications, the secondary cell is more widely used.

The *storage* or secondary cell can be completely restored to its original condition. This process, called *charging*, involves transferring back to their original electrodes the materials that have gone from one electrode to the other. The cell is usually encased in some sort of container, with terminal posts brought out that are labeled positive and negative, indicating the direction of current during discharge. Passing a direct current in the opposite direction through the cell, restores the electrodes to their original composition.

The storage battery, like that used for automobile electrical systems, is comprised of two or more secondary cells. While it does not actually store electrical energy, it does store chemical energy that can be converted to electrical energy. The two general types of storage batteries are the *lead-acid* and the *nickel-iron-alkaline* types. The lead-acid cell is constructed of two electrodes. One is of spongy lead and the other is of lead dioxide. The electrolyte is sulfuric acid and water. The sulfuric acid, which is composed of hydrogen ions and sulfate ions, loses sulfate ions to both electrodes, forming lead sulfate, and hydrogen ions to the lead dioxide electrode, forming water. During this chemical reaction electrons move from the lead electrode to the lead dioxide electrode, producing current. When all the sulfate ions have been removed from the electrode, leaving only water, the cell is completely discharged. It can then be said that in a completely discharged lead-acid cell the electrolyte and electrodes have been converted to water and lead sulfate. Since the electrodes (now both lead sulfate) are no longer dissimilar metals, current will no longer be produced. A charging current from an external source will remove sulfate from the electrodes and leave it deposited in the water, returning the system to normal and charging the battery.

28·4 Considerations. One commonly used storage battery is made up of three series-connected cells of 2.2 volts each. Although the output voltage is 6.6 volts when fully charged, it is referred to as a 6-volt battery. Each cell contains several positive and negative electrodes. The more electrodes per cell, the greater the current-carrying capability of the cell. The electrodes, often called *plates*, are connected in parallel to increase their effective surface area.

Rating. As a measure of the amount of current that a battery can deliver steadily for a given period of time, a storage battery is assigned a rating in ampere-hours. The period of time is generally considered to be 8 hr. Therefore, a 100-amp-hr battery could be expected to deliver 12.5 amp per hr for an 8-hr period. It could also deliver 1 amp per hr for 100 hr, or 50 amp per hr for 2 hr. The 8-hr period is merely a standard used in rating batteries.

Charging. The weight of the electrolyte is the best means of determining the state of charge of a lead-acid battery. As the storage battery discharges, the electrolyte loses sulfate ions, and the resultant solution, at complete discharge, is nothing but water. The weight measurement is simply a comparison between dilute sulfuric acid and pure water. This is accomplished by an instrument called a *hydrometer.* A hydrometer consists of a small glass tube fitted with a syringe for drawing the electrolyte up inside the tube. The tube contains a float that is weighted with shot and marked with a scale graduated from 1000 to 1300. At 1000 the electrolyte is pure water. At 1300 the proper electrolyte solution for full charge is indicated. Originally, the scale varied from 1.000 to 1.300, but for convenience, the decimal point was eliminated. At full charge, it can be said that the electrolyte solution is 1.3 times as heavy as pure water. Any intermediate degree of discharge will be indicated accordingly on the hydrometer. For efficient operation and longer battery life, a battery should be charged again if the hydrometer reading is as low as 1185. A battery should be charged at the same rate as it would be discharged in the standard 8-hr period. For example, a 100-amp-hr battery should be charged at the rate of 12.5 amp per hr.

Connections. Where it is desired to furnish voltage beyond the capacity of a single cell, series connections can be made. This involves connecting the negative terminal of the first cell to the positive terminal of the second. This same positive-to-negative relationship should be continued for any number of cells. The total voltage of all cells connected in series is, by equation,

$$E_t = E_1 + E_2 + E_3 + \cdots$$

If additional current is desired, cells are connected in parallel. With this arrangement, in which all negative terminals are connected together and all positive terminals are connected together, the total current from a group of cells is, by equation,

$$I_t = I_1 + I_2 + I_3 + \cdots$$

With cells (or batteries) connected in series, the total current is that of a single unit while total voltage is the sum of the unit voltages. With parallel connections, total voltage is that of a single unit while total current is the sum of the individual currents. Any number of combinations of series-parallel arrangements may be used to increase both the current and voltage capabilities as desired.

Internal Resistance. It might appear logical to assume that if a zero-ohm connection were made between the terminals of a battery, an unlimited amount of current would be produced for at least a short time. This is not the case. Even a very low-resistance ammeter placed across a cell indicates a definite amount of current—it is not an unlimited current. The assumption is made, of course, that the meter has the range capability to measure this current.

The fact that the current is not unlimited suggests the possibility that there must be some resistance that is internal to the cell itself. Another indication of this *internal resistance* is seen when comparing two cells or batteries of equal voltage rating but of different ages. The new cell will deliver much more current through a low-resistance load than will the older cell. It must be assumed, then, that the older cell has a greater internal resistance. The actual value of the internal resistance of any battery may be computed. The current that a battery delivers to the load is computed by

$$I = \frac{E}{r + R}$$

where r = internal resistance of the cell or battery
R = resistance external to the cell or battery (load, wires, etc.)
Transposing, and solving for r, it is seen that

$$r = \frac{E}{I} - R$$

Cells or batteries with large internal resistance deliver but small amounts of current; cells with low internal resistance deliver larger amounts of current. For most newer cells, and for most applications, the internal resistance is so much smaller than the external resistance that the current can be calculated simply as the ratio of the voltage applied to the external resistance, neglecting the internal resistance. The error is usually not appreciable.

REVIEW QUESTIONS

1. What are the two types of cells?
2. What components are necessary to construct a simple cell?
3. What determines the amount of emf developed by a cell?
4. Describe the action that takes place when two dissimilar metals are immersed in the electrolyte of a primary cell.
5. Why is it impractical to replace the electrolyte in a primary cell?

6. How is it possible to obtain higher voltages and currents with dry cells?

7. Describe the three types of batteries used in electronic equipment.

8. Explain the chemical action that takes place during discharge of a dry cell.

9. Explain the principle of operation of a lead-acid cell.

10. Describe the chemical action that takes place during discharge of a lead-acid cell.

11. What is determined by the hydrometer reading of a cell?

12. How are storage batteries rated? Explain.

13. Why is it sometimes necessary to connect storage batteries in parallel?

14. Explain the chemical action that takes place in a lead-acid cell during charge.

15. From a source of four batteries of 6 volts each, capable of delivering 5 amp each for 8 hr, 12 volts at 10 amp is desired. What type of connection should be used?

16. What indicates that there exists some resistance internal to the battery?

17. A battery is capable of delivering 5 amp of current for 20 hours. What is its amp-hour rating?

18. A 6-volt battery delivers only 5.9 amp of current to a 1-ohm load. What must be the internal resistance of the battery?

19. Given a 12-volt battery and a 10-ohm load, 0.1 is the internal resistance. Find the current supplied by the battery. Use Fig. 28·3.

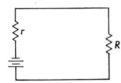

FIG. 28·3   Internal resistance of a battery.

20. In Prob. 19, if the wiring also offered 2 ohms of resistance, what would be the new value of current delivered? (All other factors remain the same.)

CHAPTER 29

INTRODUCTION TO POWER SUPPLIES

In the operation of electron tubes as components of circuit stages, different values of voltage and current are required. For example, a certain tube may require 6 volts of alternating current for heating its filament while the plate may require more than 100 volts of direct current. Rotating machinery, such as alternators or d-c generators, supplies high values of voltage and large amounts of current for higher-power applications. Since tube power requirements normally are small, the large size and high upkeep of rotating machinery make its use impractical for this purpose. Moreover, mechanical rectifying systems sometimes cause interference when used with electronic circuits. Batteries supply direct voltages; however, they require frequent charging and replacing. Batteries capable of supplying large amounts of current must be large, and therefore cannot be used where space is limited.

To overcome the many disadvantages of other systems supplying direct current to electron-tube circuits, the a-c *power supply* was developed. Because it is compact, because its components do not require frequent replacement, and because the cost of maintaining it is low, an a-c power supply system is most suitable for use in an electron-tube circuit. Basically, its purpose is to convert an alternating voltage to various values of direct voltage for use at the electrodes of electron tubes. This is accomplished by first *rectifying* the alternating voltage, then converting the pulses to a smooth value of direct voltage.

29·1 Use of Transformer. Figure 29·1 shows a basic power supply. The purpose of the transformer is to convert the a-c line voltage into one or more values to meet circuit requirements. In the example shown, one secondary winding steps down the line voltage to the value required by tube filaments. The other winding supplies voltage for the plate of the rectifier. By using one transformer with a single primary and multi-secondary, several voltages of different values may be obtained. Thus, with the use of a single transformer, both high- and low-voltage requirements can be met.

Although two secondary windings are used to supply low values of alternating voltage to the rectifier tube, other tube electrodes require direct voltage for operation. Therefore, additional circuits are employed to convert the transformer output from alternating to a suitable value of direct current. In a d-c generator, a commutator is used for rectification; in a-c meters, an electronic rectifier serves the same purpose. In a-c power supplies, either an electron-tube rectifier or a dry-metal rectifier is used. However, the output of both types is pulsating in value and must be changed to a steady value of direct current by special filter circuits.

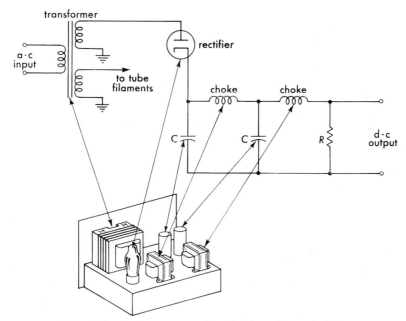

Fig. 29·1 Basic power supply and schematic equivalent.

29·2 Diode Rectifier Operation. The previously discussed diode tube, consisting of a cathode and a plate, is the most common type of electron-tube rectifier. As with all rectifiers, the principle of unidirectional impedance is utilized. Since electrons will readily flow from cathode to plate but not in the reverse direction, the diode is useful for converting alternating into pulsating direct current for use in receiver and transmitter power supplies. The low impedance offered by the tube in the direction from cathode to plate, however, is limited by the space charge and the spacing between the elements. A typical half-wave rectifier circuit employing a diode tube is shown in Fig. 29·2a. For purpose of explanation consider the cathode to be heated from a separate source and the tube to be conducting. The winding L_1 of transformer T is connected to a 115-volt a-c source and supplies a secondary voltage across the winding L_2. When the plate side of L_2 is positive, during one half of the input cycle, the diode will conduct from cathode to plate, through the secondary winding to ground, and from ground back through the load resistor to cathode. Since the secondary voltage varies as one-half a sine wave, voltage across the load resistor will vary correspondingly. On the opposite half-cycle when the voltage across L_2 changes polarity, the

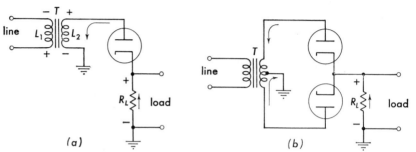

FIG. 29·2 Simple rectifiers showing direction of current. (a) Half-wave rectifier. (b) Full-wave rectifier.

tube will not conduct because the plate will be negative with respect to the cathode; therefore, no voltage is developed across the load resistor. For each cycle of input alternating current, one alternation of pulsating direct current will be developed across the output of the tube. As the positive voltage applied to the plate varies, current through the circuit will vary at the same rate. This varying current through the load resistor

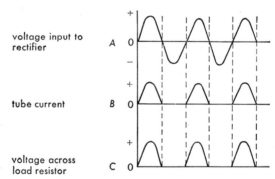

FIG. 29·3 Voltage and current relationships for half-wave rectifier.

will cause a voltage to be dropped across it that varies at the same rate. Voltage and current relationships are shown in Fig. 29·3. When voltage A is positive, current exists through the tube and a voltage C is developed across R_L. During this alternation, tube current B appears through the load resistor. During the negative half-cycle, or when a negative voltage is applied to the plate of the tube, the tube does not conduct and there is no voltage developed across R_L. Because there is current during only one half of the a-c input cycle, this type of circuit is called a *half-wave rectifier*. Output current is in one direction only but is continually varying in value and is called *pulsating direct current*. The number of pulses per second is referred to as *ripple frequency*. With half-wave rectifiers the ripple frequency is equal to the frequency of the applied voltage.

Peak Inverse Voltage. When the plate is negative and the tube is not conducting, a high potential difference exists between plate and cathode. Should this difference exceed the rating of the tube, arc-over from plate to cathode may occur and cause damage to the tube. As an example of determining *peak inverse voltage* rating, consider a tube with 700 volts alternating current applied between cathode and plate. Since this is an effective value, maximum peak voltage is 700 × 1.414, or 989.8 volts.

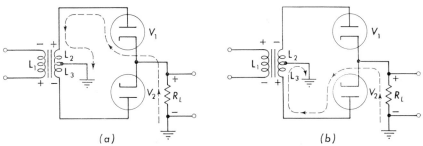

FIG. 29·4   Current paths through a full-wave rectifier. (a) Current while V_1 conducting. (b) Current while V_2 conducting.

This is the peak voltage that will appear across the tube when it is not conducting; therefore, the PIV rating must be at least 989.8 volts. To ensure long tube life, the PIV rating of a tube in a half-wave rectifier circuit should be equal to or exceed the maximum voltage across the transformer secondary.

29·3 Full-wave Rectifier. It is the purpose of a full-wave rectifier to produce a pulsating direct current in the output circuit for each alternation of a-c input. With half-wave rectifiers the efficiency is low and effective filtering made difficult by the extreme pulsating nature of the output current. For this reason, full-wave rectifiers are used more extensively.

In Fig. 29·4a, L_1 is connected to an a-c supply. Since the secondary winding is center-tapped, it acts as if two separate secondary windings were connected in series. During one half-cycle, when the plate of V_1 is positive and the plate of V_2 is negative, the center tap is negative with respect to V_1 and positive with respect to V_2. When the plate of V_1 is positive with respect to the center tap of the transformer, it is positive with respect to the cathode and there will be current. Current path is from cathode to plate, through L_2 to ground, from ground through the load resistor, and back to the cathode. During this alternation V_2 does not conduct, and only one pulse of direct current is developed across R_L. On the opposite half-cycle of input alternating current the plate of V_1 is negative while the plate of V_2 is positive, and V_2 conducts. The current path is from cathode to plate, through the secondary winding L_3 to ground, through R_L, and back to the cathode. Current through the load resistor again develops a pulse of direct current across it. The resultant output across a load resistor in a full-wave rectifier circuit is one pulse of direct current for each half-cycle of input alternating current. In a full-wave rectifier circuit the ripple frequency is twice the input frequency (Fig. 29·5).

Peak Inverse Voltage. With full-wave rectifiers the PIV rating of each tube must equal or exceed the maximum alternating voltage across the transformer secondary. For example, when V_2 of Fig. 29·4 is conducting, the voltage drop across the tube is very low; therefore, voltage at the plate

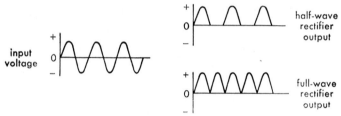

FIG. 29·5 Rectified output from half-wave and full-wave rectifiers.

of V_2 is maximum positive while the cathode is at a positive potential slightly less than that of the plate. Since the cathodes of both tubes are connected directly, they are at the same potential. At the same time that the plate of V_2 is maximum positive the plate of V_1 is maximum negative, causing the difference in potential between cathode and plate of V_1 to be equal to maximum secondary voltage less the drop across V_2.

29·4 Filter Circuits. The output from a rectifier power supply consists of a direct current varying at an a-c rate. For practical use this a-c component variation is too great. Since tube electrodes require a steady value of direct current for their operation, a means of eliminating this variation, or ripple, must be provided. In power-supply circuits filters remove the a-c component by making use of the individual properties of capacitors and inductors. The action of an inductor in opposing changes in current, and the rate of charge and discharge of a capacitor, are employed for this function.

Capacitance Filter. One of the basic types of filter circuits used in power-supply applications consists of a capacitor across the load resistor. Before the addition of the capacitor the output of the rectifier was applied across the load resistor, and there were pulses of direct current through it in the direction from ground to cathode. If the resistor was replaced by a capacitor, d-c pulses would be applied across it. Connecting the two in parallel as shown in Fig. 29·6 will result in the following action: As the rectifier conducts on one half of the cycle, it starts charging the capacitor C, whose discharge path is through resistor R_L. If the RC time of the combination is such that it cannot discharge during the time preceding the next half-cycle, it will retain some charge at the instant the second half of the rectifier starts conducting. This builds up an additional charge on the capacitor, causing it to be fully charged after the first few cycles of rectifier output current. This charge represents a supply of energy. As the rectifier output decreases to zero prior to the start of the next alternation, energy stored in the capacitor will be discharged through R_L. The resultant output is a nearly steady value of direct current.

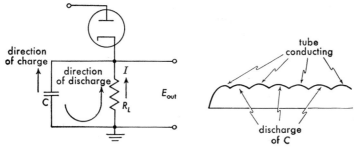

Fig. 29·6 Simple filter action.

Considerations. Increasing the size of the capacitor will result in better filter action; however, the maximum plate current that the rectifier must handle is increased. For this reason the maximum value of capacitance used is largely dependent upon the maximum safe value of rectifier plate current.

Capacitors ranging from 2 to 40 μf are generally used in power-supply circuits, the more common values being 4, 8, and 16 μf. Paper capacitors are not polarized and will last longer than electrolytic capacitors; however, those of high capacitance involve large sizes and are relatively expensive. Some paper capacitors are oil-impregnated and others wax-impregnated. High-voltage power supplies use those which are oil-impregnated because they are able to withstand higher peak voltages. Electrolytic capacitors are more commonly used because of their low cost and small size. With power supplies rated at 600 volts or less, electrolytic filter capacitors are used, but for higher voltages paper capacitors are used. Electrolytic capacitors are polarized; therefore, it is important that proper connections be made or damage to the rectifier and other circuit components may result.

Inductance Filter. Another simple type of filter is that consisting of an

inductor in series with the load resistor. This makes use of the principle
of an inductor opposing changes in current, which, effectively, causes the
inductor to store electrical energy. As current through the inductance
increases, the cemf set up will oppose the change and tend to keep the
current constant. Conversely, as current decreases, the inductance acts
to keep the current constant by opposing the change that causes the
decrease. An inductance offers a high impedance to the alternating
ripple voltage and a low resistance to direct current. Inductors used in

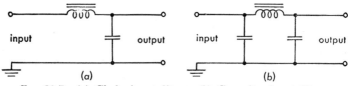

FIG. 29·7   (a) Choke-input filter.   (b) Capacitor-input filter.

power-supply filter circuits are generally called *chokes* because they choke
out the a-c component.

Filter chokes may be increased in size to increase the impedance, but
this will also increase the d-c resistance. The efficiency of a choke in
removing the ripple voltage while offering comparatively little resistance
to direct current can be visualized by considering a typical 10-henry
choke, which presents a reactance of approximately 7,500 ohms to a 120-
cycle ripple, yet offers a d-c resistance of about 200 ohms.

29·5 Filter Combinations. Although both single-capacitor and
single-inductor filters succeed in removing most of the a-c component

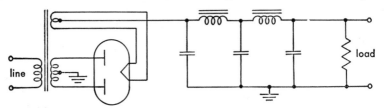

FIG. 29·8   Typical power supply employing full-wave rectifier and a two-section
capacitor-input filter.

from the rectifier output, a small amount of ripple voltage remains. In
many applications these pulsations are undesirable and must be removed
so that only a steady value of pure direct current is applied to the load
circuit. To provide improved filtering action, capacitors and inductors
are arranged in single sections which are then connected in parallel. A
single-section capacitor-input filter consists of a capacitor across the load
and an inductor in series with the load. By increasing the number of
capacitors, inductors, or sections, better filtering action will result.

Choke-input Filter. In this type of filter, shown in Fig. 29·7a, most of
the ripple voltage will appear across the high inductive reactance of the

choke, while the d-c component of the rectifier output will appear across the load. Because of its low reactance, only a small amount of alternating voltage will appear across the capacitor. Therefore, since the capacitor is in parallel with the load, most of the ripple is removed from the load. By using a single-section choke-input filter, improvement in filtering results, but output voltage is slightly less than that from a single

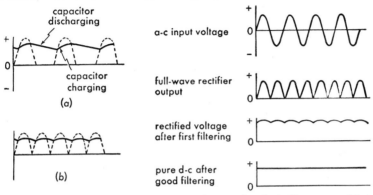

FIG. 29·9   Filter-circuit wave forms.   (a) Filter action in half-wave rectifier.   (b) Filter action in full-wave rectifier.

capacitor.   This is because the d-c resistance of the choke causes a loss of voltage that must be subtracted from the amount delivered by the rectifier.   Choke-input filters are used in power supplies which are operating with heavy or varying loads, because of their ability to limit rectifier peak current and hold output voltage constant.

Capacitor-input Filter.   Larger values of inductance and capacitance are used in this type of filter, shown in Fig. 29·7b, than in choke-input filters. Because of this and the charging and discharging action of the capacitor, filtering action is better and output voltage larger than with the choke-input filter.   Because of poorer voltage regulation and because this circuit draws large peaks of current from the rectifier tube, capacitor-input filters are used only where low-power direct current is required.

FIG. 29·10   Full-wave rectifier.   (*Radio Corporation of America.*)

Two-section Filter.   For optimum filtering action, two sections of capacitor-input (or choke-input) filters may be used, as shown in Fig. 29·8.   Both types reduce ripple voltage to an almost negligible value, although any increase in series inductances will cause a decrease in output voltage and must, therefore, be considered.

Filter-circuit wave forms for half-wave and full-wave rectifiers are shown in Fig. 29·9.

REVIEW QUESTIONS

1. What is the purpose of an a-c power supply?

2. Why are batteries and rotating machinery impractical as power supplies for electron tubes?

3. Explain the purpose of a transformer in an a-c power supply.

4. Explain the principle of operation of a half-wave rectifier.

5. Explain the principle of operation of a full-wave rectifier.

6. What is the relationship between ripple frequency, half-wave rectifiers, and full-wave rectifiers?

7. What is pulsating direct current?

8. How is the peak inverse rating of an electron tube determined?

9. Explain the process by which pulsating direct current is changed to a steady value of direct current.

10. Explain the action of a capacitance filter in smoothing out the ripples in pulsating direct current.

11. Explain the action of an inductance filter in smoothing out the ripples in pulsating direct current.

12. How do parallel filter sections result in better filtering action?

13. What are the disadvantages of capacitor-input filters?

14. What limits the size of inductance used in power-supply filters?

15. Why is the PIV rating of a tube important?

16. What limits the size of capacitance used in power-supply filters?

17. What is the effect of a single-section choke on output voltage in an inductance filter?

18. Explain the operation of a simple a-c power supply.

19. List several practical applications of an a-c power supply.

20. Design a simple a-c power supply using a half-wave rectifier and a single-section choke-input filter.

CHAPTER 30

POWER SUPPLIES AND RECTIFIERS

Vacuum-tube rectifiers are only one of the many nonrotating devices used for converting alternating to direct current. Voltage and current requirements differ with each unit of equipment to which they are to be applied. Where batteries used in portable or mobile transmitter-receiver units are to be charged, there is a need for low voltage at high current. A 50-watt audio amplifier would require a high voltage at relatively low current, while the meter movement of an a-c meter seldom needs more than 10 ma current for full-scale deflection.

To meet these many requirements and overcome the disadvantages of the high-vacuum rectifier, several different types of gaseous and dry-metal rectifiers have been perfected and will be discussed here.

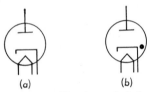

Fig. 30·1   Circuit symbols for vacuum and gaseous diodes. (a) Vacuum diode. (b) Gaseous diode. Dot indicates gas-filled tube.

30·1   Mercury-vapor   Rectifier. This type is constructed like the high-vacuum rectifier tube, except that spacing between plate and cathode is greater and a small amount of mercury is sealed into the tube at time of manufacture.

When the filament is heated, evaporation of the mercury produces vapor, or free gas atoms. Electrons are liberated from the heated filament in the conventional manner. These electrons are accelerated by the influence of a plate potential and collide with the mercury-vapor atoms in the space between filament and plate. Free electrons are produced by the collisions, leaving the mercury atoms as positive ions. This action results in many free electrons which are then attracted to the plate, causing an increase in plate current.

The positive mercury ions will drift toward the space charge surrounding the cathode and neutralize it. This affords electrons leaving the cathode an easier path, which reduces effective d-c plate resistance. Since plate resistance varies inversely with load current, the voltage drop across the tube will remain constant for a wide range of load current.

This prevents the tube from heating excessively and increases its efficiency.

As the plate voltage increases from zero toward maximum, plate current will also increase. Electrons are emitted by the cathode and accelerated toward the plate, colliding with the gas atoms. If the speed of the electron is great enough it will cause ionization of the gas atoms. The voltage necessary to produce sufficient speed for an electron to ionize a mercury-vapor atom is 10 to 15 volts. This is known as the *ionization*

potential. It causes plate current to increase to full electron emission of the cathode without any further increase in plate voltage. Where current within the tube was limited by the space charge, *ionization by collision* removes this limitation and allows maximum current.

With oxide-coated and thoriated-tungsten emitters, positive ions strike the cathode in a gas-filled tube with velocities less than those produced by a higher voltage and do not adversely affect the cathode. However, if the electron gains velocity sufficient to knock more than one electron from a gas atom, the positive ions will bombard the cathode with much greater force and cause progressive disintegration of the emitting surface. It has been found that only one electron will be removed from a mercury-vapor atom if plate voltage is not allowed to exceed approximately 22 volts.

Peak Inverse Voltage. The peak-inverse-voltage rating of any tube refers to the voltage applied during the alternation in which the tube is not a conductor of current. Since alternating current is being applied to the tube and current is being passed through the rectifier only during one alternation of the cycle, there will be one alternation of each cycle during which the tube is not conducting current.

FIG. 30·2 Mercury-vapor rectifier. (*Radio Corporation of America.*)

Where this would not unduly affect a high-vacuum type of rectifier tube, with a mercury-vapor tube the manufacturer's prescribed limit must not be exceeded. The introduction of gas into the mercury-vapor rectifier tube requires an increase in space between filament and plate to provide a comparable peak-inverse-voltage rating.

Peak Plate Current. The maximum peak plate current of any electron tube is the maximum peak current it can pass without damage or reduction of normal life. With the mercury-vapor tube, peak current is limited by total emission of the cathode at any instant. Current in amount beyond total cathode emission must be supplied by the mercury atoms, causing greater ionization and reduction of cathode life by increased bombardment. To ensure satisfactory normal life, total cathode emission must exceed rated peak current.

Associate Filter. To prevent damage to the tube, it is important that choke-input filters be used in conjunction with mercury-vapor rectifiers. Should a capacitor-input filter be used, as shown in Fig. 30·3, the following would result. After ample warmup, with the application of plate voltage the tube would be subjected to a heavy surge of plate current. This surge would last only a very short time but long enough to cause severe damage to the cathode surface. Since this current surge would be present throughout the charging of C_1, the tube would be across the secondary of T_1 until C_1 charged to the value of secondary voltage. With a

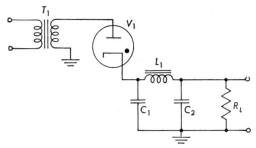

FIG. 30·3 Mercury-vapor rectifier using a capacitor-input filter.

choke-input filter the current surge would be reduced through the action of the inductance.

Summary. More care is required in the operation of mercury-vapor rectifier tubes than is ordinarily necessary with high-vacuum rectifiers. Ample time must be allowed for the filament to reach normal operating temperature before plate voltage is applied. This time delay ensures the vaporization of all the mercury within the tube. Application of plate voltage prior to warmup will result in damage to the emitting surface.

Important characteristics of this type of tube are maximum allowable peak inverse plate voltage, maximum allowable peak and average plate current, and the constant low voltage drop across the tube. Compared with the high-vacuum rectifier, the mercury-vapor rectifier has high efficiency, low internal voltage drop, low filament power, and relatively low cost per ampere output. Disadvantages are its limited inverse voltage rating, tendency to arc, damage suffered through overloads, and production of interference in nearby installations. Mercury-vapor tubes are usually operated at frequencies of 1,000 cps or below.

30·2 Tungar Rectifier.   This type of gaseous rectifier is similar in principle to the mercury-vapor rectifier, having a heated cathode and a graphite plate with a relatively large cross-sectional area and filled with pure argon gas under low pressure.   The gas enclosure has a high heat resistance, and the filament is constructed of fine tungsten wire.

Battery-charging equipment is a typical application of tungar rectifiers. With argon gas, as compared to mercury, there is less resistance offered by the space charge; consequently, the voltage drop across the tube is less (6 to 8 volts) and current-handling capabilities are greater than that of the mercury-vapor rectifier with a voltage drop of from 10 to 15 volts.

30·3 Dry-metal Rectifiers.   The assorted types of dry-metal rectifiers are somewhat similar in structure and operate on the same principle. Their many applications range from the rectification of single-phase and polyphase alternating current in power circuits to microamperes of current in meter movements.

Theory of Operation.   Based upon a principle of *unidirectional impedance,* any dry-metal rectifier must consist of a *semiconductor,* a *barrier*

FIG. 30·4   Basic construction of copper-oxide and selenium rectifiers.

layer, and a good conductor.   Unidirectional impedance is explained as an opposition or high resistance to current in one direction and a low resistance in the other.   Similar examples would be in the action of vacuum-tube rectifiers in which current from cathode to plate finds little resistance but would encounter high resistance in the opposite direction.

Action of the electrons can be described as follows: In any good conductor there is an abundance of free electrons, while in a semiconductor the number is very small.   When a negative potential is applied to the good conductor and a positive potential to the semiconductor, an electric field is set up across the barrier layer.   The barrier layer is an insulator through which the electrons must pass in transit between the two electrodes.   Because the barrier layer is very thin, the free electrons are sufficiently accelerated to penetrate the barrier layer and pass to the semiconductor.   If the polarity is reversed, the semiconductor has to furnish the free electrons.   Since there is a deficiency of free electrons, only a few will be able to penetrate the barrier layer and pass to the conductor. The unidirectional characteristic of the dry-metal rectifier is referred to as its *front-to-back ratio.*

Copper-oxide Rectifier.   One of the most common of dry-metal rectifiers is the copper-oxide type.   A copper oxide film is formed on one side of a copper sheet by partial oxidation of the copper at high temperature.

While pressure is not necessary, it is sometimes used to make low-resistance contact between soft metals. Since the copper has a larger number of free electrons than the oxide, current has a low resistance path from the copper to the oxide and a higher resistance path from the oxide to the copper.

Copper-oxide disks and plates are constructed in sizes ranging from 0.03 in. in diameter oxidized on one side, to 50 sq in. cross-sectional area oxidized on both sides. They may be used in half-wave, full-wave, or bridge circuits. For additional voltage they are connected in series, and for additional current they are connected in parallel.

Figure 30·6 is a schematic of a half-wave copper-oxide rectifier circuit. Assuming a front-to-back ratio of 1:5,000, the resistance to current from oxide to copper would be 5,000 times that of the resistance in the opposite direction. There would be a large current when the input voltage was of

FIG. 30·5 A copper-oxide rectifier. (*Conant Laboratories.*)

one polarity, and a majority of the source voltage would appear across the load resistor. With polarity reversed, most of the source voltage would appear across the rectifier because of its high resistance to current in that direction. However, there is a small amount of current in the direction of oxide to copper. This is called *reverse current*, or *back-leak*, which causes a decrease in the efficiency of the rectifier. Under certain limited

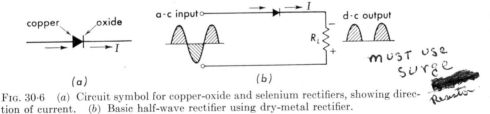

FIG. 30·6 (*a*) Circuit symbol for copper-oxide and selenium rectifiers, showing direction of current. (*b*) Basic half-wave rectifier using dry-metal rectifier.

conditions, efficiencies as high as 80 per cent can be attained; however, normal efficiency is between 60 and 70 per cent.

If pressure is to be used as a means of constructing the elements of a copper-oxide rectifier, it is important that it be applied in proper proportions. Slight pressure would increase resistance in the conducting direction while heavy pressure would lower the peak inverse voltage and cause a reduction of resistance in the nonconducting direction.

The value of voltage that a single copper-oxide rectifier will rectify is small, while the amount of current it will handle is dependent upon area of contact between copper and oxide and the amount of heat generated during conduction. The rectifiers are often connected in series or parallel to increase voltage- and current-handling capabilities. In appli-

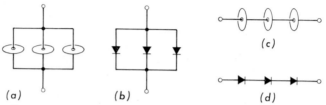

(a)   (b)   (c)

(d)

Fig. 30·7 Series and parallel connections for dry-metal rectifiers. (a) Parallel connections. (b) Equivalent circuit. (c) Series connections. (d) Equivalent circuit.

cations involving large power it is common to arrange several copper-oxide units in "stacks," with forced-air cooling, to obtain additional current. Figure 30·8 shows such stacks.

Selenium Rectifier. This type utilizes the principle of unidirectional impedance between selenium and iron. Basically it consists of an iron disk coated with metallic selenium and a thin layer of special alloy which provides a contact surface and ensures uniform current density in the active material. The selenium layer is extremely thin and is applied to one side of the roughened disk by heat. The selenium layer is then covered with a thin layer of

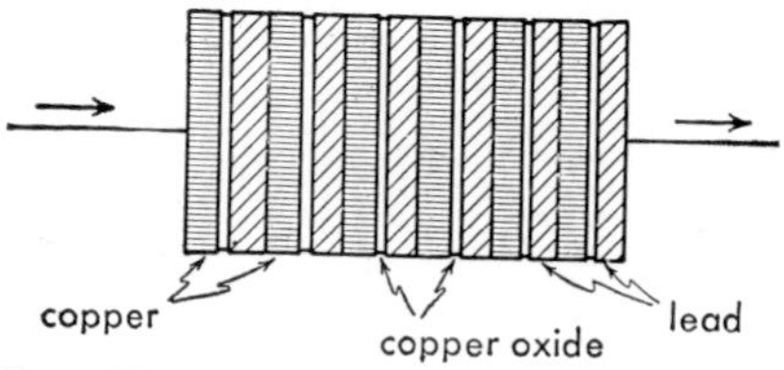

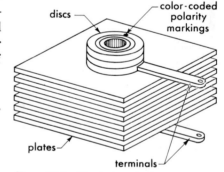

Fig. 30·8 Method of stacking copper-oxide rectifiers in series for high-power applications.

Fig. 30·9 Typical selenium rectifier showing markings and construction.

alloy to form the other electrode of the rectifier element. Electrons flow unopposed from the iron to the selenium but encounter high resistance in the opposite direction.

Although similar in principle of operation to the copper-oxide rectifier, the selenium rectifier has proved superior in many respects. As compared to a copper-oxide rectifier of equal size, the selenium rectifier has longer life span, greater ruggedness, larger current-handling capabilities, lower conducting resistance, and higher efficiency. It is normally designed for continuous operation at 50 ma per sq cm of plate area. Limiting temperatures for continuous operation are from −40 to 75°C. Selenium rectifiers may be operated at frequencies up to approximately 1,000 cps. Being able to withstand a wider range of temperatures, the life span is larger. Efficiency is between 65 and 85 per cent, depending

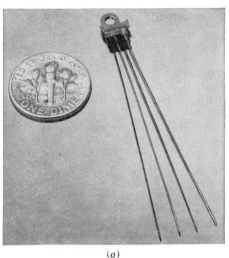

(a)

 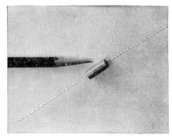 

(b)

Fig. 30·10 (a) Copper-oxide rectifier. (b) Three types of selenium rectifiers. (*Conant Laboratories.*)

upon the circuit in which used. Since pressure between the elements is not necessary for operation, its ruggedness is improved. Having lower conducting resistance than copper-oxide rectifiers, the selenium rectifier has better current-carrying capabilities.

Applications. In circuits where relatively large amounts of power are required, selenium rectifiers are used because of their superior characteristics. Copper-oxide rectifiers are generally used in small-current applications such as a-c meter movements or for furnishing direct current to circuits requiring not more than 10 amp.

Because of requirements for power in heating filaments of high-vacuum and gaseous rectifiers, over-all efficiency of dry-metal rectifiers will be greater; however, their uses are limited by physical size and ventilation requirements.

There are several other types of dry-metal rectifiers in current use, such as the magnesium-copper sulfide rectifier. Each is used in circuits where

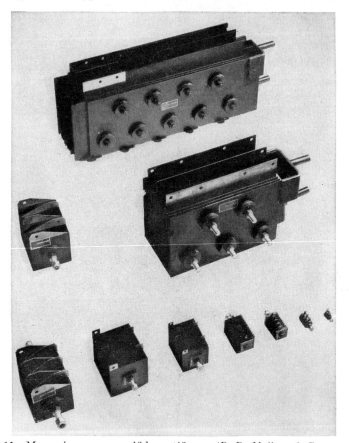

FIG. 30·11   Magnesium-copper sulfide rectifiers   (*P. R. Mallory & Company, Inc.*)

its particular characteristics best meet individual requirements. While these characteristics may differ greatly, all operate on the same principle of unidirectional impedance.

REVIEW QUESTIONS

1. Explain the principle of operation of a mercury-vapor rectifier.
2. What occurs in a mercury-vapor rectifier when its ionization potential is reached?

3. What is ionization by collision?

4. How is effective plate resistance reduced in a mercury-vapor tube?

5. How does the PIV rating of a mercury-vapor tube differ from that of conventional tubes? Why?

6. Why should a choke-input filter be used with mercury-vapor tubes?

7. Explain the principle of operation of a tungar rectifier.

8. Explain the principle of operation of dry-metal rectifiers.

9. What is meant by back-leak in dry-metal rectifiers?

10. Explain the construction and operation of a copper-oxide rectifier.

11. What is meant by unidirectional impedance?

12. How is it possible to increase the voltage- and current-handling capabilities of dry-metal rectifiers?

13. Explain the principle of operation of a selenium rectifier.

14. What are the advantages of the selenium rectifier as compared with the copper-oxide rectifier?

15. What is the main advantage of dry-metal rectifiers over gaseous and high-vacuum rectifiers?

16. Why does a tungar rectifier have greater current-carrying capabilities than a mercury-vapor rectifier?

17. In dry-metal rectifiers, what is meant by front-to-back ratio?

18. What limits the use of dry-metal rectifiers?

19. What type of rectifier would normally be found in (a) a-c voltmeters? (b) a-c ammeters?

20. What is the purpose of the barrier layer in a dry-metal rectifier?

21. List several practical applications of gaseous rectifiers.

22. List several practical applications of dry-metal rectifiers.

CHAPTER 31

VOLTAGE DIVIDERS AND REGULATORS

After the alternating line voltage has been rectified and filtered, it is in the form of steady direct current for application to electron-tube circuits. Although the filtered output from any rectifier unit is of a fixed value, the simplest electronic unit requires several different values of voltage and current. Therefore, unless more than one power supply is used with each apparatus, it is necessary to provide a means of supplying these from a single supply. This is most often accomplished by a *voltage divider*.

For proper operation of certain types of electronic circuits it is essential that the applied voltage be held at a constant value. Since load variations will cause a variation in the output circuit, it is necessary that some means be provided to compensate for these varying voltages. By use of a device known as the *voltage regulator*, power-supply output voltages can be maintained at constant values regardless of changes in line voltage.

31·1 Voltage Divider. The resistor placed across the output of a power supply can serve more than one purpose. If it performs the function of applying a fixed load to the filter circuit, it is known as a *load resistor*. If it "bleeds off" the charge on the filter capacitor after the rectifier power supply is turned off, it is known as a *bleeder resistor*. If the resistor is tapped at various points to provide several voltages which are less than the rectifier output voltage, it is called a *voltage divider*.

Any resistor placed across the output of a rectifier unit may fulfill any of these functions; however, if it is to be used only as a bleeder, it should be of a very high value of resistance. If it serves as a load resistor, its value should be such as to draw only about 10 per cent of the full load current. A load resistor may also act as a voltage divider, because the current through it produces a voltage drop equal to that of the rectifier output.

The circuit shown in Fig. 31·1 represents a simple voltage divider. Since the resistors are equal in value, the input voltage will divide in proportion to the resistance of each. If 300 volts is applied to the network, 100 volts will be available across terminals c and d, 200 volts across terminals b and d, and 300 volts across terminals a and d. Since terminal d is grounded, all output voltages will be positive in value.

The point at which the voltage divider is grounded is normally used as a reference point for measuring voltages in the circuits which it supplies. If the rectifier circuit is grounded at no other point, it is possible to ground

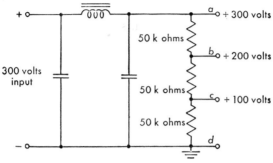

FIG. 31·1   Simple voltage divider.

the circuit at some point along the voltage divider and thus obtain voltages of both positive and negative polarity. For example, in Fig. 31·2, by grounding the divider at point c, one value of negative voltage and two values of positive voltage are available at the output. Thus, by changing the grounding point from d to c, a different polarity of voltage is obtainable. If point b is grounded, one positive and two negative voltages are available. This application is often used in standard equipment. Since there is current through the divider in the direction from point d to a, grounding point a will make all voltages negative with respect to ground.

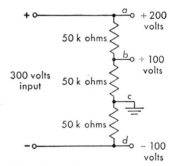

FIG. 31·2   Simple voltage divider with voltages of different polarity.

Divider with Load. In the previous examples there was no external load connected to the voltage divider; however, the divider itself was drawing current from the supply. In Fig. 31·3 additional loads are connected across R_2 and R_3. By application of Ohm's law it is obvious that current through R_2 and R_3 will be increased as a result of the added load and the voltage distribution across the divider will then change proportionately. Voltage and current across each of the resistors and loads can be determined as follows:

The resistance of the combination of R_3 and load 1 is, by equation,

$$R_{cd} = \frac{50,000 \times 50,000}{50,000 + 50,000} = 25,000 \text{ ohms}$$

The resistance of R_2 is in series with the combination. Adding this to the combination resistance of R_3 and load 1 results in a total resistance of 75,000 ohms between points b and d. Total resistance of this and load 2 in parallel is

$$R_{bd} = \frac{75,000 \times 150,000}{75,000 + 150,000} = 50,000 \text{ ohms}$$

Total resistance, then, between points a and d is the resistance between points b and d plus the resistance of R_1, or

$$R_t = 50,000 + 50,000 = 100,000 \text{ ohms}$$

Since input voltage is 300 volts and total resistance is 100,000 ohms, the current drawn by the divider and loads is, by equation,

$$I_t = \frac{300}{100,000} = 3 \text{ ma}$$

The voltage drop across R_1, therefore, is 150 volts since all the current is across it. Under these conditions one-half of the input voltage is across

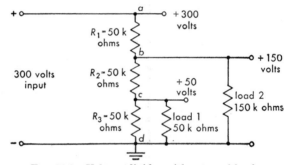

Fig. 31·3 Voltage divider with external loads.

R_1, while under no-load conditions of Fig. 31·1 only 100 volts was across it. With 150 volts across R_1 the remainder of input voltage has to be across the combination of R_2, R_3, loads 1 and 2. Therefore, since current will divide across a parallel combination of resistances, current through load 2 can be determined, by equation, as

$$I = \frac{E}{R} = \frac{150}{150,000} = 1 \text{ ma}$$

Since there is a current of 1 ma through load 2, and 3 ma in the entire circuit, then there is 2 ma through R_2 and 100 volts is dropped across it (50,000 ohms $\times$ 2 ma). Then, the voltage across R_3 and load 1 is 150 − 100 volts, or 50 volts. Since R_3 and load 1 are equal in value and there is 2 ma through the combination, there is 1 ma through each.

Thus, with the application of loads across the divider, output voltage across the terminals will vary by an amount dependent upon the size of the load. While voltage dividers are designed for the particular load conditions under which they are to be operated, the addition of loads will have no effect upon the value of applied voltage or divider distribution.

Bleeder Resistor. If the load is removed from a power supply, there is no direct voltage drop in the circuit and no discharge path for the filter capacitors. This causes the voltage across them to build up to a value approximately equal to the peak alternating current applied to the rectifier tube. With a bleeder resistor connected across the rectifier output, a discharge path is provided for the capacitors and a fixed load bleeds off the current. This type of resistor also serves to prevent any sharp increase in output voltage and thereby aids in improving power-supply regulation.

Voltage-divider Resistors. A voltage divider may consist of several resistors in series, each resistor being of such a value as to provide the proper voltages at their junctions. In some instances, resistors having several adjustable taps are used and adjusted for exact voltage values under load conditions. Fixed-tap resistors also find many applications in electronic equipment. Although the resistance value and power rating of voltage-divider resistors are determined by voltage and current ratings of the power supply, they dissipate a relatively large amount of power as heat, and should be chosen to allow ample wattage over that normally required. For example, a resistor to be used in a power supply of 400 volts and 100 ma should have a 10-watt rating. Since the resistor would draw about 10 per cent of the total rated current, current through it would be 10 ma and total resistance would be 40,000 ohms. Power dissipation would be equal to the voltage multiplied by the bleeder current, or 4 watts. Therefore, a 10-watt resistor should be used to withstand overloads or increased power dissipation.

31·2 Voltage Regulators. A simple voltage-regulator circuit would be similar to that shown in Fig. 31·4. With a variable resistor connected in series with the load, all the load current must appear through it. This causes voltage to be dropped across it in proportion to the amount of current and the size of the resistor. Should the applied voltage increase, load current will increase and voltage across the load will also increase.

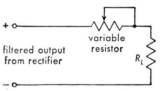

Fig. 31·4 Simple voltage-regulator circuit.

However, by increasing the series resistance, this additional voltage can be dropped across it and load voltage will remain constant. Conversely, any decrease in applied voltage can be compensated for by a decrease in series resistance. This method of voltage regulation requires manual adjustment and is, therefore, impractical.

Ballast Regulator. One type of voltage regulator often used in electronic equipment is the *ballast* tube shown in Fig. 31·5. Constructed of wire having a positive temperature coefficient, this type of regulator uses the principle of varying resistance for maintaining constant voltage. A wire which has a positive temperature coefficient will increase in resistance with an increase in temperature. In Fig. 31·5 an increase in line voltage would result in an increase in the voltage applied to the filament of the tube. Since this would increase the amount of current in the wire, its temperature would rise and cause the resistance to increase. This additional resistance in the circuit would compensate for the increase in line voltage, resulting in a constant voltage applied to the filaments of the tube. As the applied voltage decreases to its normal value, or below,

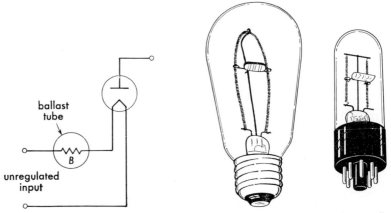

Fig. 31·5 Typical circuit using ballast tube.

Fig. 31·6 Typical ballast tubes. (*General Electric Co.*)

the reduced current through the wire would cause a proportionate decrease in temperature and resistance, thus continually maintaining secondary voltage at a prescribed level.

Voltage-regulator Tubes. The voltage-regulator tube consists of a plate made of thin wire and a cylindrical cathode surrounding the plate. Both electrodes are placed in an envelope containing an inert gas at low pressure. Since there is no filament, it is known as a cold-cathode tube.

The voltage-regulator tubes, commonly known as VR tubes, operate on the principle of varying resistance. Any change in the voltage across them results in a corresponding change in their internal resistance that compensates for the voltage change. A typical circuit is shown in Fig. 31·7. The VR tube is connected in series with a resistor across an unregulated supply, and the regulated output appears between the plate of the VR tube and ground. In any VR tube an increase of 30 per cent above its rated voltage will cause it to become ionized, and it will conduct.

For purpose of illustration, assume the tube to be rated at 150 volts. Since it is across a 300-volt supply (more than 30 per cent above the rated voltage), ionization would occur at 195 volts and the tube would conduct. As soon as the gas is ionized and the tube is conducting, the voltage across it remains at 150 volts with the remainder of the input voltage appearing across the series resistor. As current through the tube increases, due to an increase in applied voltage, the tube will become highly ionized and there will be additional current through the series resistor. Conversely, a decrease in tube current will cause it to ionize to a lesser extent and thus reduce the current. The amount of current through the series resistor is always determined by the extent of ionization within the VR tube. If the supply voltage of Fig. 31·7 should increase to 325 volts, this additional 25 volts would appear across the tube, causing greater ionization and a decrease in internal resistance. Current would then increase through the

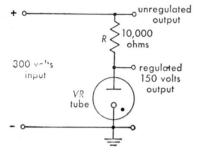

FIG. 31·7 Typical circuit using voltage-regulator tube.

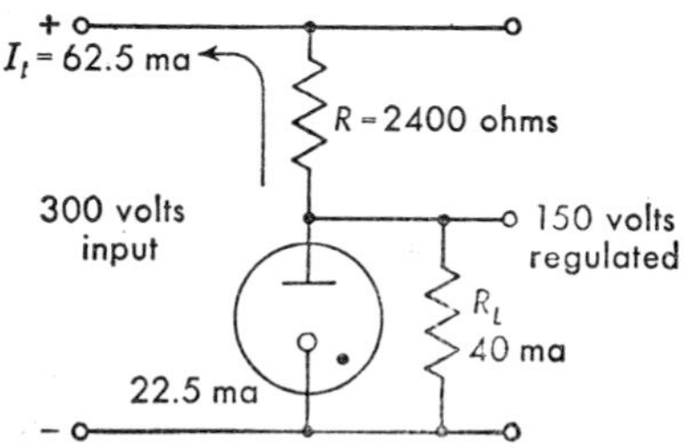

FIG. 31·8 Voltage-regulator circuit with steady load.

resistor, and 175 volts would be present across it, while the plate of the VR tube would remain at 150 volts. If the supply voltage decreased to 275 volts, ionization of the VR tube would *decrease* and its internal resistance would *increase*. Since the current through the series resistor would correspondingly decrease, only 125 volts would appear across it and the remaining 150 volts would be present across the VR tube.

VR tubes are usually designed to provide a constant voltage within an operating current range of 5 to 40 ma. If R of Fig. 31·7 is 10,000 ohms, at 5 ma the voltage across it would be 50 volts. At 40 ma the voltage across it would be 400 volts. Thus, since 150 volts will always be across the VR tube within its operating range, constant output voltage can be maintained although the applied voltage varies between 200 (50 + 150) volts and 550 (150 + 400) volts.

Figure 31·8 shows a VR tube rated at 150 volts and connected to an external load. Since this type of tube is operated between 5 and 40 ma, circuit design is such that normal current through the tube is 22.5 ma, which is the middle point between extreme limits. Total current through

R is that of the parallel combination of VR tube and load; in this case, 62.5 ma. Therefore, since 150 volts is to be dropped across R, its ohmic value must be

$$R = \frac{150}{0.0625} = 2,400 \text{ ohms}$$

If the input voltage to the network increased to 310 volts, ionization within the tube would increase and cause a reduction in its internal resistance. There would be additional current through R, and 160 volts would be across it, while the remaining 150 volts would be across the VR tube. Total current through R is, by equation,

$$I_t = \frac{160}{2,400} = 0.0666 \text{ amp}$$

Since the regulated voltage applied to the load remains constant and thus causes load current to remain constant, the additional 4.1 ma of current is supplied by the VR tube.

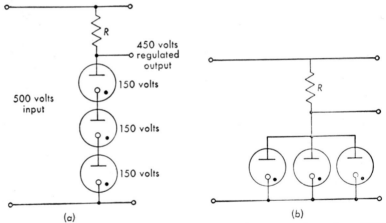

FIG. 31·9   Voltage-regulator connections. (a) Series connections for additional voltage. (b) Parallel connections for additional current handling.

Should the input voltage decrease to 290 volts, 150 volts would be across the VR tube and 140 across R. Total current would be 58.3 ma. Since load current remains constant at 40 ma, it is seen that tube current has decreased by 4.2 ma to 18.3 ma. Therefore, with a 20-volt change in supply voltage, load current was maintained constant at 40 ma and load voltage at 150 volts. Tube current varied from 26.6 to 18.3 ma, and current through the series resistor varied from 66.6 to 58.3 ma.

VR-tube Connections. In some instances, it is desired to maintain a constant value of voltage beyond the rated capacity of currently manufactured VR tubes. This can be accomplished by connecting two or more VR tubes in series, as shown in Fig. 31·9a. For example, two VR tubes rated at 75 volts each would furnish 150 volts if connected in series. Three tubes rated at 150 volts each would furnish 450 volts if series connected.

Where there are requirements for additional current handling, VR tubes are connected in parallel. Where one tube could handle a 35-ma change in current, ranging from 5 to 40 ma, three such tubes connected in parallel would be capable of handling a 105-ma change (see Fig. 31·9b).

Types of VR Tubes. While the construction of all VR tubes is basically the same, there are several types which meet most voltage and current requirements for electronic equipment now in use. Some operate at voltages as low as 55 volts while others exceed 150 volts. Although most

Fig. 31·10 Typical voltage-regulator tubes. (*Radio Corporation of America.*)

operate at current ranges of 5 to 40 ma, the 991 tube operates at a range between 0.4 and 0.2 ma. However, exact ratings and specifications may be found in any manufacturer's tube manual.

REVIEW QUESTIONS

1. Why are voltage dividers necessary?
2. Explain the purpose of a bleeder resistor.
3. What is the difference between a voltage divider and a bleeder resistor?
4. What is the difference between a bleeder resistor and a load resistor?
5. How is it possible to obtain both negative and positive voltages from a single voltage divider?
6. What are the power requirements of a resistor used as a voltage divider?
7. Explain the operation of a ballast tube as a voltage regulator.
8. Explain the operation of a voltage-regulator tube.
9. How is it possible to obtain higher current-handling capabilities than that of a single VR tube?

10. How is it possible to obtain voltages higher than the rated value of a single VR tube?

11. How does a bleeder resistor aid in improving power-supply regulation?

12. What effect does the addition of loads across a voltage divider have on the value of applied voltage?

13. How does internal resistance vary with current through a VR tube?

14. Why is it impractical to use variable resistors as voltage regulators?

15. What would be the value of current through R_2 of Fig. 31·3 if the supply voltage were increased to 500 volts?

16. What would be the value of current through R_2 of Fig. 31·3 if the resistance of R_2 was increased to 75 k ohms?

17. In Fig. 31·3, what would be the total resistance between points b and d if the resistance of load 1 was increased to 100 k ohms?

18. How much voltage would there be across R_3 and load 2 in Fig. 31·3 if the input voltage was decreased to 175 volts?

19. If point c of Fig. 31·3 was grounded, what would be the value of voltage at the ungrounded side of load 1?

20. Draw a voltage divider identical to that shown in Fig. 31·3, assign different values of resistance, then compute for voltage and current at points c, b, and a.

CHAPTER 32

VOLTAGE DOUBLERS AND BRIDGE RECTIFIERS

The voltage doubler is a circuit used to develop direct voltages of a higher value than that of the peak alternating voltage of the source without the use of a step-up transformer. It is commonly known as a *transformerless power supply* and is capable of delivering a direct voltage as high as 400 volts from a 100-volt a-c source. The voltage doubler is often used to supply high values of direct voltages to circuits requiring only a small amount of current. The picture tube in a television receiver requires a high value of d-c voltage that can be supplied more economically by a voltage doubler than by a transformer. Doublers also find many applications in test equipment and in vacuum-tube circuits, where it is sometimes more convenient to use a transformerless power supply.

Bridge rectifiers can also be used to form a transformerless power supply. Usually dry-metal rectifiers in bridge circuits are more desirable than diode tubes. Ruggedness, long life, compactness, and large current-handling capabilities are typical of the bridge rectifier.

32·1 Half-wave Transformerless Rectifier. The voltage doubler operates on the principle of rectification and the RC time of a resistor-capacitor combination. Consider the simple half-wave rectifier circuit shown in Fig. 32·1a. On one half-cycle of input voltage, when point a is positive with respect to point b, the tube will conduct and there will be current through R. With 110 volts at the input, C will charge up to the peak value of 155.5 volts (110 × 1.414). On the next alternation the plate of the tube will be negative, and it will not conduct. During this time the capacitor will discharge through R as shown. This action will be repeated with each half-cycle of input voltage, resulting in a varying value of direct current across the resistor. Each time the tube conducts, the capacitor charges to the peak value of applied voltage; however, the extent to which it discharges during the nonconducting alternation is dependent upon the RC time of the combination. There is current only for a relatively short period, because the tube will conduct only when the positive voltage on the plate is greater than that across the capacitor. Figure 32·1b shows the discharge of C for three values of R and C. Thus, with 110 volts applied, it is possible to obtain a direct output voltage of greater value by use of a rectifier and an RC circuit.

32·2 Full-wave Voltage Doubler. Figure 32·2 shows a full-wave voltage doubler whose principle of operation is similar to the half-wave

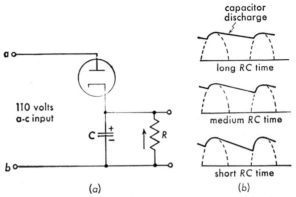

Fig. 32·1 (a) Simple half-wave rectifier. (b) Wave form resulting from discharge of C for three different values of R and C.

rectifier of Fig. 32·1. On one alternation of input voltage when point a is positive with respect to point b, V_1 will conduct, there will be current through R_1, and C_1 will charge to the peak value of 155.5 volts. On the next half-cycle the plate of V_2 is positive. During this half-cycle there

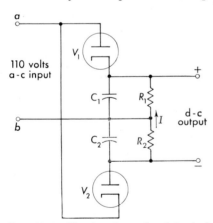

Fig. 32·2 Circuit schematic of typical full-wave voltage doubler.

is current through R_2, and C_2 charges to 155.5 volts. If the value of R_1 is relatively large so that the RC time is long, C_1 will discharge by only a slight amount during the charging of C_2. Also, if the value of R_2 is large, C_2 will retain most of its charge during the half-cycle when V_1 is conducting. Therefore, C_1 and C_2 charge while V_1 and V_2, respectively, are conducting. Since the RC time of each resistor-capacitor combination is large, it discharges to only a minor extent during each noncon- ducting alternation. With the output taken from the series combination of both resistors, its d-c value will be approximately twice the peak value of alternating input voltage.

Tube Current and Ripple. Current exists only for a short period during each alternation, as shown in Fig. 32·3; however, for each input cycle there are two pulses of current in the output.   These pulses of current find many applications in electronic circuits where current is desired only for a short duration of time.

Since there are two pulses of output current for each cycle of input voltage, the ripple frequency will be twice the input frequency.

Considerations.   With the full-wave voltage doubler, it is seen that the load circuit cannot be connected to ground or the doubling operation would not occur.   This presents certain disadvantages; however, they are not essential to this portion of the text.

Peak-inverse-voltage rating of each tube must be twice the peak value of applied voltage.

Since the load current is effectively supplied by the capacitors of a full-wave voltage doubler, the regulation is poor.   Additional output current can be supplied if the capacitors are made larger, but their size is limited by the peak current ratings of the tubes.

32·3 Half-wave Cascade Voltage Doubler.

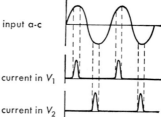

Figure 32·4*a* shows a half-wave rectifier circuit employing two diodes arranged in "cascade." It should be noted that there is current through R only during the half-cycle when V_2 is conducting. When V_1 is conducting, C_1 charges to the peak value of the applied voltage and effectively doubles it for the duration of time that V_2 conducts.

Fig. 32·3   Pulses of current for two cycles of a-c input to voltage doubler shown in Fig. 32·2.

On one half-cycle, when point *b* is positive with respect to *a*, V_1 will conduct and C_1 will charge to the peak value of input voltage with a polarity as shown.   During the next half-cycle, point *a* is positive and V_2 conducts.   Since C_1 must now discharge through the line, it is in series with the applied voltage and adds to produce a line voltage equal to approximately twice its normal peak value.

This voltage is across the combination of C_2 and R in series with V_2. While V_2 is conducting, C_2 charges to this peak voltage and the voltage across R is equal to twice the applied voltage.   On the next alternation, C_2 discharges through R and maintains a direct voltage output twice the value of the peak applied voltage.

As shown in Fig. 32·4*b*, the effect of C_1 is to raise the reference level of the applied voltage from zero to a positive value equal to its peak level. Although this type of circuit functions as a voltage doubler, it is more often used to raise the a-c reference level for use in more advanced types of circuits.

Considerations.   Since only one pulse of current is supplied for each input cycle, the ripple frequency is equal to the frequency of the applied voltage.

Since C_2 supplies all the current to the load circuit, less current is available and regulation is not as good as that of a full-wave voltage doubler.

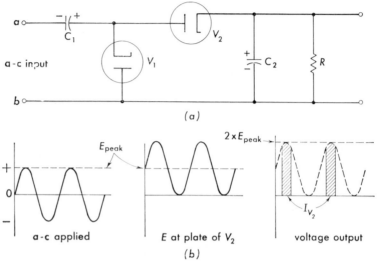

(a)

(b)

FIG. 32·4 (a) Circuit schematic of half-wave cascade voltage doubler. (b) Reference level of applied alternating voltage raised to a positive value equal to its peak level by action of C_1.

Peak-inverse-voltage rating of each tube is twice the peak of the input voltage.

Each capacitor in the half-wave circuit charges to twice the value of peak voltage; therefore, the voltage rating must be greater than those in the full-wave voltage doubler.

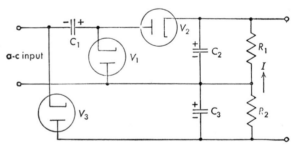

FIG. 32·5 Circuit schematic of simple voltage tripler.

32·4 Voltage Triplers and Quadruplers. It is also possible to triple and quadruple voltages by simple circuit arrangement. Figure 32·5 shows a voltage tripler which employs a half-wave rectifier and cascade voltage doubler. The outputs of both are connected in series and, therefore, add to three times the peak value of input voltage. C_1 charges to the peak value of applied voltage while V_1 is conducting, and it discharges in series with the input while V_2 is conducting. C_2 charges to twice the peak value of input while V_2 is conducting, and C_3 charges to the peak

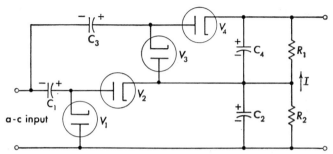

Fig. 32·6 Circuit schematic of simple voltage quadrupler.

input while V_3 is conducting. The discharge of C_2 and C_3, in series, produces a direct voltage output three times the value of the a-c input.

Voltage quadrupling can be accomplished by connecting two half-wave cascade doublers in series, as shown in Fig. 32·6. Since one cascade arrangement doubles the voltage, two in series result in a d-c output that is four times the value of peak applied voltage.

32·5 Bridge Circuits. Either diode tubes or dry-metal rectifiers are connected in "bridge" arrangements to form a type of power supply. Although the wave form of the output voltage is the same as that of a full-wave rectifier, the d-c output is twice as large. While full-wave rectifiers

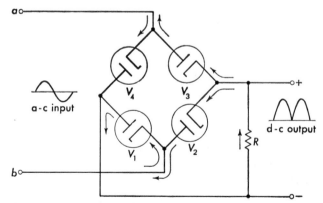

Fig. 32·7 Circuit schematic of simple bridge rectifier showing direction of current and output voltage for one cycle of a-c input.

must use a transformer with a center-tapped secondary, this is not necessary with a bridge rectifier. Unless desired for step-up characteristics, transformers are not necessary. Thus, bridge rectifiers are often referred to as transformerless power supplies.

A typical bridge circuit utilizing four half-wave rectifiers is shown in Fig. 32·7. For one half-cycle of input voltage, when point a is positive with respect to point b, there will be current through V_1, the load resistor R, and V_3. On the next half-cycle, point b is positive with respect to a, and there is current through V_4, load resistor R, and V_2 to the other side of the line. Thus, for each alternation of input voltage one pulse of

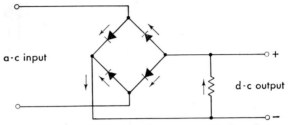

FIG. 32·8   Circuit schematic of bridge rectifier employing dry-metal rectifiers. Arrows indicate direction of current.

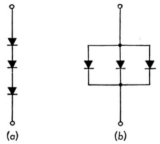

(a)　　　　　　　　　(b)

FIG. 32·9   (a) Dry-metal rectifiers connected in series for additional voltage capabilities.   (b) Parallel connections for higher current-handling capabilities.

direct current is produced across the load. The output voltage is in the form of pulsating direct current as from the conventional full-wave rectifier, except for difference in amplitude.

Where a center-tapped transformer is used, only half the secondary voltage is available at each half of the rectifier. With a bridge type of rectifier using a transformer, the available power output is doubled, since the full value of rectified secondary voltage is across the load resistor.

When one pair of tubes is conducting, peak voltage appears across the load. Since the nonconducting pair of tubes is exposed to this voltage in a reverse direction, peak-inverse-voltage rating of diodes used in bridge circuits should be at least equal to the peak voltage applied.

Although not shown on the illustration, filament transformers are necessary for the operation of diodes in bridge circuits. Since V_2 and V_3 are at the same potential, they can use a single transformer; however, V_1 and V_4 are at different potentials and must use separate transformers. Therefore, three separate transformers are necessary for supplying the filaments of bridge circuit diodes. Moreover, their insulation must be sufficient to withstand the high voltages to which they are subjected.

32·6 Dry-metal Bridge Rectifiers. Aside from eliminating the filament transformer, the principle of operation is the same as that of a bridge

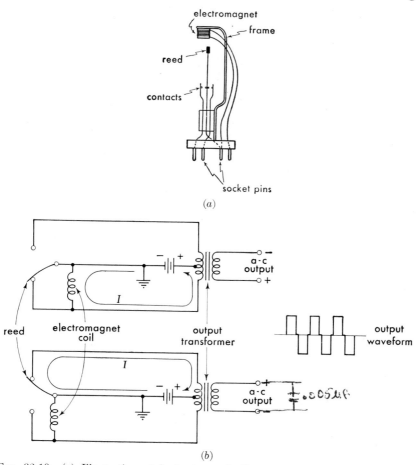

Fig. 32·10 (a) Illustration of basic type of vibrator. (b) Circuit schematic of typical vibrator power supply showing direction of current and position of contacts for one vibration.

rectifier circuit employing diodes. The peak-inverse-voltage rating of individual units is small; however, higher working voltages may be used if several units are stacked in series with each unit absorbing an equal amount of the inverse voltage. Higher current-handling capabilities are obtained by connecting units in parallel.

32·7 Vibrator Power Supply. In automobiles and in other applications where batteries are the only source of electrical energy, a type of power supply known as the *vibrator* is used to convert d-c energy into a-c energy. Since direct voltage cannot be stepped up, it is converted to alternating voltage, stepped up, and then rectified and filtered to a higher value of direct voltage than that originally available from the battery.

The vibrator mechanism is contained in a rubber-lined metal can. An electromagnet is attached to a strip of metal slightly off center from the vibrating "reed." The reed is centered between two contacts underneath the electromagnet. Circuit arrangement is as shown in Fig. 32·10*b*. The reed is centered between the contacts when no direct voltage is applied. When the battery is connected to the circuit, a magnetic field is built up around the electromagnet and the reed is attracted toward one of the contacts. This forms a closed circuit, and there will be a large direct current through the contacts, one half of the transformer primary, and back to the other side of the battery. Closing of the contacts places a direct short across the electromagnet; the magnetic field collapses, and the reed springs back and strikes the other contact. This produces a large direct current from the battery through the closed contacts, the other half of the transformer primary, and to the other side of the battery. Since the short is removed from the electromagnet, it again builds up a magnetic field and pulls the reed to the opposite contact. This cycle of events, called a vibration, usually occurs at the rate of approximately 100 times each second. The reversal of current through the transformer primary causes a high voltage to be induced in the secondary, which is rectified, filtered, and applied as a high value of direct current to external circuits. Since the reversal of current through the primary is instantaneous rather than sinusoidal, the unrectified output has square-topped peaks and is known as a square-wave voltage. However, through rectification and filtering, the net result is a pure direct voltage.

32·8   A-C/D-C Power Supply.   Still another type of power supply is that known as the a-c/d-c supply, which will operate from either an a-c or a d-c source.   Consisting of a simple half-wave rectifier and filter, it finds many applications in portable radios and other equipment where space and weight are important considerations.

Figure 32·11 shows a typical supply employing a half-wave rectifier and a capacitor input filter. Filaments of the rectifier and other tubes are connected across the source. The only requirement is that the tube filament voltages, when totaled, be approximately the value of line voltage and all tubes have the same filament current requirements. For example, a 50L6, 35Z5, 6SA7, 12SK7, and 12SQ7 would require 115 volts for filament operation in series.

Since there is no transformer, the power supply may be connected across a d-c source. If the rectifier plate is connected to the positive side of the source and the cathode to the negative side, there will be current through the resistor and a positive voltage will be available as shown. It is important that the rectifier plate be always connected to the positive side of the input or the power supply will not operate. When connected

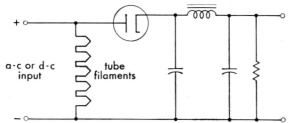

a-c or d-c input

tube filaments

Fig. 32·11   Circuit schematic of simple a-c/d-c power supply.

to an a-c source, operation is that of a conventional half-wave rectifier power supply previously discussed.

REVIEW QUESTIONS

1. What is the purpose of voltage doublers, triplers, or quadruplers?

2. Explain the operation of a half-wave transformerless rectifier.

3. How does the *RC* time of a resistor-capacitor network affect the output wave form of the rectifier in Question 2?

4. With a full-wave voltage doubler, how is it possible to obtain a direct-voltage output of approximately twice the value of a-c input?

5. Explain the operation of a half-wave cascade voltage doubler.

6. Explain the operation of a voltage tripler.

7. Explain the operation of a voltage quadrupler.

8. What is the advantage of bridge circuits in power supplies?

9. Why is the d-c output of a bridge circuit twice that of a full-wave rectifier?

10. Explain the operation of a vibrator power supply.

11. Explain the operation of an a-c/d-c power supply.

12. Name several different types of power supplies that may be used without a transformer.

13. Explain why ground connections cannot be made to the load of a full-wave voltage doubler.

14. What determines the peak inverse-voltage rating of a voltage doubler?

15. What limits the size of the capacitors used in a full-wave voltage doubler?

16. Name several applications of a vibrator power supply.

17. What is meant by "raising the reference level" as applied to the half-wave cascade voltage doubler?

18. Why are three transformers necessary to supply filament voltage to the four diodes of a bridge circuit?

19. What is the main advantage of dry-metal rectifiers over diode tubes?

20. What is the ripple frequency of a full-wave voltage doubler? Of a half-wave cascade voltage doubler?

21. Why is an a-c/d-c power supply often desirable?

22. Why is input polarity important in the operation of an a-c/d-c power supply from a d-c source?

CHAPTER 33

TETRODES AND PENTODES

Although the triode electron tube is the basis of modern electronics and is widely used in many types of circuits, it has several disadvantages in certain applications. Its inherent characteristics of low amplification and interelectrode capacitance limit its use. To eliminate these disadvantages and to achieve better results, the triode has been modified by the addition of grids to form four- and five-element tubes known as *tetrodes* and *pentodes*. While the tetrode is an improvement over the triode, it also has disadvantages that are overcome by the addition of another grid, which thus forms a pentode.

33·1 Interelectrode Capacitance. Capacitance is found to be present when two conductors are separated by a dielectric. Therefore, in a vacuum tube capacitance will exist between any two of the elements. In a three-element tube there exist grid-cathode capacitance C_{gk}, plate-cathode capacitance C_{pk}, and grid-plate capacitance C_{gp}. These are shown schematically in Fig. 33·1.

Of the three types of interelectrode capacitance present in a triode, the grid-plate capacitance is the most troublesome. In an amplifier, for example, large voltage variations are present in the plate of the tube. If the frequency of these variations is sufficiently high, the grid-plate capacitance may present such a low reactance that *feedback* from plate to grid might result. Feedback is defined as the voltage taken from the output circuit of an amplifier or tube and fed back to the input, or grid circuit. If it is applied to the input in phase with the signal voltage and tends to increase the amplitude of the output, it is called *regeneration*, or *regenerative feedback*. If the feedback is applied to the input out of phase with the signal voltage and tends to decrease the amplitude of the output, it is called *degeneration*, or *degenerative feedback*.

The amplitude of feedback resulting from interelectrode capacitance is

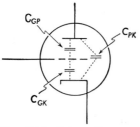

Fig. 33·1 Schematic representation of interelectrode capacitance in a triode.

usually considered negligible at audio frequencies because of the high reactance of the grid-plate capacitance. However, at high frequencies the reactance decreases and feedback is sufficiently large to affect operation. One method of counteracting interelectrode capacitance is by the addition of a capacitor which will feed energy back to the grid circuit. If this energy is equal in amplitude to and 180° out of phase with that of the interelectrode capacitance, the two will cancel. This is called *neutralization* and is almost always employed where triodes are used at radio frequencies.

33·2 The Tetrode. The grid-plate capacitance of a triode can be reduced by the addition of another grid between plate and control grid.

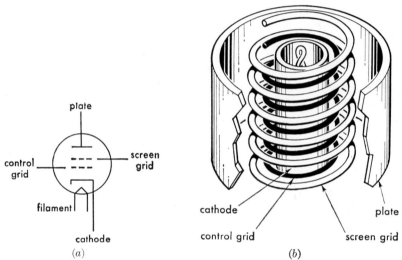

FIG. 33·2   (*a*) Schematic representation of a tetrode.   (*b*) Physical construction of a tetrode.

This grid No. 2 is called the *screen* grid, and the tube is then known as a *tetrode*, or four-element tube. The screen is made of fine-mesh wire and, like the control grid, is mostly empty space. It acts as an electrostatic shield between grid and plate and, effectively, adds another capacitor in series with the grid-plate capacitance of the tube. Since the total capacitance of any two series capacitors is smaller than that of either capacitor, total grid-plate capacitance has been reduced. This effectiveness is increased by placing a series capacitor in the external circuit between screen and cathode, thus further reducing the total grid-plate capacitance.

Amplification. In a triode tube the plate voltage has a relatively large effect on plate current. Since the amplification factor (μ) of a tube is the ratio of effectiveness on plate current of grid voltage to plate voltage, the amplification factor of a triode will be low.

Since the screen grid in a tetrode is between the plate and the space charge, it shields the space charge from the plate and thus reduces the

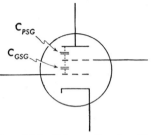

effect of plate voltage on plate current. The plate exerts very little electrostatic force on electrons near the cathode, since the screen is nearer to the cathode and provides the main attracting force for emitted electrons. Therefore, grid voltage has a greater effect on plate current, which means higher amplification with tetrodes than with triodes. Moreover, this amplification is increased and stabilized by the low grid-plate capacitance. The amplification factor for triodes is between 3 and 100, while tetrodes have amplification factors as high as 800.

Fig. 33·3 Schematic of grid-plate capacitance in a tetrode. Capacitance between plate and screen grid adds in series with capacitance between screen grid and control grid.

33·3 Dynatron Region. Under ordinary circumstances any increase in plate voltage will result in an increase in plate current until saturation

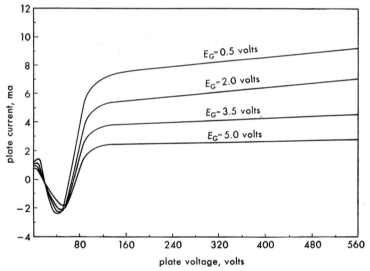

Fig. 33·4 Family of plate-characteristic curves for a typical tetrode. Each curve represents a different value of grid voltage.

is reached. With tetrodes there is a range where increasing plate voltage will cause a decrease in plate current. This is called the *negative resistance*, or *dynatron region*, of the characteristics curve.

Figure 33·4 shows a family of E_p–I_p curves for a typical tetrode. With screen voltage at a steady value, as plate voltage is increased to approximately 10 volts there is some increase in plate current. As plate voltage is further increased to approximately 60 volts, plate current decreases. This decrease in plate current with an increase in plate voltage, commonly called *dynatron effect*, is caused by secondary emission from the plate.

When plate voltage is zero, plate current will also be zero. As plate voltage is increased, there will be some current and electrons will be attracted to the plate. This continues until the velocity of the electrons is sufficiently large to cause them to strike the plate with enough force to dislodge other electrons from the plate. Electrons thus liberated are called secondary electrons and the effect is called secondary emission. Since at this point plate voltage is less than screen voltage, secondary electrons will be attracted to the screen. A further increase in plate voltage causes the electrons to increase their velocity, dislodge additional secondary electrons, and increase electron flow to the screen. During the period between initial secondary emission and the point where plate voltage is greater than screen voltage, plate current will decrease.

When plate voltage is increased to a value equal to that of the screen, secondary electrons are not as easily attracted by the screen. When plate voltage exceeds screen voltage, practically all the secondary electrons return to the plate and plate current responds linearly to plate voltage. Thereafter, plate voltage will have little effect on plate current.

Tetrodes must be operated so that plate voltage always exceeds screen voltage or unstable operation will result. While this is a disadvantage, tetrodes have the advantages over triodes of higher amplification and lower grid-plate capacitance.

33·4 The Pentode. Electron tubes having five electrodes are called *pentodes*, the fifth electrode being in the form of a coarsely wound grid placed between the screen and plate. The additional electrode, grid No. 3, is called the *suppressor grid*.

Pentodes have all the advantages of tetrodes (high μ and low interelectrode capacitance) without the disadvantage of the dynatron effect. While secondary emission is present in diodes, triodes, and tetrodes, it becomes an important consideration only in tetrodes because of the positive potential on the screen grid. The resulting dynatron effect lowers plate current and limits plate-voltage variations for tetrodes.

In a pentode the suppressor grid is placed at cathode or ground potential and is highly negative with respect to the plate. Secondary electrons are repelled by the suppressor grid back toward the plate. While it does not eliminate secondary emission, the suppressor grid prevents secondary electrons from reaching the screen and thus eliminates the dynatron or negative-resistance region evident in tetrodes. This feature allows the use of low plate-supply voltage and removes the limitation of plate-voltage variations.

Plate voltage in a pentode has much less effect on plate current than in a tetrode. Therefore, the R_p of a pentode will be considerably higher than that of a tetrode. Since grid construction of both tetrode and pentode is basically the same, transconductance will also be the same. Then, since R_p has been increased and G_m unaffected, the μ of a pentode is greater than that of a triode ($\mu = G_m R_p$). The amplification factor of a pentode may range from 70 to 5,000 as compared with that of a tetrode of 40 to 800.

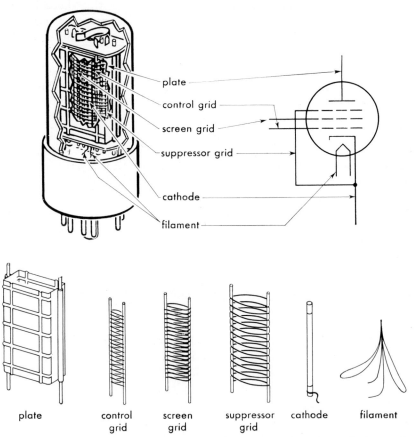

plate

control grid

screen grid

suppressor grid

cathode

filament

| plate | control grid | screen grid | suppressor grid | cathode | filament |

Fig. 33·5 Schematic representation and physical construction of a typical pentode.

33·5 Variable-μ Pentodes. In ordinary pentodes the amplification factor μ will remain constant for any value of applied voltage. This is the result of uniform construction of the control grid. The *variable-μ* pentode allows the amplification factor to vary with the amount of voltage applied to the grid. This type of tube has many applications, one of which is for high-voltage amplification at radio frequencies.

In an ordinary pentode the control grid is constructed of fine wire in the form of a coil or spiral surrounding the cathode. Spacing between each turn is uniform, and the grid itself is mostly empty space. In a variable-μ pentode the control grid is also of spiral construction and consists mostly of empty space in the center, but it is more closely wound on either end. Otherwise, tube construction is the same as that of the ordinary pentode.

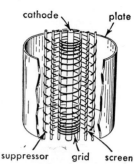

FIG. 33·6 Construction of control grid in variable-μ tube showing spacing of grid wires. (*Radio Corporation of America.*)

Nonuniform construction of the control grid in a variable-μ pentode results in the variation of the amplification factor with the input voltage. Since $\mu = G_m R_p$, a change in G_m will also cause a change in μ. High μ results from the closely spaced windings on either end of the control grid while low μ results from the widely spaced windings in the center. If a small negative voltage is applied to the variable-μ grid, the entire grid will affect the plate current. Since the closely spaced portions of the grid will have more effect upon electrons being emitted from the cathode than will the widely spaced center portion, electron flow through these areas will gradually be cut off as the grid is made more negative. When this occurs, only the widely spaced portion of the grid will allow electrons to pass through.

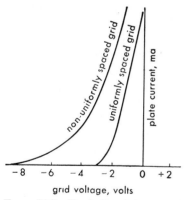

FIG. 33·7 Typical plate-current grid-voltage curve showing effect of grid voltage on plate current for both variable-μ and conventional pentodes.

Thus, transconductance is being varied as the signal applied to the grid is varied. This further varies the amplification factor of the tube. The larger the negative voltage applied to the tube, the greater the extent to which plate current is reduced until a point is reached where plate current is zero.

A relatively large negative voltage is required to cut off completely a variable-μ tube, because the last portion of the grid to have effect on plate current is the widely spaced portion. Since the wider the space between grid wires, the less the effect of grid voltage on plate current, a large negative voltage is necessary in order to reach cutoff.

However, the important characteristic of this type of tube is the varying of its amplification factor by varying the control-grid voltage. This can be accomplished by potentiometers either manually or automatically operated. Many applications of this theory will be seen in further studies.

33·6   Beam-power Tubes.   While the conventional pentode is ideal for voltage amplification, it is unsuited for power amplification.   This is because the suppressor grid in a pentode causes its plate resistance to be rather high, resulting in power losses with a large amount of plate current. Also, when pentode plate current is increased, there is an increase in screen current and additional power is dissipated in the screen circuit. Therefore, the low power output and low efficiency of the pentode eliminate its use as a power amplifier.   The tetrode is unsuitable as a power amplifier because of the dynatron region, and the triode has the disadvantage of requiring a high plate voltage.

The *beam-power tube*, shown in Fig. 33·8, is a special type of tetrode or pentode which employs beam-forming plates, at cathode potential, to concentrate the electrons in a narrow beam.

Although the suppressor grid is an optional feature, when a beam-power tube is designed without it, the dynatron effect is suppressed by the concentrated beam of electrons. Secondary-emission electrons encounter a beam of electrons that tends to force them back to the plate.   Also, secondary emission is suppressed by the space-charge effects that exist between screen and plate.   When the screen is at a higher positive potential than the plate, electrons leaving the cathode are slowed down after they leave the region of the screen en route to the plate.   This slowing down produces a space charge that is of sufficient intensity to repel secondary electrons and thus eliminate the dynatron region present in a conventional tetrode.

FIG. 33·8   Beam-power tube. (*Radio Corporation of America.*)

The absence of a suppressor grid reduces the plate resistance of the tube, which results in a higher value of plate current.   Another advantage of the beam-power tube is its low screen current.   This is because the screen grid is located in the "electron shadow" of the control grid. Both grids are so wound that each spiral of the screen is behind a spiral of the control grid, thereby shading the screen from the cathode.   The negative potential on the control grid has a repelling effect.   This effect is apparent on each spiral of the control grid and causes the electrons to converge and leave an empty space behind each turn.   Thus, very few electrons come in contact with the screen, and screen current is very low.

Because of these characteristics the beam-power tube has the advantages of high efficiency and high power output.   Its transconductance is higher than that of pentodes; its amplification factor is higher than that of triodes but lower than pentodes or conventional tetrodes.   Plate resist-

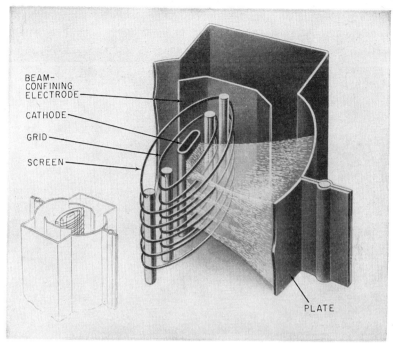

BEAM-
CONFINING
ELECTRODE

CATHODE

GRID

SCREEN

PLATE

FIG. 33·9 Beam-power tube construction. (*Radio Corporation of America.*)

ance is higher than that of triodes but lower than that of pentodes. Its main advantage is its ability to deal with large values of power.

33·7 Summary. The following important points summarize the advantages, disadvantages, requirements, and applications of the various types of electron tubes.

a. The diode, or two-electrode tube, is widely used as a rectifier and also as a detector, which will be studied later. However, its use is limited to a few applications because of its inability to control plate current effectively.

b. The triode, or three-electrode tube, has the advantage of allowing control of plate current and the ability to amplify a signal applied to its grid. The disadvantages of a triode are its interelectrode capacitance and low amplification. Triodes are generally found in audio-frequency circuits where interelectrode capacitance has a negligible effect and where only a relatively small amount of amplification is required.

c. The tetrode, or four-electrode tube, reduces the interelectrode capacitance present in a triode by the addition of a screen grid. Also, since the screen is closer to the cathode than to the plate and is at a constant positive voltage, plate voltage has less effect on plate current and the amplification is greater than that of a triode. Tetrodes are not widely used in receivers but are used in transmitters and in some special circuits where the negative-resistance, or dynatron, characteristic can be used advantageously.

d. The pentode, or five-electrode tube, also has the advantages over the triode of high amplification and low interelectrode capacitance. The suppressor grid eliminates the dynatron region and thus gives the pentode this advantage over the tetrode. Its principal disadvantage results from a higher plate resistance that reduces its current-handling capabilities. Pentodes are widely used in high-gain voltage amplifiers at both radio and audio frequencies, particularly in receivers. The pentode is commonly referred to as a "sharp-cutoff" tube.

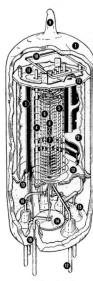

Fig. 33·10 Physical construction of a miniature pentode. (*Radio Corporation of America.*) (1) Glass envelope. (2) Internal shield. (3) Plate. (4) Grid No. 3 (suppressor grid). (5) Grid No. 2 (screen grid). (6) Grid No. 1 (control grid). (7) Cathode. (8) Heater. (9) Exhaust tip. (10) Getter. (11) Spacer shield header. (12) Insulating spacer. (13) Spacer shield. (14) Inter-pin shield. (15) Glass button-stem seal. (16) Lead wire. (17) Base pin. (18) Glass-to-metal seal.

e. The variable-μ pentode utilizes a nonuniformly constructed grid to provide an amplification factor that will vary with the input signal. It is also referred to as a "super-control" or "remote-cutoff" tube. The only difference between the variable-μ and conventional pentode is in the construction of the control grid. It is widely used as a high-gain voltage amplifier, generally at radio frequencies, and utilizes the variable-μ principle to good advantage for controlling the gain of a tube or stage.

f. The beam-power tube is a tetrode or pentode with the addition of plates to concentrate the electrons into a beam. Due to grid and screen construction, there is very little screen current. This prevents a waste of power and thus increases power output. Suppressor-grid action, in the tetrode variety, is obtained by the space-charge effect that exists between screen and plate. Beam-power tubes are designed only for specific purposes, particularly in receiver output amplifiers.

REVIEW QUESTIONS

1. Explain interelectrode capacitance.
2. Explain how feedback occurs.

3. What is the difference between regenerative and degenerative feedback?

4. How is interelectrode capacitance affected by frequency?

5. What is neutralization and why is it necessary in some instances?

6. Explain the construction of a tetrode.

7. In a tetrode, how does the addition of a screen grid reduce the grid-plate capacitance?

8. How does the screen grid affect amplification in a tetrode?

9. Explain dynatron region.

10. Explain how a pentode reduces dynatron effect.

11. How does a variable-μ pentode allow the amplification factor to vary with a varying grid voltage?

12. Explain the operation of a variable-μ pentode.

13. What are the advantages of the beam-power tube?

14. Why does a beam-power tube have low screen current?

15. What are the advantages and disadvantages of a tetrode as compared to a triode?

16. Why is the plate resistance of a pentode higher than that of a tetrode?

17. Why does a tetrode have higher amplification than a triode?

18. Explain secondary emission and how it is caused.

19. How is secondary emission suppressed in a beam-power tube?

20. Why is the conventional pentode unsuited for power amplification?

21. Why is a relatively large negative voltage necessary to cut off plate current in a variable-μ tube?

22. What is meant by electron shadow?

CHAPTER 34

AMPLIFIERS AND OSCILLOSCOPES

With the development of the third element in the electron tube, an entirely new field of experimentation and development was opened.

The addition of the control grid in the electron tube immediately brings to mind a term usually associated with its presence. That term is the amplification factor, which is described as the extent of the tube's ability to produce a comparatively large change in plate voltage and current as a result of receiving a rather small change in grid voltage. Any electron tube connected in such a manner as to utilize its amplification factor may correctly be referred to as an *amplifier.*

It is hardly possible to attach too much importance to the study of amplifiers, since there exists scarcely a unit of electronic equipment that does not utilize the principles of amplification.

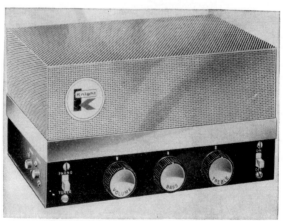

Fig. 34·1   Typical amplifier.   (*Allied Radio Corporation.*)

34·1   The Amplifier.   In electronics an amplifier may be defined as *any device that will receive at its input a signal of a given amplitude of voltage and deliver at its output a signal of greater amplitude.* The device most common to all electronic circuits in which amplification is one of the

320

requirements is the electron tube. The tube alone, however, does not function as an amplifier. There must be associated components specifically selected for the purpose of aiding in the accomplishment of this amplification.

34·2 Classification of Amplifiers. Amplifiers are best classified in terms of their characteristics and inherent limitations.

Frequency. The first and probably most important classification is that of frequency. There are three general divisions within this category, namely, audio-frequency, radio-frequency, and video-frequency amplifiers. The frequency range of audio amplifiers is approximately from 20

FIG. 34·2   Audio amplifier without cover.   (*Allied Radio Corporation.*)

to 20,000 cycles. Frequencies above this point are considered radio frequencies. Video amplifiers must be able to amplify uniformly a wide band of frequencies including the audio-frequency range and beyond. The frequency range of video amplifiers is from about 5 cycles to over 4 megacycles.

Voltage and Power. The next classification of amplifiers is one that describes their prospective use. A voltage amplifier is designed to produce as large a voltage variation in its output as possible. A power amplifier is designed to produce as much current variation at its output as possible. It is necessary to make a distinction between the two for several reasons. An example would be the problem of obtaining a large quantity of undistorted power output from a signal whose voltage is so small that more amplification is required than can be obtained from a single amplifier. In such a situation the practice is to use several amplifiers connected in such a way that the output of one is connected to the input of the next.   Each succeeding stage of amplification then receives a larger signal at its input.   The over-all amplification is multiplicative. The usual arrangement is to make all the amplifiers except possibly the last one operate as voltage amplifiers, thus reducing the drain on the power supply.   The final stage functions as a power amplifier.   The power stage then has an extremely large voltage at its input and is capable of delivering the greatest amount of power by minimizing voltage amplification.   Therefore, a large amount of current is delivered to the load, which may be a speaker, headphones, or similar devices.

Operating Level.   The third general classification of amplifiers describes the amount of bias that is to be employed.   The four general divisions in this category are Class A, Class AB, Class B, and Class C.   Classes A, B, and C will be discussed in detail in this section.   Class AB is an intermediate operating level between Class A and B.

It will be shown in this and ensuing sections that the type of amplifier to be used is governed primarily by the requirements of the electronic circuits and by grid- and plate-voltage assignments.   It is possible to make any tube with at least three elements function as an amplifier. However, tubes are generally designed to be used with a certain type of amplifier, and, when considering efficiency, care should be taken in the selection of tube types.

34·3   The Basic Amplifier.   Shown in Fig. 34·3 is a schematic of a simple triode amplifier.   For explanation purposes it should be assumed

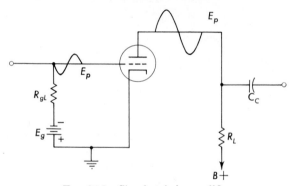

FIG. 34·3   Simple triode amplifier.

that a signal is impressed on the control grid.   A *signal* can be any varying voltage that is to be taken under consideration.   It can be discussed in terms of amplitude, frequency, phase, or any other characteristic.   A signal leaves the transmitter by way of the transmitting antenna, travels through the air, arrives at the receiving antenna, is coupled to the receiver input, and is amplified and converted to some kind of intelligence.   That intelligence may be music, voice, code, or pulses of voltage and current that are to be visualized, such as the "pip" on a radar screen or the face on a television screen.

As the signal goes negative with respect to the cathode, it causes the grid to repel the electrons being emitted by the cathode. This repulsion causes a decrease in tube plate current. Since the plate load resistor R_L is in series with the tube, the current through R_L will decrease. The decrease in current will bring about a corresponding decrease in the voltage across R_L, and the result will be that plate voltage E_p goes positive, approaching B+.

As the signal goes in a positive direction with respect to the cathode, the repulsion between control grid and cathode-emitted electrons will decrease, permitting an increase in tube current. As tube current increases, plate current I_p increases. R_L, being in series with the tube, realizes an increase in current. A corresponding increase in voltage across R_L results. This has the effect of reducing plate voltage E_p.

These plate-voltage variations are passed with a minimum of loss through the coupling capacitor C_c, to the succeeding stage. The amplitude difference between the signal voltage E_{sig} on the grid and that present on the plate is representative of the stage's amplification factor. The amplified signal may be used as an input for the next stage or to drive some audio device such as a speaker.

There are several conclusions that can be drawn from the basic audio amplifier. One is that the input signal always undergoes a "phase shift" of 180°. As the signal on the grid goes negative, E_p goes positive; as E_{sig} goes positive, E_p goes negative. Another conclusion is that element voltages are always considered with respect to the cathode. This might not be true in all cases, but for consistency's sake, it will be so assumed in this text. Another conclusion is that the frequency of the signal voltage is reproduced in the plate circuit. The ability of an amplifier to reproduce faithfully the frequency of the signal at its output is termed its *fidelity*. A fourth conclusion could be that there is current in the cathode and the plate circuits, but no grid current. In some applications, to be covered later, grid current is tolerated or even desired, but for the most part it is undesirable to have anything other than a voltage difference between grid and cathode.

34·4 Cathode Bias. There are several methods of biasing an electron tube. One of the most common for amplifiers is the technique known as *cathode bias*, employing a resistor and a capacitor in parallel in the cathode circuit. Sometimes a resistor alone is used when it is desired to introduce degeneration plus biasing into a stage.

With no signal present on the grid of Fig. 34·4, the electrons emitted by the cathode are attracted to the plate, flow through R_L to B+, to ground, and through R_k back to the cathode. C_k, the capacitor in the cathode circuit, will develop a charge equal to the voltage across the resistor R_k. This constant voltage makes the cathode positive with respect to ground. Effectively, bias is a voltage difference between control grid and cathode. The current through R_k sets up such a voltage. With no current through R_{gL}, the grid-leak resistor, the grid is at ground potential. Hence, the cathode is positive with respect to the grid, or the grid is negative with respect to the cathode. R_k is the main governing factor for the amount of bias developed. If R_k is made larger, more voltage will be across it, since the current is a function of the tube itself and tends to remain constant. With more voltage across R_k, more bias is developed and as a result, tube current will be less. C_k is selected with frequency as the main considera-

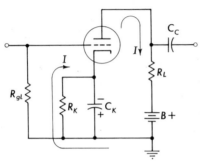

tion. The capacitance should be such that the varying signal voltage and the current changes it produces in the tube will pass through C_k. Under static conditions, C_k merely acts as a battery; under dynamic conditions, or with a signal applied, C_k acts as a means for shunting the varying current around R_k. Here it can be seen how degeneration is achieved if C_k is not connected.

FIG. 34-4   Current paths in a triode amplifier.

With no cathode capacitor, all currents will pass through R_k. This is degenerative in that a signal is being fed back that is 180° out of phase with the incoming signal.

There are two general types of biasing. *External biasing* is accomplished by applying a voltage to either the grid (negative) or the cathode (positive) that is external to the immediate stage of amplification. *Self-biasing*, of which cathode biasing is a type, is accomplished entirely within the stage itself. Any time a tube is biased by its own conduction, self-biasing is employed.

34·5 The E_g–I_p Curve. An electron tube's characteristics as well as its limitations can best be observed by curves that plot element voltages and currents. In tube manuals, published by the manufacturers, these curves are shown in groups or "families" for each tube type. In a family of curves, one element condition is usually kept constant while the other conditions are varied. In the case of the E_g–I_p curve, plate voltage is a constant and the variation in plate current is the result of variations in grid voltage. The curve shown in Fig. 34·5 is a typical E_g–I_p curve. Each segment of the curve has a name and often a purpose. The two curving portions at each end are referred to as "knees" of the curve. The more directly progressive segment between them is the *linear* portion.   The knees are also often called *nonlinear* portions.   Observe that E_g is really a composite of two different voltages.   The bias voltage, which is the true E_g, is -6 volts, while the signal voltage E_{sig} varies E_g from -4 volts through -6 volts to -8 volts.   Note also that the amplifier upon which the curve was plotted is operating well within the linear portion of the curve.   This means that both the positive and negative portions of E_{sig} will receive the same amplification.   If the plate current is through a plate load resistor of 10,000 ohms, Ohm's law shows that with a 4-ma peak-to-peak current through 10,000 ohms, the peak-to-peak voltage is 40 volts.   With a 4-volt peak-to-peak input and a 40-volt

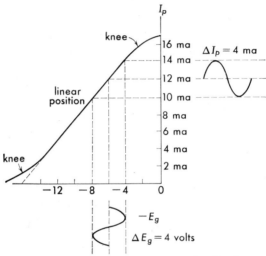

FIG. 34·5   The $E_g - I_p$ curve showing plate- and grid-voltage variations.

peak-to-peak output, the signal has been made 10 times as large and the voltage amplification is 10.

34·6   Operating Levels.   The main purpose of biasing is to fix the operating point or level of an amplifier.   Establishing this level has two other effects.   First, the tube is protected.   If the grid is near or above the cathode potential, excessive tube current will result and the tube is very likely to be damaged.   Second, the tube is more efficient.   If the grid is not operated with a negative voltage of sufficient amplitude to prevent current in the grid circuit for the entire 360° of input signal, signal-voltage variations will be lost in the grid circuit.   In addition, if grid current is allowed for any portion of the input cycle, uneven amplification will result.   This is known as *amplitude distortion*.

As was previously mentioned in this section, amplifiers are classified in terms of their prospective operating levels.   The amplifier to which the curve of Fig. 34·6a belongs is operating Class A.   Class A is defined as the level at which there is plate current for the entire 360° of input signal. The tube is usually biased in the center of the linear portion of the E_g–I_p curve. When the best fidelity is desired, Class A is the proper level of operation.

In Class-B amplifiers, as shown in Fig. 34·6b, there is plate current for only 180° of the input cycle. The tube is biased approximately at *projected cutoff*. Projected cutoff is determined by projecting a line from the lower end of the linear portion of the tube's E_g–I_p curve. The point where the line intersects the horizontal axis is projected cutoff. One main advantage of a Class-B amplifier is that, at least for one half-cycle, a large amplification can be realized. If the signal can be fed to two amplifiers, each of which at Class B will amplify a 180° segment of the signal, the over-all amplification can be extremely large. It must be remembered that the signal halves must then be combined through some

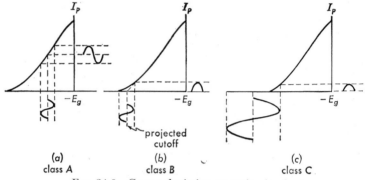

(a)
class A

(b)
class B

(c)
class C

Fig. 34·6   Curves depicting operating levels.

other network.   Class-B amplifiers are usually employed for such a separation and again for the combining.   This technique is known as *push-pull* operation.

Class-C operating level means that the tube has been biased to a point that is one and one-half to five times past the cutoff point of the tube.   It can be seen, as shown in Fig. 34.6c, that only on the extreme positive peaks of signal voltage will the tube be brought above cutoff, permitting plate current.   In Class-C operation there is plate current for approximately 120° of input cycle.   Class-C amplifiers have many uses in tuned circuits.   For example, assume that an amplifier has in its plate circuit, not a resistor, but a parallel LC circuit designed to be resonant at the frequency of the incoming signal.   The flywheel action of the tank circuit, plus the recurring "shocks" when the tube does conduct, will yield a reproduction of the incoming signal without the need of a steady current through the tube and the resultant drain on a power supply.   A Class-C amplifier is considered very efficient when used in this manner.

34·7 Determining Component Values. Generally, when determining the value of components to assist the electron tube in the accomplishment of amplification, it is well to consult the manufacturer's tube manual. Approximate component values are listed for use with the various tubes.

It has already been shown that average plate current does not change in a Class-A amplifier with signal changes. The signal always varies the same amount above and below the fixed plate-current level; therefore, average current remains unchanged. Also, since plate current emanates from the cathode, average cathode current is unaffected by the signal. It is then simple to calculate the value of R_k. If the plate current is known, and in a triode it is also the cathode current, by formula,

$$R_k = \frac{\text{bias voltage}}{\text{plate current}}$$

C_k is calculated in terms of the frequency of the incoming signal. In practical applications, the capacitive reactance of C_k is one-tenth the value of R, or, by formula,

$$X_{C_k} = \frac{R_k}{10}$$

If the amplifier is to pass signals of different frequencies, then C_k is selected by the same formula, using the lowest frequency to be amplified as the basis for computing reactance.

34·8 Oscilloscope. Much has already been said about *percentage of modulation, types of distortion, in or out of phase, filtering,* and *amplification.* These subjects will be discussed further in later portions of this text. These and many other features of a circuit can be visualized by an instrument called the *oscilloscope.* Applied to the circuit under test, it shows the phase difference, type of distortion, percentage of modulation, filtering action, and amount of amplification, in addition to several other circuit features.

An oscilloscope is basically a *cathode-ray* tube operating with an appropriate power supply and with a means of supplying the deflection and amplification voltages necessary to make visible the current or voltage being observed. The visible results are traced on the face of a cathode-ray tube.

Cathode-ray Tube. The cathode-ray tube (CRT) is a special type of vacuum tube in which electrons are emitted from the cathode and formed into a narrow beam. These electrons are caused to strike a chemically prepared screen which *fluoresces,* or glows, at the point of contact. Because the electron beam varies in accordance with the voltage or current wave under test, its behavior can be seen on the cathode-ray-tube screen.

Beam Formation. A simple method of forming an electron beam is shown in Fig. 34·8. Electrons are emitted from the cathode at right angles to its surface and are attracted toward the positively charged anode. Their speed of travel is dependent on the attraction of the anode, and a velocity of 10,000 miles per second is not uncommon. Since the anode is constructed with a narrow opening in its center, some of the electrons pass on through without any appreciable loss in velocity. Those passing through have sufficient momentum to continue on until they strike the screen, where the phosphorescent properties of the screen cause a spot to appear on its surface. Although the electrons tend to repel one another, their velocity is such that negligible scattering occurs. However, most of the electrons strike the anode and cause current to flow in the external circuit.

Fig. 34·7 Typical cathode-ray tube. (*Radio Corporation of America.*)

Electrostatic Control. In order to make the electron beam perform in accordance with the wave form under test, some means of *deflection* or focusing is necessary. While this can be accomplished by either electromagnetic or electrostatic means, only the latter will be discussed here, since the two are quite similar.

A simplified construction of an electrostatically focused and deflected CRT is shown in Fig. 34·9. When heated by the filament, the cathode emits electrons. The cylindrical grid surrounds the cathode and aids in forming the beam by controlling the number of electrons passing through

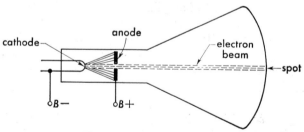

Fig. 34·8 Electron "gun."

its end opening. Control action is accomplished by varying the negative voltage on the grid through use of the INTENSITY or BRIGHTNESS controls.

Although the grid helps to narrow the electron beam, it is not capable of sufficient focusing action. While the grid does focus electrons close

by, they tend to scatter after passing through the grid opening.   Therefore, additional focusing is necessary, and is provided by two cylindrical
anodes such as those shown in Fig. 34·10.   Both anodes are positive, but
the second anode is always more positive than the first in order to continue the accelerating action.   Electrons entering into the field of the first

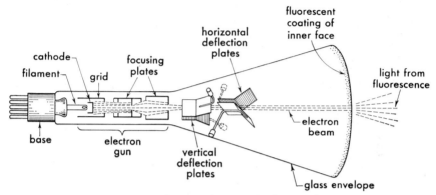

FIG. 34·9   Construction of cathode-ray tube.

anode will tend to follow one of the lines of force until they reach the
more positive cylinder.   Because the high velocity keeps the electrons in
the field for only a short time, they are subjected to negligible attraction.
However, the moving electrons are subjected to forces as they move
through the field.   For example, along the path XAB an electron will

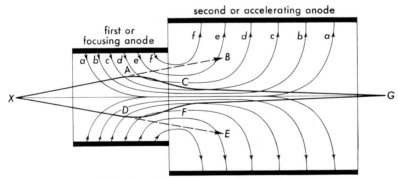

FIG. 34·10   Focusing anodes of CRT.

cross the line of force a and be attracted along the center of the cylindrical anode.   As it continues, its path will cross the lines of force b, c,
and d and the electron will be further attracted toward the center.   The
paths of the electrons will therefore be along the line AC where the lines
of force are parallel to the cylinder walls.   As a result, the electrons are
no longer attracted toward the anode itself but are accelerated along the

lines of force c and d in its center.   At this point electrons are moving at a high velocity, and the electrostatic field is becoming progressively weak. Thus, there is little tendency for any electrons to be deflected from their course, and they will finally converge at point G.

The focusing of an electrostatically-controlled CRT is usually accomplished by varying the voltage of the first anode.   This varies the amount of force that the electrostatic field exerts on the electrons.

Deflection.   The *electron gun* produces only a small spot on the screen of the CRT.   It is further necessary to deflect the beam in a pattern that conforms with the wave form being observed.   This is accomplished by *deflection plates* as shown in Fig. 34·11.   One pair of plates deflects the

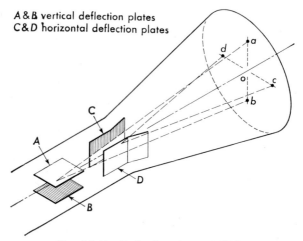

A & B vertical deflection plates
C & D horizontal deflection plates

FIG. 34·11   Deflection plates of CRT.

beam horizontally while the other pair deflects it vertically.   By functioning simultaneously, the beam can be made to trace a definite pattern across the screen.

Electrons moving in the area between the plates will be attracted by a positively charged plate and repelled by a negatively charged plate. For example, if the *vertical deflection plate A* is more positive than plate B, the electron beam will be pulled upward.   Instead of striking the screen at point o it would strike it at a.   Conversely, if plate A was negative with respect to B, the beam would strike the screen at point b.   And if both plates were at the same potential, the beam would strike at point o. The amount of deflection in either direction is dependent upon the magnitude of the voltage between the vertical deflection plates.

If the *horizontal deflection plate C* is more positive than plate D, the beam will strike the screen at point d.   When plate D is more positive than C, the beam will strike at c.   Moreover, equal voltages on plates

C and D will cause the beam to strike the screen at point o.   As in the case of the vertical deflection plates, the amount of deflection is dependent upon the magnitude of voltage between the plates.

Production of Screen Trace.   The human eye will retain an image for about one-sixteenth of a second.   This is proved by motion pictures, where the illusion of motion is created by a series of still pictures flashed on the screen so rapidly that the eye cannot follow their movement. The result is an illusion of movement.   In a CRT this same principle is

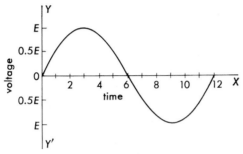

FIG. 34·12   Production of sine wave on CRT screen.

applied.   The spot is moved so quickly that a series of adjacent spots appears as a continuous line.

Oscilloscope Circuits.   The conventional way in which voltages and currents are visualized is shown by the graph in Fig. 34·12.   Voltage is plotted vertically and time horizontally.   However, to observe any wave form, it is first necessary to cause the electron beam to move horizontally across the face of the screen at a constant speed to form the time-scale line OX.   The voltage that accomplishes this is called the *sweep*

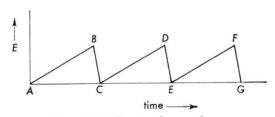

FIG. 34·13   Saw-tooth wave form.

voltage and has a *saw-tooth wave form* (see Sec. 37·1) as shown in Fig. 34·13. As the voltage increases from point A to point B, voltage on the horizontal deflection plates is varied in such a manner that the spot will move from left to right across the face of the screen.   As the voltage drops from maximum voltage at point B to zero voltage at point C, the electron beam is caused to return to its starting position and is ready to start the next sweep.

If a sine wave is applied to the vertical deflection plates with no horizontal deflection voltage, a straight vertical line will appear. However, if a sweep voltage is also applied, the up and down motion of the sine wave will be spread across the face of the screen as an exact reproduction.

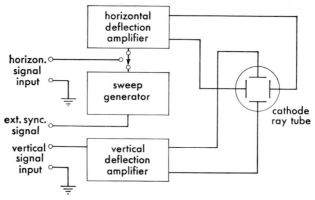

FIG. 34·14   Block diagram of basic oscilloscope, less power supply.

A block diagram of a basic oscilloscope is shown in Fig. 34·14. Sweep voltage is produced by the sweep generator and amplified by the horizontal deflection amplifier. An intensity control varies the bias on the CRT and a focus control regulates the voltage between first and second

FIG. 34·15   Typical oscilloscope.   (*Radio Corporation of America.*)

anodes to produce a sharply defined spot. Horizontal- and vertical-centering controls vary the voltage between the deflecting plates to center the spot on the screen. The saw-tooth wave form is produced by a special circuit in the sweep generator.

The signal to be observed is applied at the input of the vertical deflection amplifier where it is amplified and further applied to the vertical deflection plates. These plates cause the beam to be deflected up or down while the sweep voltage moves it from left to right. Therefore, the position of the spot on the screen at any instant is controlled by two forces—the sweep voltage and the signal voltage.

In some instances, it is desirable to apply some other signal to the horizontal deflection plates. A switch is provided so that the desired signal may be amplified by the horizontal deflection amplifier before being applied to the plates.

An external synchronization input is provided so that an external signal may be used to synchronize the frequency of the saw-tooth sweep voltage with that of the signal being observed. At other times, the signal at the input of the vertical deflection amplifier synchronizes the frequency of the sweep voltage.

REVIEW QUESTIONS

1. Why is amplification of signals necessary?
2. How are amplifiers classified?
3. Explain Class-A operation of amplifiers.
4. What is the main advantage of Class-A operation? Why?
5. Explain the operation of a simple amplifier for one cycle of signal input.
6. Explain Class-B operation.
7. What is the difference between self biasing and external biasing?
8. What is the purpose of an E_g–I_p curve?
9. Explain amplitude distortion.
10. What is one advantage of Class-C operation?
11. In amplifiers, how are component values determined?
12. Why is grid current usually undesirable?
13. Explain how cathode bias is obtained.
14. What would occur if R_{gL} in Fig. 34·3 became shorted? If it opened?
15. What would occur if R_k in Fig. 34·4 opened?
16. What would occur if C_k in Fig. 34·4 became shorted?
17. Explain how a phase shift takes place between grid and plate in a triode.
18. Why is biasing necessary in an amplifier?
19. Explain the difference between voltage and power amplifiers.
20. Name several practical uses of amplifiers.
21. Explain how an electron beam is formed in a cathode-ray tube.
22. How is a screen trace produced on the face of a cathode-ray tube?
23. Explain the principle of operation of the focusing anodes in a cathode-ray tube.
24. How is vertical and horizontal deflection accomplished?
25. Explain the principle of operation of a simple oscilloscope.

CHAPTER 35

RC-COUPLED VOLTAGE AMPLIFIERS

Voltage amplifiers can usually be distinguished from power amplifiers by the amount of resistance in the circuit. In order to allow large amounts of current in a circuit for a given voltage, and thus produce a large amount of power, the d-c resistance must be kept at a minimum. Conversely, in order to produce large voltage variations, high values of resistance are necessary so that even small changes in current will produce the desired effect. Therefore, since a voltage amplifier is designed to produce large voltage variations from small variations in current, it must have large values of a-c and d-c resistances across which these variations will occur.

Of the many types of voltage amplifiers, the *RC*-coupled is commonly used in the audio circuits of receivers, in office communication systems, and in various other electronic equipment.

35·1 Triode RC-coupled Voltage Amplifier. Although they may appear different, all amplifiers operate on the same basic principle. To

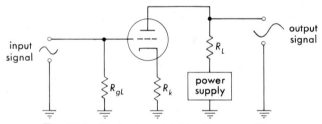

FIG. 35·1   Single-stage triode voltage amplifier.

understand this operation it is necessary to understand the purpose of each component, its approximate size, and the effect upon the circuit if improper values are used.

The object of any audio-voltage amplifier is to develop as much variation in voltage as possible so that it may be made useful. A single-stage triode voltage amplifier is shown in Fig. 35·1. As the input signal swings positive, there will be a large amount of current through the tube and

across the load resistor R_L.   Because the load resistor is large, the drop
across it will appreciably subtract from the normal voltage at the plate of
the tube.   On the negative cycle of input signal, the tube will conduct
less and the drop across R_L will be less.   As a result, the plate voltage will
increase toward a value approaching that of B+.

Because of the value of R_L the voltage variations across it are large,
and the signal at the output of the amplifier will be considerably greater
than at the input.   Voltage amplifiers are always biased Class A, which
means that amplification occurs during the entire 360° of the input signal.
One cycle of output current for one cycle of input signal is shown in Fig.
35·2.   Plate current varies in accordance with the a-c signal, and the

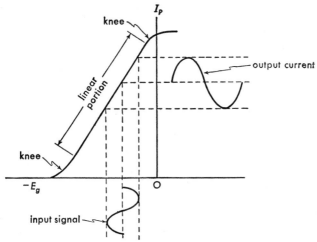

Fig. 35·2   Typical $E_g - I_p$ curve showing knees and linear portion of characteristic
curve.

amplifier is said to be operating on the linear portion of the $E_g - I_p$ curve.
It should be remembered that plate voltage varies inversely with the
input voltage, the two being 180° out of phase.

35·2   Two-stage RC-coupled Amplifier.   When more than one tube
is used to amplify signals, each tube and its associate circuit is called a
stage.   Although a resistor-capacitor network is only one method of coupling one stage to another, tubes are always connected so that the voltage
from the plate of one tube is fed to the grid of the succeeding tube.   Two
or more tubes are used where amplification is required beyond the capacity of one tube.   If the amplification of each tube is 20, the voltage at the
grid of the second tube will be 20 times as great as the voltage at the grid
of the first tube.   Moreover, grid voltage at a third tube would be 400
times as great as the original signal.

A two-stage RC-coupled amplifier is shown in Fig. 35·3. R_{gL} is known as the *grid-leak* resistor and is used as a d-c ground reference for cathode bias.   It also serves to provide a path for electrons accumulating on the grid.   Even when the grid is at a negative potential, some electrons are attracted to it because of gas ions within the tube.   With choice of a high value of grid-leak resistor, grid current will be very low. R_{gL} also forms a portion of the parallel path across which the input voltage is applied to the stage.

R_k is called the cathode resistor and, with C_k, develops bias voltage for the tube.   The cathode capacitor acts to keep the voltage across R_k constant and also to prevent cathode degeneration.   If a triode has a cathode bias voltage of -6 volts with no signal applied and a signal voltage of 6 volts peak amplitude is applied to the tube, it would add to the bias on

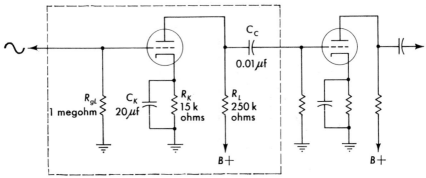

FIG. 35·3   Two-stage RC-coupled amplifier.   Area within dotted lines comprises one stage.

the negative half-cycle and become -12 volts.   On the positive half-cycle it would subtract and cause the bias voltage to become 0 volts. Since plate current would be minimum at -12 volts and maximum at 0 volts, a voltage variation would appear across the cathode resistor that is 180° out of phase with the input signal.   At maximum current more bias is developed across R_k.   Since this occurs during the alternation when the signal voltage is causing a decrease in bias, it effectively subtracts from the signal voltage.   If the voltage variations across the cathode resistor were 2 volts peak amplitude, this would subtract from the 6-volt input signal to produce a voltage variation between grid and cathode of 4 volts.

This effect is usually called *cathode degeneration* because a voltage was fed back to the input 180° out of phase with the input.   Actually, cathode voltage variations canceled 2 volts of input signal, causing degeneration by decreasing the output as shown in Fig. 35·4.

If a bypass capacitor is placed across R_k, degeneration can be eliminated. If C_k is of the proper value, it will pass only the a-c component while bypassing the d-c component through the cathode resistor. If the capacitor has a reactance approximately one-tenth that of R_k, its low reactance will easily pass all a-c variations and thus reduce the signal can-

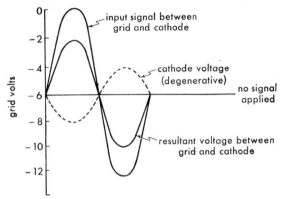

FIG. 35·4 Cathode degeneration resulting from absence of cathode-bypass capacitor.

cellation that would otherwise result from a-c variations appearing across the cathode resistor. The reactance of C_k is also found by the formula

$$X_{C_k} = \frac{1}{2\pi f C_k}$$

The value of C_k is found by the formula

$$C_k = \frac{1}{2\pi f X_{C_k}}$$

where f = lowest frequency signal to be amplified.

Example: What value of cathode capacitor would be used to bypass a 10,000-ohm cathode resistor where 60 cps was the lowest frequency to be amplified?

Solution:
$$X_{C_k} = \frac{R_k}{10} = \frac{10,000}{10} = 1,000 \text{ ohms}$$

$$C_k = \frac{1}{6.28 \times 60 \times 1,000} = 2.65 \ \mu f$$

R_L is the load resistor across which the output-voltage variations develop. These amplified variations are applied to the input of another stage or to a speaker or headphones as intelligence. For purpose of explanation, it will be assumed that plate current is 0.5 ma through the 50,000-ohm plate load resistor with no signal applied to the input of the tube in Fig. 35·5. If power-supply voltage is 300 volts, 25 volts will appear across R_L and 275 volts will be present at the plate of the amplifier. This is referred to as the reference level of the alternating output voltage. If a positive voltage is applied to the grid of the tube and the output current increases to 0.7 ma, 35 volts will be across R_L and voltage at the plate will decrease to 265 volts. If a negative voltage is applied to the grid and I_p decreases to 0.3 ma, only 15 volts will be dropped across the load resistor and E_p will increase to 285 volts. Thus a small input signal has varied the output voltage 10 volts above and below the reference level.

C_c is the coupling capacitor which serves the dual purpose of coupling the output signal to the succeeding circuit while blocking the d-c plate potential from the input of that circuit. While no voltage variations are appearing across R_L, C_c will charge to the value of plate voltage. As current through R_L increases, the voltage at the plate will decrease and C_c

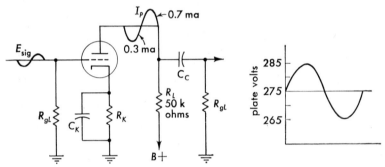

FIG. 35·5 Plate-voltage variations across a 50,000-ohm resistor caused by signal voltage varying I_p 0.2 ma.

will discharge through R_{gL} to ground, power supply, and through R_L. The discharge of C_c causes a voltage to be developed across the top of R_{gL} that is negative with respect to ground. When C_c is charging, voltage developed at the grid is positive with respect to ground.

R_L, C_c, and R_{gL} form a voltage-divider network across which the input voltage to the next stage is developed. X_{C_c} will vary inversely with the frequency of the voltage across C_c.

35·3 Calculation of Component Values. The values of R_{gL} commonly encountered in audio amplifiers range from approximately 100,000 ohms to several megohms; however, in most cases the value is not critical. Since R_{gL} forms a portion of the voltage-divider network, its value should be large as compared to that of R_L so that most of the signal voltage will be developed across it. Common practice is to select R_{gL} of a value approximately 10 times larger than that of R_L.

The values of R_k most commonly encountered in audio amplifiers range from approximately 100 to 15,000 ohms. If the value of R_k is too large, the resulting bias developed may be sufficient to shift the reference level on the E_g–I_p curve and possibly cause distortion. If the value is too small, insufficient bias will be developed and the reference level will be shifted in the opposite direction, also causing distortion.

The value of C_k is determined by the size of R_k and the lowest frequency of the signal to be amplified. If the value of C_k is too small, bias will vary at low frequencies and cathode degeneration will result. The capacitance of C_k should always be computed for the lowest frequency to be amplified.

Most audio amplifiers use a value of load resistor within the range of 25,000 to 500,000 ohms. If the value of R_L is too small, the output voltage developed across it will be small. Conversely, too large a value of R_L would cause a decrease in plate voltage and a resultant decrease in plate current. Values of R_L for the various tubes may be found by referring to the characteristics curves in manufacturers' tube manuals.

The values of C_c most commonly encountered in audio amplifiers range from approximately 0.001 to 0.1 μf. As the frequency of the signal across C_c decreases, the capacitive reactance increases. Therefore, since C_c comprises a portion of the voltage-divider network across which the signal is developed, too small a value of C_c will cause a portion of the signal to be dropped across it at low frequencies. If C_c is too large a value, leakage resistance will be low and leakage current high. This leakage current causes a voltage across the grid-leak resistor that makes the grid positive with respect to the cathode, thus subtracting from the bias, and producing excessive plate current through the tube. Excessive plate current causes the tube to be operated beyond the linear portion of the E_g–I_p curve, and severe amplitude distortion results. C_c is usually selected so that its capacitive reactance is one-tenth the value of R_{gL} at the lowest frequency to be amplified.

35·4 Effects of Component Failures. Some of the most common troubles encountered and their effect upon the circuit are discussed here so that the circuit defect causing an inoperative amplifier may be traced.

If R_{gL} were open, it is possible that a negative charge would accumulate on the grid, causing a decrease in the amplifier output or, possibly, complete cutoff. Under certain conditions the tube might operate on the lower knee of its characteristic curve and produce amplitude distortion. If R_{gL} were shorted, the input signal would be shorted to ground and no voltage variation would appear across the load resistor in the plate circuit.

If R_k were open, there would be a small amount of current due to the leakage resistance of C_k. This is because the coupling capacitor in most audio amplifiers is a low-voltage electrolytic one that has low leakage resistance. Leakage current across C_k would cause an increase in bias that would reduce current and cause plate voltage to increase beyond normal. If R_k were to be shorted, there would be no bias present between grid and cathode and the reference point on the E_g–I_p curve would shift. Plate current would therefore increase, and distortion of the output voltage might result.

If C_k opened, cathode degeneration would result. Since it is connected across R_k, a shorted C_k would produce the same effect as if R_k were shorted.

An open plate load resistor would cause plate voltage to be removed from the tube. If plate voltage is not present, there is no plate current and no output from the stage. If R_L were to be shorted, there would be no plate load impedance across which plate-voltage variations are developed. Therefore, the output would be zero.

If C_c opened, there would be no coupling to the succeeding circuit. If C_c shorted, the grid of the succeeding stage would be at the same potential as the plate of the stage preceding it. Therefore, with a high value of positive voltage on the grid, plate current would be excessive and damage to the tube might result.

35·5   Pentode RC-coupled Amplifier.   Due to secondary emission and the dynatron region, tetrodes are seldom used as RC-coupled amplifiers.

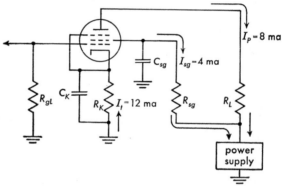

FIG. 35·6   Pentode voltage amplifier showing paths and direction of current through tube elements.

Pentodes used in amplifier circuits have the advantage over triodes of greater amplification. Figure 35·6 shows a pentode amplifier. The suppressor grid is connected to the cathode so that it is at the same potential and, therefore, will be negative with respect to the plate.

In a triode the only current through the tube is that of the plate circuit. Since pentodes utilize a screen grid at a positive potential, cathode current will divide through the plate and screen circuits. Therefore, cathode current can be considered as the sum of currents through these two circuits. If plate current in a pentode was 8 ma and screen current was 4 ma, total cathode current would be 12 ma. Current paths and examples of values are shown in Fig. 35·6.

Circuit Components. R_{sg} is called the screen-grid resistor and is used to reduce the voltage so that screen-grid voltage is less than plate voltage. The value of R_{sg} in audio amplifiers is approximately 50,000 ohms to 3 megohms. If its value is too small, screen-grid voltage will be high and plate and screen-grid currents will increase. As a result, the tube will overheat and output distortion will be produced by excessive current. The value of the screen-grid resistor is determined by the rated screen voltage of the tube as compared to the power-supply voltage. If screen voltage is rated at 250 volts at 5 ma and the power-supply voltage is 300 volts, then the value of R_{sg} must be sufficient to drop 50 volts at 5 ma. $R = E/I = 50/0.005 = 10,000$ ohms.

The purpose of the screen-grid capacitor C_{sg} is to prevent variations in screen-grid voltage that manifest themselves as screen degeneration. If

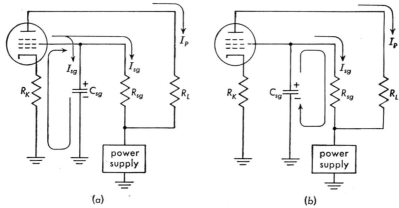

(a)   (b)

FIG. 35·7   (a) Discharge and (b) charge paths of C_{sg} in pentode amplifier.

C_{sg} were not connected, on the positive alternation of input signal there would be an increase in both plate and screen currents. This would cause an increase in voltage across R_{sg}, and the voltage at the screen of the tube would be decreased. Since screen voltage has a pronounced effect upon plate current, the reduced screen voltage would cause a decrease in plate current. Therefore, during the portion of the input cycle when the bias is being effectively reduced by action of the incoming signal, the screen grid is acting in opposition by reducing plate current. With the proper value of C_{sg} connected, it will charge to the value of screen voltage with no signal applied. On the positive alternation of input signal, screen current increases and screen voltage tends to decrease. However, C_{sg} must discharge to this lower value, as shown in Fig. 35·7a. Since there is some screen current to the positive side of C_{sg}, the amount of screen current through R_{sg} is reduced. Therefore, the increase in screen current is compensated for by an amount necessary to discharge C_{sg} to the lower value of screen voltage. On the negative alternation of input signal, screen current and the voltage across R_{sg} decrease. C_{sg} must now charge to the higher value of screen voltage. Since the charge path of C_{sg} through R_{sg} is in the same direction as I_{sg}, the two currents produce an increased voltage across R_{sg} that compensates for the increase in screen voltage.

The direction of charge current for C_{sg} is through R_{sg} and the power supply, while discharge current appears through the tube and comprises a portion of total tube current. Thus when screen current increases, the increase is supplied by the discharge of C_{sg}. When screen current decreases, the discharge of C_{sg} through R_{sg} tends to maintain screen voltage at a constant value.

REVIEW QUESTIONS

1. Explain why different values of resistance are necessary in voltage and power amplifiers.
2. Explain the operation of a triode RC-coupled voltage amplifier.
3. What is cathode degeneration?
4. What determines the value of R_k in a triode RC-coupled amplifier?
5. How is the value of C_k determined?
6. What is the purpose of C_c and how is its value determined?
7. What is the purpose of R_L and how is its value determined?
8. In Fig. 35·3, what would occur if R_{gL} were to open?
9. In Fig. 35·3, what would occur if both R_k and C_k were shorted?
10. What is the purpose of C_{sg} in a pentode amplifier?
11. What is the purpose of R_{sg} in a pentode amplifier?
12. In Fig. 35·7, what would occur if C_{sg} were shorted?
13. In Fig. 35·7, what would occur if R_L was open?
14. Why are tetrodes not used as RC-coupled amplifiers?
15. Explain how C_{sg} prevents screen degeneration in a pentode amplifier.
16. What determines the value of C_{sg}?
17. Explain the action of C_{sg} for one cycle of input signal.
18. What is meant by reference level of alternating-output voltage?
19. In a triode amplifier, what would occur if the value of R_k were too large?
20. In a pentode amplifier, what effect does screen voltage have on plate current?

CHAPTER 36

TRANSFORMER-COUPLED AMPLIFIERS
AND FREQUENCY RESPONSE

In many applications RC coupling between amplifier stages is not practical. Where it is desired to match the impedance between two stages, transformer coupling is used. This form of coupling is also used in tuned-radio-frequency circuits and where phase inversion is desired. Since the secondary voltage is 180° out of phase with the transformer primary voltage, phase inversion is realized between the output and input of successive amplifier stages by using transformer coupling.

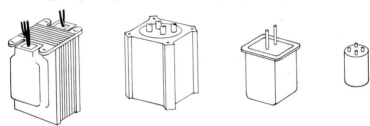

Fig. 36·1   Typical transformers common to amplifiers.

Transformers may be used in amplifiers to couple one stage to another, or between the amplifier and its load. Those used to match the output stage of a radio receiver or a-f amplifier to a loud-speaker or other load are known as *output transformers*. When used between stages they are commonly referred to as *interstage transformers*. With RC coupling the maximum gain of a stage is equal to the amplification factor μ of the tube. By using transformer coupling, the gain of a stage is equal to μ times the ratio between the number of primary and secondary turns of the transformer. This type of coupling also produces greater gain than that of RC coupling by eliminating the drop that would otherwise be present across the plate load resistor.

36·1   Transformer-coupled Amplifier.   It is seen from Fig. 36·2 that the only major difference between transformer- and RC-coupled amplifiers is the absence of R_L, C_c, and R_{gL} with transformer coupling.   While

R_L was used to develop the output-voltage variations with RC coupling, it is not necessary in this application because voltage variations are developed across the transformer primary. C_c is not necessary to block direct current from the grid of the succeeding stage because the power-supply voltage is applied only to the transformer primary and no d-c coupling exists between primary and secondary. R_{gL} in an RC-coupled amplifier serves the purpose of providing a d-c reference for bias and a path for contact current caused by electrons that accumulate on the grid.   With transformer coupling, the input signal is developed across the secondary. Under conditions of no input signal, current through R_k will develop a bias in the same manner as with RC coupling.   When an a-c input signal is

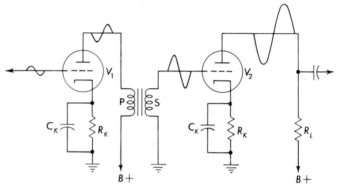

Fig. 36·2   Transformer-coupled amplifier showing phase relationship between voltages applied to succeeding stages.

applied to the grid across the transformer secondary, the resultant voltage between grid and cathode will vary around this level by an amount equal to the peak amplitude of input signal.

As the signal applied to the grid of V_1 in Fig. 36·2 swings positive, there will be current in the plate circuit through the transformer primary, through the power supply to ground and back to the cathode.   Primary current will build up a flux that causes a voltage to be induced in the secondary.   As current through V_1 increases, there is an increase in plate current and a decrease in voltage at the plate.   Therefore, the voltage across P swings negative as the voltage to the grid of V_1 swings positive. Since there is a 180° phase shift between P and S, the voltage at the grid of V_2 is in phase with the voltage at the grid of V_1.

36·2 Transformer Characteristics.   The impedance of the transformer-primary winding varies with frequency, causing the transformer-coupled amplifier to have one main disadvantage.   For example, if a transformer primary had an inductance of 5 henrys, at 60 cycles the inductive reactance would be

$$X_L = 2\pi f L = 6.28 \times 60 \times 5 = 1{,}884 \text{ ohms}$$

At 1,000 cycles the inductive reactance would be

$$X_L = 2\pi fL = 6.28 \times 1,000 \times 5 = 31,400 \text{ ohms}$$

At 100,000 cycles the inductive reactance would be

$$X_L = 2\pi fL = 6.28 \times 100,000 \times 5 = 3.14 \text{ megohms}$$

Since output-voltage variations are developed across the transformer primary, nonuniform amplification will result if a wide range of frequencies is to be considered. A graph showing comparison of RC- and transformer-coupled amplifiers is shown in Fig. 36·3.

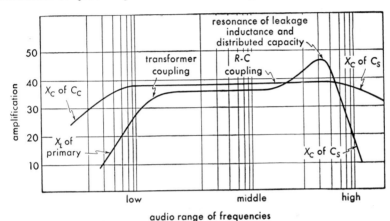

FIG. 36·3 Frequency-response graph for RC-coupled and transformer-coupled amplifiers. (C_s is shunt capacitance. See Sec. 36·5.)

To reduce eddy-current and hysteresis losses to a minimum, audio-frequency (a-f) transformers are constructed on laminated magnetic cores of special alloys.

Tubes used with transformer-coupled amplifiers usually have a plate resistance of approximately 10,000 ohms so that the shunting effect on the primary will not be too great at the low frequencies. In order to produce high amplification at low frequencies, the primary impedance should be large at these frequencies as compared to the plate impedance of the tube. Since the plate resistance of pentodes is larger than that of triodes, pentodes offer greater shunting effect at low frequencies and are therefore very seldom used where high gain is desired.

Although a high turns ratio between secondary and primary would increase the amount of signal between two stages, such a turns ratio produces distortion and loss of low-frequency gain. For example, a 6:1 step-up transformer would have the same number of secondary turns as a 1:1 transformer but only one-sixth as many primary turns. Therefore, its primary impedance is much lower at low frequencies, causing a loss in gain due to the shunting effect of the tube. Transformers with a 2:1 step-up ratio usually produce greater amplification and better frequency reproduction than those of higher step-up ratios.

36·3 Advantages and Disadvantages. *Advantages.* One advantage of the transformer-coupled amplifier is its ability to produce a high output from a low power-supply voltage. In the RC-coupled amplifier, R_L offers a high d-c resistance across which a voltage is developed that subtracts from the output voltage. With transformer coupling, the only loss is the small d-c drop across the primary. This allows a higher plate voltage to be applied to the tube than could be applied with RC coupling from the same value of supply voltage.

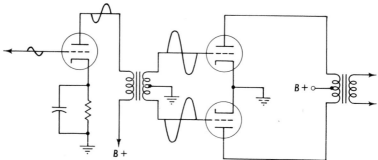

Fig. 36·4   Transformer coupling employed to furnish out-of-phase voltages to two stages in push-pull arrangement.

By eliminating the high value of R_{gL} and substituting the low d-c resistance of a transformer primary, there is less loss in input signal than with RC coupling.

Where it is desired to operate a succeeding stage in push-pull, a circuit arrangement where two out-of-phase signals are applied to two separate stages, the transformer-coupled amplifier provides another advantage. By using a center-tapped secondary, two signals, 180° out of phase, are applied to the grids of two tubes as shown in Fig. 36·4. To accomplish this with RC coupling, or to produce phase inversion between the output of one stage and the input to another, an additional stage would be required. Transformer-coupled amplifiers also have the advantage of allowing an easy means of matching the impedance of a tube with its load impedance. They also make it possible to obtain increased amplification through the use of step-up transformers.

Disadvantages. While poor frequency response is the only major disadvantage of transformer-coupled amplifiers, the considerations of increased cost, additional weight, and space requirements sometimes make them less desirable than RC-coupled amplifiers.

36·4 Effects of Component Failure. Transformers are usually designed for use with a particular type of tube, usually a triode. Primary inductance of an interstage transformer is approximately 5 henrys with a d-c resistance of from about 50 to several hundred ohms. If too few primary turns are used, there will be a reduction in the amplification of low frequencies; if too many primary turns are used, there will be an increase in the distributed capacitance, which causes a loss in signal voltage across the secondary at high frequencies.

If the primary became open, there would be no plate voltage applied to the tube and the output would be zero. If the primary shorted, there would be no plate load impedance across which output-voltage variations are developed and the output would be zero. If only a few turns of the primary were shorted, primary impedance would decrease with a resultant poor response at low frequencies. A grounded primary would remove plate voltage and reduce the output to zero.

If the secondary opened, there would be no voltage developed across it to be applied to the input of the succeeding stage. If the secondary shorted to ground there would be no signal developed across it; however, if only a few secondary turns became shorted, there would be a reduction in the amount of signal applied to the grid and a resultant reduction in output.

36·5 Frequency Response of RC-coupled Amplifiers. As shown in Fig. 36·5, with the application of a signal to the grid of a tube, the output voltage from that tube can be represented by an equivalent circuit.

The output signal from the tube is shown as the output from an alternator with the R_p of the tube represented by a series resistor that corresponds to the internal resistance of the alternator. Output voltage from the alternator is computed as the signal input times the amplification factor of the tube.

The equivalent circuit at low frequencies is shown in Fig. 36·5a. At this range of frequencies the capacitive reactance of C_c is high, causing a portion of the signal to be dropped across it. Therefore, the equivalent circuit shows the output voltage as appearing across R_L, C_c, and R_{gL}, all of which comprise a voltage-divider network.

At the middle range of frequencies, shown in Fig. 36·5b, the equivalent circuit is more simplified. The reactance of C_c is so small at these frequencies that its effect is negligible and not considered. Therefore, the output voltage can be considered as appearing across only the load and grid-leak resistors.

High frequencies are affected by shunt capacitances. Tube interelectrode and various other distributed capacitances are present at all times; however, they only become evident at the high frequencies. Since a capacitor can be defined as any two conductors separated by a dielectric, capacitance is always present between the wires and various components of the amplifier. Because capacitive reactance decreases with an increase in frequency, the reactance of the various shunt capacitances becomes so low that R_L is effectively shunted out. Since R_L is in parallel with these capacitances and becomes shunted out, they are called shunt capacitances C_s. The equivalent circuit for the high frequencies is shown in Fig. 36·5c, with C_c not present since it offers no opposition at middle and high frequencies.

The frequency-response curve shown in Fig. 36·3 shows the amount of amplification of both RC- and transformer-coupled amplifiers for low, middle, and high frequencies within the audio range. At middle frequencies, maximum amplification is realized. The reduction in amplification at low frequencies is caused by the capacitive reactance of C_c, while at high frequencies it is caused by the capacitive reactance of C_s.

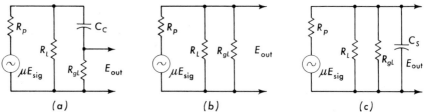

(a) (b) (c)

Fig. 36·5 Equivalent circuits for RC-coupled amplifiers at (a) low, (b) middle, and (c) high ranges of frequencies.

36·6 Frequency Response of Transformer-coupled Amplifiers.

Pentodes are seldom used in this type of amplifier due to their high R_p and the resultant difficulty in matching the impedance of the transformer primary.

As with RC-coupled amplifiers the output circuit can be represented by an equivalent circuit. Figure 36·6a represents the equivalent circuit for transformer-coupled amplifiers at the low frequencies. With a turns ratio of about 2:1, the transformer primary will have a low inductive reactance at the low range of frequencies. Therefore, only a small output voltage is developed across the primary.

At the middle range of frequencies, the equivalent circuit can be represented as shown in Fig. 36·6b. At this range the primary impedance increases until it is approximately equal to that of R_p of the tube and perfect impedance matching exists, allowing output voltage to be maximum.

Shunt capacitance has an effect upon output voltage at the higher range of audio frequencies. In addition, other component reactions have to be considered. R_s in Fig. 36·6c denotes the resistance of the secondary winding of the transformer, which has an effect upon amplification at high frequencies. Also, due to an increase in the number of lines of flux produced, some do not cut the secondary winding, and leakage inductance L_L results. Shunt capacitance has the same effect as with RC-coupled amplifiers—a loss of amplification at high audio frequencies.

The "hump" near the high end of the frequency-response curve of Fig. 36·3 is due to a condition of resonance existing between the leakage inductance and the distributed capacitance. This occurs at some point

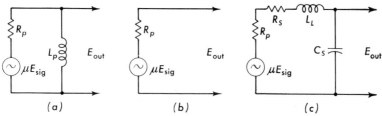

(a)   (b)   (c)

FIG. 36·6   Equivalent circuit for transformer-coupled amplifiers at (a) low, (b) middle, and (c) high ranges of frequencies.

between the middle and high range of frequencies, resulting in a gain of the stage that is equal to the Q of the circuit times the applied voltage.

36·7   Voltage Gain in RC-coupled Amplifiers.   The prime purpose of an audio-voltage amplifier is to obtain as much amplification, or *gain*, as possible with minimum distortion. Since linear amplification is found only at the middle frequency range, gain formulas are shown as being applied only to that range. Voltage gain A is the ratio between output and input voltages. By formula,

$$A = \frac{E_{out}}{E_{sig}}$$

The load on the tube shown in Fig. 36·5b at middle frequencies is comprised of R_L and R_{gL}. For all practical purposes this is a parallel com-

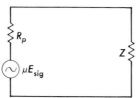

FIG. 36·7   Equivalent circuit of RC-coupled amplifier at middle range of frequencies.

bination that can be represented as shown in Fig. 36·7. The voltage of the alternator is the signal voltage times the amplification factor of the tube, and circuit current can be computed by dividing the alternator voltage by load impedance, plus the plate resistance of the tube. By formula,

$$I_p = \frac{\mu E_{sig}}{R_p + Z}$$

Since plate current through the load impedance produces the output voltage, output voltage can be determined by the formula

$$E_{\text{out}} = I_p Z$$

Substituting for I_p in the above formula,

$$E_{\text{out}} = \frac{\mu E_{\text{sig}} Z}{R_p + Z}$$

Dividing both sides of the equation by E_{sig},

$$\frac{E_{\text{out}}}{E_{\text{sig}}} = \frac{\mu Z}{R_p + Z}$$

Substituting A for $\dfrac{E_{\text{out}}}{E_{\text{sig}}}$,

$$A = \frac{\mu Z}{R_p + Z}$$

This formula requires that the amplification factor of the tube be known and is suitable only for triodes, since their amplification factor is independent of plate voltages. With pentodes, any change in plate voltage will vary the amplification factor of the tube.

36·8   Voltage Gain in Transformer-coupled Amplifiers.   The equivalent circuit for the middle frequency range of a transformer-coupled amplifier is shown in Fig. 36·6b. For a 1:1-turns-ratio transformer, output voltage will be the input signal times the amplification factor of the tube. With a step-up ratio transformer the gain for the middle range of frequencies can be determined by the formula

$$A = n\mu$$

where n = turns ratio of the transformer.

REVIEW QUESTIONS

1. Explain the difference between RC-coupled and transformer-coupled amplifiers.

2. What are the advantages of transformer-coupled amplifiers over RC-coupled amplifiers?

3. What are the disadvantages of transformer-coupled amplifiers?

4. What effect does tube plate resistance have upon transformer-coupled amplifiers?

5. What limits the turns ratio of interstage transformers?

6. What would be the effect upon the circuit if a few turns of an interstage transformer primary were shorted?

7. What causes the "hump" in the frequency-response curve of a transformer-coupled amplifier?

8. Why are pentodes seldom used in transformer-coupled amplifiers?

9. How are high frequencies affected by shunt capacitances in RC-coupled amplifiers?

10. In RC-coupled amplifiers, what causes the reduction in amplification at low and high frequencies?

11. Explain why RC-coupled amplifiers have better frequency response than transformer-coupled amplifiers.

12. Explain how the output circuit of a transformer-coupled amplifier can be represented by an equivalent circuit.

13. What is gain?

14. How is bias obtained with transformer coupling when the grid-leak resistor has been removed from the circuit?

15. What would be the effect upon the circuit if the secondary of an interstage transformer became shorted?

16. Explain how it is possible to obtain greater output from a supply voltage with transformer coupling than with RC coupling.

17. How is voltage gain determined in transformer-coupled amplifiers?

18. How is voltage gain determined in RC-coupled amplifiers?

19. What would be the effect upon the circuit if a few turns of both primary and secondary of an interstage transformer were shorted?

20. Why is the frequency response of a transformer-coupled amplifier less linear than that of an RC-coupled amplifier?

CHAPTER 37

AMPLIFIER CIRCUITS

The input signals to amplifiers have been shown as basic wave forms, or pure sine waves. However, in some of the more advanced types of circuits, waves of many different and complex shapes are used. The more frequently used of these are called *square, saw-tooth,* and *peaked* waves. Their composition must be understood in order to study their effects.

Where complex wave forms are to be amplified, distortion of three types might result. In addition to *amplitude distortion, phase distortion* and *frequency distortion* are sometimes present in circuits using improper value of components. It is necessary to understand the characteristics and causes of each type so that circuit defects may be corrected.

37·1 Harmonics. Any periodic wave, or one that repeats itself in definite intervals of time, is composed of sine waves of different frequencies and amplitudes. All these added together comprise what is known as the *fundamental* and its *harmonics.* The sine wave that has the same frequency as the complex periodic wave is called the fundamental, while the waves of higher frequency are harmonics of the fundamental. Harmonics are designated as a number of times as high as the frequency of the fundamental. For example, the second harmonic has a frequency twice as high as the fundamental, the third harmonic three times as high, the fourth harmonic four times as high, and so on. Since the first harmonic is of the same frequency as the fundamental, it is never referred to as a harmonic.

Square Waves. It is sometimes desirable to apply a square wave to the input of an amplifier or other circuit instead of a sine wave. Figure 37·1 shows a square wave and the fundamental frequency and harmonics necessary to develop such a wave. In Fig. 37·1a a square wave and a sine wave of the same frequency are shown. While the sine wave is comprised of only one frequency, square waves are made up of many frequencies. In Fig. 37·1b another sine wave B has been added to the original sine wave. Since B is of lesser amplitude and three times the frequency of A, the resultant wave form will be as shown by C. Here it should be noted that the shape of the square wave is being approached by a combination of a fundamental and a third harmonic. Wave form C is also shown in Fig. 37·1c and is combined with a fifth harmonic D to produce the resultant wave form E. The sides of the resultant wave form are becoming steeper, and the square wave form is being approached. With the addition of a seventh harmonic shown in Fig. 37·1d, the sides of

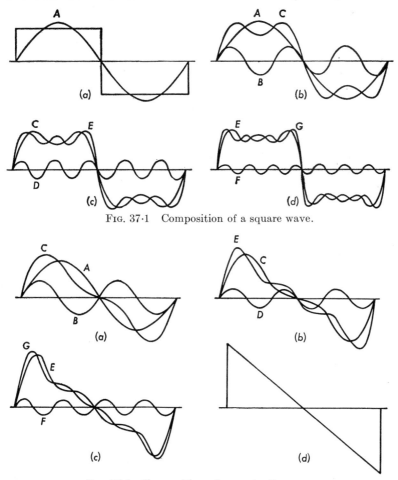

FIG. 37·1 Composition of a square wave.

FIG. 37·2 Composition of a saw-tooth wave.

the resultant wave form G are even steeper. Therefore, it is seen that with the addition of more odd harmonics, the wave form would eventually be square. Any square wave, then, is comprised of a fundamental and an infinite number of *odd* harmonics.

Saw-tooth Waves. In many advanced types of circuits it is desirable to use *saw-tooth* waves which are made up of a fundamental and an infinite number of both odd and even harmonics. Figure 37·2a shows a sine wave

A to which second harmonic *B* of smaller amplitude is added to result in wave form *C*. Figure 37·2*b* shows a third harmonic *D* added to *C* to produce the resultant *E*. It should be noted that the peak of wave form *A* has now been moved to the side, and the shape of a saw-tooth wave form is being approached. By adding the fourth harmonic *F* in Fig. 37·2*c* to *E*, wave form *G* is produced. Therefore, the addition of an infinite number of harmonics will finally produce the saw-tooth wave form shown in Fig. 37·2*d*.

Peaked Waves. The sine wave of Fig. 37·3*a* is combined with the third harmonic *B* to produce the resultant *C*. Note that the wave form *B* of

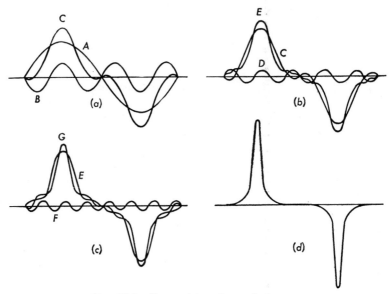

FIG. 37·3 Composition of a peaked wave.

Fig. 37·3*a* is 180° out of phase with wave form *B* of Fig. 37·1*b*, which aided in producing a square wave. In Fig. 37·3*b* and *c* the addition of fifth and seventh harmonics aids in making the peak of the resultant wave form higher and the sides steeper. Therefore, the addition to the fundamental of an infinite number of odd order harmonics will produce the resultant peaked wave shown in Fig. 37·3*d*.

37·2 Distortion. In some circuits distortion is desirable in order to produce the several complex wave forms. However, certain circuits are designed to have as little distortion as possible.

Frequency Distortion. This type of distortion occurs when some frequency components of a signal are amplified more than others or when only one component is amplified. Figure 37·4 shows a signal comprised of a fundamental and third harmonic applied between grid and cathode of an amplifier, which produces frequency distortion. The wave form of the output shows that only the fundamental frequency has been amplified. Therefore, since the third harmonic does not appear in the output, it is not an exact reproduction of the input and frequency distortion has resulted. This type of distortion is usually caused by too low a value of C_c, which presents a high capacitive reactance at the low range of frequencies to be amplified.

FIG. 37·4   Example of frequency distortion.   (a) Fundamental and third harmonic. (b) Fundamental only.

Phase Distortion. Figure 37·5 shows a signal comprised of a fundamental and third harmonic applied to the input of an amplifier, which produces phase distortion. Although the resultant amplitude of both components has been increased by identical amounts, the output wave form is not an exact reproduction of that applied to the input. It is seen that the phase of the third harmonic has been shifted with respect to the fundamental with the resultant wave form as shown. Phase distortion is caused by the coupling circuits between amplifier stages. Although the phase of the sine waves is shifted, this has no effect upon the wave

FIG. 37·5   Example of phase distortion.   (a) Fundamental and third harmonic. (b) Phase of third harmonic shifted with respect to fundamental.

form of the output. However, when complex wave forms are applied to a stage, shifting of phase will produce an output that is not an exact reproduction of the input, and special coupling circuits are required to minimize this effect.

Amplitude Distortion. Often called *nonlinear* amplification, this type of distortion usually results when a vacuum tube is operated on the nonlinear portion of its characteristic curve. If a plate-current change is not directly proportional to a change in grid voltage, distortion in the amplitude of the signal will result. This can be caused by operating the tube on the knees or any nonlinear portion of its curve. If it is operated below cutoff, plate current will be zero for any value of negative grid voltage.

Also, if operated beyond plate-current saturation, there will be no increase in plate current even though the grid swings maximum positive. Amplitude distortion for two operating points along the E_g–I_p curve is shown in Fig. 37·6.

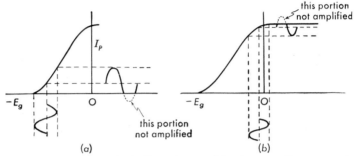

Fig. 37·6   Examples of amplitude distortion resulting from nonlinear operation.   (a) Negative peak clipping.   (b) Positive peak clipping.

37·3   Coupling Methods. In addition to being coupled by transformers or RC networks, amplifier stages may be coupled by inductance-capacitance networks, or the output of one stage may be coupled directly to the next.

Impedance Coupling. This type of coupling, shown in Fig. 37·7, is obtained by replacing the load resistor with an inductance. Since the inductance has a lower d-c plate resistance than would a plate load resis-

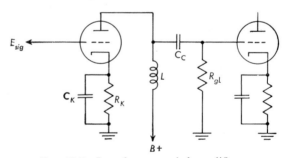

Fig. 37·7   Impedance-coupled amplifiers.

tor, the tube operates at a higher plate voltage, and higher amplification is possible than with RC coupling. However, since the plate load impedance is now higher for the a-c components of plate current, higher amplification will result in proportion to the frequency, and amplification for all frequencies will no longer be uniform. As frequency increases, the X_L of L will increase. And since amplification depends upon the voltage developed across the load impedance, for a given amount of input the output will be greater at high frequencies than at low frequencies.

Direct Coupling. This type of coupling is effectively used for amplifying low frequencies because the impedance of the coupling circuit does not vary with frequency. In a directly coupled amplifier the plate of one stage is connected directly to the grid of the next without the use of a coupling capacitor, transformer, or inductance. A typical circuit is shown in Fig. 37·8. By use of a special voltage-divider network, the requirement of proper polarity for tube elements is met. The basic requirements are that the plate of V_1 have a positive voltage with respect to its cathode and the grid of V_2 be negative with respect to its cathode.

Grid bias for V_1 is obtained by connecting the cathode at a positive point along the voltage divider with respect to the grid. When a signal is applied to the input, the drop between points A and B will develop a positive voltage at the cathode of V_1. The plate of V_1 is connected to

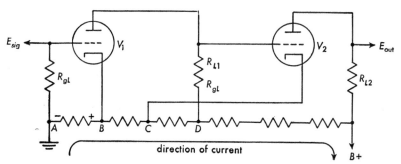

Fig. 37·8   Directly coupled amplifiers.

the voltage-divider network through R_{L1}, which also serves as the grid-leak resistor for V_2. Point D is approximately halfway between the extreme ends of the voltage divider so that one-half the available supply is used for the plate of V_1. The cathode of V_2 is connected at point C in order to obtain the proper grid-biasing and plate-operating voltages. Connections at points C and D are critical in that the voltage drop across R_{L1} produces the required grid bias. The plate of V_2 is connected through R_{L2} to the most positive point on the voltage divider.

Due to the complexity of this type of circuit, critical adjustment is necessary to ensure proper voltage at the tube elements, and the power-supply voltage must be approximately twice the value required by either tube. Since the output-voltage variations at the plate of V_1 will appear at the grid of V_2, this circuit serves as a distortionless Class-A amplifier with uniform frequency response over a wide range.

37·4   Volume Controls. Since the amplitude of all signals is not constant and no amplifier produces a constant level of amplification, some means of controlling gain is necessary. This is accomplished by means of a *volume control* which maintains the output of an amplifier at a con-

stant level.   Often referred to as *gain controls,* two methods of controlling
the output of an amplifier are shown in Fig. 37·9.   Volume controls are
potentiometers placed either in the input or output circuits of a stage.
Their value is such that at normal operation they produce the same circuit effect as the component they replace.   In Fig. 37·9a the volume control is shown as replacing the grid-leak resistor in the input circuit.   Since
bias is developed across R_k owing to current through the tube, there will
be a reference level of bias between cathode and grid.   As a signal is

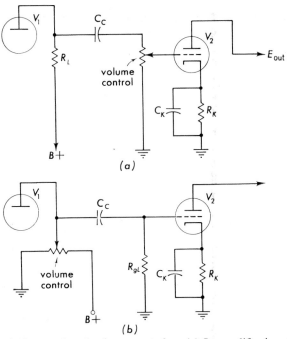

FIG. 37·9   Typical examples of volume controls.   (*a*) In amplifier input circuit.   (*b*)
In amplifier output circuit.

applied to the grid, the bias level will vary by an amount equal to the
peak amplitude of the signal.   If the peak level of the input signal is
reduced, there is less signal to be amplified and the output-voltage variations will decrease.   Conversely, any increase in input signal will cause
an increase in output voltage.   Therefore, since the output voltage of an
RC-coupled amplifier appears across the voltage-divider network consisting of R_L, C_c, and R_{gL}, it is seen that any change in the value of R_{gL} will
affect the amplitude of that voltage.   Any portion of the voltage appearing across the potentiometer can be applied to the grid.   If the arrow,
corresponding to the moving arm of the potentiometer, is moved in a
direction toward ground, the amplitude of input signal will be decreased.

Moving the arm to the extreme ground side would place the grid at ground potential, and output voltage would be reduced to zero. Conversely, moving the arm in a direction away from ground will increase the input signal, with a resultant increase in output voltage.

The example in Fig. 37·9b is another method of controlling volume by varying the amount of supply voltage applied to the plate of a tube. Any change in value of plate voltage will result in a corresponding change in output-voltage variations, thus effectively changing the gain of the stage.

37·5   Decoupling Networks.   Where more than one tube is supplied by a common supply, voltages at the plates (or screens) of the various

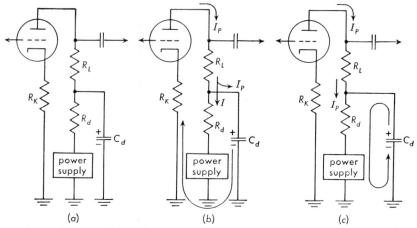

(a)   (b)   (c)

Fig. 37·10   (a) Plate-decoupling network showing (b) discharge and (c) charge paths of decoupling capacitor for decrease and increase in plate voltage.

tubes are sometimes unequal. This is because the variations at the plates of successive tubes are greater due to increased amplification. In order to maintain power-supply voltage constant at the elements of all tubes and to keep the a-c component out of the power supply, *decoupling circuits* are used. Sometimes called filter circuits, they consist of a resistor in series with the plate or screen, and a bypass capacitor. If the power-supply voltage of Fig. 37·10a is constant, there will be a voltage drop across R_d that subtracts from the voltage at the plate of the tube, and C_d will charge to that value with a polarity as shown. Should the power-supply voltage decrease due to an increase in the I_p of another stage, there will be a decrease in voltage at the plate of the tube and C_d will discharge to this new value. The discharge path of C_d is in the direction shown in Fig. 37·10b. There is some plate current to the positive side of C_d, reducing the amount of current through R_d, and the voltage drop across R_d is effectively reduced. Therefore, with a decrease in power-supply voltage there has been a compensating decrease in the drop across R_d, which tends to maintain a constant value of voltage at the plate of the tube.

Should there be an increase in power-supply voltage due to a decrease in the I_p of another stage, C_d must charge to this new value. The charge path of C_d, shown in Fig. 37·10c, is in the same direction through R_d as plate current. The two currents, being additive, increase the drop across R_d that compensates for the increase in power-supply voltage and maintains E_p constant.

This RC network also serves to prevent plate-voltage variations from reaching the power supply. Alternating currents are bypassed to ground through C_d, while R_d offers as high a resistance to a-c components as practicable for the power-supply voltage available.

The values of decoupling resistors most commonly found in a-f amplifiers range from approximately 5,000 to 50,000 ohms. If too large a value is used, there will be a large decrease in plate voltage; if too small, there will be a decrease in the RC time of the network and insufficient decoupling will result. The value of decoupling capacitors ranges from approximately 2 to 20 μf. They are usually selected to provide a capacitive reactance that is one-tenth the resistance of the decoupling resistor at the lowest frequency to be amplified.

37·6 Trouble-shooting Amplifiers. While a detailed explanation of the operation of a signal generator, shown in Fig. 37·11, is not essential to

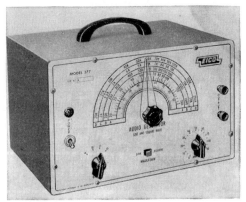

Fig. 37·11   Signal generator.   (*Electronic Instrument Company, Inc.*)

this text, it can be described as a unit of electronic equipment that generates a signal of frequencies within the audio range. Because both amplitude and frequency of output signal can be determined by settings of volume control and calibrated dial, it finds invaluable use in trouble-shooting a-f amplifiers.

By connecting the signal generator as shown in Fig. 37·12, many characteristics of the amplifier can be determined. If the volume control on the signal generator is set for a definite value, the amount of amplification can be determined by comparing the signal input of an amplifier with the output as indicated by the a-c voltmeter. Since the signal generator can be varied over the entire range of audio frequencies, frequency response of an amplifier may be determined by plotting a graph that denotes amplitude of output for the a-f band. The useful frequency range of the amplifier will be indicated by the portion of the graph with a fairly flat response.

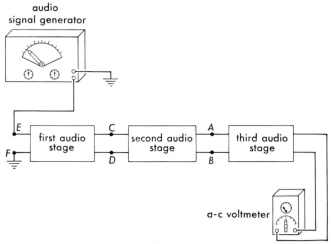

Fig. 37·12 Method of connecting signal generator and a-c voltmeter for determining characteristics of amplifiers.

The most common use of the audio-signal generator is to isolate the inoperative stage of a defective amplifier. For example, if a signal is applied from the signal generator to points A and B of Fig. 37·12 and there is no output shown on the a-c voltmeter, the third stage is inoperative. If an output voltage is indicated, then connect the signal generator to points C and D. If there is no output, then stage 2 is inoperative. By beginning at the input of the last stage and progressing to the input of the first stage, any inoperative stage may be thus isolated.

37·7 Loud-speakers. One of the most common loads into which an audio amplifier works is the *loud-speaker*. This is an electrodynamic device which converts the a-f currents into sound waves that can be heard by the human ear. These sound waves are motion-of-pressure waves through the medium of air that strike the eardrum and produce sensation.

While all loud-speakers operate on the same principle, one of the most common is the *dynamic* type shown in Fig. 37·13. In this type of loud-speaker a permanent magnet produces a strong magnetic field in the air gap. A coil of wire with relatively few turns is suspended in the air gap and attached to a paper cone. The outer edge of the cone is corrugated, allowing the cone to move in and out freely.

The amplifier output is connected to the coil of wire, which is known as the *voice coil*, through an output transformer. As the audio-frequency

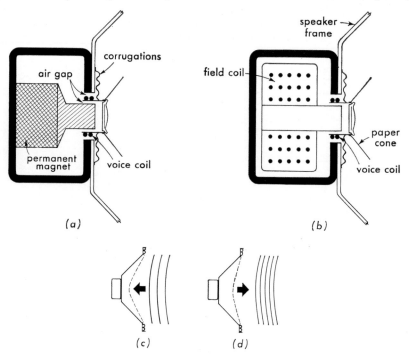

Fig. 37·13 (*a*) Dynamic loud-speaker. (*b*) Electro-dynamic loud-speaker. (*c*) Rarefied air resulting from cone moving in. (*d*) Compressed air resulting from cone moving out.

currents flow through the voice coil, a magnetic field with a changing polarity is generated. At one instant this field will *aid* the field of the permanent magnet and the cone will move *inward* and reduce the pressure of air directly in front. When the voice-coil field changes polarity and *opposes* the field of the permanent magnet, the cone will be pushed *outward* and the air in front compressed. This constant movement of the cone generates sound pressure waves at the frequency of the a-f currents that are perceptible to the human ear.

The *electrodynamic* loud-speaker operates on exactly the same principle except that it uses a field coil instead of the permanent magnet. A direct current is applied to the field coil wound on a soft iron core, producing a magnetic field that either aids or opposes the field produced by the voice coil.

REVIEW QUESTIONS

1. Define amplitude distortion.
2. What are harmonics?
3. Of what frequencies are square waves comprised?
4. Of what frequencies are peaked waves comprised?
5. What is frequency distortion and how is it caused?
6. What is phase distortion and how is it caused?
7. Explain impedance coupling.
8. Explain direct coupling.
9. What is the purpose of a decoupling network?
10. Explain the action of a decoupling network in accomplishing its purpose.
11. For what purposes are signal generators used in trouble-shooting amplifiers?
12. Why does nonuniform amplification result from impedance coupling?
13. Explain the theory of operation of volume controls.
14. How is it possible to isolate a defective amplifier stage with a signal generator?
15. How is distortion used to advantage?
16. How is the value of decoupling capacitors and resistors determined?
17. With direct coupling, why is critical adjustment of voltages necessary?
18. What is the difference between the frequencies comprising square waves and those comprising peaked waves?
19. Explain how the frequency response of an amplifier may be determined.
20. By using a signal generator and an a-c voltmeter, a certain amplifier was found to have an amplification of 500. How would this indicate whether or not the amplifier was performing according to specifications?

CHAPTER 38

MISCELLANEOUS AND HI-FI AMPLIFIERS

In addition to the types of amplifiers previously discussed, there are several others designed for specific purposes. While voltage amplifiers are designed to produce large output-voltage variations in the plate circuits for a small value of input signal, power amplifiers are designed to deliver maximum power to a load circuit while voltage amplification remains incidental.

Some amplifier circuits are designed to operate as phase inverters in which the output voltage is of the same wave form as the input signal but of opposite polarity. In some instances two input signals of opposite polarity are required where only one is available. By applying this signal to a *phase-inverter* stage, a signal of the same wave form but of opposite polarity is obtained. By combining this with the original signal, two opposite polarity signals are thus available. It is also often desirable to convert a single input to a push-pull output. This is accomplished by a *paraphase* circuit, which produces two signals of opposite polarity.

The more important types of miscellaneous amplifiers will be considered here only in minor detail. Since the principle of operation of all amplifiers is basically the same, it is only necessary to observe circuit differences in order to understand operation.

38·1 Power Amplifiers. In voltage amplifiers the amplified plate-voltage variations are used as the input signal to a succeeding stage, and plate current is relatively small. Power amplifiers, however, are designed to furnish large amounts of current to a load such as loud-speakers, headphones, or the input circuit to a transmitter. Since the d-c resistance of the load must be small in order to allow large amounts of power-producing current, load impedances usually range from approximately 1,000 to 20,000 ohms.

In voltage amplifiers there is no loss in power between stages because the output of one stage is connected to the grid of the next. Since there is no current in the grid circuit, no power is consumed. If there was grid current, there would be a loss of power that would have to be supplied by the preceding stage. In power-amplifier circuits there is a loss of power in the load circuits due to current which is necessary for their operation. Therefore, the power consumed by a loud-speaker must be supplied by the power amplifier.

Voltage amplifiers are usually operated Class A, while power amplifiers may be operated either Class A, Class B, or Class AB. Either triodes, pentodes, or beam-power tubes may be used in power-amplifier circuits. They may be operated singly, in parallel, or in push-pull, depending upon the amount of output power required. Power amplifiers must be capable of carrying large amounts of current through a small value of load impedance. Where voltage amplifiers develop large voltage variations across a high value of load impedance, power amplifiers develop large current variations across a low value of load impedance.

A typical power-amplifier stage is shown in Fig. 38·1 as supplying current to a loud-speaker. The input signal to the power amplifier is supplied by a voltage amplifier. The two circuits are similar in all respects

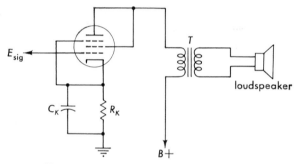

FIG. 38·1   Typical power-amplifier stage.

except for the value of plate load impedance. Plate-current variations across the primary set up a flux that produces voltage variations in the secondary that are converted into audible sound by the loud-speaker. Direct plate current through the output transformer primary produces a power loss through heating of the amplifier tube and output transformer. And since some power is consumed through operation of the loud-speaker, the total power loss must be supplied by the power amplifier.

38·2   Push-pull Amplifiers. Amplifiers connected in push-pull circuits are generally used in a-f power applications where it is desired to increase power output. They also serve to produce more uniform amplification than is usually obtained from single-tube amplifiers. With single-tube amplifiers, for an even value of grid-voltage variation there will sometimes be a larger increase in plate current for a positive grid voltage than decrease in plate current for a negative grid voltage. Therefore, the output will not be an exact reproduction of the input. Also, the nonsymmetrical plate variations often produce a wave form that is twice the fundamental frequency of the signal being amplified. By using a push-pull arrangement it is possible to balance out this second harmonic frequency. The signal from the output of V_1 in Fig. 38·2 is applied across the primary of T. During each half-cycle the grids of V_2 and V_3 are of opposite polarity. Since an alternating voltage is being applied across the transformer, the voltage across the secondary is constantly changing and the grids are always 180° out of phase. The second harmonic frequencies are canceled, since their current components set up magnetic fields in opposition. The power output of a push-pull amplifier is approximately twice that of a single-tube amplifier.

Triodes operated Class A in power-amplifier circuits usually have low efficiency, low distortion, and low power output. Pentodes in Class-A

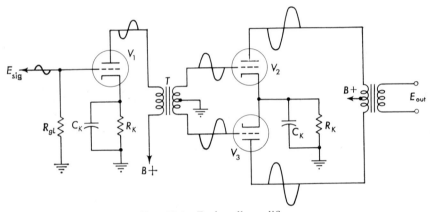

FIG. 38·2   Push-pull amplifier.

power-amplifier circuits usually have higher distortion, higher efficiency, and higher power output than triodes. Class-AB amplifiers are operated with higher plate and screen voltages than those with Class-A operation. As a result, higher power output is obtained. With Class-B operation, plate current is nearly zero when no signal is being applied. Because of this, plate current is held within the limits of the tube's plate-dissipation rating, and higher output is obtained than that available from Class-A operation.

38·3   Phase Inverters.   Any circuit which produces an output voltage with a polarity opposite to that of the input signal is called a phase inverter. For example, if the positive portion of a sine wave were applied to the input of a phase inverter, the output wave form would be a negative alternation. Although the term "phase" is usually associated with time, there is no appreciable difference in time between the input and output of a phase inverter. A circuit of this type is referred to as one which shifts polarity by 180°.

Transformers act as phase inverters by shifting the polarity of primary to secondary voltage by 180°. Vacuum tubes connected in conventional amplifier circuits also act as phase inverters. Since a positive alternation is produced in the plate circuit for a negative alternation of input signal, the polarity between input and output of an amplifier is shifted by 180°.

If two signals of equal amplitude but of opposite polarity are required for a push-pull circuit, a center-tapped transformer secondary may be employed. However, an alternate arrangement like that shown in Fig. 38·3 may also be used. Since the voltage across R_1 and R_2 is equal to the voltage across the transformer secondary, grounding the point between these resistors has the same effect as a center-tapped secondary. The only requirement is that R_1 and R_2 be of equal value.

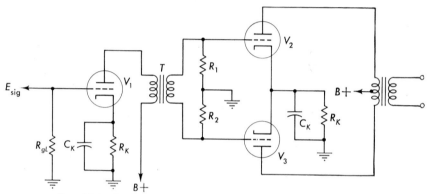

FIG. 38·3   Push-pull amplifier using voltage-divider input.

Vacuum tubes are more desirable than transformers as phase inverters. The use of a transformer in this application is limited by the amount of distortion it produces and the amount of power loss across it. Since the ratio of transformation varies with frequency, distortion will be produced. The amount of power loss will be determined by frequency, since the impedance of the transformer will increase with an increase in frequency.

Where vacuum tubes are used only for the purpose of phase inversion, some means must be provided for reducing the natural amplification to a 1:1 ratio. This can be accomplished by introducing degenerative feedback into the circuit by omission of the usual cathode bypass capacitor, as shown in Fig. 38·4. Another method is to reduce the amplitude of signal applied to the grid by an amount that will compensate for the amplification of the tube. This is similar in principle to that of a volume control, in which the input signal is developed across only a portion of the grid resistor. If the tube shown in Fig. 38·5 has a gain of 10, then the value of R_2 should be such that the voltage across it is one-tenth maximum

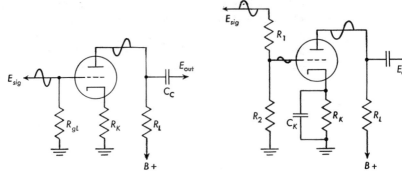

FIG. 38·4 Amplifier using cathode de-generation to reduce gain.

FIG. 38·5 Amplifier using voltage-di-vider input to reduce gain.

signal voltage. Therefore, to compensate for the tube's gain of 10, the input signal is reduced to one-tenth.

38·4 Paraphase Amplifiers. An amplifier which converts a single input into a push-pull output is known as a paraphase amplifier. This can be accomplished by the circuit in Fig. 38·6, in which the plate load is divided equally between plate and cathode. By selecting R_2 and R_3 of equal values, the voltage across them is the same and total tube current appears through both. The polarity of the output across R_4 is opposite

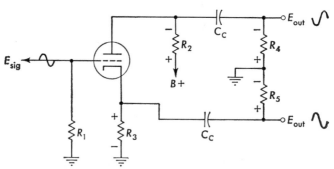

FIG. 38·6 Single-tube paraphase amplifier.

to that of R_5 because R_5 is connected to the positive side of R_3 and R_4 is connected to the negative side of R_2.

An alternate arrangement is shown in Fig. 38·7. R_3 is bypassed by C_k to avoid degeneration in this portion of the circuit and acts to limit the operating bias. R_2 and R_4 are equal in value, resulting in equal ampli-tude outputs across R_5 and R_6. When R_3 is not bypassed, its value should be such that added to R_4 it equals the resistance of R_2.

Two-tube Paraphase Amplifiers. Tubes connected in this type of cir-cuit are utilized for amplifying and phase inverting. V_1 of Fig. 38·8 amplifies the input signal and applies it to V_2 for phase inverting, thus providing two outputs of opposite polarity. R_7 of the voltage-divider network should be of a value sufficient to decrease the input signal to the grid of V_2 by an amount equal to its gain.

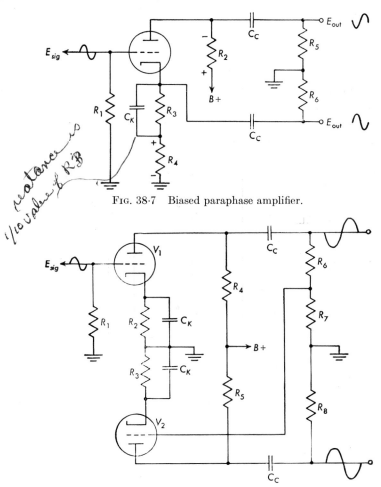

reactance of R_3 should be
$1/10$ value of R_3

FIG. 38·7 Biased paraphase amplifier.

FIG. 38·8 Two-tube paraphase amplifier.

Another two-tube paraphase-amplifier circuit utilizes the voltage difference between the output of two tubes as input voltage to the phase-inverter circuit. Tube V_1 of Fig. 38·9 acts as an amplifier; its output is applied across the voltage-divider network comprised of R_7 and R_9. The voltage across R_9 is applied to the grid of V_2, whose output is passed through C_4 and applied across R_8 and R_9. Thus, the outputs of both V_1 and V_2 are applied across the common resistor R_9 and are opposite in polarity. With R_7, R_8, and R_9 of equal value, the voltage at the grid

of V_2 is the difference between the outputs of V_1 and V_2. Therefore, the
voltage appearing across R_9 will also be the resultant voltage difference
between the opposite-polarity outputs of the two tubes.

38·5 Video Amplifiers. Video amplifiers are distinguished from conventional amplifiers in that they are required to amplify a wide range of
frequencies within and beyond the audio band. Where an audio amplifier is required to amplify frequencies within a range of approximately 20
to 20,000 cps, a video amplifier must amplify frequencies of approximately 5 to several million cps. Video amplifiers must be designed to
amplify without distortion signal inputs of square, saw-tooth, and various
other wave forms.

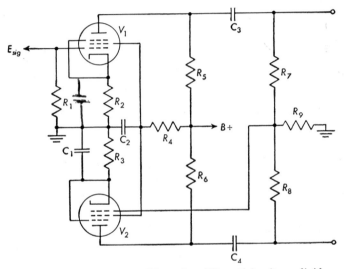

FIG. 38·9   Paraphase amplifier using differential voltage-divider.

Where transformer and impedance coupling may be used in other types
of amplifiers, RC coupling is used in video amplifiers because of its better
frequency response. The only major circuit difference lies in the values
of components. In the RC-coupled amplifier circuit shown in Fig. 38·10,
the high-frequency response is limited by the output capacitance C_1,
distributed capacitance C_2, and input capacitance C_3. Low-frequency
response is limited by the RC time of C_c and R_{gL} which must be long as
compared to the lowest frequency to be amplified. Distributed capacitance is reduced by using short wiring leads that are properly spaced.
Interelectrode capacitance is reduced by employing tubes with very low
interelectrode capacitance.

High-frequency Compensation. It was learned that the loss of gain at
the high range of frequencies with RC coupling was caused by the low
X_C of the shunt or distributed capacitances. Being in parallel with the

plate load impedance, these capacitances had a shunting effect upon the load and caused a reduction in gain. This effect can be minimized by the addition of a small inductance L in series with R_L, as shown in Fig. 38·11a, or in series with C_c, as shown in Fig. 38·11b. When used in series with C_c, it resonates with the input capacitance at high frequencies. This causes an increase in current with a resultant increase in gain at

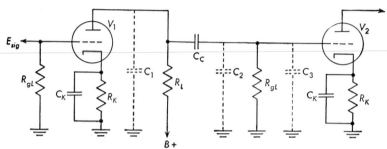

Fig. 38·10 RC-coupled amplifier showing components affecting frequency response.

these frequencies, thereby increasing high-frequency response. By using a combination of these two methods, as shown in Fig. 38·11c, the advantages of both are obtained.

Low-frequency Compensation. The value of C_c is sufficiently large to present a capacitive reactance at the lower frequencies that causes a decrease in gain. The capacitive reactance of C_c could be reduced by using a larger value; however, an increase in its physical size would result in an increase in stray capacitance that affects high-frequency response.

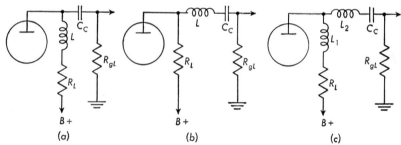

Fig. 38·11   Methods of compensating for loss of gain at high frequencies. (*a*) High-frequency shunt compensation. (*b*) High-frequency series compensation. (*c*) High-frequency shunt-series compensation.

Therefore, the maximum allowable limit for the value of C_c is about 0.1 μf. Low-frequency response may be improved by the addition of a compensating filter in series with the load resistor. Its action is to increase the plate load impedance at the low frequencies, thus maintaining constant gain. It also compensates for the shift in phase that otherwise results from the RC time of C_c and R_{gL}. This is shown in Fig. 38·12.

Bias Considerations. In ordinary amplifiers the grid bias is obtained by the drop across R_k as a result of tube current through it. Cathode degeneration is prevented by bypassing R_k with a capacitor C_k, which also serves to maintain grid bias constant. The reactance of C_k for ordinary amplifiers is about one-tenth the resistance of R_k so that it will provide a low impedance path for the a-c components. In video amplifiers the value of C_k should be greater so that too large a capacitive reactance will not be presented at the lower frequencies. The RC time of R_k and C_k should be long as compared to the lowest frequency to be amplified.

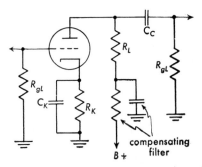

Fig. 38·12   Method of compensating for loss of gain at low frequencies.

38·6   Decibels. The difference between two sound intensities is called the *bel*, in honor of Alexander Graham Bell, who invented the telephone. The unit *decibel* (db), which is one-tenth of a bel, is the difference between two sound intensities which is just barely discernible to the human ear. This unit is commonly used to express the gain or loss of various circuits or equipment. The total gain of a circuit may be found by adding the individual decibel gains of each circuit stage. The decibel represents a power ratio that is referred to some power level. This reference, or zero, level is determined by the manufacturer of the equipment. For example, it is common for telephone engineers to use 6 mw as a reference level. Some broadcast engineers use 12.5 mw as a standard. However, if it is understood that these are merely reference levels, the output can be determined as a certain number of decibels above zero level. For example, if a manufacturer rated an amplifier at 40 db, it would mean that the power-output capability was 40 db above reference level. Computation of decibel gain is not considered essential to this text. Decibel gain varies logarithmically with variations in sound intensity. This means that the ear responds more readily to changes in volume of sound at low levels than at high levels.

It is common practice to specify the power output of an amplifier in addition to its over-all decibel gain.   Unless otherwise specified, 0 db is usually considered to be 6 mw.

38·7 Hi-Fi Amplifier. In this field, fidelity is defined as the degree of exactness with which a system or unit reproduces an input signal. High fidelity (hi-fi) is a term generally applied to an audio component, amplifier, or system.   Ideally, it is the ability to reproduce faithfully, that is, with a minimum of distortion, the full audio range of frequencies. While many units or systems are incapable of reproducing this range of frequencies, the term is nevertheless loosely applied to them.

The audio range of frequencies is from about 20 to 20,000 cps.   However, the human ear is rarely capable of perceiving frequencies above 15,000 cps.   Therefore any system capable of reproducing signals of frequencies up to this limit can be considered as being hi-fi.   Actually, hi-fi can be any reproduction of sound that is pleasing to the listener. While research has proven that many animals are capable of detecting frequencies above the audio range, a system designed to reproduce signals above 15,000 cps would have little value to the human listener.

Any hi-fi system can be compared to a chain, because the reproduction will be no better than the capabilities of the weakest unit.   By this it is meant that an amplifier with a response of from 20 to 20,000 cps would be wasted if used with a loud-speaker with a response of only 50 to 10,000 cps. The over-all response of the system would be no better than that of the loud-speaker.   Further, if these two units were used in a system that had a phonograph *pickup* with a 100 to 8,000 cps response, the over-all response would be reduced to that of the pickup.   A pickup is the device which is actuated by the variations in the grooves of a record and delivers a-f power to an amplifying system.   It usually consists of a tone arm, cartridge, and needle.

While hi-fi systems can be extremely expensive, there are some available at relatively low cost.   Amplifiers, for example, can be purchased in "kit" form and assembled by almost anyone interested in building his own hi-fi system.   If the result is pleasing to the ear, then it is truly hi-fi. Manufacturers have gone to great lengths to produce a large variety of systems to please a correspondingly large variety of tastes.

Typical Amplifier. Figure 38·13 shows one of the many amplifier kits available.   With a 12-watt output and a frequency response of 30 to 15,000 cps, it is capable of reproducing almost all audio frequencies perceptible to the human ear.   The input J_1 is for use with a tuner, a crystal or ceramic phonograph cartridge, or a tape recorder.   The input J_2 is used only for a record player with a magnetic cartridge.   Since many tape recorders perform better when used with an external amplifier, an amplifier of this type may be used for this or several other purposes.

FIG. 38·13   Typical hi-fi amplifier.   (*Allied Radio Corporation.*)

FIG. 38·14   Amplifier chassis wiring.   (*Allied Radio Corporation.*)

However, to realize the full-frequency response of the amplifier, all associated equipment should have equal or better response.

Circuit Operation. The amplifier can be operated at full-rated output by introducing a signal from a tuner or crystal cartridge at *J*-1, or a signal from a magnetic cartridge at *J*-2 (Fig. 35·15). The switch *S*-1 selects either tuner input or phonograph preamplifier, grounding out the input not in use to prevent pickup of undesirable noises from this source. *R*-1 is the terminating resistor for magnetic cartridges.

The circuits of *V*-1 provide preamplification and equalization for magnetic cartridges. Equalization is necessary in order to provide a uniform response when using either input *J*-1 or *J*-2. The two sections of *V*-1 are connected as a cascade amplifier to obtain the high gain needed. Both cathodes are grounded to provide better shielding and thus reduce hum. Bias is developed across the grid-leak resistors *R*-2 and *R*-7. Equalization is achieved by plate-to-plate feedback through *C*-3 and *R*-4, with *R*-5 limiting the bass boost to prevent rumble.

V-2 is connected as a modified self-balancing phase inverter and provides two signals, 180° out of phase, for driving the push-pull output stage. Phase inversion takes place because the cathode of *V*-2A is connected to the cathode *V*-2B, with the grid of *V*-2B in effect grounded. *V*-2A operates as a conventional amplifier, with a positive signal at the grid resulting in a negative signal at the plate and a positive signal at the cathode. This results in a positive output signal at the plate of *V*-2B at the same instant that the output of *V*-2A is negative.

Precision results are achieved with ordinary-tolerance components because of the self-compensating features of this circuit. Self-balancing features include the use of a common cathode resistor *R*-15 to provide a large amount of degeneration. The mid-point between *R*-18 and *R*-19 is used as a reference level for balancing purposes. When the two halves of *V*-2 are perfectly balanced, this point will be at zero potential. However, if one half has more gain than the other, a correction signal appears at this point that is applied to the grid of *V*-2B and corrects the unbalance.

One signal from *V*-2 is coupled through *C*-11 to the grid of *V*-3. The other signal from *V*-2, 180° out of phase with that applied to *V*-3, is coupled through *C*-12 to the grid of *V*-4. These output tubes are connected for push-pull operation, with cathodes connected to the opposite ends of the output transformer primary. This results in combining the output of both *V*-3 and *V*-4 in the output transformer, which reduces distortion by canceling out both hum and harmonics.

Feedback voltage is taken from the secondary of *T*-2 and serves the dual purpose of reducing distortion and providing tone control. This voltage is diverted by filters, with high frequencies being applied to the TREBLE control and low frequencies to the BASS control. Moving either

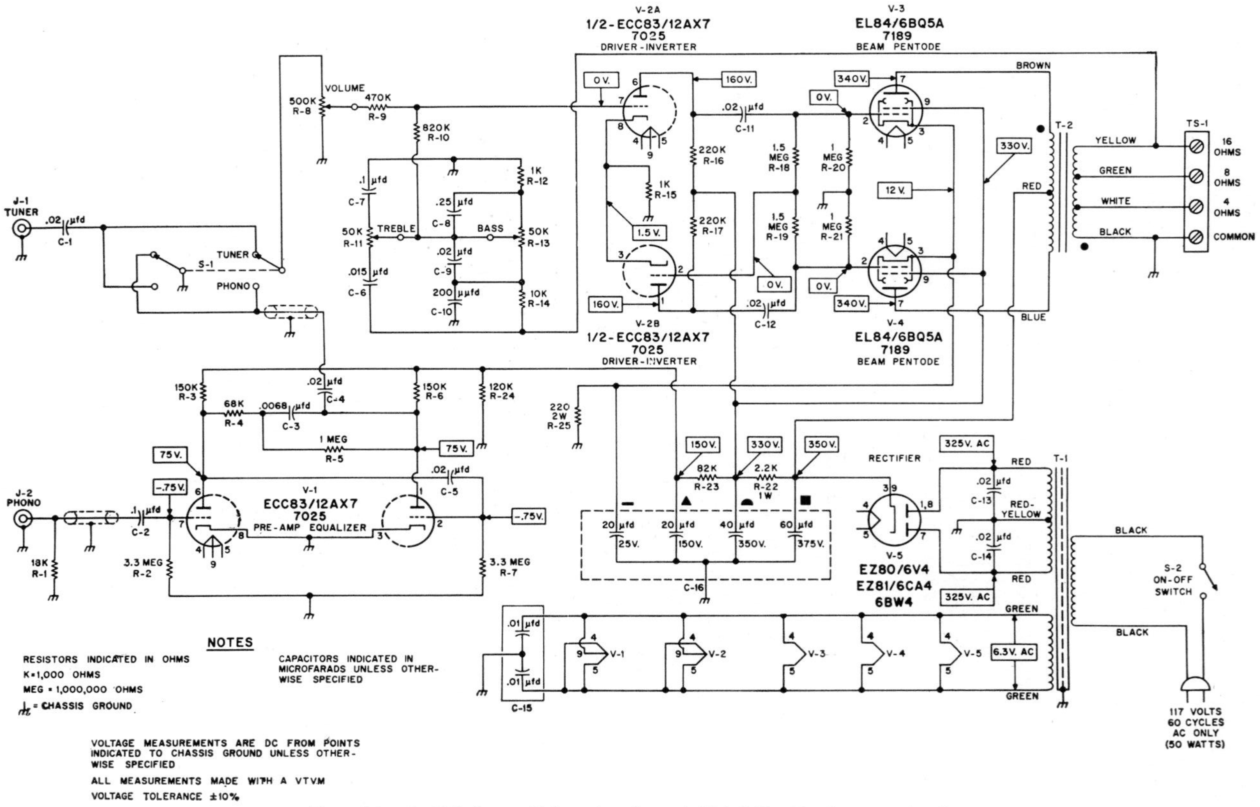

Fig. 38-15   Hi-fi amplifier circuit.   (Allied Radio Corporation.)

376

'control clockwise (upward on the schematic in Fig. 38·15) reduces the amount of feedback on the selected frequencies. This causes an increase in either treble or bass.

The output transformer T-2 has a 10,000-ohm primary to match the impedance of the output tubes. The secondary has taps to match 4-, 8-, or 16-ohm speakers.

The power supply includes the power transformer T-1, an indirectly heated rectifier tube V-5, and a multisection filter capacitor C-16. The capacitors C-13, C-14, and C-15 further improve the power supply by filtering out rectifier "hash."

REVIEW QUESTIONS

1. Explain the difference between power and voltage amplifiers.
2. Explain the operation of a phase inverter.
3. What is the purpose of a paraphase circuit?
4. Explain the operation of a push-pull amplifier.
5. Why are vacuum tubes more desirable than transformers as phase inverters?
6. Explain the operation of a paraphase amplifier.
7. How do video amplifiers differ from ordinary amplifiers?
8. How is high-frequency compensation accomplished in video amplifiers?
9. How is low-frequency compensation accomplished in video amplifiers?
10. Explain the difference between bias for ordinary amplifiers and bias for video amplifiers.
11. Explain decibels.
12. What is the plate-load impedance of a power amplifier?
13. Explain how the second harmonic frequencies of single-tube amplifiers are eliminated.
14. What are the advantages of operating power amplifiers Class B rather than Class A?
15. How is interelectrode capacitance reduced in video amplifiers?
16. Why is RC coupling always used with video amplifiers?
17. How is distributed capacitance reduced in video amplifiers?
18. In phase-inverter circuits, how is it possible to replace a center-tapped transformer with two resistors and still obtain two signals of opposite polarity?
19. What determines the values of C_k used in video amplifiers?
20. Explain what is meant by hi-fi.
21. In the circuit of Fig. 38·15, what would be most likely to occur if R_{10} opened?
22. In the circuit of Fig. 38·15, what would be most likely to occur if R_{17} became shorted?
23. In the circuit of Fig. 38·15, what would be most likely to occur if R_{16} increased in value to 300 K ohms?

CHAPTER 39

OSCILLATORS

In the study of transmitters it will be found that the oscillator plays an important part. A *transmitter* can be described as a device which supplies r-f energy of sufficient power to be radiated by an antenna over long distances. The frequency of this energy is determined by a vacuum tube and associated circuit components operating as an *oscillator*. Although all transmitters do not employ the same principles of operation, there are basic functions characteristic of all transmitters.

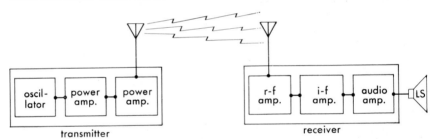

Fig. 39·1   Simple communication system.

Home radio or television sets receive transmitted energy of a specific frequency within the radio-frequency spectrum. This is considered the useful spectrum of radio waves and is divided into major bands. Where the radio receiver is designed to receive r-f waves within the "broadcast" band, the television receiver is designed for reception of higher-frequency waves. Therefore, each transmitter must be designed for a specific purpose.

Figure 39·1 is a "block" diagram of a simple communication system. The oscillator is the unit of the transmitter which generates an r-f signal that is amplified by two or more power amplifiers and radiated into space by the transmitting antenna. The receiving antenna picks up the signal and transfers it to the receiver where it is converted into a-f sound-pressure waves that can be heard by the human ear.

39·1   Introduction to Oscillators.   Although oscillators perform definite functions in both receiver and transmitter circuits, in all cases they can be considered as devices used for the purpose of generating frequencies. The frequencies generated are determined by the value of circuit components.

Any oscillator functions on the ability of a vacuum tube to amplify. By applying a portion of the amplified output to the grid circuit as regenerative feedback, grid-circuit losses can be overcome and the circuit will "oscillate." Therefore, any amplifier supplying its own input is called an *oscillator*. However, before an amplifier will oscillate, energy fed back to the grid must be of sufficient amount to overcome losses in the grid circuit. It must also be in phase with the voltage at the grid. Since there is a 180° phase shift between the input and output of any amplifier, a means of effecting regenerative feedback must be provided.

Considerations. If the foregoing requirements are met, the circuit will oscillate and provide an output signal of constant amplitude. The most important function of an oscillator is frequency stability. Since the stability of transmitter output frequency is dependent upon stability of oscillator frequency, it is important that any oscillator generate a signal of constant frequency.

One major cause of frequency instability in oscillators results from improper loading of the tank circuit. If power is taken from the tank, Q decreases and the circuit losses increase. Since these losses determine the difference between circuit-operating frequency and tank-resonant frequency, loading the tank beyond certain limits will change the operating frequency of the oscillator. This condition is minimized by lightly loading the oscillator with a fixed load. Once the frequency is determined for a particular load, it will thereafter remain constant.

Oscillator stability is also affected by changes in ambient or local temperatures around the frequency-determining elements of the circuit. This is because the capacitors and inductors change their physical dimensions with a change in temperature around them, thereby changing the resonant frequency of the tank. This effect is reduced by placing the oscillator, or tank, in a temperature-controlled oven.

Changes in supply voltage will also have an effect upon frequency. Since R_p is calculated by dividing plate-voltage changes by plate-current changes, it is seen that a change in supply voltage will effect a change in plate current and R_p. The effect is much the same as that of improper loading. A change of current in the tank circuit causes a change in Q which also changes frequency. This effect is minimized by using a regulated power supply.

Mechanical vibration will cause the frequency of an oscillator to shift. Tube capacitance is determined by spacing of elements. If this spacing is constantly changing through mechanical vibration, total circuit capacitance will change and affect the frequency. Also, coils wound on air cores undergo a change in the value of inductance if subjected to mechanical vibration. In order to maintain frequency stability and reduce this effect, oscillator circuits are often shock-mounted in rubber mounts to eliminate vibration.

39·2 Tank-circuit Oscillations.

A tank circuit will generate a sine wave of a frequency determined by the value of L and C components. If C of Fig. 39·2a is charged to its maximum value and then connected across L, it will discharge in the direction shown, causing current through L. This current sets up a magnetic field around the inductor which will exist until the capacitor has completely discharged. After current ceases, there is no means of sustaining the magnetic field and it will start to collapse. As the field collapses, it tends to maintain current in the same direction as during the discharge of C (Fig. 39·2b). This charges C with a polarity opposite to that of the original charge. The capacitor again discharges and sets up about the inductance a field which in turn collapses and recharges the capacitor. This flywheel, or "oscillatory," action continues until all the energy stored in the capacitor has been expended due to power losses in the tank circuit. Therefore, it is seen that oscillations will not be sustained unless sufficient energy is supplied to the tank. The basic vacuum-tube oscillator utilizes the amplifying ability of a tube to supply this energy.

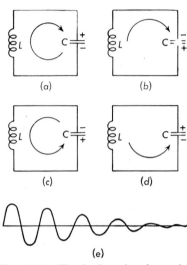

FIG. 39·2 Flywheel action in tank circuit and resultant wave form if losses not sustained. (a) C discharging through L, setting up magnetic field. (b) Magnetic field around L collapsing and recharging C with opposite polarity. (c) C discharging through L, setting up field with polarity opposite to that of (a). (d) Magnetic field around L collapsing and recharging C to original polarity. (e) Resultant tank-circuit wave form.

Although different in design, all oscillators are basically the same in that they are comprised of a tank circuit, r-f amplifier, feed-back circuit, and timing circuit. The tank circuit is merely a combination of inductor and capacitor in parallel. The r-f amplifier is of ordinary design. The feed-back circuit provides a means of transferring energy from the plate to tank circuit in proper phase and amplitude to sustain oscillations. In a vacuum-tube oscillator the timing circuit is the bias circuit which governs the amount of energy supplied to the tank for sustaining oscillations.

39·3 Armstrong Oscillator. This type of oscillator, shown in Fig. 39·3, was the first practical vacuum-tube oscillator ever developed. Plate direct current appears through the tube, through L_2, the r-f choke and power supply, to ground. Plate alternating current appears through the tube and through L_2, where it sets up a magnetic field. The remainder appears through the r-f choke (rfc) and is bypassed to ground through the filter capacitor in the power supply. There is grid current in oscillators, because they are always operated Class C. Path of grid current is from cathode to grid through R_{gL}, L_1, to ground, and back to the cathode. Output voltage is taken from across L_1, and grid-leak bias is obtained from the combination of R_{gL} and C_{gL}. With this form of bias the oscillator is considered as self-starting; that is, the circuit will oscillate as soon as operating potentials are applied. If fixed bias was used, some means

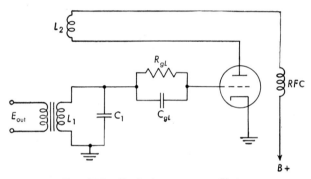

Fig. 39·3   Basic Armstrong oscillator.

of external excitation would be required before the circuit would oscillate.

Operation. When operating voltages are first applied to the tube, there will be plate current through L_2, which sets up a magnetic field around it. L_2 is positioned so that coupling exists between it and L_1; therefore a voltage will be induced in L_1 of such a polarity that the grid is made positive. This causes an increase in current which increases the magnetic field around L_2. This action continues until plate saturation is reached, at which time the magnetic field around L_2 remains steady.

During the time the grid is positive, C_{gL} charges to the value of voltage developed across the tank circuit. When plate saturation is reached, it has charged to the value of voltage across C_1 and L_1. When there is no longer an increase in voltage across L_1, there is nothing to sustain the magnetic field and it begins to collapse. This tends to produce current in the same direction through the tank, and C_1 charges to a negative potential on the grid side.

As the voltage across L_1 decreases, the grid becomes less positive and the charge on C_{gL} flows through R_{gL}.   This maintains bias on the tube through the entire cycle due to the long time constant of the combination. The discharge of C_1 through L_1 induces a magnetic field around it with a polarity that adds to the negative charge on C_{gL}, thus holding the tube at cutoff during this portion of the cycle.

The discharge of C_1 causes a field to be built up around L_1 that collapses upon complete discharge of C_1 and maintains current in the same direction.   In so doing, C_1 is recharged with the grid side positive, thus completing the first cycle of operation.

As the grid side of C_1 becomes positive, tube bias is reduced and it will conduct.   Again a field is built up around L_2 which induces a voltage in L_1 that is additive to the voltage across the tank circuit.   This amount of

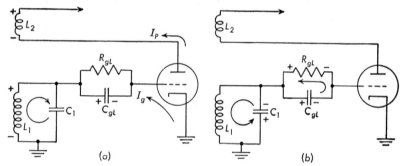

(a)   (b)

Fig. 39·4   Armstrong oscillator.   Action of tank and grid-leak capacitor in either allowing tube to conduct or maintaining cutoff conditions.   (a) Grid side of tank positive.   Tube conducting and drawing grid current. C_1 and C_{gL} charging until tube biased to cutoff.   (b) Grid side of tank negative. C_1 and C_{gL} discharging, biasing, and keeping tube cut off until bias reduced to a point where tube can again conduct.

feed-back voltage is sufficient to overcome losses and thereby sustain oscillations.   When the voltage across the tank is positive enough to overcome the charge on C_{gL}, the tube again draws grid current and C_{gL} will recharge.   At this point of operation, C_1 is completely charged and must discharge through L_1.   This discharge builds up a field around L_1 while C_{gL} discharges through R_{gL} and maintains bias on the tube.   As C_1 becomes less positive, at some point it will be unable to overcome the bias and the tube will be at cutoff.   When C_1 is completely discharged, the field about L_1 will collapse and recharge C_1 with an opposite polarity.

In summary, the charge and discharge of C_1 through L_1 either adds to or subtracts from the bias developed across the combination of R_{gL} and C_{gL}.   Therefore, the tube is varying between the conditions of saturation and cutoff with plate current pulsating through L_2.   Current through the tank is first in one direction and then in the other.   The frequency of these oscillations of current is dependent upon the size of L_1 and C_1.   The pulses of plate current shock-excite the tank and thereby maintain oscillations by overcoming losses in the grid circuit. Feedback is by means of the magnetic field existing between L_1 and L_2. The amount of feedback can be controlled by varying the coupling between the two coils. By varying either L_1 or C_1 of the tank, the frequency of the oscillator may also be varied.

39·4 Hartley Oscillator. The Hartley oscillators shown in Fig. 39·5 are commonly used for developing r-f signals in transmitters and have better frequency stability than the Armstrong oscillator. In Fig. 39·5a the plate supply is connected in series with the plate section and is called a *series-feed* circuit. In Fig. 39·5b the plate circuit provides paths for both a-c and d-c components and is called a *parallel-feed* circuit. The latter type is more commonly used because only the a-c component of plate current appears across any portion of the tank circuit. Except for

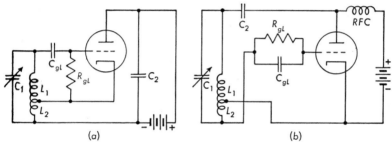

FIG. 39·5 Basic Hartley oscillator circuits. (a) Series feed. (b) Parallel feed.

this respect, the operation of both types is identical. As with the Armstrong oscillator, amplified energy from the plate circuit is fed back to the grid circuit through inductive coupling. Although in the Hartley oscillator only one coil is used, for purposes of explanation it is shown as two sections with L_1 in the grid circuit and L_2 in the plate circuit. The amount of feedback is dependent upon the number of turns in the plate circuit as compared to the number of turns in the grid circuit. By increasing the number of plate turns, the amount of feedback will be increased.

Operation. When operating potentials are applied, the tube will start to conduct and current will increase toward maximum. This current through L_2 and back to the cathode will set up a magnetic field around L_2. Since inductive coupling exists between L_2 and L_1, a voltage will be induced in L_1 with a polarity that causes the grid side of the tank to be positive. This further increases plate current until saturation is reached. During the time the grid is positive, grid current is through R_{gL}, and C_{gL} is charging. When saturation is reached, the magnetic field around L_1 and L_2 will no longer be sustained and will collapse. This charges C_1

with a polarity which, with the discharge of C_{gL} through R_{gL}, biases the tube at cutoff. Thereafter, circuit operation is essentially the same as that of the Armstrong oscillator previously discussed. The charge and discharge of C_1 through L_1 and L_2 either adds to or subtracts from the bias developed across the RC network in the grid circuit, causing the tube to vary between conditions of plate-current saturation and cutoff. The purpose of C_2 in the series-feed circuit is to bypass a-c components of plate current from the power supply.

In the parallel-feed circuit the rfc keeps the a-c component out of the power supply, while C_2 acts to prevent direct current from being present in the a-c circuit.

39·5　Colpitts Oscillator. The Colpitts oscillator shown in Fig. 39·6 has the best frequency stability of all basic oscillator circuits. Feedback

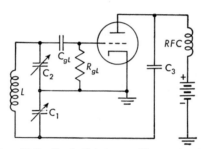

FIG. 39·6　Basic Colpitts oscillator circuit.

from plate to grid circuit is accomplished by means of electrostatic coupling. Except for the manner of feedback, this circuit is similar to the parallel-feed Hartley oscillator.

When operating potentials are applied, the tube will conduct and there will be a voltage across rfc that decreases the voltage at the plate. This decrease in plate voltage leaves C_3 and C_1 charged to a higher value than source voltage, and they will start to discharge through the tube. The discharge path is in a direction that causes the grid to swing positive and increase plate current until plate saturation is reached. At this point plate current remains constant, and there is no further current in the feedback or tank circuit. The field around L will then collapse, charging C_2 and starting tank-circuit oscillations. Thereafter, the charge and discharge of C_2 will add to or subtract from the bias developed across the RC network in the grid circuit. The tube will then vary between conditions of saturation and cutoff as in any other oscillator circuit.

Grid-excitation voltage is obtained from across C_2 and is 180° out of phase with plate voltage, since it is taken from the opposite side of the tank. Total tank capacity is equal to the resultant capacity of C_1 and C_2 in series. Frequency of oscillations is determined by the size of C_2, while the amount of feedback is determined by the size of C_1. Increased frequency stability is due to the design of the tank circuit, which features a reduced L/C ratio with a resultant higher circuit Q. However, C_1 and C_2 must be variable capacitors. This necessitates two adjustments for proper operation and makes the Colpitts oscillator less convenient to operate as a variable-frequency oscillator than the single-adjustment Hartley circuit.

39·6 Crystal Oscillators. *Crystals.* A property of Rochelle salts, quartz, and tourmaline is known as the *piezoelectric* effect. This is the ability of a substance to produce a difference of electrical potential between opposite sides when subjected to a mechanical ~~strain~~ *stress* that changes its physical dimensions. Conversely, this property causes the

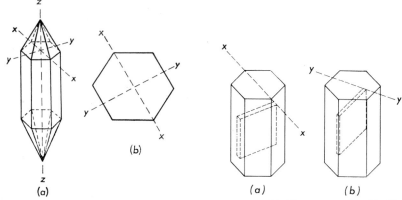

FIG. 39·7   Natural shape of quartz crystal showing axes.

FIG. 39·8   (*a*) X-cut crystal. (*b*) Y-cut crystal.

substance to expand or contract when a voltage is applied across opposite sides.   The most commonly used is quartz because of its ruggedness and active electrical qualities.   It is also the least expensive and is available in large quantities.

Crystal Characteristics.   Quartz crystals are found in the natural shape shown in Fig. 39·7a and have three main axes.   The Z, or optical, axis joins the two extreme points at the ends of the crystal.   The X, or electrical, axis joins opposite hexagonal points, while the Y, or mechanical, axis joins opposite hexagonal sides, as shown in Fig. 39·7b.   The greatest amount of piezoelectric effect is realized from crystals cut along the X axis.   Crystals used for electronic purposes, such as oscillators, are cut into thin plates along one of the three axes.   Those cut with flat surfaces perpendicular to the Y axis are known as *Y-cut crystals*, while those cut with flat surfaces perpendicular to the X axis are known as *X-cut crystals.* as shown in Fig. 39·8.   *Z-cut-crystals* are cut perpendicular to the Z axis.

Crystals are cut for a specific resonant frequency as determined by their thickness; the frequency of vibration varies inversely with thickness. The X-cut crystal has a negative temperature coefficient, while the Y-cut crystal has a positive temperature coefficient. This means that an increase in temperature will cause the frequency of an X-cut crystal to decrease and the frequency of a Y-cut crystal to increase. Crystals used in oscillators are usually housed in temperature-controlled ovens.

Equivalent Circuit. Crystals are mounted between two metal plates to which electrical contact is made, in such a manner that mechanical vibration will occur when operating potentials are applied. Since this vibration will induce a difference of potential between the two plates, the crystal and mounting plates can be considered as an electric resonant circuit, as shown in Fig. 39·9b. C_2 represents the capacitor formed by the two

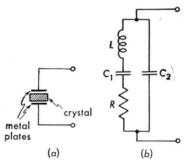

Fig. 39·9   (a) Crystal mountings and connections.   (b) Equivalent electric circuit.

mounting plates separated by the crystal dielectric. C_1 represents the elasticity of the crystal, L represents its mass, and R represents the electrical equivalent of resistance offered to mechanical vibration by friction. Because the inductance of the crystal is large as compared to its resistance, the crystal represents a high-Q tank circuit. Therefore, crystals can be used instead of conventional tank circuits for determining the operating frequency of an oscillator.

Basic Crystal Oscillator. The crystal oscillator shown in Fig. 39·10 is similar to other oscillators except for the substitution of the crystal for the tank circuit. Feedback from plate to grid circuit is through the C_{gp} of the tube, utilizing the otherwise undesirable plate-grid capacitance. The crystal and plate circuit act as two separate parallel-resonant circuits, with the plate circuit tuned to a frequency slightly below that of the crystal. Voltage fed back to the grid circuit is applied to the crystal and causes it to vibrate. These vibrations develop a voltage that is applied to the grid and determines the amount of current. Maximum feedback will occur at the parallel-resonant frequency of the crystal. Since the frequency of oscillation is determined by the parallel-resonant frequency of the crystal, maximum vibration will occur at this frequency and voltage induced by crystal vibration will be maximum.

The load is taken from the plate tank circuit of a crystal oscillator. Although loading affects the Q of the tank, a properly adjusted crystal

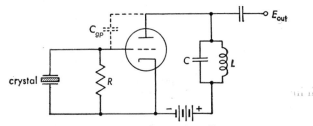

Fig. 39·10   Simple crystal oscillator.

oscillator requires very little feedback because of its high Q. Therefore, very little energy is dissipated in the grid circuit.

REVIEW QUESTIONS

1. What requirements must be met in order for an oscillator to function properly?

2. Explain how a tank circuit oscillates.

3. What are some of the causes of frequency instability in an oscillator?

4. Explain the operation of an Armstrong oscillator.

5. Explain the operation of a Hartley oscillator.

6. Explain the operation of a Colpitts oscillator.

7. What is piezoelectric effect?

8. Explain how oscillator crystals are cut.

9. How can a crystal function as the frequency-determining element of an oscillator?

10. How is the frequency of oscillators usually varied?

11. Explain how a crystal and its mounting plates can be considered as an electric resonant circuit.

12. Explain the operation of a crystal oscillator.

13. How is the frequency of a Colpitts oscillator determined?

14. Which of the oscillators discussed in this chapter is the most desirable?   Why?

15. How is regenerative feedback effected in a Hartley oscillator?

16. How does a change in supply voltage have an effect upon the frequency of an oscillator?

17. What effect would increasing the value of L_1 in Fig. 39·3 have on the frequency of oscillations?

18. What effect would increasing the number of turns in L_2 in Fig. 39·5 have on the frequency of oscillations?

19. What would occur if RFC in Fig. 39·6 became shorted?

20. How would the shorting of C_2 in Fig. 39·5b affect oscillations?

CHAPTER 40

TRANSMITTER CIRCUITS

The purpose of any transmitter is to radiate electrical energy into space. This could be accomplished by connecting the oscillator directly to the antenna. However, an oscillator is not primarily a producer of power, and such an arrangement would have a low power output which would limit the distance over which the "transmitted" signal could be "received." Also, frequency stability would be lost because of the comparatively large amount of power being drawn from the oscillator.

Practical transmitters consist of an oscillator and several stages of amplification. The stage connected to the antenna is usually referred to as the *final power amplifier*, while stages between the oscillator and final stage are known by several names. They are sometimes referred to as

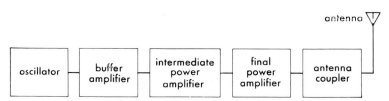

FIG. 40·1   Block diagram showing stages of typical transmitter.

first and *second power amplifiers, first doubler, second doubler,* or simply as *intermediate power amplifiers.* In some instances the first power amplifier is called a *buffer* because it serves to isolate the oscillator from the load and thus increases frequency stability.

40·1 Typical Transmitter. A block diagram of a typical transmitter is shown in Fig. 40·1. The oscillator circuit is chosen for frequency stability and furnishes a relatively small amount of power. Oscillator frequency is determined by the values of circuit components. The first power amplifier, or buffer, is usually a Class-A r-f amplifier that serves to prevent loading of the oscillator. The intermediate power amplifier is operated Class C and is used to increase the power of the signal generated by the oscillator. This stage may be operated as a *doubler*, that is, to double the frequency of the oscillator signal. For example, if the transmitter is to operate at 1,000 kc, the oscillator can be designed for 500 kc and its frequency doubled in one of the intermediate stages. If more power amplification is required, additional intermediate stages are used. The number of stages operating as doublers is determined by the frequency for which the transmitter is designed. The final power amplifier is operated Class C and as a "straight-through" amplifier; that is, it is never operated as a frequency doubler. The antenna coupler is a circuit that provides a means of transferring maximum energy from the final amplifier to the antenna. Current through the antenna sets up magnetic and electrostatic fields around it and causes the energy to be radiated into space.

40·2 Buffer Amplifier. The buffer amplifier shown in Fig. 40·2 is untuned and operated Class A. A combination of grid-leak and cathode

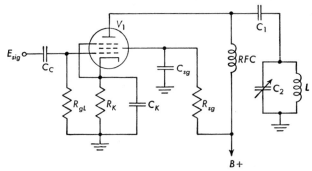

FIG. 40·2 Circuit schematic of typical buffer amplifier.

bias is provided by C_c, C_k, R_k, and R_{gL}. The r-f coil in the plate circuit serves as a plate load resistance while offering a high impedance to the r-f signal, thus keeping it out of the power supply. R_{sg} reduces the power-supply voltage to a proper value for the screen grid. C_{sg} is the screen bypass capacitor, and the input signal from the oscillator is connected into the stage through C_c across R_{gL}. The amplified signal from the output of V_1 is coupled through C_1 to the input of the intermediate power amplifier across the tuned circuit consisting of L and C_2. If this tank circuit is tuned to the frequency of the signal from the oscillator and buffer amplifier, it is said to be operating "straight through." If the oscillator frequency is to be doubled, L and C_2 are tuned to a frequency twice that of the oscillator; if tripling is desired, the tank is tuned to three times the oscillator frequency.

The true buffer circuit is an untuned Class-A r-f voltage or power amplifier that places no load on the oscillator circuit. However, it may also be a tuned r-f amplifier operated either Class B or C with fixed bias. Regardless of type or class of operation, grid current must not be drawn

in the buffer circuit.   Should grid current be drawn, the oscillator would
be required to furnish the power, which would place a load upon the
oscillator and defeat the purpose of the buffer.   Buffers may be connected
to associated stages by means of transformer coupling, direct coupling, or
impedance coupling.

40·3   Class-C R-F Amplifiers.   Since Class-A amplifiers are only about
25 per cent efficient and are costly in space and materials, high-efficiency
amplifiers require the use of Class-C bias.   When operated Class C, fewer
power stages are required for a given output and efficiencies of from 60 to
80 per cent are attainable.

A basic Class-C r-f power amplifier is shown in Fig. 40·3.   Bias is
obtained from a separate supply and is of sufficient value to cause the
tube to conduct during only one-third of the input cycle.   In Class-C

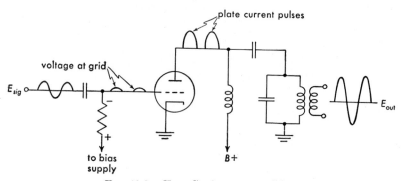

Fig. 40·3   Class-C r-f power amplifier.

operation the grid is biased at approximately $1\frac{1}{2}$ to 5 times the value of
cutoff voltage.   Therefore, the tube remains cut off for approximately
two-thirds of each input cycle, and there is current only when the input
signal increases grid voltage above cutoff.   For maximum power output
the excitation voltage must drive the tube almost into the plate-current
saturation region.   Since there will be grid current during the portion of
the excitation cycle that the grid is positive, power is consumed in the grid
circuit.   Therefore, grid-driving power must be supplied by the preceding
stage, which must be a power amplifier.

In Fig. 40·3 the input signal is shown as a sine wave of a certain amplitude.   Due to the fixed bias present on the grid, only the positive peaks
of the input signal are applied to the grid and the tube will conduct during
the time the grid is positive.   Tube current pulsates as shown.   These
pulses supply the energy to the plate tank circuit that causes it to oscillate
like the conventional oscillator.   With the plate load impedance consisting of a parallel-resonant circuit tuned to the excitation frequency, maximum impedance is offered at resonance and a high value of output volt-

age is developed across the load. Because of the flywheel action of the tank circuit, whose losses are replaced by the plate-current pulses, the output voltage will be similar to a sine wave.

Plate Power and Efficiency. Maximum positive grid voltage, maximum current, and minimum plate voltage occur simultaneously. Therefore, at the time of maximum current, the potential between plate and cathode is relatively small. Thus a minimum amount of power is dissipated in heat at the plate of the tube. Since useful power is the power that is actually delivered to the tank circuit, plate efficiency can be determined by dividing power delivered to the tank by the d-c power input to the stage. Power delivered to the tank is equal to $E_p I_p$ minus the power dissipated in heat at the plate.

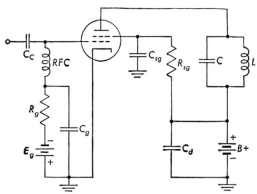

FIG. 40·4   Class-C r-f power amplifier employing tetrode.

Tetrode Amplifier. A Class-C r-f amplifier using a tetrode is shown in Fig. 40·4. For purpose of illustration, batteries are shown as supplying both grid bias and plate voltage. The signal from the preceding stages is connected across C_c, R_g, the rfc, and E_g. A portion of the bias is developed across R_g, the grid-bias resistor. C_g acts as a bias supply filter for bypassing radio frequencies around the bias supply. The rfc also serves to prevent radio frequencies from reaching the bias supply. C_{sg} and R_{sg} are the screen bypass capacitor and screen dropping resistor, respectively. C_d bypasses radio frequencies from the d-c plate supply. Plate-current pulses supply the energy to sustain oscillations in the tank, and the output is an amplified voltage closely resembling a sine wave.

40·4 Frequency Multipliers. For good frequency stability at very high frequencies, crystal oscillators are used. Since frequency varies inversely with crystal thickness, it is impractical to cut crystals to vibrate at high frequencies without being easily broken. In order to use crystal oscillators in transmitters operating at high frequencies, and because any oscillator operates more satisfactorily at low frequencies, a means of frequency multiplication is employed. For example, with the transmitter shown by block diagram in Fig. 40·5 the oscillator could operate at 2 Mc. By employing two stages of doubling, the final power amplifier would operate at 8 Mc; if two stages of tripling were used, the output would be 18 Mc. Any number of doubler or tripler stages may be used; however, power output is appreciably decreased through each multiplier stage. An amplifier operating straight through and capable of delivering 50 watts would deliver about 35 watts as a doubler and less than 30 watts as a tripler. For this reason the final power amplifier is never used for frequency multiplication.

Although the output of a highly biased Class-C amplifier closely resembles a sine wave, it is actually composed of a fundamental and many of

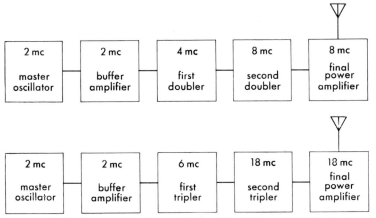

FIG. 40·5   Block diagram showing methods of doubling and tripling frequency.

its harmonics. If the frequency of a crystal is 1 Mc, the second harmonic is 2 Mc, the third harmonic is 3 Mc, and the tenth harmonic is 10 Mc. Therefore, by using several stages of doubling or tripling, a 1-Mc crystal could operate with a transmitter of almost any desired output. In the first doubler stage of Fig. 40·5 the frequency of the 2-Mc crystal is doubled to 4 Mc; in the first tripler stage, it is tripled to 6 Mc.

Frequency multiplication is accomplished by tuning the plate tank circuit of the stage to the desired harmonic of the grid signal frequency. Thus, the desired harmonic is amplified while all other harmonics are rejected. If the grid signal is 2 Mc, these pulses of current will appear from cathode to plate and energize the tank circuit. Because the tank is resonant to a higher harmonic of 2 Mc, it will oscillate at that frequency. The pulses of current supply the energy necessary to sustain oscillations at the same time during alternate cycles of either the doubled or tripled frequency. Between each pulse of plate current the tuned circuit will continue to oscillate, and the output will be a wave form either twice or three times the frequency of input signal, depending upon the frequency to which the plate tank is tuned. The plate tank may be tuned to higher-order harmonics, but because of the resultant loss of power, only doubling or tripling has been found practical.

40·5 Tube Considerations. The intermediate stages in transmitters usually employ tetrodes, while the final power amplifier stage may use either tetrodes or triodes. Tetrodes are used as final power amplifiers in low- and medium-power applications but produce excessive harmonics at higher power ranges and are not practical for high-power transmitters. Forced-air- or water-cooled triodes are used with transmitters producing high power.

Because of large current-carrying requirements, transmitting tubes usually have directly heated cathodes connected as shown in Fig. 40·6.

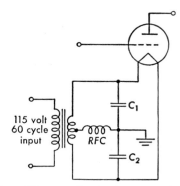

FIG. 40·6   Filament circuit of transmitting tube.

The cathode is connected across a 60-cycle filament transformer which is center tapped to prevent the a-c component from appearing in the plate circuit. Therefore, heater current appears only through the center-tapped secondary and cathode, reversing in direction with each alternation. R-f current exists from ground through C_1 and C_2 but not through the transformer secondary because of the presence of the r-f choke; then it divides through both halves of the filament, through the tube, and back to ground. By employing this arrangement and using tubes with tungsten cathodes, long tube life results although large currents are handled.

40·6 Bias Circuits. For Class-C operation the necessary bias may be obtained from fixed sources or developed across circuit components. If the bias remains fixed although the strength of the input signal varies, it is called *fixed bias*. If bias is the result of current through a grid or cathode resistor, it is called *self-bias*. It is common practice to use a combination of these two methods, each of which has certain advantages and disadvantages.

Fixed Bias.　One method of obtaining fixed bias is from a negative power supply.　By grounding the positive side of the supply and varying the output with a potentiometer, as shown in Fig. 40·7, any desired value of negative voltage can be made available for biasing purposes.　Fixed bias may also be obtained from small d-c generators or from batteries. Each method will place the grid at the proper negative direct voltage for Class-C operation.　The advantage of this type of bias is that the tube

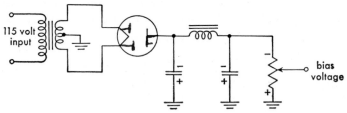

Fig. 40·7　Negative power supply for producing fixed bias.

is always cut off when no signal is applied.　However, the amplifier output will vary in accordance with input-signal variations.　This is a disadvantage, because the transmitted signal should remain constant; therefore, the amplified output from each stage should also remain constant. Fixed bias sometimes allows the tube to be overloaded.　Since voltage at the grid is equal to the signal voltage minus bias voltage, an excessive value of input signal might cause the tube to be overloaded.

Self-bias.　One method of obtaining self-bias is by utilizing the current from cathode to grid on the positive peaks of input signal.　This is called

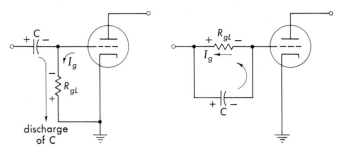

Fig. 40·8　Grid-leak-bias circuits showing paths of grid current and discharge of grid capacitor.

grid-leak bias and is shown in Fig. 40·8.　With grid current the capacitor charges to the polarity shown, and the grid is made more negative. After the grid ceases to draw current, C discharges through R_{gL} and a negative voltage remains on the grid.　The value of bias is determined by the size of the grid-leak resistor and the amplitude of the input signal. Therefore, it has the advantage of providing voltage regulation in the grid circuit.　If the signal voltage increases, voltage at the grid will also increase and produce additional bias that tends to maintain a constant output. Conversely, a decrease in input signal will cause a decrease in bias, thus providing amplitude stability over a wide range of input-signal variations. The main disadvantage of this method of bias is the lack of protection offered the tube in the event of loss of excitation.

Cathode bias is another form of self-bias produced by current through a cathode resistor, as shown in Fig. 40·9a. The d-c component of plate current appears through this resistor, and the amount of bias developed is determined by the size of R_k and the value of current through it. Current through R_k causes the grounded side to be negative with respect to the cathode side. Since the grid is connected to the negative side through L, it will be negative with respect to the cathode by an amount equal to the voltage across R_k. Cathode bias has the advantage of compensating

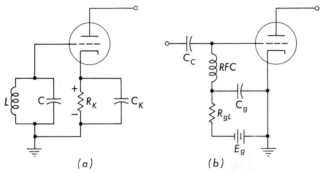

(a)   (b)

Fig. 40·9   (a) Cathode-bias circuit.   (b) Combination-bias circuit.

for changes in input-signal variations. Because the amount of bias is determined by plate current, which is further determined by the amplitude of input signal, any change in input is automatically compensated for by a change in bias. C_k bypasses the a-c component of plate current which would otherwise cause a continual variation in grid voltage.

The most common bias network is that known as *combination bias*, which employs both fixed- and self-bias circuits. With this method the fixed bias is adjusted so that it is sufficient merely to cut off the tube in case of loss of excitation, while the remainder of the necessary bias is developed across a grid-leak resistor, as shown in Fig. 40·9b. When the input signal is sufficiently large to drive the grid positive, there is grid current, which develops a bias that stabilizes the amplifier output.

40·7 Transmitter Output. In summary, a transmitter consists of an oscillator which generates the signal, one or more intermediate stages, and a power amplifier that is connected to the antenna through a coupling circuit. The r-f signal that is transmitted to the receiving antenna is called the *carrier* and may be of several types. It is this signal which "carries" the intelligence, or message, that is to be transmitted over some distance. However, the steady carrier signal produced at the

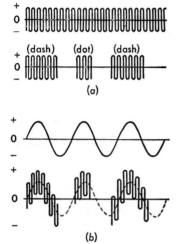

(a)

power-amplifier output cannot be interpreted as having any meaning unless it is changed. The process by which a carrier wave is changed so that it can convey intelligence is called *modulation*.

The most common methods of transmitting messages are by code or by voice. In one code method, the carrier is trans-

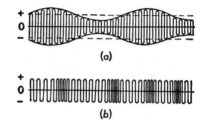

Fig. 40·10 (a) C-w transmission. (b) Mcw transmission.

Fig. 40·11 (a) Amplitude modulation. (b) Frequency modulation.

mitted as a continuous wave but is interrupted at intervals to produce dots and dashes in a sequence that corresponds to code. This is known as *continuous-wave* transmission (c-w). Another form of code transmission is known as *modulated-continuous-wave* transmission (mcw), in which an audio-frequency signal of constant amplitude is superimposed upon the r-f carrier. The carrier is then interrupted at intervals as with c-w transmissions. The carrier wave for c-w transmission is shown in Fig. 40·10a as a constant-amplitude signal of a certain frequency which is interrupted at intervals to convey intelligence. In mcw transmission the interrupted carrier is shown as a signal of constant frequency but varying in amplitude because of the audio signal superimposed upon it (Fig. 40·10b). Because of the wide bandwidth, mcw transmission is used for emergency communication only.

Fig. 40·12 Typical transmitter tube. (*Radio Corporation of America.*)

Voice transmission for broadcast-transmitters is of two types. In the a-m (amplitude-modulation) method the amplitude of the carrier is varied, as shown in Fig. 40·11*a*, to convey intelligence. In the f-m (frequency-modulation) method the frequency of the carrier is varied, as shown in Fig. 40·11*b*. To *modulate* a carrier is to vary it in frequency, pitch, amplitude, or other quality of sound. The modulating component is developed by a circuit known as a *modulator*, to be studied later. It is

FIG. 40·13   Typical transmitter capacitors.   (*Cornell-Dubilier Electric Corporation.*)

a sine wave varying at an audio frequency, which is superimposed upon the r-f carrier to convey intelligence.

REVIEW QUESTIONS

1. Explain the operation of a typical transmitter.

2. Why is the final power amplifier operated Class C?

3. What is the purpose of a buffer amplifier?

4. What are the bias requirements of a simple transmitter?

5. Why is it important that grid current not be drawn in a buffer circuit?

6. Explain the operation of a Class-C r-f power amplifier.

7. Why are frequency multipliers usually necessary in transmitters?

8. Why is frequency quadrupling not practical?

9. What are the tube requirements for a simple transmitter?

10. Explain two methods of obtaining self-bias.

11. Why is it necessary to modulate the r-f carrier of a transmitter?

12. Explain the difference between c-w and mcw transmissions.

13. What is a modulator and what purpose does it serve?

14. Explain the difference between amplitude modulation and frequency modulation.

15. What components are present in a modulated carrier?

16. Explain the principle of operation of a frequency multiplier.

17. What is combination bias, and what is its main advantage?

18. Why is the final power amplifier of a transmitter always operated "straight through"?

19. Why are tetrodes never used in high-power transmitters?

20. Why does bandwidth play an important part in limiting the use of mcw transmissions?

CHAPTER 41

TRANSMITTER TUNING AND KEYING

If a transmitter is properly tuned, the plate tank of each stage resonates with the grid input signal and the final amplifier is effectively coupled with the antenna, or load. Under these conditions, the transmitter will operate at a specified frequency with maximum power output.

It should not be assumed that the problem ends once a transmitter is made to radiate. There are numerous techniques for making the transmission itself as efficient a process as possible. Further, some means must be devised for turning the transmitter on and off. Often the rate at which the transmitter is turned on and off is the actual intelligence. This intelligence is termed a *code*, and the process of transmitting a code is called *keying*.

41·1 Transmitter Tuning. The plate tank circuit of a Class-C amplifier can be compared to a variable resistance in series with the plate. When the plate circuit is resonant to the grid circuit, impedance is maximum. If tuned either above or below the resonant frequency, impedance will decrease proportionately. If the plate circuit is completely detuned, plate-circuit resistance is negligible and plate voltage will be approximately equal to the supply voltage. When the input signal drives the grid above cutoff, plate current will appear in large pulses. Because the plate tank is off resonance, it will have a lower impedance and will set up no appreciable value of alternating voltage. By tuning the tank circuit to a frequency approaching that of the input signal, impedance of the plate circuit will increase and some value of alternating voltage will be set up across this impedance. As with any amplifier, an increase in the positive grid signal will cause a decrease in plate voltage because of the current through the plate load. Conversely, a decrease in plate current will reduce the drop across the plate load and cause the value of plate voltage to increase. In a parallel-resonant circuit, impedance is maximum when the lagging component of current through the inductive branch is equal to the leading current through the capacitive branch. Therefore, plate impedance is maximum and line current is minimum. However, the cir-

culating current will be greater than line current by an amount equal to
Q times line current.

Circulating current through the inductive reactance creates flux lines
that induce in the secondary a voltage which is applied to the grid input of
a succeeding stage. This is shown in Fig. 41·1. In tuning individual

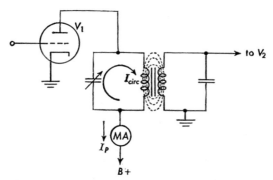

FIG. 41·1   Flux lines caused by circulating current in plate circuit of V_1 inducing
voltage in grid circuit of V_2.

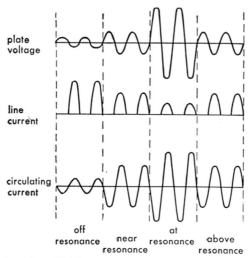

FIG. 41·2   Examples of amplitude of plate voltage and line and circulating currents
as plate tank is tuned through its resonant frequency.

stages of a transmitter, the plate tank is tuned to the resonant frequency
of the grid input signal as indicated by minimum line current through the
milliammeter. Under these conditions the stage is delivering maximum
power output to the following stage or antenna circuit. Comparative
examples of plate voltage and line and circulating currents are shown in
Fig. 41·2.

When tuning a transmitter, the first step is to set the oscillator to the desired frequency. This is accomplished with a standard frequency meter by means of *heterodyne* action, which will be discussed later. The next stage to be tuned is that following the oscillator. Tuning is performed by making either the capacitance or inductance variable. By rotating the tuning control, the inductance or capacitance will be varied until resonance is reached. This will be indicated by a "dip" on the plate-current milliammeter. This dip, or minimum indication, occurs when the plate tank circuit offers maximum impedance to line current. After one stage is tuned, each successive stage is then tuned. Tuning may also be accomplished by observing a milliammeter in the grid circuit of a succeeding stage. When the plate-current meter indicates minimum current, the grid-current meter will indicate maximum at the same instant. Thus, when a stage is tuned to resonance, there is maximum drive to the following stage.

As a stage is tuned, the plate tank will resonate at higher-order harmonics of the grid input signal. This will be indicated by several dips on the plate-current milliammeter. However, because of resulting power losses when a stage is used as a doubler or tripler, successive dips will be progressively smaller and the grid-current meter will indicate a reduced amount of drive to the following stage.

41·2 Antenna Tuning and Coupling. Antenna-coupling systems are used to couple maximum energy from the final power amplifier to the antenna. Because an antenna radiates most efficiently when its electrical length is equal to one-quarter of a wavelength or a multiple thereof, coupling units provide a means of varying the electrical length. Some of the most common coupling methods are shown in Fig. 41·3. For example, the electrical length of an antenna may be increased by using the series-inductance method of Fig. 41·3a. An antenna may be electrically shortened by using the series-capacitance method shown in Fig. 41·3c.

Antenna Characteristics. An antenna shows the same characteristics as either a series-resonant or a parallel-resonant circuit, depending upon the length. At one-quarter wavelength, or any odd multiple of one-quarter wavelength, it appears as a series-resonant circuit and acts as a low-resistance load to the source of excitation. Under these conditions the antenna is said to be "current fed" because the input to the antenna is a high value of current at low voltage. At one-half wavelength, or any even multiple of one-quarter wavelength, it appears as a parallel-resonant circuit and acts as a high-resistance load to the excitation source. This is known as "voltage feed" because the input to the antenna is a high value of voltage at low current (see Chap. 43).

Because inductive reactance increases with frequency, inductive coupling allows very little harmonic transfer from final power amplifier to antenna.   With capacitive coupling, harmonic transfer is great because capacitive reactance decreases with an increase in frequency.   However, of these two methods, capacitive coupling is easier to adjust and is simple in design.   Link coupling provides a means of varying the degree of coupling.   Regardless of method or design, the coupling circuit serves the

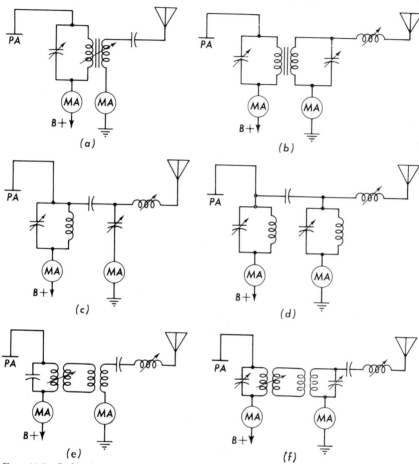

FIG. 41·3   Inductive coupling: (*a*) series feed (current), (*b*) parallel feed (voltage). Capacitive coupling: (*c*) series feed, (*d*) parallel feed.   Link coupling: (*e*) series feed, (*f*) parallel feed.

purpose of matching the antenna and final power amplifier while varying the electrical length of the antenna.   The antenna must be a resonant circuit at the frequency of the power amplifier to radiate efficiently. Also, the impedance of the antenna must be matched to that of the power amplifier for maximum transfer of energy.   Therefore, resonance is realized when the antenna is adjusted to the required electrical length by means of a variable inductance or capacitance in the coupling circuit. Maximum transfer of energy is realized when the coupling circuit is adjusted to match antenna impedance with that of the power amplifier.

41·3 Transmitter and Antenna Tuning Procedure. Individual steps to follow in the tuning of almost all transmitters are outlined below.

1. Allow ample time for transmitter to warm to operating temperature.

2. Determine output frequency and adjust oscillator to the desired frequency, depending upon number of stages doubling or tripling.

3. Tune buffer amplifier to frequency of oscillator.

4. Tune IPA to desired frequency, either straight through or as a doubler or tripler. Tune for dip on plate-current meter or maximum grid current in following stage. If more than one IPA is used, tune last IPA for maximum grid-current indication on power-amplifier grid-current meter.

5. Tune PA to frequency of last IPA as indicated by a dip on PA plate-current meter.

6. Adjust antenna inductance or capacitance until approximate antenna resonance is reached as indicated by a slight rise in PA plate current or an indication of current on the antenna meter.

7. If type of feed is not known, tune for indications of maximum antenna current. In some instances, resonance will be indicated on both current and voltage feed. However, the method resulting in the sharpest resonant indications of maximum antenna current is that for which designed.

8. Increase coupling in small steps, retuning antenna for maximum current and PA plate tank for minimum plate current. As loading is increased, PA plate current at resonance will increase. Antenna and PA plate circuits should be tuned until the PA plate current has reached the tube's rated value.

9. After completing these steps it is usually advisable to check the frequency of the oscillator and slightly retune all stages to compensate for any drift that may have occurred during the original tuning.

Maximum plate current due to coupling should occur simultaneously with a dip in plate current resulting from PA plate tank tuning, and both should occur at the tube's rated value of plate current. This condition indicates correct coupling, PA tank tuning, and electrical length of antenna for maximum transfer of power at the desired frequency. With current feed, a large value of current will be indicated on the antenna current meter. It is therefore advantageous to use this indication for tuning purposes. However, with voltage feed, there will be little indication of antenna current. With either type of feed, maximum antenna current for a rated plate current provides the best transfer of energy from power amplifier to antenna.

41·4 Neutralization and Parasitic Suppression. When a tube is to function as an amplifier, under no circumstances should it develop oscillations. When triode tubes are used in both transmitting and receiving systems, the grid-plate capacitance is often sufficiently large to produce sustained oscillations in the grid circuit. Therefore, some means of *neutralization* is necessary to cancel energy fed back from plate to grid circuit through interelectrode capacitance. A neutralizing circuit is one which transfers an equal amount of energy in the opposite direction to

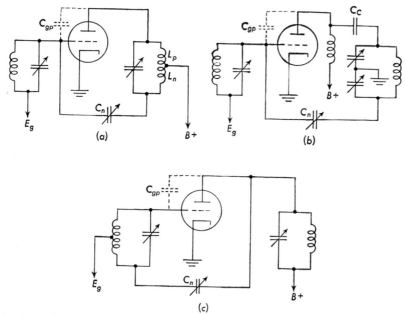

FIG. 41·4 Commonly used neutralization systems. (a) Hazeltine system of plate neutralization (series feed). (b) Hazeltine system of plate neutralization (shunt feed). (c) Rice system of grid neutralization.

that between plate and grid, thereby neutralizing its effects and preventing oscillations. Feedback of proper phase and sufficient amplitude to cause oscillations may result from either inductive or capacitive networks. In all instances, undesirable oscillations are produced that must be eliminated if the circuit is to function as designed.

Although many methods of neutralization may be employed, those shown in Fig. 41·4 are the most common. Consider the circuit of Fig. 41·4a, in which a voltage from the plate tank is fed through C_n to the grid of the tube. The circuit is that of an ordinary tuned amplifier, connected so that the voltage from the L_n side of the plate tank transformer is opposite in polarity to that applied to the plate through L_p. With C_n of proper size, the voltage applied to the grid will be of opposite polarity and sufficient amplitude to neutralize the feedback from plate to grid resulting from tube capacitance. Because close coupling exists between L_n and L_p, neutralization by this method is almost independent of frequency. However, the effects of stray capacitance and changes in leakage inductance prevent its being independent of frequency over a wide range. The circuit shown in Fig. 41·4b performs the same function and in the same manner as that of a except that a tuned circuit is utilized for obtaining polarity reversal of feed-back voltage.

Another method of neutralizing is that shown in Fig. 41·4c, in which the input transformer supplies the neutralizing voltage. This is known as the Rice method and is different from the Hazeltine methods previously discussed in that it produces the necessary polarity reversal across the input transformer rather than across the output transformer. In the Rice circuit, with C_n properly adjusted, voltage developed in the plate circuit will be of the same magnitude as that resulting from tube capacitance. Since these two voltages produce currents and effects in the grid circuit that are in phase opposition, neutralization is accomplished.

Before a transmitter is neutralized, plate voltage must be removed from the stage to be neutralized. With plate voltage off, the plate tank circuit is tuned through its range and the grid-current meter of that stage is observed. If tuning the tank circuit causes any change in grid current, the stage requires neutralizing. Once C_n has been adjusted so that plate tuning has no effect upon grid current, the stage is properly neutralized.

Parasitic Oscillations. Any undesirable oscillation occurring in an oscillator or amplifier is referred to as a *parasitic* oscillation. These oscillations occur in resonant circuits comprised of tube capacitances, lead inductances, and stray capacitances within the circuit. Some of their effects are power losses, excessive voltage stresses, and distortion. Also, low-frequency parasitics sometimes cause carrier amplitude to vary at the low-frequency rate of the parasitic oscillation. Existence of these undesirable oscillations may be determined by first removing excitation voltage to the stage being considered, then reducing grid voltage to nearly zero and plate voltage to within rated limits of the tube. By attaching a neon bulb to an insulated rod and moving the bulb near the circuit components within the stage, parasitic oscillations will be indicated by a glow of the neon bulb.

Parasitics may be eliminated by methods shown in Fig. 41·5. A small resistor connected in the grid circuit is effective for eliminating high-frequency parasitics. Either a choke or a combination of choke and resistor placed between plate and tank is also effective for eliminating parasitics of high frequency. However, the use of a choke sometimes introduces low-frequency parasitics, so its value must be such that any resonant frequency set up in the plate circuit is less than that of the grid circuit.

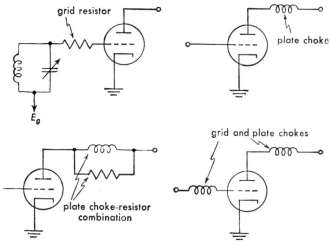

grid resistor

plate choke

plate choke-resistor combination

grid and plate chokes

FIG. 41·5   Commonly used methods of parasitic suppression.

41·5   Transmitter Keying.   The process of interrupting a transmitter carrier at intervals so that it will conform to a code is called *keying*.   The primary requirement of a good keying system is zero output when the key is open and desired output when the key is closed.   The absence of "key clicks" or "chirps" is essential to optimum transmitter performance.

One method of interrupting the carrier is known as *plate-circuit keying*. This circuit is shown in Fig. 41·6a, in which the output of the transmitter is controlled by connecting a key in the plate supply of the power amplifier.   By applying and removing plate voltage at proper intervals, carrier output will conform to a coded signal.   This method is best suited to transmitters handling exceptionally low power.   Plate keying is not used in high-power applications because the key must pass total current drawn by the transmitter, thereby endangering the operator.   Also, excessive arcing would be produced at the keying contacts and a chirping note would be present in the output signal.

Another method of interrupting the carrier is known as *grid-block keying*.   In the circuit of Fig. 41·6b a negative voltage is applied to the grid of one or more stages when the key is open.   Under these conditions, the tube is cut off and there is no plate current or carrier output.   When the key is closed, all or part of the blocking bias is removed and the tube is allowed to conduct.   The advantage of this method is that only a low value of voltage has been interrupted, eliminating chirps and clicks.

One of the most common methods is known as *filament center-tap keying*. In the circuit of Fig. 41·6c the key is placed in the filament ground return lead.   When the key is open, there is no return path for plate current and the tube will not conduct.   When the key is closed, the keying contacts provide a complete return path for the plate current.

The *vacuum-tube keying* method of Fig. 41·6d employs a keying tube which keeps the stage cut off when the key is open.   Under these conditions, V_2 is conducting and the drop across R_2 reduces the screen voltage

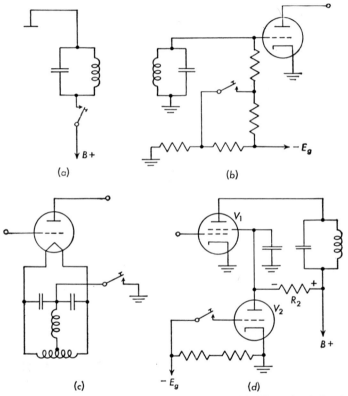

Fig. 41·6   Typical methods of keying transmitters.   (*a*) Plate-circuit keying.   (*b*) Grid-block keying.   (*c*) Filament center-tap keying.   (*d*) Vacuum-tube keying.

on V_1 to a value sufficient to prevent plate current.   When the key is closed, the grid of V_2 is placed near ground potential, there is no current through R_2, the screen of V_1 assumes normal operating voltage, and the tube conducts.

Improper Keying Effects.   An effect of improper keying is known as *back waves*, which occur when the carrier does not completely drop to zero when the key is open.   This may result from too low a value of blocking voltage when grid-block keying is being used.   As a result, the amplitude of the carrier is merely reduced instead of being cut off completely.   Back waves cannot be produced if the oscillator is keyed or filament center-tap keying is employed.

Key clicks are caused by an instantaneous rise to full power, or an instantaneous drop from full power to zero power. Arcing of the keying

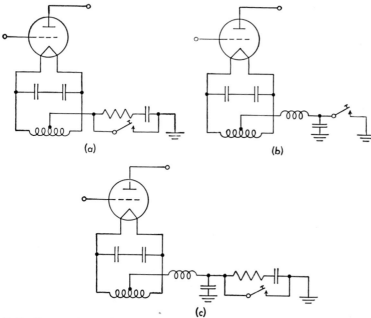

Fig. 41·7 Commonly used filter and lag circuits. (a) Key-click filter circuit. (b) Lag circuit. (c) Combination filter and lag circuits.

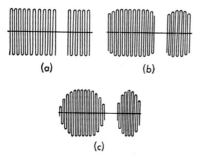

Fig. 41·8 Keyed carrier wave showing effect upon amplitude of lag circuits. (a) Insufficient lag. (b) Proper lag. (c) Excessive lag.

contacts will also produce key clicks in the output which may cause high-frequency components to be introduced into the signal and interference with adjacent channels. These may be eliminated by the filter or lag circuits shown in Fig. 41·7. Inductance affects the rise time while the capacitance affects the decay time, thus introducing the proper amount of lag into the circuit. A proper amount of lag is shown in Fig. 41·8b, in which the leading and trailing edges of carrier output are rounded off.

If the transmitter frequency varies while the key is closed, a chirp will be noted. Any keying methods causing chirps by loading the oscillator circuit are undesirable.

REVIEW QUESTIONS

1. What is the purpose of tuning a transmitter?
2. Explain the procedure necessary to tune an ordinary transmitter correctly.
3. Why is it necessary to tune the antenna circuit in a transmitter?
4. What is the difference between current-fed and voltage-fed antennas?
5. Why is neutralization necessary in transmitters?
6. How is neutralization of a transmitter accomplished?
7. Why is parasitic suppression necessary in a transmitter?
8. How is it possible to determine the presence of parasitics?
9. Explain how parasitic suppression in a transmitter is accomplished.
10. Explain the plate-circuit method of keying a transmitter.
11. Explain the grid-block method of keying a transmitter.
12. What are the detrimental effects of back waves?
13. Why are key clicks undesirable?
14. How may the electrical length of an antenna be increased or decreased?
15. How is it possible to determine whether or not a transmitter requires neutralization?
16. What indication would be used for tuning to a third harmonic of the oscillator frequency?
17. Why is proper electrical length of the antenna important to correct tuning?
18. What are the advantages of grid-block keying over plate keying?
19. What is one advantage of capacitive coupling over inductive coupling between transmitter and antenna?
20. What circuit action is taking place in the plate circuit of an amplifier when tuned for minimum line current?

CHAPTER 42

MODULATION PRINCIPLES

In order for r-f energy to be useful for radiotelegraphy or radiotelephony, it must contain intelligence. The process of superimposing intelligence on a carrier wave is known as *modulation*. In c-w transmitters oscillator circuits generate the r-f voltage known as the *carrier* wave. This carrier, however, contains no signal and must be interrupted at a coded rate to convey any intelligence to the listener.

In radiotelephone systems speech is converted to an a-f voltage, amplified, and superimposed upon the carrier. When a signal containing intelligence has been added to the carrier, it is said to be *modulated*. Modulation is defined as the process by which some characteristic of a periodic wave is varied with time in accordance with a signal of another frequency.

42·1 Modulated-wave Components. The superimposition of a voltage of one frequency on a voltage that is varying at another frequency is accomplished in one of three ways. A carrier wave may be expressed as

$$e = E_0 \sin (2\pi f_0 t + \theta)$$

where E_0 = average amplitude

f_0 = frequency of r-f oscillation

θ = phase angle

Therefore, the wave form can be varied by varying average amplitude, frequency of r-f oscillation, or phase angle. If, in the course of modulation, the amplitude of the carrier is varied while its frequency remains constant, it is said to be *amplitude modulated*. If the carrier amplitude is held constant while carrier frequency is varied, it has been *frequency modulated*. *Phase modulation* occurs when the phase angle θ is varied while frequency and amplitude remain constant. It will not be discussed in detail in this text because of its similarity to frequency modulation.

A *signal* is defined as the a-f wave, or modulating wave, which contains the intelligence to be transmitted. A *modulated wave* is one whose amplitude, frequency, or phase has been varied in accordance with the information to be transmitted. *Side bands* are bands of frequencies produced, by modulation, on either side of the carrier frequency. A modulated wave is not a single sinusoidal oscillation but several waves superimposed on each other. The single carrier wave is converted into a complex wave by superimposing on it the many waves which comprise speech or music.

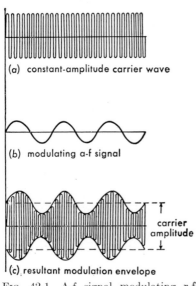

(a) constant-amplitude carrier wave

(b) modulating a-f signal

(c) resultant modulation envelope

FIG. 42·1   A-f signal modulating r-f carrier.

42·2   Amplitude   Modulation.

An example of amplitude modulation is shown in Fig. 42·1. The carrier wave of constant amplitude and frequency shown in *a* has been modulated by a signal in *b* with the resultant *modulation envelope* shown in *c*.

A phenomenon resulting from the process of modulation is *heterodyne action*. When two voltages of different frequencies are combined to obtain a voltage of a third value of frequency, two new frequencies are produced which are known as *side bands*. The lower side band will have a frequency equal to the difference in frequency between modulating signal and carrier wave. The upper side band, or sum frequency, is equal to the sum of carrier frequency and modulating frequency. Figure 42·2 shows a steady carrier frequency of 1,000 kc modulated by a 7,500-cps audio frequency. Two additional frequencies are produced, one

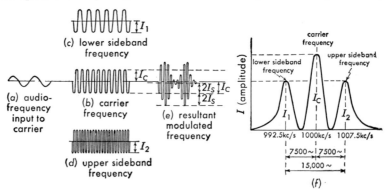

(c) lower sideband frequency

(a) audio-frequency input to carrier

(b) carrier frequency

(e) resultant modulated frequency

(d) upper sideband frequency

carrier frequency

lower sideband frequency

upper sideband frequency

992.5kc/s 1000kc/s 1007.5kc/s

7500~ 7500~

15,000 ~

(f)

FIG. 42·2   Relationship of side bands to carrier frequency. (*Nilson and Hornung, "Practical Radio Communications," McGraw-Hill Book Company, Inc., 1943.*)

of 1,007.5 kc and the other of 992.5 kc. These, also known as *beat frequencies*, have values equal to the sum and difference of the modulating and carrier frequencies. The interaction of the three frequencies produces a resultant wave form as shown in e of Fig. 42·2. The amplitude at any time is equal to the algebraic sum of the instantaneous values of the three waves.

Bandwidth. All the intelligence in an a-m wave is carried in the side bands. The side bands contain the modulating frequencies, which, effectively, are the information to be transmitted. Since an a-m wave contains side bands on either side of the carrier, it is apparent that a band of frequencies will be involved rather than a single frequency. Music contains many frequency components up to 15 kc; therefore, music modulated upon a carrier would produce side-band components extending to 15 kc on each side of the carrier frequency. In Fig. 42·2f with 7.5-kc modulation, there are side-band frequencies extending 7.5 kc above and below the 1,000-kc carrier. Although the resultant frequency due to the interaction of the three frequencies is 7.5 kc, the *bandwidth* is 15,000 cps, or from 992.5 kc to 1,007.5 kc.

Power Relations and Modulation Percentage. A measure of the amount by which the amplitude of the carrier is varied is called the *modulation factor, degree of modulation,* or *modulation percentage.* It is usually expressed as a percentage and can be determined by the equation

$$m = \frac{E_s}{e} \times 100$$

where m = per cent of modulation

E_s = maximum value of modulating signal, volts

e = maximum value of carrier, volts

Figure 42·3 shows modulation envelopes and their relation to carrier amplitude for 50 per cent modulation, 100 per cent modulation, and over 100 per cent modulation. If the audio-frequency power applied produces modulation in excess of 100 per cent, the carrier is said to be *overmodulated* and distortion results. Therefore, modulation may be varied to any percentage between 0 and 100. Because the modulating frequencies contain the information to be transmitted, as much power as possible should be contained in the side bands. Thus, the modulation envelope should be varied in amplitude as much as possible, up to 100 per cent. With 100 per cent modulation, total side-band power is equal to one-half the carrier power, with each side band containing an equal amount that corresponds to one-quarter the carrier power. With less than 100 per cent modulation, carrier power remains the same but power in the side bands decreases. From the standpoint of power and resultant optimum transmission, modulation as close as possible to 100 per cent is desirable.

42·3 Frequency Modulation. One main disadvantage of amplitude modulation is the presence of interference and static, which may be of almost any frequency within the spectrum. If the amplitude of the

transmitted signal is increased, noise amplitude also increases.   With frequency modulation the amplitude of the modulated wave is held at a constant value while the frequency of the wave is varied at a rate determined
by the frequency of the intelligence to be transmitted.   F-m systems
require a greater bandwidth, and it has been determined that the *signal-
to-noise ratio* of the transmitted signal is increased by the increase in useful

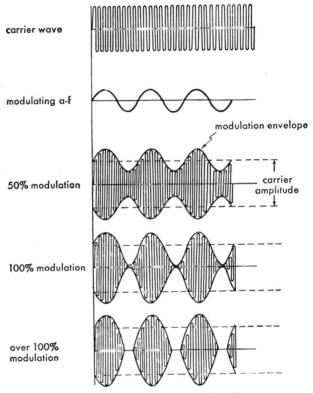

carrier wave

modulating a-f

modulation envelope

50% modulation

carrier
amplitude

100% modulation

over 100%
modulation

FIG. 42·3   Percentage of modulation.

signal strength which results from greater bandwidth.   Where a-m broadcast stations are allocated a bandwidth of only a few kc either side of the
carrier frequency, f-m stations are sometimes more than 100 kc apart,
thus preventing interference between stations.

Figure 42·4 shows a carrier wave of constant amplitude modulated by a
sine-wave signal.   It is seen that the amplitude of the carrier remains
constant for the signal of each frequency; however, the modulating signal
varies the carrier frequency at the rate of its own frequency.   The frequency of the carrier of an f-m transmitter is known as the *center*, or
resting, frequency.   When a modulating signal is applied, the amount of

frequency change above or below the resting frequency is known as the *frequency deviation*. Total variation between minimum and maximum values of frequency is known as *carrier swing*. Figure 42·5 shows a carrier wave of 5 cycles modulated by a weak signal of 2 cycles and a stronger signal of 4 cycles. These are shown only for purpose of explanation, for, actually, f-m transmitters operate on a band of frequencies within the vhf spectrum.

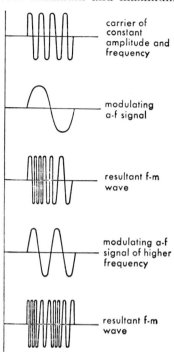

carrier of constant amplitude and frequency

modulating a-f signal

resultant f-m wave

modulating a-f signal of higher frequency

resultant f-m wave

The major difference between a-m and f-m transmitters is in the method of modulating the carrier. The f-m wave, like the a-m wave, is a carrier plus side bands. However, the degree of modulation is expressed in terms of frequency deviation. By equation,

$$m_f = \frac{\text{maximum frequency deviation}}{\text{maximum signal frequency}}$$

where m_f = modulation index or phase deviation, radians.

A frequency deviation of 75 kc is considered the equivalent of 100 per cent modulation in a-m systems.

Fig. 42·4 F-m carrier for a-f signal of two different frequencies.

The f-m wave is a carrier of frequency f_0 plus side bands of frequency $f_0 \pm f_m$, $f_0 \pm 2f_m$, $f_0 \pm 3f_m$, etc., where f_m is the modulating frequency. The number of side bands large enough to be important is determined by the frequency deviation imposed on the carrier and by the modulation frequency. Although an a-m wave has the same components as an f-m wave, the two are not the same. The difference lies in the fact that the carrier phases with respect to side-band phases differ by 90° for the two types of modulation. Because the carrier is out of phase with the side bands in an f-m wave, no additional energy is supplied to the f-m wave during modulation. Only the distribution of energy in the frequency spectrum is varied. Therefore, because amplitude variations are not involved, f-m transmitting tubes can be operated at their maximum ratings and efficiencies. Also, for a given power output, f-m transmitters are physically smaller than a-m transmitters.

42·4 Amplitude-modulation Circuits. Block diagrams of amplitude-modulated transmitters are shown in Fig. 42·6, in which an r-f signal is generated, amplified, modulated, and delivered to the antenna to be radiated into space. The complete unit is known as a *transmitter*, which may be further classified as to power output, method of operation, type of modulation, etc. Although the power rating of a transmitter is relative, those with 3 kw or less output are known as *low-power* transmitters while those whose output is above 3 kw are known as *high-power* trans-

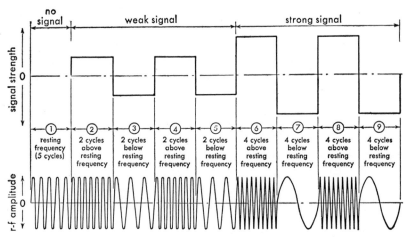

FIG. 42·5   Wave shapes of a carrier wave that is frequency-modulated by square-wave signal voltages. (*Cooke and Markus, "Electronics and Nucleonics Dictionary,"* *McGraw-Hill Book Company, Inc., 1960.*)

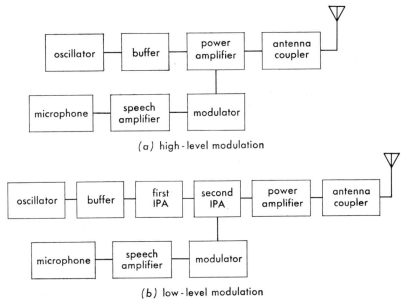

FIG. 42·6   Block diagrams of transmitters for high- and low-level modulation.

mitters. Output is determined by the number and type of tubes and by the type of modulation employed.

Modulation may be classified as to method and level. With *grid modulation*, the output of an a-f amplifier is used to vary the grid bias of a Class-C r-f amplifier. *Plate-modulation* methods utilize the output of an a-f amplifier to modulate the plate of an r-f amplifier. In all methods the r-f output of the stage modulated varies in accordance with the modulating signal. *Cathode modulation* is a combination of grid and plate modulation while *suppressor-grid modulation* is similar to control-grid modulation.

Although modulation may be accomplished in any of the r-f amplifier stages, the stage to which it is applied determines the level of modulation. In *low-level modulation* systems the modulation occurs in a stage preceding the final r-f amplifier, or at a low power level. Low-level modulation may be accomplished by either grid or plate methods, although the plate method is normally used. This type of modulation is used in high-power transmitters and has the advantage of requiring less audio power than high-level modulation of a similar transmitter. It has the disadvantage of reduced efficiency as compared with high-level methods. With low-level modulation all stages following that of the stage modulated must be linear amplifiers (Class B) of the modulated carrier and are often of the high-efficiency type in transmitters involving high power. This prevents distortion of the modulated signal.

High-level modulation occurs when the last r-f amplifier stage is modulated. With this type of modulation, the r-f amplifiers preceding the modulated stage do not have to be linear; therefore, high-gain amplifiers, which increase the efficiency of a transmitter, may be used. High-level modulation is used in low-power transmitters. Figure 42·6a is an example of high-level modulation, while Fig. 42·6b shows low-level modulation. The a-f portion of the transmitter consists of a microphone, a speech amplifier that increases the output of the microphone, and the modulator which produces the a-f modulating signal.

42·5 Grid Modulation. Figure 42·7a shows a circuit in which an r-f amplifier V_1 is modulated by the a-f output of another tube V_2. The r-f carrier is coupled into the grid of V_1 through transformer T_1. The a-f output of V_2 is also coupled into the grid of V_1 through T_2. C_2 prevents the r-f signal from entering the a-f circuit. The modulated output of V_1 is then coupled to the next stage through the plate output transformer, T_3.

Because the peak power of the modulated amplifier is four times carrier power, the stage must be adjusted so that with no modulation the output power is one-fourth that of an ordinary Class-C amplifier. This is accomplished by first adjusting the tube's bias for Class-C operation, then increasing until zero output results. Proper bias will then be at a point midway between zero output and Class-C operation. A comparison of grid bias, signal voltage, and cutoff bias is shown in Fig. 42·7b, while the resultant plate voltage is shown in Fig. 42·7c.

By utilizing the amplification factor of a tube, grid modulation has the advantage of requiring only a small amount of a-f power to modulate a transmitter carrier wave and produce a high power output.

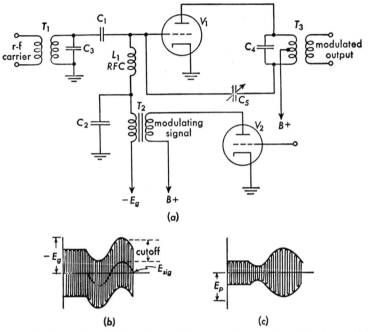

FIG. 42·7   Grid-modulated Class-C amplifier.   (a) Schematic.   (b) Comparison of grid bias, signal voltage, and cutoff bias.   (c) Voltage at plate.

42·6   Plate Modulation.   The basic system of *plate modulation*, often called the Heising system, is shown in Fig. 42·8.   This is the most widely used method of obtaining amplitude modulation.   The carrier signal is applied to the grid of V_1, an ordinary Class-C amplifier.   The modulating voltage from V_2 is applied across T_1 to the plate of V_1.   By superimposing the modulation voltage upon the plate direct voltage of V_1, the total voltage will be the sum of the two, which varies in accordance with the modulation envelope. L_1 is an r-f choke to isolate the plate-supply circuit. C_1 prevents direct current from entering the plate tank circuit.

V_1 is a triode, Class-C r-f power amplifier that must be operated at lower power during modulation to protect the tube.   Input power is usually reduced to about two-thirds its normal value. V_2 is either a Class-A or Class-B a-f power amplifier.   Audio voltage is coupled to V_1 across T_1, whose turns ratio is such that the impedance of the primary matches that of the Class-C amplifier plate.

Plate voltage increases and decreases in accordance with the amplitude of the audio voltage. Although the effective voltage varies between zero and a value twice that of the d-c supply, the circuit should be adjusted so that at $2E_p$, the r-f amplifier operates Class C with good efficiency and an output that is four times carrier power.

Both modulator and modulated amplifier must have linear characteristics so that a unit change of plate voltage will produce a unit change in r-f output. For single sinusoidal input, 100 per cent modulation is possible and the carrier varies from zero to twice normal. However, for voice or music modulation, average modulation is approximately 60 per cent. Under these conditions audio voltage is less than that required for 100 per cent modulation, and good linearity characteristics are required

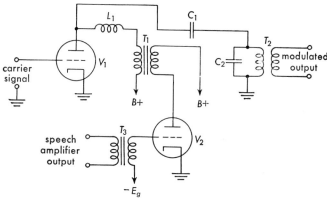

Fig. 42·8   Schematic of plate-modulated Class-C amplifier.

so that the carrier will vary in accordance with both frequency and amplitude of the voice or music.

By comparison with grid modulation, plate modulation produces a larger output from a given tube but requires greater modulation power. The plate-modulated amplifier has better linearity and higher efficiency, thus making it preferable in almost all applications, except where large modulation power produces bandwidth in excess of limits.

42·7   Miscellaneous Modulation Methods. *Suppressor-grid Modulation.* As shown in Fig. 42·9, suppressor-grid modulation is similar to control-grid modulation. A bias is applied to the suppressor grid, and the a-f voltage is superimposed across this bias. As the modulating voltage causes the suppressor to become more negative, plate voltage increases. Likewise, a positive swing of the modulating voltage will increase plate current and decrease plate voltage. Therefore, as the modulating voltage varies the suppressor voltage, the output will also vary. The suppressor is biased to a point halfway between zero and cutoff, and the peak audio voltage is equal to one-half cutoff bias for 100 per cent modulation.

Suppressor-grid modulation can be compared to control-grid modulation when the control grid is driven positive. Plate efficiency is about the same, although screen-grid losses are high and thereby limit the output power.

Cathode Modulation. A combination of grid and plate modulation is known as cathode modulation. With the audio-signal transformer coupled to the cathode of the r-f amplifier, it produces the same effect as if applied to the grid because of the grid return circuit to ground. Since the plate is also returned to ground through the power supply and back to the cathode, it has the same effect as being applied to the plate.

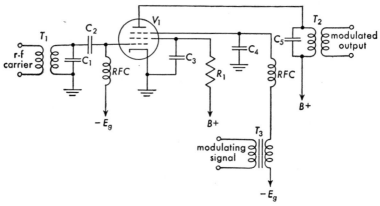

Fig. 42·9   Schematic of suppressor-grid-modulation circuit.

A cathode-modulated r-f amplifier is easier to adjust than one which is grid-modulated. Audio modulating power required is less than for plate modulation but greater than for grid modulation.

Screen-grid Modulation. This method, not widely used, is a variation of plate modulation with tetrodes or pentodes. The screen grid controls plate current, and a linear relationship exists between screen voltage and plate current. With tetrodes, the screen grid should always be operated at a potential lower than that of the plate. To ensure this condition, the screen grid and plate are modulated together.

42·8   Frequency-modulation Method. In frequency modulation the a-f signal is applied to the circuit to be modulated in such a manner that the frequency of the output varies in accordance with the amplitude and frequency of the modulating signal. Frequency- and phase-modulation methods are similar in that a frequency change is produced as a result of a change in phase of the modulating wave. The carrier frequency is obtained from a vacuum-tube oscillator, whose output is changed in frequency by the a-f signal. A block diagram of a simple f-m system for varying frequency is shown in Fig. 42·10. The output from the speech amplifier is fed to a *reactance modulator*, which controls the oscillator frequency.

The *reactance tube* in the modulator of Fig. 42·10 draws a reactive current that varies with the modulating voltage. The system operates on

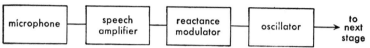

FIG. 42·10 Block diagram of f-m system for varying oscillator frequency.

the principle that any shift in phase will result in a corresponding shift in frequency. This is a comparatively simple method of producing frequency modulation and has the advantage of requiring the speech amplifier to deliver only a small value of output voltage.

A basic reactance-tube modulator circuit is shown in Fig. 42·11, in which a reactance tube and associated circuit is connected in parallel with an oscillator. The oscillator circuit consists of the tank circuit L_3 and

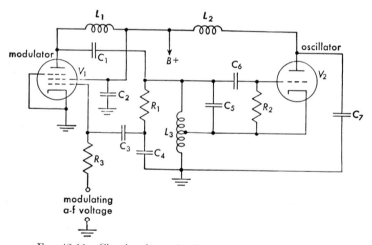

FIG. 42·11 Circuit schematic of reactance-tube modulator.

C_5, the grid capacitor C_6, the grid-leak resistor R_2, and the tube V_2. The output of the modulator tube, V_1, is connected through C_1, R_1, and C_4 to ground. This path is also parallel to that of the plate-supply circuit, which is through L_1, the plate supply, and to ground. Thus, the circuit comprised of C_1, R_1, and C_4 is in parallel with the internal resistance of V_1 to form a phase-shifting circuit connected across the oscillator tank. V_1, the reactance tube, draws a reactive current that will vary in accordance with the a-f voltage. This component of current appears through C_1, R_1, C_4, and to ground. Current through R_1 and C_4 is in phase with voltage across the tank circuit due to the low reactance of C_4 as compared with the resistance of R_1. Because the resistance of R_1 is purposely higher than the reactance of C_4, voltage across C_4 will lag the current by 90°. This voltage is applied through C_3 to the control grid of V_1, whose output current is in phase with the input voltage and thus lags tank-circuit voltage of V_2 by 90°. This reactive current has the effect of associating a reactance with the oscillator tank, which will affect the oscillator frequency. Therefore, frequency modulation with this method is obtained by applying the a-f modulating voltage to the control grid of the reactance tube, superimposed upon the r-f voltage. V_1 acts as an inductance in parallel with L_3, the effective inductance of both being less than that of a single inductance. As the inductance of V_1 is varied by the a-f voltage on its control grid, oscillator tank-circuit inductance is also varied, and the frequency of the oscillator will be modulated in accordance with variations of the a-f voltage.

REVIEW QUESTIONS

1. What is modulation and why is it necessary?
2. What is the difference between amplitude modulation and phase modulation?
3. What are side bands and how are they produced?
4. By what amount does each side band differ in frequency from the carrier?
5. What is modulation percentage?
6. What is one advantage of frequency modulation over amplitude modulation?
7. What is the difference between frequency deviation and carrier swing in frequency modulation?
8. Explain the difference between low-level and high-level modulation.
9. Explain the theory of plate modulation.
10. Explain the operation of a reactance-tube modulator.
11. What are the frequencies of interference and noise?
12. What determines bandwidth?
13. How is modulation percentage for an a-m wave computed?
14. Explain heterodyne action.
15. How is the modulation index of an f-m wave computed?
16. What would be the frequency of upper and lower side bands if a 700-kc carrier was modulated by 10.5 cps?
17. Why is cathode modulation considered to be a combination of grid and plate modulation?
18. What amount of power is contained in each side band of an a-m wave for 100 per cent modulation?
19. What are beat frequencies?
20. Explain the relation between carrier, side bands, and beat frequencies.

CHAPTER 43

ANTENNAS AND TRANSMISSION LINES

The prime function of a transmitter is to deliver r-f energy to an antenna so that it may be radiated through space and detected by remote receiving antennas. It is the purpose of the antenna to act as a connection between the transmitter, or receiver, and the conducting medium. Where the transmitter generates the energy and the receiver converts it to some form of intelligence, the antenna is the unit that couples these with space.

An antenna operates upon the principle of a voltage difference between two points setting up an electric field. Current between these two points of voltage difference sets up a magnetic field at right angles to the electric field. These two fields alternate about the antenna, building up to a peak, collapsing, and then building up to a peak in the opposite direction. As the fields alternate, a portion of the energy escapes, or is "radiated," into space in the form of electromagnetic waves that carry intelligence to receiving antennas, where the process is reversed.

43·1 Fundamental Principles. The principle of electromagnetic radiation is based on the law that a moving electric field creates a magnetic field and a moving magnetic field creates an electric field. The new field is always in phase in time with the moving field that created it; however, it is perpendicular to the parent field in space.

If a piece of wire is cut into two lengths and attached to the terminals of an r-f generator, as shown in Fig. 43·1a, the result is a basic *dipole* antenna. The length of the wire should be such that each section represents one-quarter of a wavelength of the generator frequency. At some instant when one side of the generator is positive and the other negative, there will be current, as shown in Fig. 43·1b. Electrons will flow away from the negative end of the antenna toward the generator terminal, while the positive end of the antenna will draw electrons toward it. Since the antenna is not a closed conductor and there is no place for the electrons to continue their travel after they reach the end, current at each end is zero and current distribution over the antenna is as shown. Although current distribution will always be the same, regardless of amount, cur-

rent amplitude at any given point will be determined by the amount of
voltage developed by the generator.   Therefore, if the generator output
is a sine wave, current amplitude will vary as a sine wave.

After one-quarter of a cycle, generator voltage is maximum and current
will decrease to zero, as shown in Fig. 43·1c.   Although there is no current,
there are extra electrons on one end of the dipole and a deficiency at the

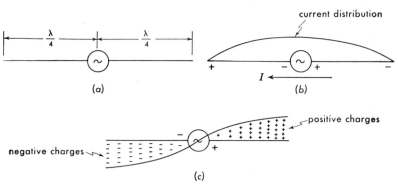

Fig. 43·1   Half-wave dipole charge and current distribution.

opposite end.   Since like charges repel, the charges will travel away from
the generator terminals towards the ends of the dipoles.   Therefore, as
with current distribution, charge distribution will be the same all along
the antenna.   The magnitude of charge will vary with the magnitude of
generator voltage.   Thus, the following conclusions can be drawn.   (a)
Current distribution will always be as shown in Fig. 43·1b, and its amplitude will vary sinusoidally with the gen-
erator voltage.   (b) A sinusoidal distribution of charge will exist on the antenna,
as shown in Fig. 43·1c, reversing position
every half-cycle.   (c) The sinusoidal
variation of charge magnitude lags the
sinusoidal current variation by 90°.

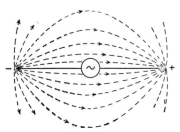

Fig. 43·2   Electric field around an
antenna.

43·2   Electric Field.   Of the two fields
set up around an antenna the *electric*, or
radiation, field is most important.   This
is shown in Fig. 43·2.   As the polarity
of generator voltage changes, the charges that produce this field are
constantly moving from one end of the antenna to the other.   First
one end of the antenna is positive, then at the zero point along the
sine wave no charge will exist, while on the next half-cycle, the antenna
will be positive at its opposite end.   The manner in which energy is
radiated is shown in Fig. 43·3.   In a, flux lines are shown to exist between
positive and negative charges.   In b the generator is approaching the zero

point of its sine wave, the antenna is nearly discharged, and the flux lines should reduce to zero and completely collapse; however, some flux lines are repelled by other lines nearer the antenna. These lines sometimes form a closed electric field in space, as shown in *c*. After these independent fields have been formed, the antenna charges in the opposite direction, as shown in Fig. 43·3*d*, and produces new flux lines that repel the fields

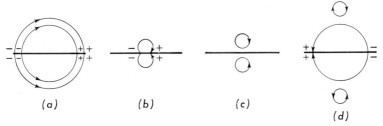

(a)   *(b)*   *(c)*

(d)

Fig. 43·3   Principle of electromagnetic radiation.

into space at the speed of light. Thus electromagnetic radiation has occurred, and it is these waves that carry the intelligence to a receiving antenna.

43·3   Magnetic Field. The magnetic field set up around an antenna is caused by the current through it. This is shown in Fig. 43·4. Because the current and charges which produce the two fields are 90° out of phase, the two fields will also be 90° out of phase. The amplitude of the magnetic field varies inversely as the square of the distance from the antenna. Although the magnetic field effect is quite local, magnetic lines of force may be "detached" from the antenna. Since these lines move away from the antenna, they will generate a perpendicular inphase electric field. Therefore, electromagnetic radiation from an antenna is comprised of the electric-generated and magnetic-generated fields.

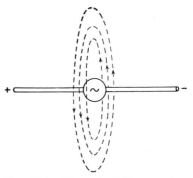

Fig. 43·4   Magnetic field around an antenna.

43·4   Basic Considerations. An antenna is a conductor or system of conductors which couples transmitters and receiving equipment with the conducting medium. It may consist of a single length of elevated wire for use with the ordinary broadcast receiver. However, for most other functions, many factors enter into the design, such as height above the ground, conductivity of the earth beneath it, and physical dimensions of the antenna. Also, in some applications, the antenna radiation must be directed between certain angles in either or both of the horizontal and vertical planes.

An antenna may be constructed to resemble a resonant two-wire line with the wires so arranged that the fields produced by the currents are added rather than canceled. Figure 43·5a shows an example where the earth acts as one conductor and enables the field to expand further in space than if the other conductor were nearby. Further, the fields will be detached more easily by rapid reversals of current. In Fig. 43·5b the currents cancel each other's fields. However, by spreading the ends of the two wires as shown in Fig. 43·5c, the currents now aid in producing a field in space.

Electrical Length. An antenna constructed of extremely fine wire and isolated perfectly in space will have an electrical length approximately

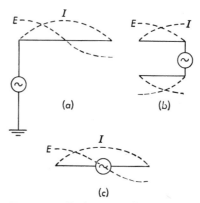

Fig. 43·5 Basic types of antennas.

equal to its physical length. Thus, a one-wavelength antenna for 20 meters would be 20 meters in length; a two-wavelength antenna for 20 meters would be 40 meters long; and a half-wavelength antenna for 20 meters would be 10 meters in length. This is under optimum conditions, however, since an antenna is rarely perfectly isolated. Because of this, a correction factor is employed. Although antenna length might vary with different installations, the following formula can be applied to determine the desired length of a half-wave antenna for a given frequency.

$$l = \frac{492 \times 0.95}{f} = \frac{468}{f}$$

where l = length, ft
f = frequency, Mc

Radiation Resistance. In a half-wave antenna the current is maximum at the center, whereas the voltage is minimum, as for a series-resonant circuit. Therefore, the impedance is minimum at the center and maximum at the ends. A generator supplying power to a series-resonant circuit works into only the resistance of the conductors because X_L and X_C cancel each other. Similarly, a half-wave dipole acts as a pure resistance consisting of the resistance of the wire and an intangible resistance known as *radiation resistance*. For a half-wave antenna it has been found to be approximately 73 ohms and represents the equivalent resistance which, if connected in place of the antenna, would dissipate the same amount of power as the antenna radiates into space.

Input Impedance. Antenna input impedance determines antenna current at the feed point for the value of r-f voltage at that point. It may be expressed mathematically by Ohm's law for alternating current:

$$Z = \frac{E}{I}$$

where Z = antenna impedance
E = r-f voltage
I = r-f current
Or it may be expressed:

$$Z = \sqrt{R^2 + X^2}$$

where R = input resistance
X = reactance

Because a half-wave dipole acts like a series-resonant circuit, it will exhibit either inductive or capacitive properties as the applied r-f signal is varied in frequency. If operated at its proper frequency, a half-wave dipole will be exactly one-half-wavelength long and offer a resistive impedance that is equal to its radiation resistance. If the frequency of the r-f signal increases, the antenna will no longer be one-half-wavelength long. It then represents a series circuit that is operating above its resonant frequency. Therefore, the inductive reactance is larger than the capacitive reactance and the antenna appears inductive to the transmitter. Conversely, as the frequency of the r-f signal decreases, the antenna will be less than a half-wavelength long, the capacitive reactance will be larger, and the antenna will appear capacitive.

Antenna Tuning. One of the purposes of antenna coupling circuits should now become obvious. A transmitter is designed to operate over a range of frequencies and usually with one antenna. As the frequency of the transmitter is shifted, the antenna input impedance varies and causes the electrical length of the antenna to vary. For maximum radiation it is necessary to have the antenna offer a resistive impedance. Coupling circuits accomplish this by the addition of inductors or capacitors which effectively increase or decrease the antenna's electrical length. An antenna whose input impedance at its base is resistive and capacitive can be electrically lengthened by the addition of sufficient inductance to counteract the increased capacitance. Conversely, an antenna that appears inductive could be electrically shortened and thus resonated by the addition of capacitance to counteract the increased inductance.

Polarization and Radiation. The position of an antenna in space determines the polarization of the radiated wave. Thus, an antenna which is vertical with respect to the earth will radiate a vertically polarized wave,

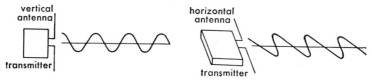

FIG. 43·6 Wave polarization.

while one which is horizontal will radiate a horizontally polarized wave. This is shown in Fig. 43·6.

Maximum radiation from a dipole antenna takes place at the center, because current is greatest at this point. The antenna is said to be directional along the line of strongest radiation, which is at right angles to a point of maximum current on the antenna. If a dipole antenna could be isolated in space, its radiation would be at right angles to the plane of the conductor and would resemble a doughnut, as shown in Fig. 43·7.

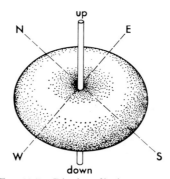

FIG. 43·7 Dipole radiation pattern.

43·5 Basic Antennas. The *Hertz* antenna consists of two lengths of wire, or tubing, each one-quarter-wavelength long at the desired frequency. It is known as a half-wave dipole, or half-wave *doublet*, and operates independently of ground. It thus has the advantage of allowing installation far above the surface of the earth or other absorbing bodies. A typical Hertz antenna is shown in Fig. 43·1.

The *Marconi* antenna is a vertical, quarter-wavelength antenna which utilizes the earth as one half of a half-wave antenna, as shown in Fig. 43·8.

Maximum current, therefore, is at the base rather than at the center, as with the half-wave dipole. When the Marconi antenna is used, the earth beneath it must be a good electrical conductor. This is sometimes done by driving copper tubing into the ground to increase conductivity. Where it is necessary to operate the antenna in some location far removed from the earth, a simulated ground is provided by using grounded metal rods at least a quarter-wavelength long placed at the base of the antenna. This simulated ground is called a "counterpoise."

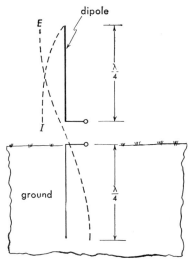

FIG. 43·8 Marconi antenna.

43·6 Transmission Lines. The term *transmission line* applies to a line that is used to conduct or guide electrical energy from one point to another. A common application would be in carrying 60-cps power from the generator where it is produced to the external circuit or equipment using it. An important application of transmission lines is in antenna systems, since almost all antennas are coupled or matched to transmitters by means of transmission lines. This is because transmitters are usually located within an installation while antennas are located outside at some distance from the transmitter.

Any transmission line has two ends, the end to which power is applied and the end at which it is delivered. Although various terminology is used in referring to these ends, in this text they will be referred to as the *input* end and the *load* end.

Equivalent Circuit. Any r-f transmission line will have a certain amount of resistance, inductance, and capacitance along its length, as shown in Fig. 43·9a. The resistance is that of the wires, with also a high leakage resistance between the two wires, because no material is a perfect

insulator. The capacitance is produced by the two conductors acting as
two plates of a capacitor separated by a dielectric, which, in this case, is
air or the insulating material. The inductance is generated as a result of
current which creates a magnetic field that expands and collapses along
the entire length of the line. For a short transmission line, the equivalent
circuit can be represented as consisting of a series LCR network, as shown
in Fig. 43·9b. In a transmission line, LCR quantities are distributed
throughout its length instead of being present in definite "lumps."
Therefore, where a short line may be represented by single values of LCR,
long lines must be represented by separated "segments," each corresponding to the distributed quantities of LCR along its length. Figure 43·9c
shows the equivalent circuit of three segments of a long transmission line
with the four properties of each segment lumped for explanatory purposes.

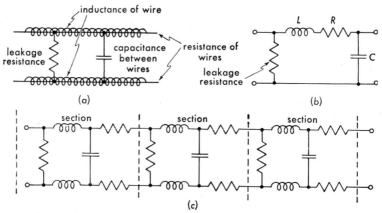

FIG. 43·9   Properties affecting transmission-line impedance and equivalent circuits.

When a transmission line is short as compared to the wavelength of r-f
energy it carries, opposition to input voltage is mainly at the load end.
For a line that is long compared to wavelength, the load must be of a
proper value or a mismatch will exist, resulting in a loss of energy between
transmitter and antenna.

Characteristic Impedance. When a transmitter is supplying r-f energy
to a transmission line, a voltage is impressed across the line, producing
current through it. The amplitude of current is determined by the LCR
of the line, which comprises its impedance. The ratio of voltage to current is its input impedance. To find the input impedance of a transmission line, the impedance of each section shown in Fig. 43·9c must be calculated by the formula $Z = E/I$. After each section has been calculated
and combined with those preceding, the over-all impedance will be found
to be of a lower value. The combined impedance of any number of consecutive sections is known as its *characteristic impedance* (Z_0), which has

an important function in transmission-line design. If a load equal to this impedance is placed across the load end of a line, the same impedance will appear at the input end. With an infinitely long line, r-f energy from the transmitter will travel down the line indefinitely. Therefore, the infinite line acts like a resistance equal in value to its characteristic impedance. If the line is replaced by a resistance equal to Z_0, the same amount of transmitted r-f energy will be dissipated in the resistor as was in the line. Under these conditions maximum transfer of power is realized. For example, a half-wave dipole has approximately 73 ohms impedance at its center. If a transmission line is constructed so that it has a Z_0 of 73 ohms, maximum power transfer will result and the line is said to be matched to the antenna.

43·7 Types of Lines. General sine waves of voltage and current exist along the length of an infinite line. Maximum points of voltage and current appear at the same points along this line; however, because of line losses their amplitude decreases with length in the form of damped oscillations. These waves of energy travel down the line toward its load end at a speed slightly less than the speed of light, or 186,000 miles per sec. If the load end of the line is open-circuited, the current must collapse to zero because there is no place for the electrons to go. This collapse of current causes the magnetic field set up by current to collapse also. Thus, the magnetic field cuts the conductors near the load end and induces additional voltage across the line, which sets up new voltage and current waves that travel back along the line toward the input end. These are known as *reflected waves*. In an open-end line, since current is zero and voltage is high at the output end, current and voltage are 90° out of phase after the reflected waves start. These reflected waves combine at some points with the input waves and reinforce, while at other points they cancel. The result is that the input and reflected waves combine and produce what are known as *standing waves* along the line. In either the closed-end or the open-end line, no power is delivered to the antenna. Moreover, a transmission line terminated in either a high or a low resistance as compared with Z_o will produce the same effect as with an open or closed end. Standing waves will be as shown in Fig. 43·10, in which the line used is a half-wavelength at the operating frequency, and the waves are shown only on one wire for simplicity.

Impedance Matching. When a line is terminated in a resistance equal to Z_o, the maximum and minimum values of current are the same, and the load is matched to the line. With the exception of line losses, all the energy is absorbed by the load and there are no standing waves.

If a transmission line with a characteristic impedance of 100 ohms were to be used to feed an antenna with 75-ohms resistance and 30-ohms inductive reactance at the operating frequency, a mismatch would occur. To overcome this mismatch, an intermediate element must be used between line and antenna. Such an element is called an *impedance-matching device*. For this purpose, a carefully constructed section of transmission line can be used. Because a line presents an impedance that varies with length, the properly selected additional length can serve as the matching element. Thereafter, the line would appear infinitely long.

Nonresonant Lines. If a load resistance equal to Z_o terminates the line, then the line is *matched*, or *flat*. There are no standing waves or reflected waves. By definition, a matched line is *nonresonant*. That is,

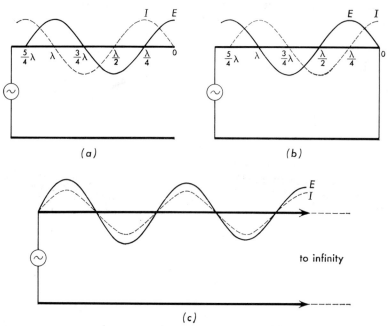

Fig. 43·10 Voltage and current comparisons for (*a*) open-end and high-resistance, (*b*) closed-end and low-resistance, and (*c*) line terminated in its characteristic impedance.

there is no reflection of energy and the transfer of energy to the load is maximum.

Resonant Lines. A line of finite length which is not terminated in its Z_o is called a *resonant* line. Such a line possesses reflected waves and standing waves of current and voltage. A resonant line is sometimes said to be resonant at an applied frequency, which means it is acting as a resonant circuit at some particular frequency. It may be either open or closed at its load end and is cut to some multiple of one-quarter wavelength.

Two-wire Open Line. This derives its name from the fact that the dielectric medium is air. It is also known as the *parallel-conductor* line because it is comprised of two parallel conductors separated by *insulators* or *spacers*. Although the balanced conductors act to reduce radiation loss, the balance is critical, and nearby metallic objects will cause unbalance which results in large radiation losses.   Its characteristic impedance, however, is relatively constant.   Current flows through the two parallel conductors in opposite directions.   If they are 180° out of phase, the fields nearly cancel and radiation losses approach zero.   This condition can be approached at relatively low frequencies; however, at higher frequencies the two currents tend to be more out of phase and radiation loss results.   The loss can be in turn reduced by moving the conductors

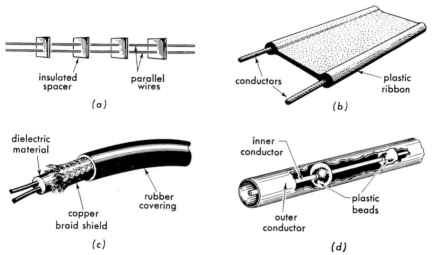

FIG. 43·11   Types of transmission lines.   (*a*) Two-wire open line.   (*b*) Insulated two-wire line.   (*c*) Shielded pair.   (*d*) Coaxial line.

closer together, but this lowers the characteristic impedance of the line. A two-wire open line is shown in Fig. 43·11*a*.

Insulated Two-wire Line.   The line shown in Fig. 43·11*b* is encased in a solid dielectric and has several advantages over the open line.   It is flexible and thus lends itself better to installation, while the dielectric is solid enough to maintain uniform spacing even when bent.   The main disadvantage is in the higher dielectric losses which lower its characteristic impedance.

Shielded Pair.   Another type of transmission line which represents an improved development is the shielded pair shown in Fig. 43·11*c*.   The two parallel conductors are imbedded in a solid dielectric, such as plastic copaline.   The insulated pair then is enclosed in a tube of braided copper, and the entire assembly is given a weatherproof coating.   Its principal advantage over other types is low radiation loss.   This is because the shield provides a uniform ground for both conductors, resulting in a well-balanced line and preventing stray pickup from external fields.

Coaxial Lines.   Another line is the coaxial, or concentric, type shown in Fig. 43·11*d*.   In this type of line one conductor is placed inside another to form a transmission line.   Usually, the line consists of a wire conductor placed inside a metal tube in an air dielectric.   The inner wire is maintained along the center axis of the metal tube by spacers, usually plastic beads.   This line operates efficiently at relatively high frequencies. Radiation losses are negligible because the outer conductor confines radiation to the space inside the line.   Therefore, external objects have no effect on transmission, and the result is a line definitely superior to the ordinary two-wire type.   A solid dielectric, such as flexible plastic, can be used to provide greater flexibility than with air; however, this increases the dielectric losses.

REVIEW QUESTIONS

1. What is the purpose of an antenna?
2. Explain how an electric field is set up around an antenna.
3. Explain the principle of radiation as applied to antennas.
4. Explain how a magnetic field is set up around an antenna.
5. Why is the electrical length of an antenna an important consideration?
6. How is antenna-input impedance determined?
7. Explain the polarization of antennas.
8. What effect does input frequency have upon the properties of an antenna?
9. Where does maximum radiation take place on an antenna?   Why?
10. Explain the principle of operation of a Hertz antenna.
11. Explain the principle of operation of a Marconi antenna.
12. What is the purpose of a transmission line?
13. How can a transmission line be expressed as an equivalent circuit?
14. What is characteristic impedance?
15. Why is it necessary that a transmission line work into a load equal to its characteristic impedance?
16. What are standing waves?
17. How are reflected waves produced?
18. What is the difference between resonant and nonresonant lines?
19. What is the advantage of a shielded pair over a two-wire open line?
20. How is impedance matching between transmission line and load accomplished?
21. What is antenna radiation resistance?
22. Explain the complete procedure involved in connecting a transmitter through a transmission line to an antenna.

CHAPTER 44

TYPICAL TRANSMITTER

The ultimate purpose of any circuit component is to function as an integral part of a complete unit. In transmitters, for example, each component performs a definite function toward the end result of generating and transmitting some form of intelligence to receiving antennas at remote points. This portion of the text deals with a typical transmitter that is in actual commercial use. It was chosen for its simplicity of design and because it incorporates almost all the principles previously studied. The various circuit components discussed in earlier chapters will be seen functioning individually to achieve the end result of comprising a basic transmitter. Moreover, this particular transmitter represents the fundamental type of system from which more complicated and elaborate transmitters are designed.

It is recommended that applicable portions of the text be reviewed in order to visualize more clearly how each component performs its individual function in conjunction with associate circuits.

44·1 General. Figure 44·1 is a block diagram of a basic transmitter that is available in "kit" form and specially designed for maximum versatility without involving complicated circuits. It features up to 75 watts input with three switch-selected crystal positions. Also included is controlled carrier-phone operation with provisions for variable-frequency oscillator (vfo) excitation. Output impedance is 50 to 1000 ohms through a pi-network (coaxial) output coupling. Either cw or phone operation is possible with the frequency of operation determined by crystals of vfo. The tuning range is limited to the 80, 40, 20, 15, 10, and 11 meter bands.

The transmitter consists of one power supply, three r-f stages, and two dual-triode audio stages. The pi-network output coupling is used to facilitate antenna matching. Panel controls consist of a key jack, operation switch, band switch, drive control, pilot light, final tuning, meter switch, and antenna tuning. The microphone connector, crystal switch, output connector, vfo input, and auxiliary power socket are located on the rear chassis apron.

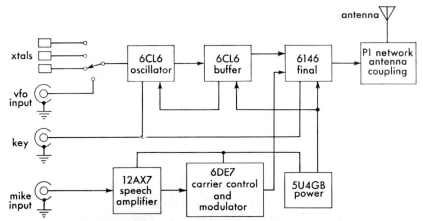

Fɪɢ. 44·1   Block diagram of basic transmitter. (*Heath Company.*)

44·2   Circuit Description.   *Oscillator.*   The oscillator circuit employs a type 6CL6 tube in a Colpitts circuit to provide efficient harmonic output for use on the high-frequency bands.   The plate tank circuit consists solely of a slug-tuned coil which is broadly resonant on 40 meters but serves as an r-f choke on 80 meters.   For operation on 80 through 10 meters, the oscillator-plate circuit tunes to 40 meters.

One of three crystals may be switched into the circuit by means of a double-pole switch which breaks both connections to the other two crystals to prevent interaction.   In the fourth position, the 6CL6 grid is connected to a jack for external vfo control and the cathode r-f choke is bypassed to ground.

Plate and screen voltage for the oscillator stage are derived from the buffer-stage cathode.   The two 6CL6 tubes are operated in series across the 600-volt power supply and are furnished approximately 300 volts each.   This arrangement eliminates the need for dropping resistors, which wastes power.

The 6CL6 buffer stage, in most cases, tunes the second, third, or fourth harmonics to obtain the desired frequency.   Because the r-f level required by the buffer stage is quite low, 80- or 160-meter crystals may be used for output on 80 meters without the necessity of resonating the oscillator-stage plate circuit to these frequencies.   It is recommended that only 160-, 80-, or 40-meter crystals be used, with 80- and 40-meter crystals preferred.   This is because some additional feedback may be required in the oscillator circuit for certain 160-meter crystals.   Sufficient grid drive to the 6146 final should be obtained from an 80-meter crystal for operation on 80 through 10 meters.   Only slightly more efficient operation is evident on the higher frequency bands by using a 40-meter crystal.

Buffer.   The buffer stage is coupled to the 6146 final amplifier by a pi-network circuit which has a tuning range limited to the amateur bands. This limitation prevents the tuning of a wrong harmonic which would be amplified by the 6146 stage. This method of coupling helps materially in stabilizing the final amplifier, at the same time attenuating higher order harmonics. The buffer stage has an independent filament supply to prevent heater-to-cathode breakdown, as the cathode potential is 300 volts above that of the other tubes.

Final Amplifier. The plate circuit of the final amplifier is shunt fed with a 2.5 mh r-f choke, and is capacity coupled into the pi-network tank

FIG. 44·2   Typical transmitter.   (*Heath Company.*)

circuit. For operation on 80 meters, a 68-$\mu\mu$f 4-kv fixed capacitor is automatically paralleled with the plate tuning capacitor by means of the band switch. A 900-$\mu\mu$f variable capacitor is permanently connected across the output of the pi circuit for antenna loading.

Modulator. A type 12AX7 tube is used as a high-gain, two-stage, resistance-coupled speech amplifier. The output of the speech amplifier is coupled to the 6DE7 through a low-capacity coupling capacitor. This low-capacity coupling, along with the 470-k and 100-$\mu\mu$f capacitor which forms the feedback circuit from the modulator cathode back to the speech-amplifier cathode, shapes the response to favor the voice frequencies. This permits the maintenance of a higher average level where it will be most effective.

Audio energy from the speech amplifier is coupled to the grid of one triode section of a 6DE7, which contains two triode sections. One section is rated at 1.5 watts dissipation and the other at 7 watts dissipation. The lower rated triode is used as a direct coupled driver, its plate being tied to the control grid of the heavier-duty triode which forms the modulator. This second triode is biased sufficiently to limit its conduction and therefore to limit the screen voltage on the final amplifier. This results in a low resting carrier.

With modulation, the conduction of the heavy-duty triode is varied in accordance with the average voice level. This gives a controlled carrier

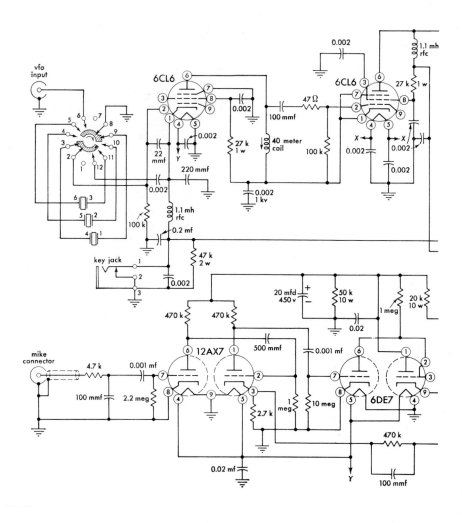

FIG. 44·3   Transmitter circuit

effect by varying the screen voltage on the 6146 tube at the same time as the audio signal is superimposed on this variable voltage. The net result is a carrier output which increases with the percentage of modulation applied.

Power Supply. The power supply consists of a transformer-operated, full-wave rectifier circuit with a choke-input filter. Two capacitors are operated in series to withstand the voltage involved. Two identical resistors across the filter capacitors serve a dual purpose of equalizing the filter voltage and acting as a bleeder resistor to stabilize the output under

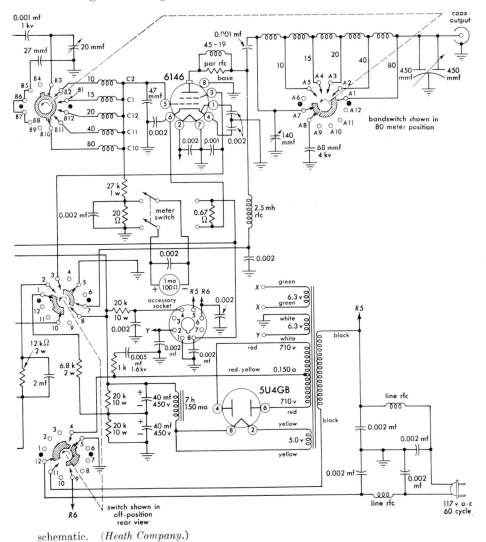

schematic. *(Heath Company.)*

varying load conditions. A 5U4GB tube is used as a rectifier. This is a heavy-duty version of the regular 5U4G. Some tube ratings have been slightly exceeded while others are operating under the maximum permissible. However, tests have indicated that by using the heavy-duty tube with a choke input and a light current load, no difficulty should be encountered.

44·3 Tuning Procedure. For the following tuning adjustments, an 80-meter crystal in the 3,500 to 3,600-kc range or a 40-meter crystal in the 7,000 to 7,200-kc range should be used. A vfo that tuned within these limits would also suffice. Install the crystal in any one of the three sockets and set the crystal selector switch for this socket or the vfo position. Set the band switch to 10 meters and connect a dummy load, such as a 40-watt light bulb, from the ground bolt to the center of the coaxial connector. Switch the meter to read GRID CURRENT. Set the operation switch to STAND BY and plug the line cord into a power source. Set the loading coil (antenna tuning) to zero, which is the position in which the capacitor is fully meshed. After about 2 minutes time for tube warmup, switch to the TUNE position. With the meter switched to read GRID CURRENT, depress the key and adjust the drive control for maximum grid-current reading. When this has been accomplished, release the key.

With an alignment tool or small screwdriver, turn the 40-meter adjustment coil counterclockwise to the end of its travel. Close the key and turn the coil in a clockwise direction until maximum grid current is indicated, then release the key. This does not mean that the oscillator-plate coil is tuned exactly to the frequency, however. Because the oscillator provides more than sufficient drive for the buffer stage, maximum grid-current reading to the 6146 final amplifier sometimes occurs when the oscillator coil is slightly off-tuned. In general, the coil should be adjusted for the highest grid-current reading near the range of frequencies in which operation is planned. Once adjusted, it can be left alone as long as sufficient drive is obtained.

On 10 meters with a 40-meter crystal, a higher reading is obtained with the tuning slug screwed out farther than with an 80-meter crystal. This, in effect, means that the oscillator is overdriving the buffer stage with a 40-meter crystal, and detuning the oscillator-plate circuit reduces the excess drive to the buffer stage.

Upon obtaining a reading at or near 3-ma grid current to the final amplifier, switch the meter to read PLATE CURRENT. Switch the operation switch to PHONE position and adjust the tuning control to obtain the lowest reading of plate current. This "dip" should occur near No. 90 on the dial with the band switch on 10 meters.

To load the antenna or dummy load, start with the antenna tuning control in the closed or "0" position. The final amplifier is always tuned to resonance. However, when the loading coil is moved during antenna tuning, the output circuit of the final amplifier is detuned and this has to be compensated for by redipping the final tuning control to resonance. Starting from a closed position, open the loading coil by adjusting the antenna tuning to No. 20 on the dial. Now return to the final amplifier and redip to minimum plate current by using the tuning control. Increase the loading to approximately No. 40 on the dial, then again redip the final amplifier. Continue increasing the loading and retuning for minimum final plate current until the dip is at or near the recommended "loaded" current of 125 ma in the c-w position.

Loading to the c-w rating and then shifting to the PHONE position is the customary procedure. With a constant audio tone of sufficient amplitude, the r-f output can be adjusted to maximum with greater ease.

44·4 Antenna Coupling. Since this transmitter is designed for single-ended, unbalanced operation, some means of balancing the output to the

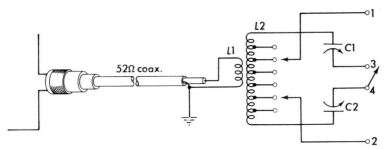

FIG. 44·4   Antenna coupler.   (*Heath Company.*)

transmission line must be provided. Balanced antenna systems should be fed through an antenna coupler so that neither the antenna nor either leg of the line will be at ground potential. Normally, the output of the transmitter is unbalanced since one side of the output circuit is grounded. Basically, an antenna coupler is an impedance matching device which transforms the impedance of the transmitter to the impedance of the transmission line.

A recommended antenna coupler is shown in Fig. 44·4. Coil $L1$ should match the impedance of the coaxial cable as closely as possible at the frequency of operation. The circuit consisting of $L2$, $C1$ and $C2$ must tune to the transmitting frequency. If it is desired to series tune the transmitter, the shorting bar between terminals 3 and 4 is opened and the transmission line connected at these points. For parallel tuning, terminals 3 and 4 are shorted and the transmission line is connected to terminals 1 and 2. Taps are provided on $L2$ to facilitate matching the transmission line.

The transmitter may be operated with several different types of antennas. For example, a tuned antenna fed with untuned feeders may be used. However, it should be cut to one-half wavelength for the frequency of operation and directly fed in the center with a 73-ohm coaxial line. A folded dipole could also be used if cut to one-half wavelength at the operating frequency and fed with balanced lines. Additionally, a long wire antenna equal to one-half wavelength at the lowest operating frequency could be used if connected through a suitable antenna coupler.

The proper antenna must be selected if the transmitter is to be effective. Attempting to load the transmitter to the wrong antenna will cause high percentages of reflected power to flow in the final amplifier tank circuit. This may damage the components in the final stage. Moreover, a mismatched antenna will be more susceptible to interference. Therefore, experimentation is sometimes necessary in order to produce the ideal choice.

REVIEW QUESTIONS

All questions are based on the circuit schematic in Fig. 44-3.

1. What would occur if the inductance of the plate tank coil of the oscillator increased in value?

2. What would be the effect upon circuit operation if the capacitor between pin 5 and ground in the buffer stage opened?

3. How would shorting one of the 470-k resistors in the 12AX7 plate affect circuit operation?

4. What effect would shorting the 27-k resistor in the screen circuit of the oscillator stage have upon circuit operation?

5. What is the purpose of the 12-k resistor in the cathode circuit of the 6DE7 tube?

6. What is the purpose of the two capacitors in the filament circuit of the buffer?

7. Explain the operation of the oscillator stage.

8. Explain the operation of the buffer stage.

9. Explain the operation of the final amplifier.

10. Redraw the power supply in simple form, showing it removed from the circuit in its entirety.

CHAPTER 45

RECEIVER INTRODUCTION

Another member of the family of equipment which comprises one basic electronic situation is the *receiver*. Where a transmitter originates, amplifies, converts, and broadcasts r-f signals through the medium of air, it is the function of the receiver to receive, amplify, and convert these signals to something useful, such as code, speech, music, or pictures.

Each receiver is designed for a specific purpose, such as for broadcast-band reception. Others are designed for the reception of frequencies in the vhf or uhf bands. The receiver which brings the television picture into the living room is also of a specific design.

45·1   Receiver Considerations. The basic communication receiver consists of a pickup device, which is the antenna; at least one tuned stage, tuned to the frequency of the desired incoming r-f signal; a demodulator or detector stage for converting the r-f to an a-f signal; and one or more amplifier stages to increase the amplitude of the signal to such an extent that it can be utilized. Additionally, for aural reception, a reproducer is necessary to convert the audio frequency energy to sound energy.

Any reliable receiver should have the following characteristics:

Sensitivity. This is generally defined as the receiver's ability to pick up and use weak signals. Actually, it is the characteristic which determines the minimum input-signal strength required for a given signal-output value. It is a measure of the receiver's ability to amplify the voltage induced into the antenna circuit until a specified level is present at the reproducing end. Sensitivity is largely determined by the number of amplification stages preceding the loud-speaker.

Signal-to-Noise Ratio. The amount of amplification in a receiver can be increased indefinitely; however, while the desired signal is being amplified, unwanted noises such as static and internal noises generated within the tubes are also being amplified. Thus, with excessive amplification, the noise may be loud enough to "drown out" the desired signal. Signal-to-noise ratio is defined as the ratio of the radio field intensity of a desired received wave to the radio noise field intensity received with the desired wave. A practical signal-to-noise ratio is about 10:1; that is, with a 10-μv signal, the noise level should be no greater than 1 μv.

Selectivity. A receiver should be designed so that it will select only the signal desired and discriminate against all others. Selectivity is defined as the characteristic which determines the ability of a receiver to reject undesired and untuned signals. The quality of the tuned circuits within the receiver mainly govern its selectivity.

FIG. 45·1 Communication receiver. (*Hammarlund Manufacturing Company.*)

Stability. This can be defined as freedom from change due to any cause. In a receiver it is the characteristic which determines the ability to remain tuned to a desired signal without being affected by changes in voltage, temperature, or amplitude. In a receiver with good stability there will be no fluctuations or frequency drift from the signal to which it is tuned.

Fidelity. This is defined as the degree of exactness with which a receiver reproduces an input signal. To maintain a high degree of fidelity, the receiver must be as free as possible from internally generated distortion and the tubes must be operated at their proper levels— normally Class A for all amplifiers.

45·2 Basic Requirements. It is the function of any receiving system to select one desired r-f signal out of the medium of air and convert it to intelligence of usable amplitude. In order to perform this function the receiving system must fulfill several basic requirements.

Antenna. In the study of transmitters, it was shown that the transmitted signal was produced by current through the transmitting antenna, causing an electromagnetic field to be radiated into the air. At the receiving antenna, this process is reversed. The flux lines in the electromagnetic field induce a current in the receiving antenna that is of the same phase and frequency as the transmitted signal. Although not of the same amplitude, it will contain the same type of *amplitude variations* that were present on the original signal. Therefore, one of the basic requirements of a receiving system is the antenna, which picks up the signal of r-f energy emanating from a transmitter.

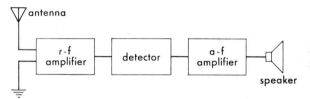

Fig. 45·2 Block diagram of a basic receiver.

Station Selector, or Tuner. Many unwanted signals are constantly present in the medium surrounding a receiving antenna. To select only the desired signal, some means of *tuning*, or *station selection*, must be provided. The tuning circuit consists of appropriate values of L and C, one or both of which will be variable so that the receiver may select one signal over a band of frequencies.

R-f Amplification. The signal at the receiving antenna is only of the order of microvolts and is therefore of little use unless amplified. Almost all receivers employ one or more stages of r-f amplification to increase the amplitude of the signal to a value sufficiently large to be useful.

Demodulator or Detector. Since some form of modulation is used in order that all signals may carry intelligence, some form of demodulation is necessary at the receiving end to convert the signals to their original form. The modulation envelope varies at an audio rate by an equal amount above and below zero. However, the average value of the modulation envelope is zero volts. It is the purpose of the demodulator, or detector, to rectify and change the average value of the modulated signal so that it varies at an audio rate.

A-f Amplification. Generally, the audio signal from the output of the detector is not large enough in amplitude to operate the reproducing device. One or more stages of a-f amplification are employed to increase the amplitude of the signal so that it may be converted into sound energy of useful amplitude. Audio amplifiers are inserted between the detector and the reproducer.

Reproducer. This is the headphone, loud-speaker, or any device that converts the electrical energy to sound energy that may be heard by the human ear.

45·3 Reception. Radio-frequency waves emanating from a transmitter travel through space at a speed of about 186,000 mi per sec. These waves strike receiving antennas in which they induce currents. The currents induced are alternating and of the same frequencies as the waves causing them. Since many transmitters operate at the same time as and in the vicinity of the receiving antenna, the antenna must select only the desired signal from all the others. Moreover, if several transmitting stations are operating within the receiving capabilities of the receiver, one may wish to tune the receiver through the range of frequencies involved. To do this, the receiver must be capable of selecting individually any of the frequencies within the band.

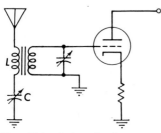

FIG. 45·3 A tuned-primary antenna circuit.

This may be accomplished by a circuit like that shown in Fig. 45·3. By selecting appropriate values of L and C, the antenna circuit may be made tunable over the entire band. When tuned to a particular frequency, the series-resonant antenna circuit will offer a very low impedance to this frequency, and current through the antenna will be maximum. Conversely, the antenna coil and associated capacitor will offer a high impedance to all other frequencies. At resonance, the high current through the antenna coil will cause flux lines to be set up around it. Because the secondary coil is within the area of influence of these flux lines, currents of the same frequency will be introduced into this coil. By tuning the secondary circuit to the same frequency as the primary, it will also select only the desired frequency and discriminate against all others. Thus both primary and secondary circuits combine in selecting only one desired frequency. With this arrangement it is possible to tune over the entire band, selecting any one of numerous frequencies at which signals are being transmitted.

45·4 Detection. The r-f amplifier produces both selectivity and amplification, and provides large pulses of voltage when properly tuned to the desired signal. However, the frequency of these voltages is within the r-f range, therefore some means must be provided to convert the r-f signal to an a-f signal.

Detection, or *demodulation,* is the process of recovering the intelligence from a modulated wave. When a modulated wave has been received, it is necessary to separate its audio component from its radio-frequency component and thus bring it within the audio range.

A simple detector is shown in Fig. 45·4. The r-f carrier is made to vary in amplitude at an audio-frequency rate at the transmitter. For any given cycle or combination of cycles, the average value of voltage is

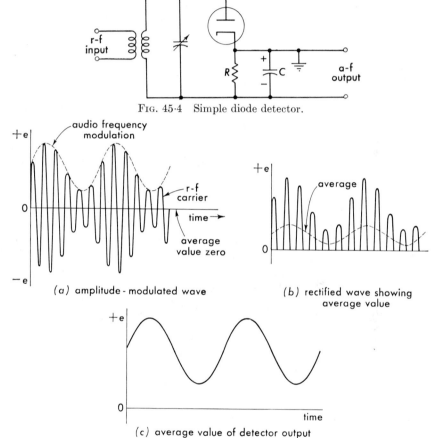

FIG. 45·4 Simple diode detector.

(a) amplitude - modulated wave

(b) rectified wave showing average value

(c) average value of detector output

FIG. 45·5 Diode detector input and output wave forms showing shifting of average value.

zero as shown in Fig. 45·5a. The modulated wave is induced in the tuned circuit by transformer action. Current will flow only on the positive half-cycles of the r-f voltage, or when the plate is positive with respect to the cathode. The rectified output, shown in Fig. 45·5b, consists of a series of r-f pulses that increase and decrease at an a-f rate. However, the average value of voltage has been shifted and is no longer zero but some greater value as shown in Fig. 45·5c. Moreover, its frequency is the same as the frequency of the modulating signal.

Filtering. Although a diode detector produces an audio voltage, the output is not a smooth outline or envelope. However, by proper selection of *C*, the output voltage will more closely approach a smooth audio wave. For example, in Fig. 45·6a, *C* charges to the peak value of r-f voltage during the first quarter-cycle. As the applied r-f voltage falls below its peak value, *C* discharges through *R* and helps maintain this voltage as shown between points *b* and *c*. When the r-f voltage on the next cycle exceeds the value at which *C* maintains a voltage at the cathode (point *c*), current again flows and *C* charges to the peak value of the second half-cycle as shown at point *d*. Thus the voltage across the capacitor follows the peak value of the applied r-f voltage and reproduces the a-f modulation. Therefore, the detector output after rectification

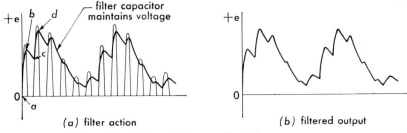

(a) filter action   (b) filtered output

Fig. 45·6   Action of filter on diode detector output.

and filtering is a direct voltage that varies at an audio rate as shown in Fig. 45·6b.

The detector output shown is not a smooth audio wave form. However, the r-f component is negligible, and, after being amplified, the original intelligence is faithfully reproduced.

45·5 Reproduction. The output of the a-f amplifier in a receiver is in the form of alternating current varying at an a-f rate. It is the purpose of a reproducing device such as a headphone or loud-speaker to change these variations into sound waves. Therefore, the sound reproducer must be designed to vary the surrounding air pressure in accordance with the a-c signal.

Any device, such as the human vocal chords, that produces sound must vary the pressure of the surrounding air. Musical instruments, for example, make use of this principle. When a piano key is struck, a taut wire is caused to vibrate. This wire vibrates on both sides of its normal resting point and either compresses or rarefies the air around it, as shown in Fig. 45·7. When the wire vibrates in the direction of the ear, the air on that side will be compressed; when it vibrates in the opposite direction, the air on the side nearest the ear will be rarefied. These varying pressure waves strike the eardrum and produce the sensation of sound. The number of complete vibrations per second determines the frequency or pitch of the sound wave. The intensity is determined by the amount of displacement of the wire from its resting point.

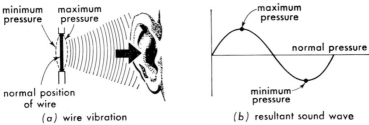

(a) wire vibration   (b) resultant sound wave

FIG. 45·7 Action of vibrating wire in producing sound waves.

The human voice covers the range of approximately 60 to 10,000 cps and has an intensity, or amplitude, that may vary in the ratio of 10,000 to 1. The frequency range of music is in the range of approximately 40 to 15,000 cps with an intensity variation that may be as great as 100,000 to 1.

Crystal Headphone. One type of reproducing device is the crystal headphone shown in Fig. 45·8a. This makes use of the piezoelectric

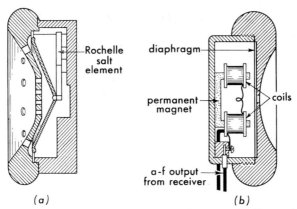

(a)   (b)

FIG. 45·8 Types of headphones. (a) Crystal. (b) Dynamic.

effect of Rochelle salt crystals, which generates a voltage under the stress of a mechanical pressure and produces a mechanical force when a voltage is applied. The amplified a-f signal is applied to the metal plates of the Rochelle salt-crystal element, causing the crystal to change its shape by contracting and expanding. This movement of the crystal produces pressure variations in the surrounding air that result in audible sound.

Magnetic Headphone. Most headphones are of the dynamic type shown in Fig. 45·8*b*. A coil of wire is wound on each pole of a U-shaped permanent magnet, with the coils in series and the a-f signal applied to external connections. A movable diaphragm of soft iron is placed a fraction of an inch from the pole ends.

When there is no signal to the coils, the permanent magnet exerts a constant pressure on the diaphragm and causes it to be pulled some distance from its normal position. When the a-f signal flows through the coils, they become electromagnets and create a magnetic field that either aids or opposes the field of the permanent magnet. On one half-cycle the fields will aid the field of the permanent magnet and the diaphragm will be pulled further inward toward the permanent magnet's poles. On another half-cycle, the field will oppose the field of the permanent magnet and the electromagnetic field produced by the coils will cancel some of the permanent-magnet field. This causes the diaphragm to move outward and compresses the air in front of it. By moving in and out at the rate of the a-f signal applied, the diaphragm produces sound waves of the same frequency.

Output. Normally, one or more stages of audio-frequency amplification are inserted between the detector's output and the input to the headphone or loud-speaker. This accomplishes two purposes. First, all the r-f components of the detected modulation envelope are eliminated, leaving only an a-f variation. Second, the audio variation is amplified in terms of current so that the reproducer will receive sufficient current to reproduce properly. Therefore the final audio amplifier should in almost all cases be a power amplifier.

45·6 Receiver Antennas. The type of antenna used with a receiver should have the same characteristics as the transmitting antenna. If the transmitting antenna is horizontal, the receiving antenna should also be horizontal. An example of aspects of similarity is offered by the smaller, lightweight two-way radios used by police patrols, taxis, etc. These use a switching arrangement whereby on TRANSMIT an antenna is connected to the transmitter output and on RECEIVE the same antenna is switched and connected to the receiver input.

A receiving antenna should feed as much desired signal and as little noise and undesired signal as possible to the receiver. The term *noise*, such as that from internal-combustion engines, electric razors, fluorescent lights, etc., is meant to include all frequencies. A noise signal may have a basic frequency but is also comprised of almost an infinite number of odd and even harmonics. Filters can hardly eliminate all frequencies, especially at the receiver's input, which must be tunable over a range of frequencies. Therefore, receiving antennas are usually placed as far as possible from such interferences.

At some fixed installations where the reception is to be from one direction, the antenna can be made highly directional. There are several types of directional antennas, the theories of which are not essential to this text. However, increasing the directivity, or "beaming," of both the transmitting and the receiving antenna can increase the distance over which a useful signal may be utilized. Beaming techniques are employed considerably for commercial and government broadcasting.

45·7 Antenna Coupling Systems. Designing the receiving antenna to pick up maximum energy from the ether with a minimum of interference accomplishes nothing if some inefficient method of coupling the signal into the receiver is employed. The better the antenna and the more efficient the coupling system, the fewer stages of amplification and the less power required to operate the receiver.

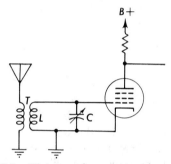

Fɪɢ. 45·9   High-impedance antenna coupling.

One of the most common methods of coupling the signal voltage induced in the antenna to the grid of the first r-f amplifier is the *high-impedance coupling* circuit shown in Fig. 45·9. In this circuit the voltage induced in the antenna causes a current in the primary of the antenna coil. This current induces a voltage in the secondary circuit, which consists of a series LCR network. The resistive component is the effective resistance of the coil itself. Although schematically the circuit might appear to be a parallel arrangement, it is in every respect a series connection. L is in series with its own resistance R, and C. If the circuit is operating at resonance, the impedance will be low, and a large secondary current will be produced. This large current will develop a large voltage across C, which will appear as the voltage difference between grid and cathode of the tube. The greater the amplitude of the voltage variation on the grid, the greater the amplitude of changes in tube current and output variations. Any signal picked up by the antenna other than the resonant frequency to which the secondary circuit is tuned will still be coupled through in this type of system. However, impedance offered to this unwanted signal will be considerably greater. Thus current will be less, and negligible voltage will be developed across the capacitor, with a resultant reduction in plate variations.   Therefore, the secondary circuit is contributing to the receiver's selectivity.

There are two major requirements for any antenna coupling system. First, the system must have a uniform gain over the entire operating frequency range of the set.   Second, the primary winding, together with stray capacitances, should not become resonant at any frequency within the range of the receiver.   These two requirements should be satisfied regardless of the type of coupling system or antenna employed.   The first requirement can usually be satisfied by use of an antenna that will be at least one-quarter-wavelength long at the lowest frequency.   The second can be satisfied by using as much inductance in the primary coil as is necessary to ensure resonance with the stray capacitances at a frequency below the range of the receiver.   Since the antenna wire and the surface of the earth effectively form two plates of a capacitor, raising or lowering

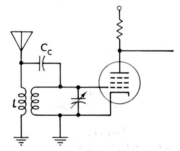

Fig. 45·10   High-impedance coupling with a compensating capacitor.

the antenna to separate or bring together the "plates" may also assist in satisfying the second requirement.

There is a second advantage in using a high value of primary inductance in the antenna coil.   If L is high, then X_L will be rather high even at the lower frequencies.   This prevents a loss in signal and aids in maintaining a uniform response over the entire range of the receiver.   However, at higher frequencies an increase in X_L, together with a decrease in the X_C of the stray capacitances, might produce a loss in the desired signal.   Figure 45·10 shows the corrective measure to be taken to preclude such a signal attenuation.   A capacitor is connected across the top, or "hot" side, of the antenna coil from primary to secondary.   At low frequencies X_C is large enough so that little or no energy is coupled by any means other than inductive coupling between primary and secondary.   At higher frequencies, as the X_C of the stray capacitances begins to shunt the signal around L, the X_C of C_C also decreases and an increased amount of energy is coupled indirectly into the secondary circuit.   In the interests of economy this is accomplished in many antenna coils by a turn of wire wrapped around the secondary.   This single turn acts as one plate while the secondary acts as the other.   The result is approximately 5 $\mu\mu f$ of capacitance which, in an ordinary broadcast-band receiver, is enough to offset most of the losses.

The amount of inductance in the secondary circuit is determined by the range of frequencies to be covered by the receiver.   It is usually computed by solving for an inductance whose reactance equals that offered by the variable capacitor in the middle of its range.   The inductance of the secondary is usually less than that of the primary; this results in a loss of gain.   However, the loss of gain is not usually considered as important as the uniformity of gain obtained with a large primary inductance.   The over-all signal gain between antenna and grid of the first r-f amplifier is usually from about three to eight.

REVIEW QUESTIONS

1. What are the basic parts of a receiver?   Explain the purpose of each.
2. Define sensitivity.
3. What is meant by signal-to-noise ratio?
4. Define selectivity.   What determines the selectivity of a receiver?
5. What is stability and how is it obtained?
6. How is good fidelity achieved?
7. What are the basic requirements of a typical receiver?
8. Explain how it is possible to select one signal from several around a receiving antenna.
9. What is the purpose of demodulation?
10. Explain the operation of a diode detector.
11. Why is the output of a diode detector not a smooth wave form?
12. Why is it necessary to filter the output of a diode detector?
13. Explain the principle of operation of a crystal headphone.
14. Explain the principle of operation of a dynamic headphone.
15. What are some of the characteristics of a receiver antenna?
16. What is the purpose of an antenna coupling system and why is this system necessary?
17. Explain the operation of a high-impedance antenna coupler.
18. Explain how filtering helps smooth the output of a diode detector.
19. What are some of the requirements of an antenna coupling system?
20. Which is the most important of the five basic receiver characteristics?   Why?

CHAPTER 46

TRF RECEIVER AND RECEIVER CIRCUITS

The tuned radio-frequency (trf) receiver employs one or more stages of r-f amplification, a detector, and one or more stages of a-f amplification. Antenna considerations are similar to those of the basic receiver discussed in Chap. 45. However, the trf differs from the basic in that ganged tuning procedures are employed. Also, the trf might use any one of several detector circuits, depending upon several considerations, such as strength of signals to be detected, strength of audio signal required, and the type of transmission (c-w, mcw, voice, etc.) to be received.

46·1 TRF Receiver Considerations. Figure 46·1 shows a block diagram of a basic trf receiver. The r-f amplifier may consist of several

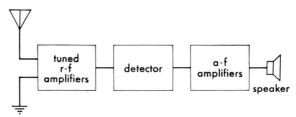

Fig. 46·1   Trf receiver block diagram.

amplifier tubes together with their associated tuned circuits. The a-f amplifier section may consist of one or more audio-amplifier tubes together with their associated a-f components. The last or final a-f amplifier may be of either voltage or power type depending upon the type of reproducer to be employed. If headphones are to be used, a voltage amplifier will usually suffice; if a speaker is to be used, power amplification is necessary.

Ganged Tuning. Figure 46·2 is a diagram of the first two stages of a trf receiver and the input to a detector. The dotted lines attached to each variable capacitor and the horizontal dotted line comprise a schematic indication that the three capacitors are tuned simultaneously. There are several justifications for this means of varying the frequency of the r-f amplifiers. To tune the entire receiver effectively to the frequency of the desired signal, each stage must itself be tuned.   Tuning each stage individually would necessitate too many front-panel controls. Another and more important reason for ganged tuning is that unless the stages are individually calibrated and the frequency of the incoming signal is known, considerable time would be required to adjust each control for maximum signal through that stage.   With *ganged* tuning it is not necessary to know the frequency of the incoming signal.   The one tuning control is varied through the range of frequencies until the circuit is resonant at the frequency of the desired signal.   Moreover, it is more economical to utilize three separate capacitors mounted on a single shaft, connected to the front panel, and controlled by only one knob.

The stators of each capacitor are electrically separated from each other and are the "hot" sides.   The rotors of each are connected to the shaft,

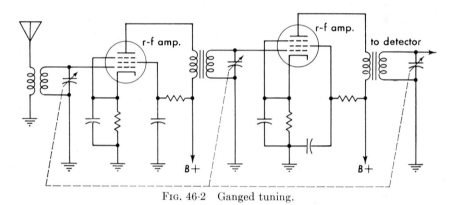

Fig. 46·2   Ganged tuning.

which is grounded.   This protects the operator from any voltages and also tends to eliminate stray interference introduced into the circuits from the operator's body.   Such interference is called *body capacitance* and, besides causing interference, can effect a shift in frequency of the tuned circuits.   Body capacitance results when the operator's body acts as one plate of a capacitor while the ungrounded shaft and rotor plates act as the other.   This added "capacitor" changes the total capacitance in the circuit and thus changes the resonant frequency.   Therefore, rotor shafts must be grounded.

Alignment is the one minor disadvantage of ganged tuning.   Since there can be no perfect capacitor and since the degree of imperfection varies slightly in each one, no two capacitors even if rated the same will possess the same capacitance.   For example, the rotors on the second capacitor in Fig. 46·2 might not be perfectly aligned with the rotors of the capacitor in the detector input circuit.   Therefore, as the shaft is rotated, at no point will the amount of mesh between rotors and stators be the same for both capacitors.   As a result, at no time will both tuned circuits be tuned to exactly the same frequency.

Trimmers.   Usually, by means of a small compression-type variable capacitor in parallel with each individual capacitor, the total capacitances of each circuit can be made the same.   This additional capacitor is called a *trimmer*.   Another aid in alignment is to employ capacitors with one rotor positionable, or slotted, so that the effective surface area can be varied slightly or the distance between the one rotor and its stator can be varied.   In alignment procedures it is general practice to use the parallel trimmer capacitor for alignment at the low end of the frequency band and to adjust the rotors at the high end of the band.   Alignment has been defined as *the process of adjusting all the tuned circuits of a receiver so that they receive, with maximum sensitivity, any desired signal within the frequency range of the receiver.*

The equipment needed to accomplish alignment of almost any type of receiver consists primarily of an r-f signal generator to develop the signals with known amplitude and known frequencies; an aligning screw driver, usually of Bakelite or something equally nonconducting; and some form of a-c voltmeter to observe the receiver's output, because the human ear is not sufficiently sensitive to peak adjustments.

46·2   Pentodes in the TRF Receiver.   Pentodes have a higher gain than triodes and are usually more desirable as amplifiers in most receivers. They permit operation with circuits of higher values of Q and thus cause the receivers to be more selective than if triodes were used.

Sometimes triodes operate with a tuned grid circuit and are transformer-coupled to another tuned circuit.   Under these conditions there is always a tendency for the triode to act as a tuned-plate–tuned-grid oscillator and introduce unwanted spurious noise signals into the receiver. Because of the rather large value of plate-grid capacitance, there is always a possibility that regenerative feedback of sufficient amplitude might cause the circuit to oscillate.   Conversely, it is possible that a degenerative signal might be fed back from plate to grid and reduce the gain to a point of unsatisfactory receiver operation.   For these reasons, triode amplifiers are generally unsatisfactory.

46·3   Heterodyne Action.   The terms *beat note, zero beat, sum frequency,* and *difference frequency* each pertain to some function of *heterodyne* action referred to in Fig. 46·3.   *Hetero* means *to mix* and *dyne* is a unit of force, thus, heterodyne action in receivers can be considered as a mixture of two signals.

When two signals of different frequencies are received across a nonlinear impedance, new frequencies will be generated.   A *nonlinear impedance* is any device that will not deliver the same voltage or voltage variations at its output that it received at its input.   For example, an amplifier that is operating on a nonlinear portion of its E_g–I_p curve is considered a non-linear impedance device. Any signal received by the amplifier would not be amplified linearly, and new frequencies would be generated. These new frequencies are equal to the sum of the original frequencies and the difference between them. Further, the two original frequencies would be present in the output.

Heterodyne Detection. C-w transmission consists only of a carrier frequency interrupted at a coded rate. There is no amplitude modulation from which speech intelligence can be determined. Therefore, a detected c-w transmission is without variations, even though its average value may be something greater than zero. In Fig. 46·3 the carrier frequency

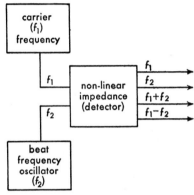

Fig. 46·3   Heterodyne action.

and an oscillator frequency are fed into a detector which functions as a nonlinear impedance. The oscillator is operating at, say, 1,000 cps above the carrier frequency. If the carrier frequency is assumed to be 100 kc, the oscillator will be operating at 101 kc, or carrier frequency plus 1,000 cps. The combining or "mixing" takes place in the electron stream of the tube, or at its input. The *sum frequency* will be 100 plus 101 kc, or 201 kc. The *difference frequency* will be 101 minus 100 kc, or 1,000 cps. The difference frequency is in the audible range and can be heard by the human ear. At the output of the detector there is usually a filter of the π type that will reject any frequencies other than those within the audible range. Thus, the 1,000-cps signal will be passed, amplified, and delivered to the speaker. During the time when no carrier frequency is present, there will be no heterodyne action and the 1,000-cps oscillator frequency will not be heard. Therefore, only when the carrier is present will there be an audible note from the speaker and will the code that was originated at the transmitter be reproduced. Although there are a few other methods for detecting c-w transmissions, none seem to be as simple or practical.

Beat Frequency Oscillator. The oscillator that generates the mixing signal is called the *beat frequency oscillator* (BFO) because its frequency and that of the carrier are "beat" together. The BFO has a variable capacitor which is almost always gang-tuned with those of the amplifier to ensure that the difference frequency remains the same. Further, a trimmer capacitor with a front-panel control is also used to vary the frequency of the BFO by a few hundred cycles so that the difference frequency need not be exactly 1,000 cps. Because some persons find listening to certain audio frequencies unpleasant, for operator convenience a c-w pitch control is employed.

Frequency Measurement. Another useful example of heterodyne action is in frequency measurement. If two equal frequencies are combined across a nonlinear impedance, their difference frequency will be 0 cps. If one frequency is variable, beating it with an unknown frequency will produce an audible beat note when both are approaching the same frequency. The tone of the note will depend upon the frequency difference between them. By varying one frequency until the pitch of the audible note decreases and it fades out entirely, zero beat is reached and the two signals are of the same frequency. Thus, the zero beat between two frequencies indicates that the two frequencies are the same, and the unknown frequency is determined by comparison. This is the theory of most equipment-tuning and -measuring operation.

46·4 Multiunit Tubes. For purposes of economy and simplicity, tubes have been designed for receiver use that employ the elements of two

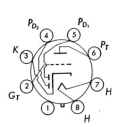

FIG. 46·4 A circuit schematic of a type 6SQ7 multiunit tube.

or three tubes in one glass or metal envelope. One example is the type 6SQ7 dual diode-triode shown in Fig. 46·4. With tubes where the cathode or filament voltage is common, the same cathode or filament may be used for more than one type of screen or anode. This provides the advantage of less power required for one filament, or fewer connecting wires for one cathode. The 6SQ7 often uses the diode sections for full-wave detection and the triode section for the first a-f amplifier. Full-wave detection is the same in principle as half-wave detection, although average voltage is slightly higher. However, one of the diode sections is more often used for half-wave detection while the other is used to provide automatic-volume-control (avc) voltage (Sec. 47·2).

46·5 Grid-Leak Detector. The grid-leak detector shown in Fig. 46·5 functions like a diode detector and triode amplifier. The grid and cathode are connected as a diode detector, with the triode grid acting as the plate of a diode. The grid-leak resistor forms the load for the diode circuit and the grid capacitor is the r-f bypass, or filter capacitor, in the circuit. This capacitor should have a high impedance at audio frequencies and a low impedance at radio frequencies. The grid is operated at zero bias under no-signal conditions.

When a modulated signal is applied to the circuit, current flows only on the positive half-cycles and rectification results. When the plate is positive, the voltage across the grid-leak resistor causes the triode grid (diode plate) to be negative with respect to the cathode. This results in biasing the triode grid.

Because the bias for the triode is produced by rectifying the modulated signal voltage, the bias increases and decreases at an a-f rate. Although the tube is operated at zero bias initially, after the signal is applied the grid draws current, and after a few cycles a steady d-c bias is established

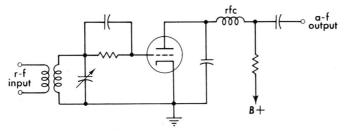

FIG. 46·5   Grid-leak detector.

between grid and cathode. Thereafter, the a-f signal varies the grid voltage above and below the steady d-c bias under approximately Class-A conditions during normal signals.

Maximum plate current occurs when no signal is being received. This is because there is no bias voltage being developed by the grid leak during the time when no signal is applied. Because the triode-plate current is determined by the grid voltage, the a-f voltage appears across the external plate resistance. The r-f voltage also appears in the plate circuit but is bypassed to ground by the plate capacitor. Therefore, in a grid-leak detector, the detection occurs in the grid circuit and the resulting a-f voltage is amplified in the plate circuit.

46·6 Plate Detector. In the plate detector shown in Fig. 46·6, the r-f signal is first amplified in the plate circuit and then detected in the same circuit.

The grid is biased almost to plate current cutoff by the average plate current flowing through the cathode resistor. As a result, the negative half-cycles of the r-f voltage cause little or no variations in plate current. Moreover, the average value of plate current increases as the strength of the applied signal is increased, which is an effect opposite to that of the grid-leak detector.

On the positive half-cycles of r-f input, a plate current will be produced that varies with the amplitude of the modulating wave. This variation corresponds to the desired a-f voltage. Bias voltage is held constant across R_k between positive half-cycles by the action of C_k. This action is similar to that of the capacitor across the load of a diode-detector circuit. However, the time constant of the RC network should be long compared with the lowest a-f cycle.

Filtering is accomplished by the two capacitors and rfc in the plate circuit, which comprise a low-pass filter. Audio frequencies are passed while radio frequencies are rejected.

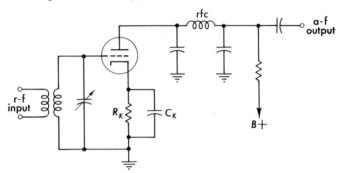

Fig. 46·6   Plate detector.

46·7 Detector Characteristics. *Diode.* The diode detector will handle strong signals from local stations with little or no distortion. It also provides avc voltage which other types of detector do not provide, unless additional tubes and associated circuits are used.

The diode detector draws power from the input circuit which prevents it from being a sensitive type of detector. The diode and its load form a low-impedance shunt across the tuned input circuit. This causes the sensitivity, selectivity, and Q of the circuit to be lowered. Moreover, diode-interelectrode capacitance limits its usefulness on high-carrier frequencies. Because the diode detector distorts on weak signals, several stages of amplification are usually needed to build the signal to a sufficient value for detection.

Grid-Leak Detector. One disadvantage of the grid-leak detector is its inability to reproduce large input signals faithfully. Because signals of large amplitude will cause the grid bias to shift considerably beyond normal, incomplete rectification will result. Therefore, since this type of detector depends for operation on a certain amount of grid current, a loading effect is produced which lowers the sensitivity of the input circuit. It has a high sensitivity, however, on low-amplitude signals.

Plate Detector. The plate detector has fair sensitivity, but its selectivity is excellent. This is because it does not draw grid current on normal signals and therefore has little loading effect on the input-tuned circuit. Additionally, distortion is negligible on uniformly large signals. One disadvantage is its inability to handle very large signals without being overloaded.

46·8 Cross Talk, or Cross Modulation. The E_g-I_p curve shown in Fig. 46·7 is that of a sharp-cutoff tube. The bend of the knee of the curve is very shallow, and plate-current changes are very rapid for corresponding grid-voltage changes. When a receiver is tuned to a weak signal that is close in frequency to a strong signal, the latter will often be sufficiently large to develop a grid-to-cathode signal. This signal operates the tube over the rapidly changing portion of its E_g-I_p curve, sometimes to the extent that plate current will be cut off for portions of the strong input signal.

If a tube is cut off for a portion of the input cycle, it is detecting or rectifying. The resultant plate current will contain components of the

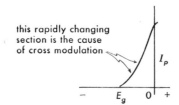

FIG. 46·7 E_g-I_p curve of sharp-cutoff tube.

desired signal and its modulation, together with a new component caused by plate detection of the strong signal. This new component is an additional modulation of the weak signal and contains the a-f modulation component of the strong signal. Since the a-f component of the strong signal is now superimposed on the weak signal, no extent of tuning or filtering will enable the receiver to be sufficiently selective to eliminate the undesired component. The result is that the receiver will have two signals at its output at the same time. This is known as *cross modulation*, or *cross talk*. In this example, cross modulation resulted from plate detection in the first r-f amplifier.

Another source of cross modulation is that which could result from detection in the antenna circuit across a high-resistance point, for example, the point across which the antenna coil secondary is connected to the grid of the first r-f amplifier.

Variable-μ Tube. A tube type which has reduced cross modulation is the variable-μ, or remote-cutoff tube. In this type the grid spacing, or the physical distance between the wires of the grid mesh, is varied. When large signals are being received, the effect of this varied spacing is not too pronounced; however, when the tube is operating on the nonlinear portion of the curve with weak signals, more electrons reach the plate. This is because the grid spacing does not stop as many electrons as would a grid with more closely spaced wires. Therefore, the slope of the knee of the $E_g–I_p$ curve is changed, and the rate of change in plate current for a corresponding change in grid voltage is not as rapid. Thus, when a strong signal is picked up and a large grid-to-cathode voltage is developed,

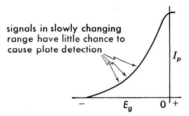

signals in slowly changing
range have little chance to
cause plate detection

Fig. 46·8 $E_g–I_p$ curve for variable-μ tube.

the tube is not as likely to be cut off. If plate current is not cut off, no detection will result and cross modulation is eliminated.

R-f Gain. Another function of the variable-μ tube is to control the r-f gain of a receiver. This is accomplished in conjunction with a variable resistor connected in series with the cathode to vary the bias of the stage. For a given current, as cathode resistance increases, bias will also increase and shift the operating level of the tube. As operating level is shifted,

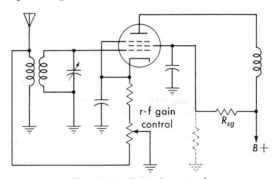

Fig. 46·9   R-f gain control.

the gain of the stage will vary. Therefore, increasing cathode resistance will decrease the gain of the stage.

A basic r-f gain control circuit is shown in Fig. 46·9. This circuit has the disadvantage of screen voltage varying and opposing an increase in stage gain. As the gain control is adjusted for an increase in gain, the bias on the tube will decrease. However, space current and screen current will increase, causing screen voltage to decrease and thus oppose the increase in gain. With the addition of a bleeder resistor as shown by the dotted lines, screen current will comprise only a portion of the total current through the resistor. Therefore, screen-current changes resulting from bias changes will have less effect upon screen voltage. This added resistor is called the *screen-grid stabilizing resistor*.

The resistor shown in series with the r-f gain control in Fig. 46·9 is to maintain a minimum bias on the tube when the gain control is set for maximum gain. This is to protect the tube and minimize grid current which introduces distortion of the desired signal that is manifested as noise.

The top of the antenna primary coil is connected to the bottom of the r-f gain control to provide positive control at minimum gain. Without this arrangement, strong signals might overcome the cathode resistance and be passed to the cathode of the tube. However, this is prevented by shorting the antenna to ground at the minimum-gain point.

REVIEW QUESTIONS

1. Explain how ganged tuning is accomplished.
2. Explain the process of aligning a receiver.
3. What is the purpose of trimmer capacitors?
4. What is the purpose of ganged tuning in a receiver?
5. Why are pentodes used as amplifiers in receivers?
6. Explain heterodyne action.
7. What is meant by zero beat?
8. What are sum and difference frequencies? How are they produced?
9. Explain heterodyne detection.
10. What is the purpose of a vfo?
11. Explain how heterodyne action is used in frequency measurement.
12. Explain the operation of a grid-leak detector.
13. Explain the operation of a plate detector.
14. What is cross modulation and why does it occur?
15. How does the use of a variable-μ tube reduce cross modulation?
16. What is a screen-grid stabilizing resistor and why is it used?
17. Two signals, of 650 and 870 kc, are combined across a nonlinear impedance. What new frequencies will be produced?
18. How is the r-f gain of a receiver controlled?
19. Explain how c-w reception is accomplished in a trf receiver.
20. Explain the basic circuits of a trf receiver and the function of each.

CHAPTER 47

RECEIVER CIRCUITS AND WAVE PROPAGATION

Most of the circuits discussed up to this point are to be found in both the trf and *superheterodyne* receivers. While they may not seem identical to those previously studied, they are basically the same. Each has an individual function in the over-all performance of the receiver. It is therefore recommended that a review of the chapters on amplifiers, oscillators, detectors, filters, power supplies, and tuned circuits be made so that a clearer understanding of the action of any particular circuit or component may be acquired.

The final aim of this text, which has been to analyze the circuits which are combined in conventional transmitters and receivers, should now be evident.

47·1 Wave Propagation. To understand how communication over great distances is possible, it is necessary to understand something about the propagation of radio waves. Energy is radiated into space through the medium of the earth's atmosphere, is picked up by receiving antennas, and is then converted back to its original form. Radio waves travel between transmitting and receiving antennas in two principal ways. One is by means of *ground waves*, which follow the curvature of the earth in a direct line. The other is by means of *sky waves*, which travel upward at various angles and are reflected back to earth by the electrically conducting layers of the earth's atmosphere.

Ground Wave. The ground wave is that part of the radio wave which does not make use of reflections from the ionosphere. The intensity of ground waves, and the resultant distance they travel, is dependent upon several factors. Some of these are transmitting power, characteristics of the transmitting antenna, frequency of waves, "bending" of waves around the curvature of the earth, conductivity of local terrain, nature of the transmission path, and water vapor content of the atmosphere. Most of the intensity of the ground wave at the receiving point can be accounted for in terms of some of these factors. Additionally, the earth itself is a partial conductor, and contact by the radiated wave will cause some of the wave to be absorbed and dissipated as heat. Because of the many factors which contribute to losses of radiated field intensity, ground-wave communication is generally limited to low-frequency applications and communication limited to no more than several hundred miles. Ground waves can easily be reflected by obstructions along the transmission path, or refracted in the earth's surface or troposphere. Figure 47·1 shows how a ground wave may take a direct course or be reflected or refracted along the transmission path. Radiated energy refracted into the earth or troposphere is lost.

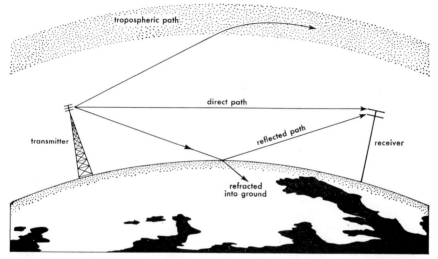

Fig. 47·1   Ground-wave paths.

Ionosphere. This is the name given to layers of ionized air in the earth's atmosphere which extend from about 50 miles above the surface of the earth to the limits of the atmosphere. The English scientist, Heaviside, and the American scientist, Kennelly, showed that the region contained layers of ionized gases, and the name *ionosphere* was given to the region. Two of the layers were named the Kennelly-Heaviside layers in honor of the scientists.

The ionosphere consists of four layers, E_1, E_2, F_1, and F_2. The E_1 and E_2 layers are generally known as the Kennelly-Heaviside layer, which begins at about 50 miles above the earth's surface. The F_1 and F_2 layers are sometimes called the Appleton layer. The E_1 layer is closest to the earth's surface, and the others are progressively more distant in the order named.

In the ionosphere, the air is extremely thin, having about the density of the gas in a vacuum tube. When the atmospheric particles are ionized by ultraviolet radiation from the sun or by other radiation, they tend to remain ionized because few collisions occur between ions. It is the ionosphere which makes possible the reception of signals from much greater distances than would be possible with only the ground wave component of a radiated wave.

Sky Wave. As defined above, the sky-wave component of a radio wave is that component which travels upward and is reflected by the ionosphere back to the earth at some distance.

The ionosphere exerts the greatest influence on the propagation of radio signals because energy which is radiated upward in the form of the sky waves is in part absorbed by the ionized air and in part refracted or bent downward toward the surface of the earth. Figure 47·2 shows some

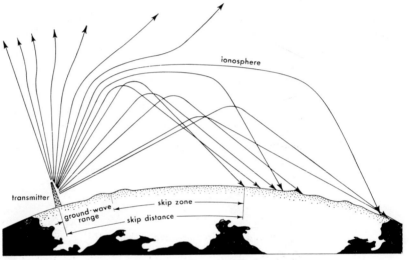

FIG. 47·2   Sky-wave paths.

of the many possible paths of radio waves from transmitter to receiver. Note that some of the waves are of too high a frequency to be reflected back to earth. This is because the amount of reflection decreases as frequency increases. In other words, it is possible that some frequencies will be so high that they will not be reflected by the ionized layer but will pass on through and be lost in space. Other components of the sky wave are of the correct frequency for reflection and are reflected back to the earth. The distance between the point of origin and the point at which the wave returns to the earth depends on the height of the ionized layer and the degree to which the wave's path is bent while traversing the layer. The amount of bending depends on the frequency of the wave as compared to the ion density required to refract or bend the wave. For some extremely high frequencies, refraction is nonexistent. Therefore, radio waves such as those used for frequency modulation and television cannot be transmitted over long distances.

A comparison of the atmospheric layers is shown in Fig. 47.3, along with their effect on waves of certain frequencies. However, it should be pointed out that there are regular variations of the ionosphere as a result of the regular behavior of the sun. For example, the E_1 layer appears after dawn and disappears at night. The E_2 layer has a height that is

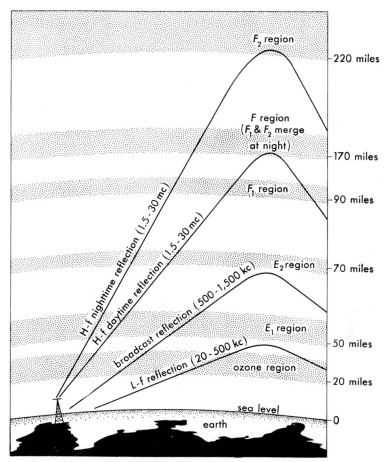

FIG. 47·3   Ionosphere layers and wave reflection.

approximately constant and a density that follows the vertical angle of the sun, and it is practically nonexistent at night. The F_1 layer decreases in height and density at night, and increases in both after dawn. The F_2 layer changes only seasonally with a height increase in summer and a decrease in winter. Therefore, it is obvious that long-distance communications will be affected by both daily and seasonal variations of the ionosphere. This explains why signals picked up by a receiver during the late afternoon or early morning will vary in intensity. Sometimes a signal will be received for a period of time at reasonable strength, then will fade out completely and not be picked up again until some time later. Such incidents are the result of the shifting of the atmospheric layers or a change in their density.

Fading. In receivers, fading is defined as a variation in the intensity of a signal at a given location. It occurs when the ground waves and the reflected sky waves arrive at the receiving antenna out of phase and interfere with each other. If the paths are of different lengths because of fluctuations in the height of the ionospheric layers, the waves arrive at slightly different times and alternately cause reinforcement or cancellation of the field intensity. This is known as *interference fading.*

Skip fading is observed at places near the limit of the skip distance and is caused by the changing angle of refraction. It is most noticeable near sunrise or sunset when the ionization density of the ionosphere is changing.

Skip Distance. The distance from the transmitter at which the ion density of the ionospheric layer will support reflection is known as *skip distance.* As shown in Fig. 47·2, it extends over an area beginning at the transmitting antenna and terminating at the point where the lowest frequency sky waves are reflected back to the earth.

Skip Zone. This is the zone that extends from the usable limit of the ground-wave range to the extreme limit of the skip distance. If the ground-wave range equals or exceeds the skip distance, there is no skip zone. Skip zone and skip distance can be compared in Fig. 47·2. Where a skip zone exists, reception is impossible.

47·2 Automatic Volume Control. If the sensitivity of a receiver is constant, fading will cause the amplitude of audible output to vary; and if short-duration signals of large amplitude are received, the output will alternately increase and decrease in intensity. While this is annoying to the listener, it is even more annoying if the manual r-f or a-f gain must be continually changed. It is the purpose of an avc system to automatically vary the receiver's sensitivity by controlling the over-all gain. Thus, the output will remain fairly constant for signals of varying intensities. In addition to compensating for fading, avc will appreciably reduce overdriving the receiver. This occurs when the receiver is tuned for weak signals past a strong signal. Since the manual gain control must be adjusted for maximum gain, the strong signal would overdrive the receiver. With avc, the sensitivity is automatically decreased as the strong signal is received, then automatically increased so that weak signals may be received.

Figure 47·4 shows a simple avc circuit with the avc voltage applied to the control grid of a remote-cutoff tube that is being operated as an r-f amplifier. Voltage developed across the diode load resistor at the detector is essentially a direct voltage with an a-f variation superimposed upon it. The polarity of this direct voltage is negative with respect to ground, and its value is a direct function of carrier amplitude. The stronger the carrier, the greater the value of direct voltage developed. A remote-cutoff pentode characteristically produces a decrease in tube gain with an increase in negative grid bias. Therefore, if the negative voltage developed across the detector load is applied to the grid of the remote-cutoff pentode, its gain will be reduced. If the r-f amplifier delivers a strong carrier signal to the detector, the diode load resistor will develop a large direct voltage. Coupling this voltage back to the grid of

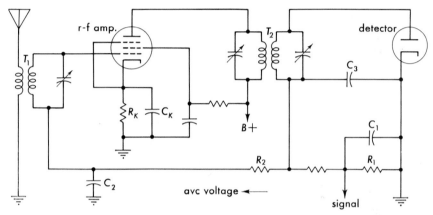

Fig. 47·4   Simple avc circuit.

the pentode will decrease the gain of the r-f stage, and carrier strength will correspondingly decrease. Since avc action is almost instantaneous, the time elapsed between the reception of a large amplitude carrier and its reduction to a practical level will not be perceived by the listener.

A small value of bias is required on the r-f stage so that the tube will not draw grid current and produce distortion during reception of weak signals when avc voltage is low. To obtain this bias, a cathode resistor R_k and cathode bypass capacitor C_k are employed. This reduces the noise level of the tube.

The low-pass filter network (C_2 and R_2) is used to keep the audio component of voltage developed across the diode from being applied to the pentode grid. If the audio variation was applied to the r-f amplifier, it would vary the gain of the stage at an a-f rate. This variation would reduce the gain of the stage and effectively demodulate the carrier. Further, the receiver output would be greatly reduced. Common values for the filter network are approximately 0.5 μf for C_2 and 500 kilo-ohms for R_2. This results in an RC time of 0.25 sec. If the RC time is shorter than 0.1 sec, audio variations might be passed through the amplifier; if the *RC* time is longer than 0.3 sec, receiver sensitivity will not respond to rapid changes and strong signals may be passed through the receiver. Avc voltage is for the purpose of controlling the gain of a stage or stages preceding that developing the avc voltage.

Avc Decoupling. When avc voltage is applied to more than one r-f stage, a decoupling network is necessary to prevent the stages from oscillation due to their common grid return. This is avoided by isolating the grid circuits of each r-f amplifier through individual low-pass filters.

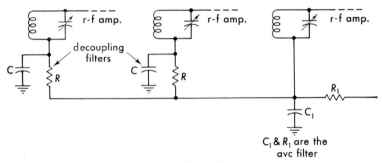

Fig. 47·5 Avc decoupling system.

These filters are chosen in value so that they will not appreciably add to the time constant of the avc circuit. An example of this type of decoupling is shown in Fig. 47·5.

Avc action has the disadvantage of supplying an avc voltage regardless of the value of carrier voltage. With weak signals, even though the reduction in gain is small, it is sometimes sufficient to render a weak signal unusable. In order to realize maximum sensitivity during the reception of weak signals, a delayed voltage is supplied in opposition to the instantaneous avc voltage. Thus, the signal must reach some appreciable amplitude before the avc voltage overcomes the delayed voltage. This system is known as *delayed automatic volume control* (davc).

47·3 Shortcomings of the TRF Receiver. Although the trf receiver is often used for the reception of frequencies below the broadcast band, it has many disadvantages which make it generally less desirable and dependable than the superheterodyne receiver. One disadvantage is that gain increases with an increase in frequency. An r-f amplifier using an untuned primary and a tuned secondary will increase in amplification as operating frequency increases if Q is relatively constant. Since, by formula,

$$Q = \frac{X_L}{R}$$

it would appear that as frequency is increased, Q would also increase. However, the resistance of the inductance is not limited to the resistance that could be measured by an ohmmeter.   Owing to the magnetic effects within the wire itself, an alternating current is not distributed evenly over the entire cross-sectional area of the wire.   Instead, it tends to concentrate in the outer layers of the conductor and is known as *skin current.* As frequency is increased, skin current becomes more pronounced until current appears almost exclusively on the outer surface of the wire when the frequency is of the order of megacycles.   This has the effect of reducing the cross-sectional area of the wire.   If cross-sectional area is reduced, the resistance of the conductor increases while Q remains almost constant. Thus, at higher frequencies, resistance increases and the gain is increased because of the increase in X_L.

The gain of a trf receiver is also increased with an increase in frequency because of additional interstage coupling.   This results from the decreased reactance of stray capacitances between wires, tube sockets, etc., at higher frequencies.

Although it might appear that greater gain at higher frequencies would in many instances be desirable, this is not the only consideration.   As gain in a trf receiver increases, so does its tendency toward regeneration. Further, effective avc action cannot be realized if the inherent gain is not constant over the frequency range of the receiver.

Bandwidth.   Another disadvantage of the trf receiver is that bandwidth increases with an increase in frequency.   Greater bandwidth is usually desirable, but only within certain limits.   Since bandwidth is equal to f_0/Q, an increase in frequency will cause an increase in bandwidth and fidelity.   However, an excessive increase in bandwidth will reduce the selectivity and increase the possibility of receiving two stations at the same time.   Broadcast-band stations are required by the FCC to limit bandwidth of transmitted signals to a few kc.

47·4   Superheterodyne Receiver.   Figure 47·6 is a block diagram of a typical superheterodyne receiver which overcomes most of the disadvantages of the trf receiver.   The signal is picked up by the antenna and passed to the first r-f amplifier, which is tunable over a range of frequencies.   The output of the r-f amplifier is coupled to a *mixer* stage which acts as both amplifier and nonlinear impedance.   The output of the *local oscillator* is combined with the output of the r-f amplifier within the mixer tube.   Thus, through heterodyne action, two new frequencies are produced—the sum and difference frequencies.

One advantage of the superheterodyne receiver is that the high frequency of the carrier is changed to a lower fixed frequency and then amplified, thus providing more uniform gain and better selectivity.   This is in opposition to the method used in the trf, where the carrier is amplified at its original frequency. The superheterodyne receiver has a fixed intermediate frequency, usually 456 kc, and the oscillator is tuned to "track" above the carrier frequency by an amount equal to the intermediate frequency. For example, if the frequency of the desired signal was 1,200 kc modulated by 2,000 cps, the r-f amplifier would be tuned to resonate at 1,200 kc and the oscillator would be tuned to 1,656 kc. Thus, the 1,656-kc oscillator frequency and the 1,200-kc r-f signal would be beat together to produce sum and difference frequencies of 2,856 kc and 456 kc. Since the primary of the i-f transformer will be tuned to the

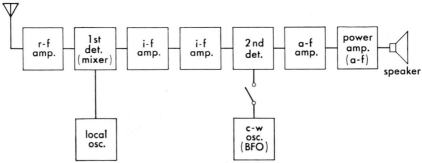

Fig. 47·6 Block diagram of a superheterodyne receiver.

fixed frequency of 456 kc, it will offer a low impedance to all other frequencies and negligible voltage will be developed across it. Therefore, only the difference frequency will be passed and amplified through the i-f stages. This frequency is then detected in the second detector circuit to remove the r-f component, and the remaining a-f component is amplified and fed to the reproducer.

Only two circuits are tuned in a superheterodyne receiver, the input circuit of the first r-f amplifier and the oscillator tank circuit. Since only a narrow band of frequencies is present in the i-f stages at all times, coupling methods and circuit components can be selected to provide optimum performance at these frequencies. Where almost any superheterodyne receiver employs five tuned circuits contributing to selectivity, a comparable trf would require a five-gang variable capacitor. Since this type of capacitor is bulky and would require costly shielding and long leads, the superheterodyne has the advantage of economy and simplicity. Other advantages are (1) uniform selectivity, (2) better stability, (3) better adjacent-channel selectivity, (4) uniform gain throughout the range, and (5) lower cost for equivalent performance.

Beat Frequency Oscillator. The beat frequency oscillator shown in Fig. 47·6 is for the purpose of c-w reception. The signal fed into the second detector is an unmodulated carrier that would be affected by the r-f bypass capacitor of the detector circuit. Without the BFO this carrier would appear in the plate circuit of the detector as a signal of insufficient amplitude for reception. It is the purpose of the BFO to furnish an audio component to modulate the carrier so that an audible tone will be heard in the output. The BFO is tuned to a frequency slightly different from the carrier so that the two frequencies can heterodyne and produce a beat note. If the i-f section of the receiver is fixed at 456 kc, the BFO is usually tuned 800 cps above 456 kc so that an 800-cycle note will be produced in the a-f stage of the receiver.

Side Bands. If a modulated signal is being received, the i-f section must pass a narrow band of frequencies. For example, if a 1,200-kc carrier is modulated by 3,000 cps, upper and lower side bands will be present. Therefore, signals of 1,203, 1,200 and 1,197 kc will be present at the tuned input circuit of the mixer. If the i-f input is resonant at 456 kc, across the plate load there will appear the upper side-band frequency of 459 kc, the lower side band of 453 kc, and the 456-kc difference frequency. Since i-f transformers normally have a band-pass of approximately 10 kc, all three frequencies will be passed with equal efficiency. Furthermore, the audio component will remain because the 3-kc relationship between carrier and side band frequencies still exists in the i-f stages.

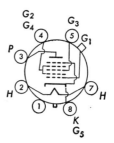

Fig. 47·7 Circuit schematic of hexode mixer tube.

The intermediate frequency of a superheterodyne is generally of a value lower than the lowest frequency within the range of the receiver. Although 456 kc is more commonly used, other values are sometimes used in special receivers. The local oscillator is usually designed to operate above the frequency of the incoming signal. This is mainly an economy measure in that smaller capacitors can be used. Further, maintaining oscillator frequency above that of the signal frequency minimizes *image frequencies* (Sec. 48·4).

Hexode Mixer. A common type of mixer tube used in superheterodyne receivers is the 6L7 hexode mixer shown in Fig. 47·7. This tube employs five grids, an indirectly heated cathode, and a plate. The carrier signal is fed to G_1, which is an ordinary control grid similar to that of any variable-μ tube. G_2 and G_4 are screen grids, connected in conventional arrangements, while G_5 is an ordinary suppressor grid. G_3 is also a suppressor grid; however, it is referred to as an *injector* grid because the oscillator signal is injected through G_3 into the electron stream developed by G_1 and G_2. Thus, suppression modulation results and new frequencies are produced. The upper side band will be equal to the carrier plus modulating frequency, the lower side band will be equal to the carrier minus modulating frequency, and the sum and difference frequencies will be determined by the values of carrier and oscillator frequencies.

REVIEW QUESTIONS

1. Explain how radio waves are radiated through the earth's atmosphere.

2. Explain the difference between the ground and sky components of a radio wave.

3. What is the ionosphere?

4. How are radio waves refracted?

5. What are some of the paths that a ground wave may take between transmitter and receiver?

6. What effect does frequency have on the reception of high-frequency sky waves?

7. Explain the action of the various ionospheric layers on radio waves of different frequencies.

8. What causes received signals to vary sometimes in intensity or fade out completely?

9. Define skip zone.

10. Define skip distance.

11. What causes fading?

12. What is the purpose of avc in receivers?

13. Explain the action of a simple avc circuit.

14. What are some of the shortcomings of a trf receiver?

15. Explain how an increase in frequency will result in an increase in gain in a trf receiver.

16. Why is a trf receiver less selective than a superheterodyne receiver?

17. Explain the action of the local oscillator in a superheterodyne receiver.

18. What is the purpose of the BFO in a superheterodyne receiver?

19. Explain how "tracking" between r-f amplifier and local oscillator is accomplished in a superheterodyne receiver.

20. Explain the step-by-step process by which a modulated signal is received by a superheterodyne receiver and converted to an audible signal.

CHAPTER 48

SUPERHETERODYNE RECEIVER AND CIRCUITS

The principle of operation of all superheterodyne receivers is the same. The only difference between individual sets is in the particular circuit employed. It is the purpose of a superheterodyne receiver to give high amplification, good fidelity of reproduction, and outstanding selectivity. This chapter will discuss the various circuits that comprise each section of a superheterodyne receiver and the methods by which these purposes are realized.

48·1 Mixers and Converters. The mixer has a twofold purpose. It is the nonlinear impedance across which the carrier and local oscillator frequencies are heterodyned, and the detector which passes the difference frequency to the i-f section. A simple mixer circuit is shown in Fig. 48·1a.

If two frequencies are mixed, only the original frequencies are present, but the envelope of the combined wave will vary in amplitude at a beat-frequency rate. If the wave is applied to a nonlinear impedance, the positive and negative portions will not be symmetrical and a difference frequency will be developed.

The oscillator voltage is mixed with the incoming signal in the tuned circuit of Fig. 48·1a. Since the diode will conduct in one direction only, the resultant wave will be a rectified output containing only half of the difference-frequency envelope. The diode load circuit is resonant to the difference frequency and a large voltage will be developed across it at this frequency. The diode tank circuit will appear highly capacitive to higher-order frequencies and no voltages will appear across the inductance other than the difference frequency. Further, a sine wave of voltage will be generated by the flywheel action of the tank circuit as a result of the pulses of current on the positive half-cycles of the difference-frequency envelope. Therefore, the difference frequency will be applied across the tuned secondary to the grid of the first i-f amplifier.

Signals produced by this type of mixer would be extremely weak and hardly usable. A more satisfactory type of circuit employs a triode which is biased so that it operates as a plate detector. In addition to rectifying, the triode amplifies the signal and provides a higher value of difference frequency. Although this type of circuit is fairly satisfactory, ordinary triodes have low gain and have been generally replaced by pentodes in most mixer circuits.

Pentode Mixer. In the pentode mixer shown in Fig. 48·2 the oscillator voltage is injected into the suppressor grid. This separates the signal and oscillator voltages, which reduces interaction. Two voltages are effectively modulating the plate current, and mixing action takes place in the

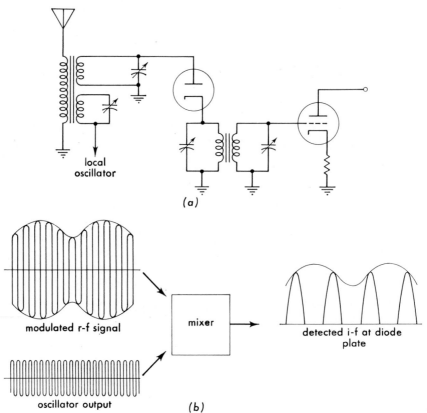

local
oscillator

(a)

modulated r-f signal

mixer

detected i-f at diode
plate

oscillator output

(b)

FIG. 48·1 (*a*) Simple diode mixer. (*b*) Mixer input and output wave forms.

electron stream. When two signal voltages are applied to separate grids, current past the control grid G_1 varies at the signal-voltage rate. The oscillator voltage is applied to the suppressor grid G_3 and causes the same current to vary at the rate of the oscillator frequency. Thus, the two voltages are modulating plate current.

Detection of these two voltages is accomplished by the suppressor grid, which is biased at approximately cutoff by space current through the cathode resistor and by grid current. Grid current is produced when the oscillator voltage causes the suppressor grid to become positive over a portion of the oscillator voltage. The suppressor draws electrons which flow through the grid resistor to ground and back to the cathode. Therefore, the suppressor is negative with respect to ground and to the cathode.

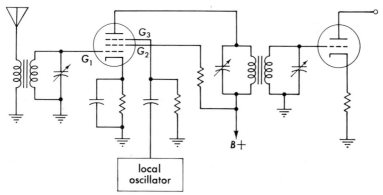

FIG. 48·2   Pentode mixer.

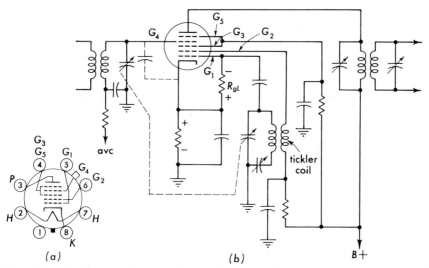

FIG. 48·3   (a) Circuit schematic of type 6A8 pentagrid converter.   (b) A pentagrid converter circuit.

This negative voltage is sufficient to drive the tube into cutoff on the negative half-cycles of oscillator voltage. Thus rectification occurs, and the difference frequency is produced for further amplification.

   Pentagrid Converter.   A tube often employed as a mixer is the *pentagrid converter* shown in Fig. 48·3a.   In addition to performing the same function as a mixer, it incorporates the local oscillator within the same envelope.　In some receivers, this type of tube alone performs the functions of r-f amplifier, nonlinear impedance, local oscillator, and detector.

The 6A8 converter is one of the results of attempts to improve tube performance and efficiency of the superheterodyne receiver by reducing the number of tubes required.　However, its one main disadvantage is frequency limitations.　Although satisfactory operation results from broadcast-band operations, interelectrode capacitance tends to render the local oscillator unstable at higher frequencies.　Further, gain tends to decrease at higher frequencies.　This is because a cloud of electrons forms around G_4 that alternately varies in distance from the signal grid. When the distance increases, gain must necessarily decrease.

The ordinary pentagrid converter like that shown has four grids that are normal in appearance and construction.　However, G_2 (Fig. 48·3b) is composed of two rods placed between G_1 and G_3.　G_1 acts as the control grid of the oscillator and G_2 as the oscillator plate.　Electrons are emitted

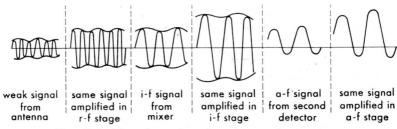

| weak signal from antenna | same signal amplified in r-f stage | i-f signal from mixer | same signal amplified in i-f stage | a-f signal from second detector | same signal amplified in a-f stage |

FIG. 48·4　Wave forms through various receiver sections.

by the cathode, with about 5 per cent drawn by G_1 to sustain oscillations. Another 40 per cent is collected by the oscillator plate G_2; approximately 25 per cent is collected by G_3 and G_5; while the remainder goes to the main plate of the tube.　G_4 should collect no electrons or distortion of carrier frequency and difference frequency might result.　Because of the physical location of the oscillator grid, oscillator voltage impressed upon this grid will modulate the electron stream.　When the receiver is energized, G_1 is at 0 volts until the cathode begins to emit electrons.　After emission begins, regenerative feedback occurs between plate and grid of the oscillator section, and oscillations occur.　Regenerative feedback occurs due to the magnetic coupling between the oscillator plate, or *tickler*, coil and tank coil.

As oscillations occur, G_1 is driven alternately positive and negative. On the positive variations there is current through R_{gL}, and G_1 is made negative with respect to the cathode.　This voltage stabilizes and becomes the reference level for the oscillator bias.　A value of bias is developed that would normally cut the tube off; however, there is a secondary source of electrons from which the signal grid G_4 can be supplied.

Since G_4 has a small value of bias present, this negative voltage will cause some of the electrons to be stopped after they leave the vicinity of G_3. Thus, the "stalled" electrons form a *virtual cathode* and provide a source of electrons from which G_4 can draw to modulate the carrier frequency. In the converter plate there are four frequencies: (1) sum frequency, (2) difference frequency, (3) oscillator frequency, and (4) signal frequency. However, the plate tank is resonant only to the difference frequency.

48·2 Local Oscillator. The operation of a superheterodyne receiver depends to a large extent upon the correct adjustment of its local oscillator. If optimum performance is to be realized, the oscillator must meet exacting requirements as to tracking, stability, amplitude of oscillations, and frequency range.

Local oscillators may be any of those previously discussed; however, some are better adapted to superheterodyne-receiver operation than others. And even though some superheterodyne oscillator circuits appear to differ from the examples in this text, their electrical characteristics are basically the same.

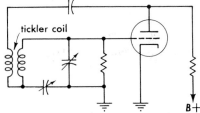

Fig. 48·5 A combination Colpitts and tickler oscillator.

The Hartley oscillator finds little adaptability in superheterodyne circuits but is used quite extensively in others. Figure 48·5 shows a combination Colpitts and tickler oscillator that is quite commonly used. In this circuit, oscillations are developed by the same method as in the conventional Colpitts, but oscillations are sustained by both inductive and capacitive feedback. By careful selection of circuit constants, this type of oscillator provides good amplitude and frequency stability over a wide range of frequencies. Further, because the capacitive and inductive feedbacks are additive, fewer turns are required on the tickler coil and the possibility of tickler resonance is reduced.

The local oscillator may be beat with the signal voltage in either the control-grid, cathode, screen, or suppressor-grid circuit of the first detector. Coupling between oscillator and first detector, where separate tubes are involved, can be effected in one of five generally accepted methods: (1) inductive coupling between oscillator plate coil and detector grid coil; (2) inductive coupling between oscillator plate coil and coil in series with detector cathode circuit; (3) inductive coupling between oscillator tank coil and coil connected in detector-grid return circuit; (4) electron coupling by introducing oscillator voltage to detector screen grid; and (5) electron coupling by introducing oscillator voltage to detector suppressor grid.

As long as the requirement of producing a suitable, distortion-free intermediate frequency is satisfied, the method of coupling is not too important.

48·3 Tuning Methods. If maximum receiver sensitivity is to be realized with gang-tuned capacitors, each stage must be tuned to exactly the same frequency for any one dial setting. Further, the capacitor sections must each provide the same rate of capacitance change between any settings throughout the range. Therefore, individual stages must be adjusted to the same frequency, and the stages should track together over the entire range of the receiver. If one stage is off frequency, signal amplification will be reduced.

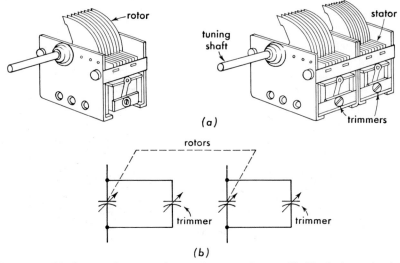

FIG. 48·6 (*a*) One- and two-section tuning capacitors. (*b*) Equivalent circuit of two-section unit.

To provide maximum amplification, the capacitance and inductance of each tuned circuit must be exactly equal, or resonant, at the desired frequency. Further, the stray capacitances and inductances of each tuned circuit must be equal. It is therefore sometimes necessary to vary both capacitance and inductance in a tuned circuit. Where many factors, such as the collection of dust or dirt in the rotors and stators of variable air-dielectric capacitors, can affect frequency, inductors are similarly affected.

Permeability Tuning. Inductance of tuned circuits is sometimes varied by means of a powdered-iron plug inserted into the coil of the tank circuit. If the position of the plug is varied with respect to the coil, the permeability of the core is also varied. Since the iron possesses greater conducting ability than air, its presence in the core of the coil will result in an increase in inductance and a decrease in frequency. Thus, by positioning the plug within the core by means of a screw-driver adjustment, compensation may be made for stray inductances and capacitances. In many circuits "coarse" tuning is provided by means of a variable air-dielectric capacitor, while "fine" tuning is provided by permeability methods.

Permeability tuning is also accomplished by means of a brass rod or other material whose permeability is less than that of air. Inserting the rod within the coil will cause a decrease in inductance and an increase in frequency. This is in opposition to the powdered-iron-plug method of inductive tuning, although both realize similar advantages.

Transmitters often employ a shorting-bar device for varying the inductance of tuned circuits. In this method a positionable bar is adjusted

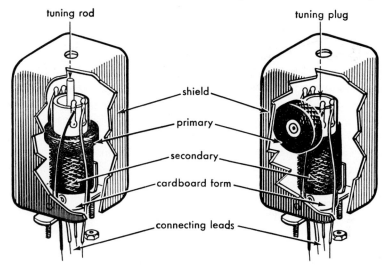

FIG. 48·7   Two types of tuning coils, or tuned circuits.

across a certain number of turns of the coil. As a number of turns are shorted out of the circuit, inductance and frequency will be varied proportionately.

Tuned Circuits. Input and output circuits of i-f amplifiers are usually constructed inside small metal containers which act as electrostatic shields to prevent noise being picked up from adjacent circuits. The entire arrangement is referred to as i-f "cans," in which there is an opening to allow screw-driver alignment of either the trimmer capacitors or a powdered-iron plug. Connection terminals are brought out at the bottom of the can for convenience, and a tunable, self-contained tank circuit is thus provided.

48·4   Image Frequencies and Spurious Responses. Several factors must be taken into consideration in the choice of an intermediate frequency to be used with superheterodyne receivers. This is because the i-f amplifiers provide the principal amount of gain and adjacent-channel selectivity.

By adjacent-channel selectivity is meant the ability of a receiver to choose between several signals being broadcast on adjacent channels. The frequency allocation of adjacent channels for broadcast stations is such that stations are only a few kc apart. If a trf receiver was tuned to a signal at 1,000 kc and another station was operating at 1,010 kc, the frequency difference between the two signals would be 10 kc, or 1 per cent. Therefore, both signals would be picked up, and this frequency difference would be maintained throughout the entire r-f section. Further, both signals would pass through the receiver unchanged in frequency.

If the same signals were picked up by a superheterodyne receiver, there would be the same 1 per cent difference between the desired and interfering signals. The oscillator would be operating at 456 kc above the desired signal, or at 1,456 kc. Therefore, the mixer would produce at its output the sum and difference frequencies of oscillator and r-f signals. Further, the sum and difference frequencies of the oscillator and interfering signal would be present at its output. Thus, signals of 456 and 446 kc would be passed to the input of the i-f amplifier. Although the frequency separation is still the same, the *percentage difference* is now greater. Where before there was a 1 per cent difference, the difference between the two signals is now approximately 2.2 per cent ($10 \times {}^{100}\!/_{456}$). Therefore, the superheterodyne provided 2.2 per cent better adjacent-channel selectivity than a trf with comparable r-f selectivity. Since the i-f amplifier is tuned to 456 kc, further selectivity is realized.

By arithmetic it will be found that a 10-kc difference between desired and interfering signals will produce a percentage difference for several values of i-f frequency as follows:

Intermediate Frequency, kc	Frequency Difference, %
100	10
175	5.7
456	2.2
700	1.4

As the percentage difference in frequency increases, separation becomes easier and the interfering signal will be attenuated in the i-f amplifier tuned circuit. Moreover, it appears that a low i-f value should be employed to increase the difference. Although this applies within certain limits, there are other considerations.

Image Frequencies. The most serious disadvantage of the superheterodyne receiver is the problem of *image frequencies.* These are produced in several ways and are an important consideration in the selection of an intermediate frequency.

Since the difference frequency is produced by heterodyne action between oscillator and carrier, for any oscillator setting there is a frequency above and below that will produce the same difference frequency. For example, if a 100-kc i-f section was used and the oscillator was operating 1,000 kc above the i-f amplifier, the oscillator would be tuned to 1,100 kc if a 1,000-kc signal was being received. Moreover, it could be tuned 100 kc below the carrier frequency, or to 900 kc, and still produce a 100-kc difference frequency. If the oscillator was tuned to 1,100 kc, it would beat with the desired 1,000-kc signal and produce a difference frequency of 100 kc for the i-f amplifier. It would also beat with an undesired signal of 1,200 kc and produce a 100-kc difference frequency. If

Fig. 48·8   Superheterodyne receiver.   (*Hammarlund Manufacturing Company.*)

the oscillator was tuned below the desired signal by 100 kc, it would produce 100-kc difference frequencies for carrier signals of both 1,000 and 800 kc. These undesired frequencies are called *image frequencies*. It is also possible for two signals to heterodyne in the first detector and produce a difference frequency equal to that of the i-f amplifiers. One or both stations may be passed through to the output. For example, carrier signals of 1,150 kc and 1,250 kc could heterodyne and produce a 100-kc difference frequency.

The intermediate frequency is chosen so that interfering signals of sufficient strength will appear as other than the correct frequency to cause images. By formula,

$$f_1 = f_0 + 2f_i$$

where f_1 = image frequency

  f_0 = desired frequency

  f_i = intermediate frequency

Since the ordinary receiver is designed to operate over the frequency range of the broadcast band—550 to 1,600 kc—by the above formula it has been found that approximately 456 kc will produce fewer image frequencies and is commonly used.

Spurious Response. This is defined as reception in a receiver at one or more frequencies other than that to which the receiver is tuned. The reception of an image frequency would be considered one form of spurious reception. Spurious response may be eliminated by proper selection of tuned circuits and the frequency of the intermediate stages.

I-F Amplifiers. It is the purpose of i-f amplifiers in a superheterodyne to perform three main functions: (1) amplify the desired signal so that satisfactory gain will be realized; (2) provide suitable band-pass characteristics so that both carrier and side bands will be amplified and passed to the second detector; and (3) sharply attenuate all undesired carriers and associate side bands in adjacent channels.

REVIEW QUESTIONS

1. Explain the principle of operation of a simple mixer.

2. Explain the operation of a pentode mixer.

3. What is the purpose of a pentagrid converter?

4. How is a virtual cathode formed in a pentagrid converter?

5. What is the purpose of the local oscillator in a superheterodyne receiver?

6. Explain the action of a combination Colpitts and tickler oscillator in providing frequency stability.

7. How does the combination Colpitts and tickler oscillator provide good amplitude stability over a wide range of frequencies?

8. What are some of the requirements for properly tuning a receiver?

9. What are image frequencies?

10. What image frequency could result from an oscillator tuned to 850 kc and an r-f stage tuned to 1050 kc?

11. How are image frequencies eliminated?

12. Explain why 456 kc is desirable as an intermediate frequency.

13. Explain why a superheterodyne receiver provides better adjacent-channel selectivity than a trf receiver.

14. Since it provides better adjacent-channel selectivity in a superheterodyne receiver, why is 175 kc not a better intermediate frequency than 456 kc?

15. Explain permeability tuning.

16. What is the local oscillator frequency of a receiver with an i-f of 465 kc that produces an image frequency of 1450 kc?

17. How does an i-f amplifier provide selectivity?

18. Explain how four frequencies are present in the plate circuit of a converter.

19. What are some of the coupling methods used between detector and oscillator?

20. Explain the purpose, function, and operation of each of the stages of a super-heterodyne receiver.

CHAPTER 49

TYPICAL RECEIVER

The receiver discussed in this chapter is typical in the sense that it is similar to many commercial receivers designed for broadcast-band operation. It will be used to illustrate the employment of most of the individual components discussed in previous portions of the text. The principles of operation and the circuits of this receiver are similar to those

Fig. 49·1   Typical receiver.   (*Allied Radio Corporation.*)

which have been discussed in previous chapters. Therefore, to ensure a thorough understanding of the purpose and function of individual components, it is suggested that appropriate portions of the text be reviewed. Each component will be seen functioning individually to form one of the several basic circuits of which the receiver is comprised. This receiver represents the fundamental ideas from which almost all receivers are designed.

49·1   General.   The receiver shown in the various figures in this chapter is typical of many basic receivers available from manufacturers in "kit" form. These kits are so designed that even the novice may assemble components with ease. The kit contains a chassis, connecting wires, tubes, resistors, capacitors, and all other essential components, as well as explicit step-by-step instructions.

The receiver shown covers the frequency range of 540 to 1640 kc with a maximum audio output of 1 watt, and has automatic volume control and a permanent-magnet speaker. Designed as a superheterodyne, it

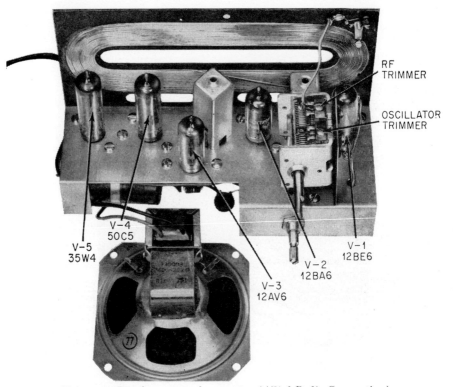

FIG. 49·2   Receiver parts placement.   (*Allied Radio Corporation.*)

has the added feature of using multiunit tubes that provide 6-tube performance from a 4-tube circuit. An acoustically designed cabinet produces a clear, full tone, while the built-in loop antenna combines with the avc circuit to minimize blasting and fading. Input power can be either a-c or d-c.

In assembling the components of any receiver, all connections should be made close to the chassis and leads kept as short as possible. Long leads between terminal points provide means of picking up undesirable noises, which, once introduced, are amplified and result in listening discomfort. As shown in the wiring diagram, resistors and capacitors may be placed close together. However, leads to the grid and plate connections on the tube sockets should be well separated.

All connections should be securely soldered, preferably using rosin-core solder. The soldering iron should be sufficiently hot to ensure a smooth, even flow of solder, thus providing connections that are both mechanically and electrically secure. Work should be performed slowly so that each connection may be checked as it is made. If more than one wire is to be connected to one terminal or point, soldering of that terminal should be accomplished only after all connections are made. Careful wiring

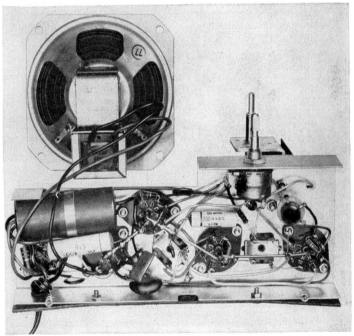

FIG. 49·3   Receiver chassis wiring. (*Allied Radio Corporation.*)

and inspection of each circuit during construction can save hours of trouble shooting after construction. I-f circuit transformers should always be wired first. The remaining circuits can then be wired by following the pictorial diagram, observing polarities where necessary— particularly with respect to tubular capacitors.

49·2   Circuit Description.   The transmitted signal is picked up by the loop antenna, or by an external antenna if it is desired to use the latter. The loop antenna with the r-f section of the tuning capacitor C-2 tunes the receiver to the desired frequency. The signal is then applied to the grid of V-1.

The converter tube V-1 serves two purposes. One section functions as an oscillator and is connected to the oscillator coil L-2 with the oscillator section of the tuning capacitor C-2. The tuned circuit, consisting of the oscillator coil L-2 and the oscillator section C-2B, is tuned to a frequency that is always 455 kc higher than the frequency of the incoming signal from the transmitting station. The other, or mixer, section of V-1 delivers this 455 kc difference frequency to the primary winding of the first i-f transformer T-1 at terminals 3 and 4.

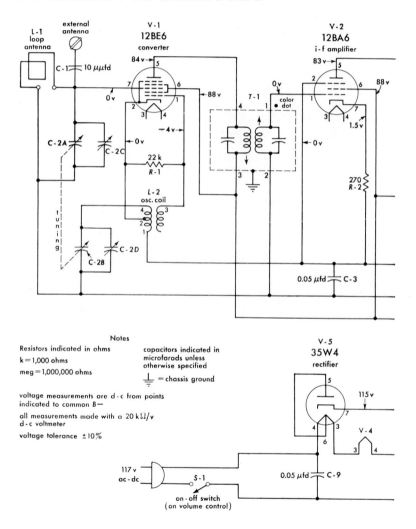

Fig. 49·4   Receiver circuit

The secondary winding of T-1, at terminals 1 and 2, couples the 455 kc signal to the grid of V-2, the i-f amplifier tube. After the signal is applied to V-2 it is amplified and passes through the primary winding of the second i-f transformer T-2 at terminals 3 and 4 to the secondary winding at terminals 1 and 2. From the secondary winding of T-2 the 455 kc signal is applied to the detector section of V-3, the detector-avc-audio amplifier tube. The detector section of V-3 changes the 455 kc i-f signal

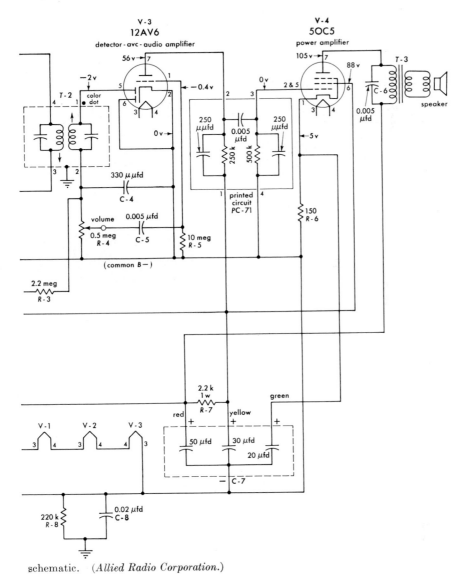

schematic. (*Allied Radio Corporation.*)

to an a-f signal. This a-f signal is then fed to the grid of V-3 in the a-f amplifying section of the tube. After amplification by V-3, the amplified signal is coupled to the grid of the power amplifier tube V-4.

V-4 provides a high degree of power amplification to the a-f signal, raising the level to about 1 watt for operating the loud-speaker. The a-f output of V-4 is coupled to the loud-speaker through the output transformer T-3, and converted by the loud-speaker from electrical to sound energy.

Fig. 49·5 Television control board. (*Radio Corporation of America.*)

Positive voltage for the various tube electrodes is supplied by the rectifier tube V-5. The rectified alternating voltage is filtered by a network consisting of the resistor R-7 and the 50 μf and 30 μf sections of C-7.

49·3 Alignment. When the receiver is constructed and wiring is completed, tubes should be inserted in their proper sockets and the set energized. Ordinarily, some stations may then be received because some circuits have been factory-aligned. However, for optimum performance, additional alignment is usually necessary.

A superheterodyne receiver can often be aligned merely by adjusting the dial pointer until it corresponds to the known frequency of a broadcast station. With more complex sets covering stations of unknown frequencies, a signal generator and an a-c output meter are necessary. Although they provide the most dependable and accurate method of alignment, signal generators and output meters are costly and not always available for ordinary broadcast-band receiver alignment.

An alternate method is on-the-air alignment. First, close the plate of the tuning capacitor C-2 so that it is fully meshed, remove both knobs from the receiver, temporarily install the receiver in the cabinet, and replace the tuning knob of the shaft of C-2.

Turn the tuning knob so that the arrow points to a dial setting between 14 and 16, then select a known frequency between 1,400 and 1,600 kc on which some local station transmits. Next, carefully remove the tuning knob without disturbing the setting of C-2, and remove the receiver from the cabinet. Replace the volume-control knob on the shaft of R-4, turn the volume control fully clockwise, and energize the receiver.

After approximately 2 minutes for tube warmup, with a screwdriver turn the oscillator trimmer C-2D in either direction until the desired local station is heard. Using a plastic or similar type of alignment tool, adjust the cores of the i-f transformer T-1 and T-2 to obtain the loudest signal from the loud-speaker. Start with T-1, top and bottom, then T-2, top and bottom, and repeat in sequence until maximum volume is obtained. During this procedure reduce the volume control as necessary to maintain a comfortable level of output signal.

Place the tuning knob on the shaft of C-2 and rotate the tuning control to a point where no station is heard, preferably at a point where the plates of the tuning capacitor are widely opened. With a screwdriver, turn the screw of the r-f trimmer C-2C until maximum noise is heard in the loud-speaker. This completes the alignment of all circuits in the receiver.

Turn the volume control counterclockwise, deenergize the receiver, remove the knobs, and return the receiver to its chassis.

REVIEW QUESTIONS

All questions are based on the circuit schematic in Fig. 49-4.
1. What is the purpose of R-5 and C-5?
2. What is the purpose of R-3 and C-3?
3. What would occur if the inductance of the oscillator coil L-2 increased in value?
4. What would be the effect upon circuit operation if C-4 opened?
5. What is the purpose of C-1?
6. What would most likely occur if R-1 became shorted?
7. What is the purpose of the 20μf section of C-7?
8. What is the purpose of R-7?
9. What is the purpose of C-9?
10. What would most likely occur if pin 1 of V-1 became grounded?

CHAPTER 50

TRANSISTORS

One of the most important recent developments in the field of electronics is the *transistor*, a name taken from the words "transfer resistance." Although it is not conceivable that the transistor will ever completely replace the electron tube, transistors will improve existing types of equipment and they will be employed in other equipment in which electron tubes had never before been used.

The transistor can now perform many of the functions of an electron tube and, in some instances, perform them better and more efficiently. Unlike the electron tube, which depends on the flow of electrons through a vacuum, vapor, or gas, the transistor makes use of the flow of electric charge carriers through a semiconductor. One advantage of the transistor is that it has no vacuum, no grid, no plate, no cathode, and therefore requires no warmup delay.

50·1 General. Although many scientists and engineers have been associated with its development, key investigations which brought the transistor to reality were carried out by J. Bardeen and W. H. Brittain of the Bell Telephone Laboratories technical staff. Since then, transistors have developed into practical and dependable devices, and the use of these solid-state components has expanded rapidly.

A transistor has numerous advantages over the electron tube. Since it has no filament and requires low operating voltages and currents, it consumes little power. This results in longer battery life and considerable reduction in the size and weight of equipment. Transistors are therefore useful in equipment where limited space, portability, or reliability are prime considerations. Since a transistor has low power consumption, there is less heat radiation. Because it is rugged and solidly constructed, it has no movable elements which can produce microphonics. Small in size, transistors are generally housed in tiny cylinders less than an inch long. Moreover, the transistor requires no pre-heating; it functions the instant it is energized. A transistor can be made impervious to weather and can even be operated under water. In addition to their ability to amplify, detect, or oscillate, transistors can serve as electronic switches, mixers, or modulators. Engineers are designing many new products to make use of the many advantages offered by transistors.

Although the *junction triode* is the most commonly used type of transistor, others in use are the point-contact, junction, point-junction, surface barrier, drift, field-effect, and hook. Each has its own characteristics, advantages, and areas of application, although the principle of operation is similar.

By having the ability to act as an amplifier, oscillator, detector, etc., the transistor solves a problem that many scientists and engineers have been pondering for years—how to make semiconductors perform the functions of an electron tube and thus provide a smaller, simpler, and yet

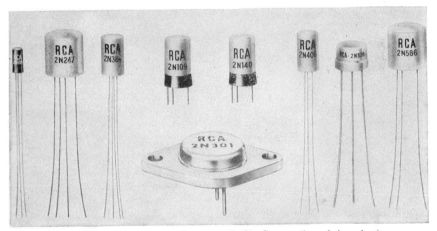

FIG. 50.1   Typical transistors.   (*Radio Corporation of America.*)

more rugged device. In one type of transistor, for example, two point contacts only 0.002 in. apart are made to a semiconductor. Input power to one of these contacts is amplified over 100 times and transmitted to the other terminal for further delivery to the output circuit. This large amount of amplification is produced as the result of energy supplied from a small battery with a power consumption of less than one-tenth of that used by an ordinary flashlight. Several transistors of approximately actual size are shown in Fig. 50.1.

50·2   Semiconductors. A semiconductor can be defined as a material having a conductivity lower than that of conductors but higher than that of insulators. This can best be explained by considering the structure of matter and the basic difference between conductors and insulators.

Each atom of which matter is comprised has a nucleus around which electrons revolve in different orbits or rings. The basic difference between the various elements is the number of protons in the nucleus of its atom and the number of electrons orbiting around the nucleus. An

atom of any element has a number of electrons rotating around its
nucleus. A hydrogen atom, for example, has one proton in its nucleus
and one orbital electron. Uranium is more complicated with 92 orbital
electrons. The germanium atom has 32 orbital electrons while the silicon
atom has 14. In other words, the atoms of each element have a different
number of orbital electrons and a different number of outer rings. It is

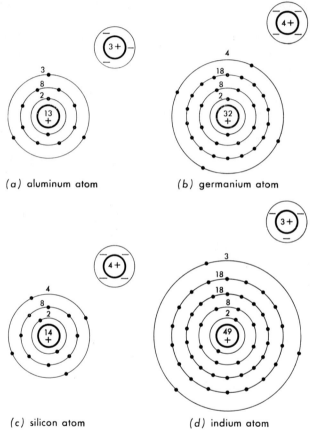

(a) aluminum atom   (b) germanium atom

(c) silicon atom   (d) indium atom

FIG. 50·2   Four different atoms with net charge due to valence electrons.

this outer ring which determines whether an element is a good conductor,
insulator, or semiconductor.

In Fig. 50·2 are shown four atoms and the equivalent of their outer ring
electrons. These electrons in the outer ring are called *valence* electrons,
and are an important consideration in the study of transistors. To be a
good conductor, an element must have an outer ring of only one, two, or
three electrons. This is because the more electrons in the outer ring,
the greater the potential required to break them free from the attraction

of the nucleus to cause current. Moreover, the greater the number of electrons in the outer ring, the better the element will act as an insulator. Elements having five, six, or seven electrons in the outer rings of their atoms are considered good insulators. The maximum number of valence electrons in most of the known elements is eight.

Since valence electrons are not as tightly bound to the nucleus as the electrons in the inner rings, it is possible to simplify the drawing of various atoms as shown in Fig. 50·2. The aluminum atom, for example, can be shown as having a net positive charge of three protons in the nucleus, with the three valence electrons shown as equal negative charges. The net positive charge is equal to the number of valence electrons.

50·3 Transistor Material. Although a wide variety of materials can be used as semiconductors, the most common in the manufacture of

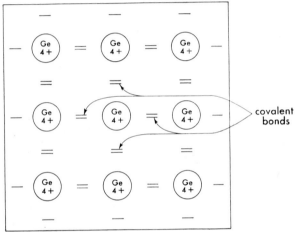

FIG. 50·3 Germanium crystal with net valence charge and resultant covalent bonds.

transistors are silicon and germanium. Because these two materials are similar, only germanium will be considered in this text.

Any material whose number of valence electrons is between that of an insulator and a conductor is considered a semiconductor. Germanium, with four valence electrons, is considered to be a good semiconductor. However, it is necessary to control the properties of germanium to produce transistor action. This is accomplished by the addition of minute quantities of impurities such as arsenic, aluminum, gallium, antimony, or indium to the pure germanium. A pure germanium crystal is shown in Fig. 50·3. The four valence electrons of an atom are associated with the valence electrons of adjacent atoms, forming *covalent bonds*.

N-type Germanium. When impurities such as arsenic or antimony are added to germanium, the covalent bonding between pure germanium atoms becomes unbalanced. Since arsenic and antimony have five valence electrons, only four of these electrons will form covalent bonds between adjacent germanium electrons. The fifth electron is in excess for covalent bonding between the four valence electrons of the germanium and is free to drift through the crystal structure. When this type of semiconductor is connected to a battery, or when voltage is applied across it, the free electron will move through the material in a manner that constitutes current. The free electron will be attracted by the positive potential and enter the external circuit, while an electron will be given up at the negative terminal and enter the semiconductor. Thus, a continuous flow of electrons is maintained through the semiconductor between the negative and positive terminals (Fig. 50·5).

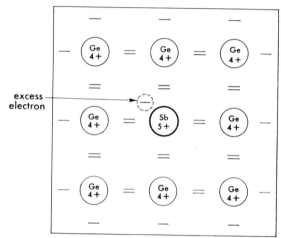

Fig. 50·4   Excess electron resulting from adding antimony to germanium.

The effect of adding impurities to the germanium is shown in Fig. 50·4. Antimony, arsenic, or other impurities having a valence of five are known as *pentavalent-type* impurities. They are also known as *donors* since they donate electrons to the semiconductor. Germanium to which donor impurities have been added is characterized by an abundance of electrons and is called negative or *N-type* germanium.

P-type Germanium. When the added impurity has fewer valence electrons than the germanium, it is known as a *trivalent-type* impurity, or *acceptor.* This is because it accepts electrons from the germanium. Germanium to which trivalent impurities have been added is characterized by a deficiency of electrons and is known as a positive or *P-type* germanium.

Some of the materials used to produce P-type germanium are gallium, aluminum, or indium. The result of adding indium, for example, is to create an incomplete covalent bonding between the atoms. As with the pentavalent impurities, each trivalent atom forms a covalent bond with adjacent germanium atoms. However, since there is a deficiency of one electron in the indium outer ring as compared to the outer ring of the germanium, one covalent bond is incomplete. This results in the presence of a "hole." In order to complete the four-electron bond, the impurity will rob an electron from an adjacent germanium bond. This creates a hole in a different place within the crystal structure. As this action continues, the hole moves from place to place within the crystal in much the same manner as an electron moves from atom to atom in the

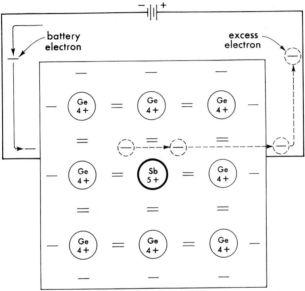

Fig. 50·5   Electron movement in N-type germanium with external voltage applied.

N-type germanium. While movement of the excess electron in the N-type germanium was considered as a negative-type current carrier, the hole in the P-type germanium can be considered as a positive-type current carrier. The structure of a germanium crystal with a trivalent-type impurity added is shown in Fig. 50·6.

By applying a difference of potential across a P-type semiconductor, the hole will move from positive to negative. It may be considered to move through the material in exactly the same manner as an electron, except that it moves in the opposite direction because it involves an opposite charge. The instant voltage is applied to the semiconductor, an electron from an adjacent covalent bond will move from its position and fill the hole. The movement of this electron creates a hole in the covalent bond just vacated. Another adjacent electron fills this hole

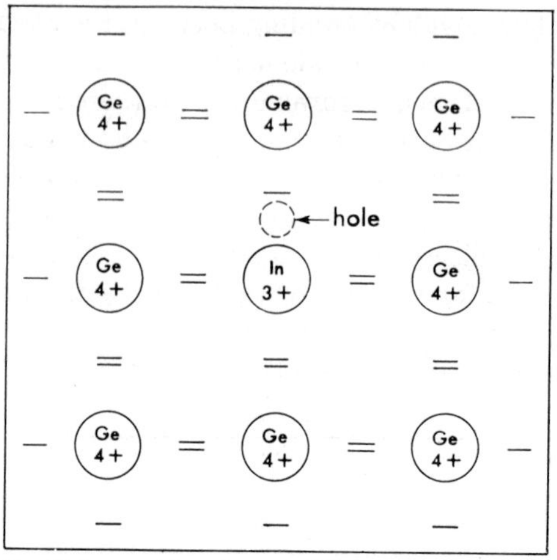

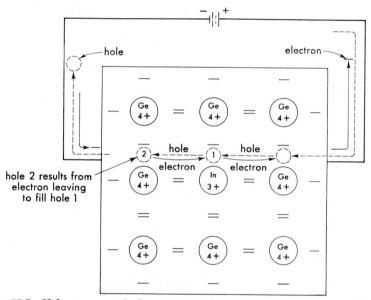

FIG. 50·6   Hole resulting from adding indium to germanium.

FIG. 50·7   Hole movement in P-type germanium with external voltage applied.

and creates still another hole as a result. As the hole reaches the extreme end of the semiconductor, an electron from the external circuit moves in and fills the hole. As an electron enters the semiconductor from the negative terminal, an electron near the positive terminal will leave the semiconductor and enter the external circuit. In effect, the hole seems to be moving from the positive terminal through the semiconductor to the negative terminal. This is shown in Fig. 50·7.

50·4 PN Junction. If P-type and N-type semiconductors are joined together, the area in the center is known as the *PN junction*. This is shown in Fig. 50·8a. Although movement of electrons and holes through the semiconductors is continuously going on, neither semiconductor exhibits a charge unless a difference of potential is applied from an external source. By joining the two types, it would seem that some of the electrons in the N-type would diffuse across the junction. However, this does not occur, because the negative charge exerted by the fixed impurity atoms in the P-type repel them. Moreover, the holes in the P-type semiconductor remain because they are repelled by the fixed donor atoms in the N-type which exhibit a positive charge. Therefore, a

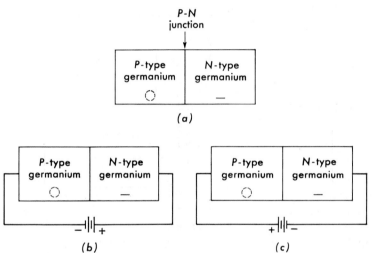

FIG. 50·8 (a) PN junction. (b) Reverse-bias connection. (c) Forward-bias connection.

potential exists across the junction because of the unlike charges on either side. This is known as the *potential energy barrier*.

If a difference of potential is connected across a PN junction as shown in Fig. 50·8b, the holes will move toward the negative terminal and the electrons will move toward the positive terminal. This increases the potential energy barrier and there is more opposition to current through the junction. Connecting in this manner is referred to as *reverse bias*. By reversing the connection, electrons in the N-type semiconductor will move toward the junction, where some will be repelled across and into the P-type semiconductor. As this occurs, covalent bonds near the positive terminal are broken and the liberated electrons enter the positive terminal. This produces a hole which moves toward the junction. Current is produced as a result of electron flow in the N-type and hole movement in the P-type. Connecting in this manner is referred to as *forward bias.*   If an a-c signal were applied across the PN junction, current would be produced during the positive half-cycles and the N- and P-type semiconductors would be operating as a rectifier.   When operating in this manner the transistor is functioning as a *junction diode.*

50·5   Types of Transistors.   Although there are various types of transistors, only three will be discussed here.   However, because their operation is similar, knowledge of one type is sufficient for an understanding of most basic types.

NPN Transistor.   One of the most common types of transistor is the *NPN junction.*   It is comprised of a thin layer of P-type germanium sandwiched in between two relatively thick layers of N-type germanium, as

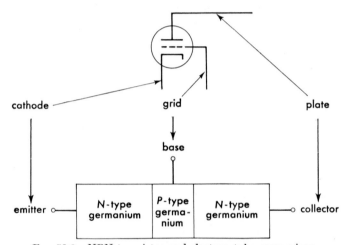

Fig. 50·9   NPN transistor and electron tube comparison.

shown in Fig. 50·9.   Two junctions are thus formed and the three elements are known as the *emitter, base,* and *collector.*   The similarity between this type of transistor and a triode electron tube is also shown in Fig. 50·9.   The emitter and cathode supply the source of electron flow, the base is similar to the control grid in that it also serves to control electron flow, and the collector acts as part of the output circuit in the same manner as the plate of an electron tube.

In the NPN transistor, neither the free electrons nor the holes will overcome the potential energy barrier unless external voltage is applied. Therefore, no current will exist.   If connected as shown in Fig. 50·10, battery 1 will reduce the potential energy barrier between the emitter and base regions.   Further, battery 2 will increase the barrier between collector and base regions.   This permits electrons to flow from the emitter to the base.   However, because of the thin construction of the base, most of the electrons will not combine with the holes in the base but will pass beyond into the collector region. After reaching the collector region, the electrons are attracted to the positive terminal of the battery and thus complete the passage through the transistor.

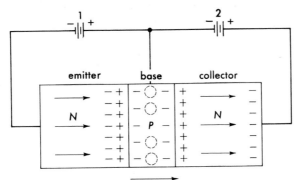

direction of electron movement

FIG. 50·10   Electron movement in NPN transistor.

If an a-c signal were applied to the transistor emitter, the potential energy barrier would increase on the positive half-cycles and reduce electron flow through the emitter. On the negative half-cycles, the potential energy barrier would be reduced and electron flow through the emitter would increase. Effectively, reverse bias exists on the positive half-cycles, and forward bias exists on the negative half-cycles. On the negative half-cycles, most of the electrons will pass through the thin base into the collector and constitute current.

PNP Transistor. The PNP transistor is comprised of a thin layer of N-type germanium sandwiched in between two relatively thick layers of

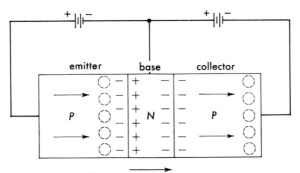

direction of hole movement

FIG. 50·11   Hole movement in PNP transistor.

P-type germanium. Battery connections to the emitter and collector are the opposite in polarity to that of the NPN transistor. Holes in the emitter region are repelled toward the PN junction by the positive battery voltage.   This reduces the potential barrier and some holes pass on through the base to the collector.   However, a small number of holes are lost in the base region through combining with base electrons.   The holes entering the collector are filled by electrons entering from the negative battery terminal.   As each hole is lost by combination with electrons in the base or collector regions, an electron from one of the covalent bonds near the emitter electrode enters the positive battery terminal.   This creates a new hole with the net effect of a continuous flow of holes from emitter to collector (Fig. 50·11).

Point-contact Transistor.   The point-contact transistor is constructed of germanium to which pentavalent impurities have been added.   Into the surface of the germanium are placed small inserts of P-type germa-

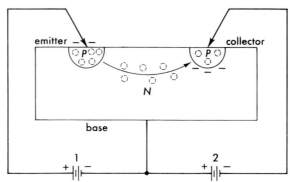

Fig. 50·12   Hole movement in a point-contact transistor.

nium.   Pressed down upon these inserts are two metal electrodes.   One electrode is thus attached to the emitter region and the other to the collector region, with the N-type germanium forming the base.   Potential energy barriers exist between each insert and the base material.   Since this is a P-type transistor, the current is carried mainly by holes.

If connected as shown in Fig. 50·12, battery 1 biases the emitter in a manner to produce greatest current while battery 2 biases the collector in a manner to reduce current.   Electrons leave the emitter and enter the external circuit, producing holes that are filled by adjacent electrons breaking their covalent bonds.   As electrons move from the negative battery terminal to fill the holes, additional holes are created in a progressive direction toward the negative terminal at the collector.   And although the collector is biased negatively, holes in its vicinity allow many more electrons to leave the negative terminal.   This reduces the resistance of the collector, which further increases electron flow.   The net effect in a point-contact transistor is movement of electrons through the base from collector to emitter, and a movement of holes from emitter to collector.

From this it can be seen that an a-c signal can be applied to the emitter area and produce amplification. As holes are formed in the emitter region, the resistance of the collector region is controlled and a corresponding change in electron flow in the collector circuit results. Thus, a small variation in emitter electron flow can produce and control a far greater electron flow in the collector region.

50·6 Applications. Transistors can be operated in circuits by various methods comparable to the operation of electron tubes. For example, there are three basic triode circuits: grounded-grid, grounded-plate, and grounded-cathode circuits. Transistors can be operated in the same manner with a resulting variation in the ratio between input and output impedance. Operating a transistor with a grounded base in a circuit is similar to the operation of an electron tube used as a grounded-grid amplifier. Since in this application the input impedance is low and the output impedance is high, it produces greater amplification. With a high resistance in the output of the collector circuit, a small change in collector current will produce a relatively large voltage change across this resistance.

Operating a transistor with a grounded collector is similar to the operation of an electron tube as a *cathode follower*. With the collector grounded, the input impedance is high and the output impedance is low. A cathode follower is essentially an impedance-matching or impedance-lowering device that has less than unity voltage gain but is capable of producing power gain.

A third method of operating a transistor in a manner comparable to electron-tube operation is by grounding the emitter. This is similar to a grounded-cathode electron-tube circuit, in that the input impedance varies from medium to low while the output impedance varies from medium to high. This method of operation is generally employed in conventional circuits. Moreover, by choosing the proper method of connection, almost any desired impedance ratio can be produced to meet existing requirements.

It should be pointed out that the manner of amplification in a transistor is different from that of an electron tube. While an electron tube is a voltage-operated device, depending upon an alternating voltage on the grid to control current between cathode and plate, the transistor is strictly a current-operated device. It is the current in the emitter and base circuits that controls current in the collector circuit.

Coupling. The coupling between transistor stages is accomplished in much the same manner as between electron-tube stages. The only difference is that input and output resistances of transistors vary more than those of tubes. In a transistor, an increase in load resistance will result in a decrease in input resistance; while in an electron tube, any plate-load change would have no effect on the grid circuit. Input and output resistances of transistors also vary with operating conditions and types of transistors used. Ordinarily, transformer, impedance, RC, or direct coupling can be used with good results.

Gain Controls. As with electron-tube circuits, it is necessary to provide gain controls for controlling the volume level of transistor circuits. Controls are used with RC, transformer, and direct coupled circuits. Generally, these controls vary the amount of potential applied to the base of the transistor in the same manner that grid potential is varied to an electron tube.

Miscellaneous. Transistors are used as oscillators, power amplifiers, video amplifiers, and other conventional circuits where electron tubes are normally used. Transistor oscillators, for example, function in the same manner as electron-tube oscillators. Inphase feedback is necessary to sustain oscillations, although an amplifying device with a gain greater than 1 is required. They can be operated in Hartley, Colpitts, or almost

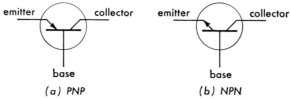

emitter   collector   emitter   collector

base   base
(a) PNP   (b) NPN
Fig. 50·13   Schematic symbol of transistors.

any other conventional circuit. Power amplifiers using transistors are of the single-ended or push-pull type. Moreover, they can be classified as Class A, Class B, etc., depending upon the mode of operation.

In short, transistors can perform most of the functions of the ordinary electron tube and in some cases perform them better.

50·7   Transistor Radio. The transistor radio shown in Fig. 50·14 is typical of the many radios of this type available in kit form from manufacturers. Light, compact, and small in size, it is ideal for portable use. Using one dual and two single PNP transistors, plus a germanium diode, the radio consists of five basic stages in a superheterodyne circuit. The stages are r-f converter or mixer, i-f amplifier, second detector, first audio amplifier, and power output audio amplifier.

Circuit Description. The incoming signal is picked up by the antenna loop coil $L1$ and is coupled through the low-impedance secondary winding to the base of the r-f transistor $PH6$. The incoming signal is selected, or tuned, by $C1A$. As in all r-f circuits, the greatest transfer of energy occurs when the impedances of the two circuits are matched. Since the input impedance of transistors in this type of circuit is low, it is imperative that the signal source also be of a low impedance in order to transfer maximum energy. Therefore, the secondary of $L1$ has fewer turns than the primary. This results in the transfer of the higher voltage and lower current from the high-impedance primary to a lower impedance in the secondary. Because of the lower voltage and higher current in the secondary, there is no loss of power transfer since the secondary winding produces a greater current than the primary winding.

The oscillator coil $C2$, because of close coupling between the two windings, feeds back a signal to the emitter of $PH6$ from the collector through $C4$. This produces oscillations at a frequency determined by the setting of tuning capacitor $C2A$. The frequency of oscillation is always maintained at 455 kc above the incoming signal. It is maintained at this difference through the tuning range by means of a combination of the

Fig. 50·14   Transistor radio.   (*Philmore Manufacturing Company, Inc.*)

Fig. 50·15   Transistor-radio construction.   (*Philmore Manufacturing Company, Inc.*)

difference in inductance of the antenna loop coil winding and the oscillator coil winding, and because of the difference in capacitance between the two-ganged variable capacitor sections of $C1A$ and $C2A$.

The two signals are mixed and amplified by the transistor $PH6$, which is a PNP-type in a conventional converter circuit. The 455-kc difference signal is present across the collector load and is applied to part of the tuned circuit on the primary winding of the i-f transformer $T1$.

Resistors $R13$ and $R14$ form a voltage divider across the battery-source voltage from whose tap a voltage is applied to the base of $PH6$ as a bias. In conjunction with the emitter resistor $R9$, this acts to determine the proper collector current and correct operating conditions for proper converter and amplifier action on the signal. In this circuit, the collector current will increase with an increase in the negative bias on the base element and with a lowered emitter resistance.

The 455-kc signal present at the collector of the converter stage is applied to a portion of the primary winding of $T1$ in order to correctly match the collector impedance of the converter transistor. The signal is then stepped down in impedance but not in power to match the low i-f transistor impedance of the base element of $PH3$. The i-f amplifier stage acts as a straightforward amplifier, and the amplified output is applied to the primary winding of the i-f transformer $T2$.

Capacitor $C3$ acts as a neutralizing capacitor and its purpose is the prevention of self-oscillation in this triode-type transistor stage. Oscillations might otherwise occur due to internal inphase feedback of the signal voltage from collector to base elements. Neutralization is accomplished by feeding an out-of-phase signal back from the primary of $T2$ through $C3$ to the base of $PH3$. This signal is of sufficient magnitude to cancel the internally generated inphase feedback voltage from collector to base. Selection of the proper amount of feedback voltage is accomplished through selection of $C3$ capacitance and positioning of the tap on the primary of $T2$ for proper inductance.

The secondary winding of $T2$ is low in impedance in order to match the equally low input impedance of the germanium crystal diode $PH4$, which is the second detector. $PH4$ demodulates the a-c signal output of the i-f amplifier. In this process of amplitude-modulation detection, the a-f component is separated from the i-f signal and transferred through the volume control $R17$ to the a-f amplifier. A small portion of this voltage is simultaneously applied to the base element of the i-f stage through resistors $R11$ and $R5$ and the secondary of $T1$. This voltage acts as automatic volume control. From $R17$ the audio signal is applied to the base element of the first audio transistor $PH5$ through $C12$. Resistors $R12$ and $R15$ form a voltage-divider network from whose junction point a correct bias voltage is applied to the base of $PH5$. In conjunction with the emitter resistor $R8$, this network determines the collector current needed for the transistor to operate on the linear portion of its characteristics for maximum output and minimum distortion. Capacitor $C16$ bypasses a-f variations to ground and thus eliminates degeneration. The amplified signal is coupled from the collector of $PH5$ to the primary of the audio driver transformer $T3$. It is then stepped down to match the low-impedance input of the power-output audio transistor.

In the power-output stage the signal is further amplified and then applied to the primary winding of the output transformer $T4$. The secondary of $T4$ is low in impedance in order to match the 4-ohm impedance of the loud-speaker voice coil. Resistors $R3$ and $R10$ in the base circuit determine the base bias and, with $R1$ in the emitter circuit, act in the same manner as $R12$, $R15$, and $R8$ in the first audio stage. Capacitor $C14$ forms a low-impedance path between emitter and base, and bypasses a-f variations to ground to prevent degeneration.

The speaker voice coil is automatically disconnected when the head-

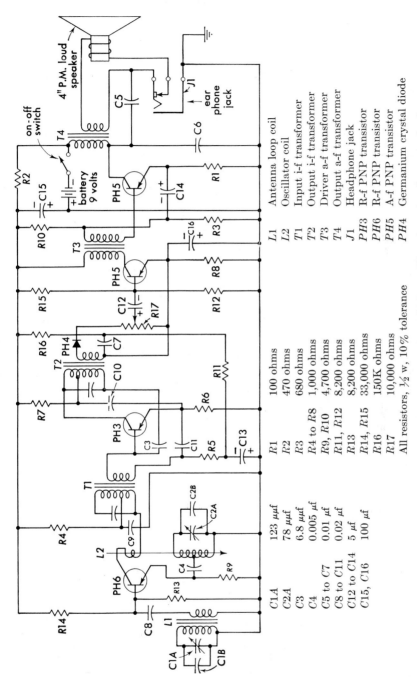

C1A	123 $\mu\mu f$	
C2A	78 $\mu\mu f$	
C3	6.8 $\mu\mu f$	
C4	0.005 μf	
C5 to C7	0.01 μf	
C8 to C11	0.02 μf	
C12 to C14	5 μf	
C15, C16	100 μf	

R1	100 ohms	
R2	470 ohms	
R3	680 ohms	
R4 to R8	1,000 ohms	
R9, R10	4,700 ohms	
R11, R12	8,200 ohms	
R13	8,200 ohms	
R14, R15	33,000 ohms	
R16	150K ohms	
R17	10,000 ohms	
All resistors, ½ w, 10% tolerance		

L1	Antenna loop coil
L2	Oscillator coil
T1	Input i-f transformer
T2	Output i-f transformer
T3	Driver a-f transformer
T4	Output a-f transformer
J1	Headphone jack
PH3	R-f PNP transistor
PH6	R-f PNP transistor
PH5	A-f PNP transistor
PH4	Germanium crystal diode

FIG. 50-16 Transistor-radio circuit schematic. (*Philmore Manufacturing Company, Inc.*)

phone plug is inserted into jack $J1$.   Audio voltage for the headphones
is taken from the output collector winding through $C6$.

REVIEW QUESTIONS

1. What are some of the uses of transistors?
2. Explain the basic difference between transistors and electron tubes.
3. What are semiconductors?
4. What are valence electrons?
5. What is the effect of adding impurities to germanium?
6. What is a pentavalent impurity?   A trivalent impurity?
7. Explain how N-type germanium is produced.
8. Explain how P-type germanium is produced.
9. What are covalent bonds?
10. Explain how a hole is produced in P-type germanium.
11. Explain how an excess electron is produced in N-type germanium.
12. What is meant by potential energy barrier?
13. Explain the difference between forward and reverse bias.
14. Explain the operation of an NPN transistor.
15. Explain the operation of a PNP transistor.
16. Explain the operation of a point contact transistor.
17. What is the basic difference between a PNP and an NPN transistor?
18. How can a transistor be compared to an electron tube?
19. What are some of the advantages of transistors over electron tubes?
20. How does amplification in transistors differ from amplification in an electron
tube?

The following questions are based on the schematic in Fig. 50·16.

21. What would be most likely to occur if the resistance of $R14$ increased?
22. What is the purpose of $C7$?
23. What is the purpose of $R2$ and $C15$?
24. If $R7$ shorted, what would be the effect upon circuit operation?
25. Moving the tap on the primary of $T2$ in a manner to increase the inductance
would be most likely to produce what effect?

APPENDIX

I   The Chemical Elements*

Atomic number	Name of element	Symbol	Atomic weight	Chemical valence	Melting point, C°	Density,† g/cm³
89	Actinium........	Ac	227.	3	1600.	
13	Aluminum.......	Al	26.98	3	660.	2.699
95	Americium......	Am	[243.]	3,4,5,6		11.7
51	Antimony.......	Sb	121.76	3,5	630.5	6.62
18	Argon..........	A	39.944	0	−189.4	.00166
33	Arsenic.........	As	74.91	±3,5	814@36At	5.73
85	Astatine.........	At	211.			
56	Barium.........	Ba	137.36	2	704.	3.5
97	Berkelium.......	Bk	[245.]	3,4		
4	Beryllium.......	Be	9.013	2	1280.	1.82
83	Bismuth........	Bi	209.00	3,5	271.3	9.80
5	Boron..........	B	10.82	3	2300.	2.3
35	Bromine........	Br	79.916	±1,5	−7.2	3.12
48	Cadmium.......	Cd	112.41	2	321.	8.65
20	Calcium........	Ca	40.08	2	850.	1.55
98	Californium.....	Cf	[246.]	3		
6	Carbon.........	C	12.011	±4,2	3700.	2.22
58	Cerium.........	Ce	140.13	3,4	600.	6.9
55	Cesium.........	Cs	132.91	1	28.	1.9
17	Chlorine........	Cl	35.457	±1,5,7	−101.	1.51
24	Chromium......	Cr	52.01	2,3,6	1930.	7.19
27	Cobalt.........	Co	58.94	3,2	1492.	8.9
29	Copper.........	Cu	63.54	1,2	1083.	8.96
96	Curium.........	Cm	[243.]	3		
66	Dysprosium.....	Dy	162.51	3		(8.56)
99	Einsteinium.....	E	[253.]			
68	Erbium.........	Er	167.27	3		(9.16)
63	Europium.......	Eu	152.0	2,3		(5.24)
100	Fermium........	Fm	[255.]			
9	Fluorine.........	F	19.00	−1.	−223.	1.14
87	Francium.......	Fr	223.0	1		
64	Gadolinium.....	Gd	157.26	3		(7.95)
31	Gallium.........	Ga	69.72	3	29.8	5.91
32	Germanium.....	Ge	72.60	4	958.	5.36
79	Gold...........	Au	197.0	1,3	1063.	19.32
72	Hafnium........	Hf	178.50	4	1700.	11.4
2	Helium.........	He	4.003	0	−271.4	.00017
67	Holmium........	Ho	164.94	3		(10.12)
1	Hydrogen.......	H	1.0080	1	−259.4	.00008
49	Indium.........	In	114.82	3	156.4	7.31
53	Iodine..........	I	126.91	−1,5,7	114.	4.93

Atomic number	Name of element	Symbol	Atomic weight	Chemical valence	Melting point, C°	Density,† g/cm³
77	Iridium.........	Ir	193.1	3,4,6	2443.	22.5
26	Iron............	Fe	55.85	2,3	1539.	7.87
36	Krypton........	Kr	83.80	0	−157.	.00349
57	Lanthanum......	La	138.92	3	826.	6.15
82	Lead...........	Pb	207.21	2,4	327.3	11.34
3	Lithium.........	Li	6.940	1	186.	0.53
71	Lutetium........	Lu	174.99	3		(9.74)
12	Magnesium......	Mg	24.32	2	650.	1.74
25	Manganese......	Mn	54.94	2,3,4,6,7	1245.	7.43
101	Mendelevium....	Mv	[256.]			
80	Mercury........	Hg	200.61	1,2	−38.87	13.55
42	Molybdenum....	Mo	95.95	3,5,6	2625.	10.2
60	Neodymium.....	Nd	144.27	3	840.	7.05
10	Neon...........	Ne	20.183	0	−248.6	.00084
93	Neptunium......	Np	237.	3,4,5,6	640.	
28	Nickel..........	Ni	58.71	2,3	1453.	8.9
41	Niobium........	Nb	92.91	3,5	2415.	8.57
7	Nitrogen........	N	14.008	2,−3,5	−210.	.00116
76	Osmium.........	Os	190.2	4,6,8	2700.	22.5
8	Oxygen.........	O	16.0000	−2	−218.8	.00133
46	Palladium.......	Pd	106.4	2,4	1552.	12.0
15	Phosphorus......	P	30.975	±3,5	44.1	1.82
78	Platinium.......	Pt	195.09	2,4	1769.	21.45
94	Plutonium.......	Pu	[242.]	3,4,5,6		
84	Polonium........	Po	210.	2,4	254.	(9.24)
19	Potassium.......	K	39.100	1	63.	0.86
59	Praseodymium..	Pr	140.92	3	940.	6.63
61	Promethium.....	Pm	[145.]	3		
91	Protactinium....	Pa	231.	5	3000.	
88	Radium.........	Ra	226.05	2	700.	5.0
86	Radon..........	Rn	222.	0	−71.	4.40†
75	Rhenium........	Re	186.22	−1,4,7	3170.	20.5
45	Rhodium........	Rh	102.91	3,4	1960.	12.44
37	Rubidium.......	Rb	85.48	1	39.	1.53
44	Ruthenium......	Ru	101.1	3,4,6,8	2500.	12.2
62	Samarium.......	Sm	150.35	3	1300.	7.7
21	Scandium.......	Sc	44.96	3	1200.	2.5
34	Selenium........	Se	78.96	−2,4,6	220.	4.81
14	Silicon..........	Si	28.09	4	1430.	2.33
47	Silver..........	Ag	107.880	1	961.	10.49
11	Sodium.........	Na	22.991	1	98.	0.97

Atomic number	Name of element	Sym-bol	Atomic weight	Chemical valence	Melting point, C°	Density,† g/cm³
38	Strontium.......	Sr	87.63	2	770.	2.6
16	Sulfur	S	32.066	−2,4,6	119.	2.07
73	Tantalum.......	Ta	180.95	5	2996.	16.6
43	Technetium.... .	Tc	99.	7	2140.	11.46
52	Tellurium.......	Te	127.61	−2,4,6	450.	6.24
65	Terbium........	Tb	158.93	3	327.	(8.33)
81	Thallium........	Tl	204.4	1,3	300.	11.85
90	Thorium........	Th	232.05	4	1800.	11.5
69	Thulium........	Tm	168.94	3		(9.35)
50	Tin	Sn	118.70	2,4	232.	7.298
22	Titanium.	Ti	47.90	3,4	1820.	4.54
74	Tungsten........	W	183.86	6	3380.	19.3
92	Uranium........	U	238.07	3,4,5,6	1133.	18.7
23	Vanadium.......	V	50.95	2,4,5	1735.	6.0
54	Xenon..........	Xe	131.30	0	−112.	.0055
70	Ytterbium.......	Yb	173.04	2,3		(7.01)
39	Yttrium.........	Y	88.92	3	1490.	5.51
30	Zinc............	Zn	65.38	2	419.5	7.133
40	Zirconium.......	Zr	91.22	4	1750.	6.5

* Courtesy of W. M. Welch Manufacturing Company.
† Density @ 20°C except Rn @ −62°C.

II Greek Alphabet*

Name	Capital	Lower case	Commonly used to designate—
Alpha............	A	α	Angles, area, coefficients
Beta.............	B	β	Angles, flux density, coefficients
Gamma...........	Γ	γ	Conductivity, specific gravity
Delta............	Δ	δ	Variation, density
Epsilon...........	E	ε	Base of natural logarithms
Zeta.............	Z	ζ	Impedance, coefficients, coordinates
Eta..............	H	η	Hysteresis coefficient, efficiency
Theta............	Θ	θ	Temperature, phase angle
Iota.............	I	ι	
Kappa...........	K	κ	Dielectric constant, susceptibility
Lambda..........	Λ	λ	Wave length
Mu..............	M	μ	Micro, amplification factor, permeability
Nu..............	N	ν	Reluctivity
Xi...............	Ξ	ξ	
Omicron..........	O	o	
Pi...............	Π	π	Ratio of circumference to diameter = 3.1416
Rho.............	P	ρ	Resistivity
Sigma...........	Σ	σ	Sign of summation
Tau.............	T	τ	Time constant, time phase displacement
Upsilon..........	Υ	υ	
Phi.............	Φ	φ	Magnetic flux, angles
Chi.............	X	χ	
Psi.............	Ψ	ψ	Dielectric flux, phase difference
Omega..........	Ω	ω	Capital, ohms; lower case, angular velocity

* Reprinted by permission from *Mathematics for Electricians and Radiomen* by Nelson M. Cooke, published by McGraw-Hill Book Company, Inc., New York.

III   Common Abbreviations and Letter Symbols in Electronics

Term	Abbreviation	Symbol
Alternating current	a-c	
American Standards Association	ASA	
Ampere-turns	amp-turns	NI
Amperes	a, amp	
Amplification factor		μ
Amplitude modulation	a-m	
Angular frequency		ω
Area	A	
Audio frequency	a-f	
Automatic frequency control	afc	
Automatic volume control	avc	
Average current		I_{av}
Average voltage		E_{av}
Capacitance		C
Capacitance reactance		X_c
Capacitor	C	
Cathode		K
Centimeters	cm	
Charge		Q
Circulating current		I_{circ}
Conductance		G
Continuous wave	c-w	
Control-grid current		i_g, I_g
Control grid (multigrid tube)		G_1
Control-grid supply voltage		E_g
Control grid (triode)		G
Cosine	cos	
Counter electromotive force	cemf	
Coupling coefficient		$k,\ \kappa$
Current		I
Cycles	c	
Cycles per second	cps	
Decibels	db	
Diameter	d	
Direct-current	d-c	
Double-pole, double-throw switch	dpdt	
Double-pole, single-throw switch	dpst	
Effective (rms) current		I
Effective resistance		R_{eff}
Effective (rms) voltage		E
Electromotive force	emf	
Farads	f	
Figure of merit		Q
Filament or heater supply voltage		E_k
Flux		Φ

Term	Abbreviation	Symbol
Frequency		f
Frequency modulation	f-m	
Grid-cathode capacitance		C_{gk}
Grid-plate capacitance		C_{gp}
Grid-plate transconductance		G_m
Heater		H
Henrys	h	
Impedance		Z
Inductance		L
Inductive reactance		X_L
Instantaneous current		i
Instantaneous voltage		e
Institute of Radio Engineers	IRE	
Intermediate frequency	i-f	
Intermediate power amplifier	IPA	
Interrupted continuous wave	icw	
Joint Army-Navy	JAN	
Kilocycles (per second)	kc	
Kilovolt-amperes	kva	
Kilovolts	kv	
Kilowatt-hours	kw-hr	
Kilowatts	kw	
Master oscillator power amplifier	mopa, MOPA	
Maximum current		I_{max}
Maximum voltage		E_{max}
Megacycles (per second)	Mc	
Meters	m	
Microfarads	μf	
Micromicrofarads	$\mu\mu f$	
Milliammeter	ma	
Milliamperes	ma	
Millihenrys	mh	
Millimeters	mm	
Millivolts	mv	
Milliwatts	mw	
Minimum current		I_{min}
Minimum voltage		E_{min}
Modulated continuous wave	mcw	
Modulation index		m_f
Mutual inductance		L_m
Permeability		μ
Phase modulation	p-m	
Plate		P
Plate-cathode capacitance		C_{pk}
Plate current		I_p
Plate resistance		R_p
Plate supply voltage		E_p
Power amplifier	PA	

Term	Abbreviation	Symbol
Primary	p, pri	
Radio frequency	r-f	
Radio, Electronics, & Television Manufacturers Association	RETMA	
Reactance		X
Reluctance		$\Re$
Resistance		r, R
Resonance frequency		f_0
Revolutions per minute	rpm	
Revolutions per second	rps	
Root mean square	rms	
Screen grid		G_2
Screen-grid current		I_{sg}
Screen-grid supply voltage		E_{sg}
Secondary	s, sec	
Self-inductance		L
Signal voltage		E_{sig}
Sine	sin	
Single-pole, double-throw switch	spdt	
Single-pole, single-throw switch	spst	
Super high frequency	shf	
Suppressor grid		G_3
Switch		S
Tangent	tan	
Time		t, T
Transformer		T
Turns, number of		N
Tuned radio frequency	trf	
Ultra-high frequency	uhf	
Vacuum tube		V
Vacuum-tube voltmeter	VTVM	
Variable frequency oscillator	vfo	
Very-high frequency	vhf	
Voltage		E
Voltage regulation	VR	
Volt-amperes	v-a	
Volts	v	
Watts	w	
Wavelength		λ

IV Standard Color Coding for Resistors

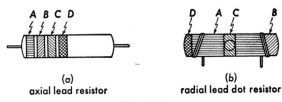

(a)
axial lead resistor

(b)
radial lead dot resistor

FIG. A·1

The two methods of identifying resistors are shown in Fig. A·1. For axial-lead types, band A represents the first significant figure, band B the second significant figure, band C the decimal multiplier, and band D the tolerance. For example, an axial-lead resistor whose colors are as follows:

<table>
<tr><td>Band A—gray</td><td>Band C—silver</td></tr>
<tr><td>Band B—red</td><td>Band D—gold</td></tr>
</table>

would have a resistance of 0.82 ohms and a tolerance of 5 per cent. (For additional information refer to Appendix VI.)

For radial-lead-dot-type resistors, the body color represents the first significant figure, band B represents the second significant figure, the dot (or sometimes a band) represents the decimal multiplier, and band D represents the tolerance. For example, a radial-lead-dot resistor colored as follows:

<table>
<tr><td>Body—orange</td><td>Dot (or band)—brown</td></tr>
<tr><td>Band B—white</td><td>Band D—silver</td></tr>
</table>

would have a resistance of 390 ohms and a tolerance of 10 per cent.

EXAMPLES OF COLOR CODING

Resistance, ohms	A	B	C	Resistance, ohms	A	B	C
0.47	Yellow	Violet	Silver	200	Red	Black	Brown
1.0	Black	Brown	Black	300	Orange	Black	Brown
4.7	Yellow	Violet	Gold	330	Orange	Orange	Brown
10	Brown	Black	Black	470	Yellow	Violet	Brown
15	Brown	Green	Black	620	Blue	Red	Brown
20	Red	Black	Black	820	Gray	Red	Brown
30	Orange	Black	Black	1000	Brown	Black	Red
33	Orange	Orange	Black	1100	Brown	Brown	Red
47	Yellow	Violet	Black	1500	Brown	Green	Red
51	Green	Brown	Black	1600	Brown	Blue	Red
68	Blue	Gray	Black	2200	Red	Red	Red
82	Gray	Red	Black	3000	Orange	Black	Red
100	Brown	Black	Brown	3900	Orange	White	Red
110	Brown	Brown	Brown	5100	Green	Brown	Red
150	Brown	Green	Brown	6800	Blue	Gray	Red

EXAMPLES OF COLOR CODING (*Cont.*)

Resistance, ohms	A	B	C	Resistance, ohms	A	B	C
10 k	Brown	Black	Orange	160 k	Brown	Blue	Yellow
11 k	Brown	Brown	Orange	200 k	Red	Black	Yellow
12 k	Brown	Red	Orange	220 k	Red	Red	Yellow
16 k	Brown	Blue	Orange	330 k	Orange	Orange	Yellow
20 k	Red	Black	Orange	470 k	Yellow	Violet	Yellow
24 k	Red	Yellow	Orange	510 k	Green	Brown	Yellow
30 k	Orange	Black	Orange	680 k	Blue	Gray	Yellow
33 k	Orange	Orange	Orange	1.0 meg	Brown	Black	Green
43 k	Yellow	Orange	Orange	1.5 meg	Brown	Green	Green
47 k	Yellow	Violet	Orange	2.0 meg	Red	Black	Green
56 k	Green	Blue	Orange	3.0 meg	Orange	Black	Green
62 k	Blue	Red	Orange	5.1 meg	Green	Brown	Green
82 k	Gray	Red	Orange	10 meg	Brown	Black	Blue
100 k	Brown	Black	Yellow	15 meg	Brown	Green	Blue
120 k	Brown	Red	Yellow	20 meg	Red	Black	Blue

V   Standard Color Coding and Markings for Capacitors*

In so far as designation of numbers by color is concerned, color coding for capacitors is the same as for resistors. All capacitance values are in micromicro-farads. While the larger types are usually marked as to capacitance, tolerance, and working direct voltage, small capacitors are color-coded in a variety of sizes and shapes. Three-dot capacitors indicate a working voltage of 500 volts, a tolerance of more than 10 per cent, and a capacitance of less than 10 $\mu\mu f$. Additional dots or bands are used to indicate the exact working voltage, tolerance, and temperature coefficient.

Because so many types of capacitors are manufactured, it is almost impossible to prescribe a standard method of identification that will apply in all cases. Figure A·2 shows typical examples of the most commonly used capacitors.

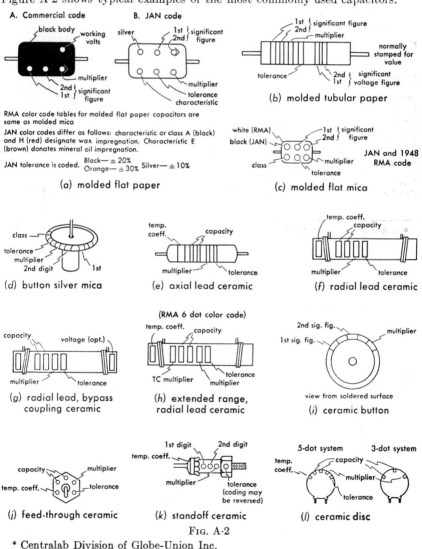

Fig. A·2

* Centralab Division of Globe-Union Inc.

VI   Composite Capacitor and

Color	Significant figures	Molded-paper tubular capacitors			Molded-mica RMA†-standard–JAN-specification capacitors			
		Decimal multiplier	Tolerance	Voltage, volts	Decimal multiplier	Tolerance, %	RMA voltage rating (all capacitors)	Class
Black.........	0	1	± 20	...	1	± 20 (JAN 1948 RMA)	....	A
Brown........	1	10	....	100	10	....	100	B
Red..........	2	100	....	200	100	± 2	200	C
Orange.......	3	1,000	± 30	300	1,000	± 3(RMA)	300	D
Yellow........	4	10,000	± 40	400	10,000	....	400	E
Green........	5	10^5	± 5	500	......	± 5 (RMA)	500	F (JAN)
Blue..........	6	10^6	....	600	......	....	600	G (JAN)
Violet........	7	......	....	700	......	....	700	......
Gray.........	8	......	....	800	......	....	800	I (RMA)
White........	9	......	± 10 (RMA)	900	......	....	900	J (RMA)
Gold.........	.....	0.1	....	....	0.1	± 5 (JAN)	1,000	......
Silver........	.....	......	± 10 (JAN)	....	0.01	± 10	2,000	......
No color......	.....	......	....	.....	......	± 20 (old RMA)	500 (old RMA)	

* Centralab Division of Globe-Union Inc.   † Now EIA.

Resistor Color-code Table*

	Ceramic RMA-standard–JAN-specification capacitors					Resistors; RMA and JAN	
Decimal multiplier	Tolerance		Temp. coeff., ppm/°C.	Temp. coeff. for extended-range TC HiCap		Multiplier	Tolerance, %
	Capacitance of 10 μμf or less, μμf	Capacitance of more than 10 μμf, %		Significant figures	Multiplier		
1	±2.0 (JAN)	±20	−0	0	−1	1	
10	±0.1	±1	−33	...	−10	10	
100	....	±2	−75	1	−100	100	
1,000	....	±2.5 (RMA)	−150	1.5	−1,000	1,000	
10,000 (RMA)	....	....	−220	2.2	−10,000	10,000	
....	±0.5	±5	−330	3.3	+1	100,000	
....	....	....	−470	4.7	+10	10^6	
....	....	....	−750	7.5	+100	10^7	
0.01	±0.25	....	+30	...	+1,000	10^8	
0.1	±1.0	±10	−330 ± 500	...	+10,000	10^9	
....	....	....	+100 (JAN)	...	......	0.1	±5
....	....	....	....	...	......	0.01	±10

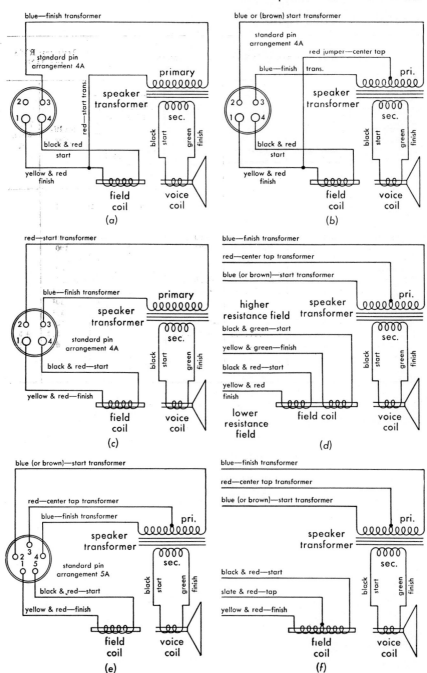

Fɪɢ. A·3.   Identification of leads of typical electrodynamic loud-speakers.

Standard Color Coding*

The diagrams below and opposite indicate the standard color coding for loud-speaker and transformer leads as adopted by the RMA (now the RETMA). It should be noted that the start, tap, and finish of all speaker windings occur in clockwise order around the plug when viewed from the socket end. Also, when two fields are used on a single speaker, the field of lower resistance will be indicated by leads having a common red color. The field of higher resistance will be indicated by leads having a common green color. When three fields are used, the highest-resistance field will be indicated by common orange leads.

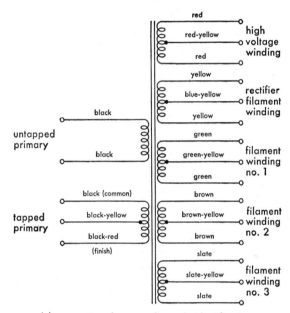

(a) power transformer color code identification

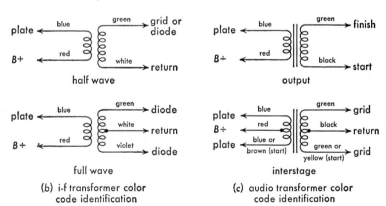

(b) i-f transformer color code identification

(c) audio transformer color code identification

Fig. A·4.   Identification of leads of typical transformers.

* Centralab Division of Globe-Union Inc.

VIII Miscellaneous Color Coding*

CHASSIS WIRING COLOR CODE, RADIO

Seq. no.	Color	Circuit name
0	Black	Grounds (grounded elements and returns)
1	Brown	Heaters or filaments, off ground
2	Red	Power supply B+
3	Orange	Screen grids
4	Yellow	Cathodes
5	Green	Control grids
6	Blue	Plates
7	Violet	Not used
8	Gray	A-c power lines
9	White	Above- or below-ground returns (avc, etc.)

COLOR CODE IDENTIFICATION, BATTERY CABLES

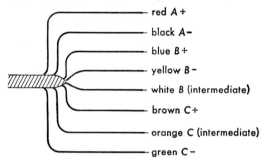

red A+

black A−

blue B+

yellow B−

white B (intermediate)

brown C+

orange C (intermediate)

green C−

CHASSIS WIRING COLOR CODE, TELEVISION

Body and Tracer Colors	Circuit name
Black (solid)	Grounds (grounded elements and grounded returns)
Black-Brown	Identified grounds (grounded heater or filament)
Black-Red	Identified grounds (grounded B−)
Black-Yellow	Identified grounds (grounded cathode)
Black-Green	Identified grounds (grounded grid)
Brown (solid)	Heaters or filaments (above or below ground)
Brown-Red	Identified heater or filament (rectifier heater or filament)
Brown-Yellow	Identified heater or filament (any auxiliary heater or filament)
Brown-Green	Identified heater or filament (any auxiliary heater or filament)
Brown-White	Heater or filament center tap (not grounded)

* Centralab Division of Globe-Union Inc.

Body and Tracer Colors	Circuit name
Red (solid)	Power-supply B+ (general or main stem)
Red-White	Identified B+ (unfiltered B from filament)
Red-Blue	Identified B+ (above main stem)
Red-Yellow	Identified B+ (below main stem)
Red-Green	Identified B+ (intermediate voltage)
Red-Black	Identified B+ (intermediate voltage)
Red-Blue-Yellow	Identified B+ (intermediate voltage) (see black-red and white-red for B−)
White (solid)	Bias supply, B or C− (main stem)
White-Red	B− (below ground, max. value)
White-Orange	C− (intermediate fixed value)
White-Yellow	C− (intermediate fixed value)
White-Green	C− (preferred for avc bias)
White-Brown	C− (intermediate avc bias)
White-Black	Alternative ground or offground connection
White-Blue	Internal antenna or to antenna coil
White-Blue-Red	Universal substitute wire
Green (solid)	Control grids and diode plates (general)
Green-White	Diode plate (if identified from control grid)
Green-Red	Identified grid (as thyratron control grid)
Green-Yellow	Identified grid (as oscillator control grid)
Blue (solid)	Plates, except diode plates (general)
Blue-Red	Identified plate (as rectifier plate & HV a-c)
Blue-Yellow	Identified plate (as oscillator plate or "anode **grid**")
Yellow (solid)	Cathodes (above and below ground)
Yellow-Red	Identified cathode (as power-amplifier cathode)
Yellow-Green	Identified cathode (as picture-tube cathode)

COLOR-CODE IDENTIFICATION, TELEPHONE SWITCHBOARD CABLE
(sometimes used in electronic installations)

20-pair cable:

Blue	Blue-Green	Green-White
Orange	Blue-Brown	Green-Brown
Green	Blue-Slate	Green-Slate
Brown	Orange-White	Brown-White
Slate	Orange-Green	Brown-Slate
Blue-White	Orange-Brown	Slate-White
Blue-Orange	Orange-Slate	

The color of the mate wire to each is white.

21-pair cable: as above but extra pair is red-white
40-pair cable: as above but pairs 21 to 40 incl. have a red mate
60-pair cable: as above but pairs 41 to 60 incl. have a black mate
80-pair cable: as above but pairs 61 to 80 incl. have a red-white mate
100-pair cable: as above but pairs 81 to 100 incl. have a black-white mate

IX Common Schematic

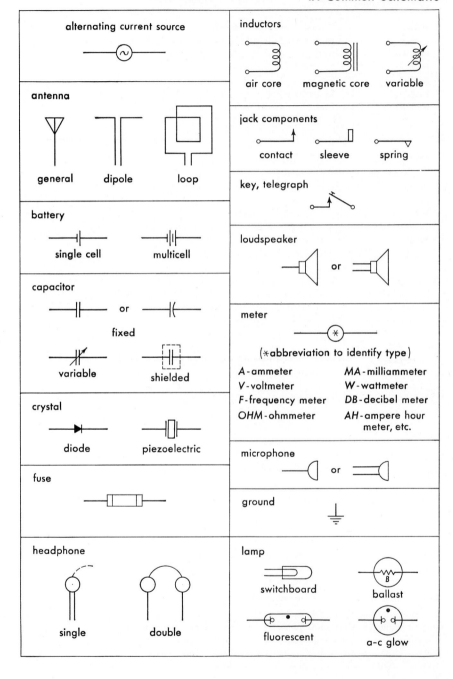

Symbols in Electronics

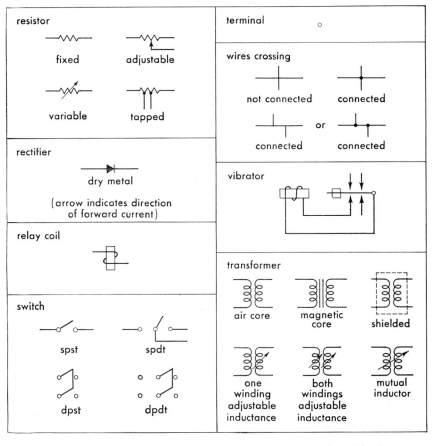

X   Conversion of Units

Given	To obtain—	Multiply by—	Divide by—
amperes...............	milliamperes	1,000	
amperes...............	microamperes	10^6	
amperes...............	micromicroamperes	10^{12}	
centimeters...........	feet	......	30.48
centimeters...........	inches	......	2.54
centimeters...........	meters	......	100
centimeters...........	millimeters	10	
centimeters...........	mils	393.7	
circular mils	square centimeters	......	197,300
circular mils	square inches	......	1,273,000
cycles.................	kilocycles	......	1,000
cycles.................	megacycles	......	10^6
degrees................	minutes	60	
degrees................	seconds	3600	
degrees................	radians	......	57.3
farads.................	microfarads	10^6	
farads.................	micromicrofarads	10^{12}	
feet...................	meters	......	3.281
gauss.................	lines per square inch	6.452	
gilberts................	ampere turns	......	1.257
grams.................	dynes	980.7	
grams.................	kilograms	......	1,000
grams.................	ounces	......	28.35
grams.................	pounds	......	453.6
henrys................	millihenrys	1,000	
henrys................	microhenrys	10^6	
horsepower.............	foot-pounds per second	550	
horsepower.............	kilowatts	......	1.341
horsepower.............	watts	746	
inches.................	meters	......	39.37
joules.................	watt-hours	......	3600
kilograms..............	dynes	980,665	
kilograms..............	pounds	2.205	
mhos....	micromhos	10^6	
microseconds...........	seconds	......	10^6
microvolts.............	volts	......	10^6
microvolts.............	millivolts	......	1,000
microwatts.............	watts	......	10^6
microwatts.............	milliwatts	......	1,000
miles..................	kilometers	1.609	
ohms..................	megohms	......	10^6
ohms..................	micro-ohms	10^6	
ohms..................	micromicro-ohms	10^{12}	
ohms..................	milliohms	1,000	
units..................	kilounits	......	1,000
units..................	milliunits	1,000	

XI Annealed Copper-wire Table (Solid)*

Gage number	Diameter, mils	Area, cir mils	Resistance, ohms per 1,000 ft, 25°C (77°F)	Weight, lb per 1,000 ft
0000	460.0	211,600.0	0.0500	641.0
000	410.0	167,800.0	0.0630	508.0
00	365.0	133,100.0	0.0795	403.0
0	325.0	105,500.0	0.100	319.0
1	289.0	83,690.0	0.126	253.0
2	258.0	66,370.0	0.159	201.0
3	229.0	52,640.0	0.201	159.0
4	204.0	41,740.0	0.253	126.0
5	182.0	33,100.0	0.319	100.0
6	162.0	26,250.0	0.403	79.5
7	144.0	20,820.0	0.508	63.0
8	128.0	16,510.0	0.641	50.0
9	114.0	13,090.0	0.808	39.6
10	102.0	10,380.0	1.02	31.4
11	91.0	8,234.0	1.28	24.9
12	81.0	6,530.0	1.62	19.8
13	72.0	5,178.0	2.04	15.7
14	64.0	4,107.0	2.58	12.4
15	57.0	3,257.0	3.25	9.86
16	51.0	2,583.0	4.09	7.82
17	45.0	2,048.0	5.16	6.20
18	40.0	1,624.0	6.51	4.92
19	36.0	1,288.0	8.21	3.90
20	32.0	1,022.0	10.4	3.09
21	28.5	810.0	13.1	2.45
22	25.3	642.0	16.5	1.95
23	22.6	509.0	20.8	1.54
24	20.1	404.0	26.2	1.22
25	17.9	320.0	33.0	0.970
26	15.9	254.0	41.6	0.769
27	14.2	202.0	52.5	0.610
28	12.6	160.0	66.2	0.484
29	11.3	127.0	83.4	0.384
30	10.0	100.0	105.0	0.304
31	8.9	79.7	133.0	0.241
32	8.0	63.2	167.0	0.191
33	7.1	50.1	211.0	0.152
34	6.3	39.8	266.0	0.020
35	5.6	31.5	335.0	0.0954
36	5.0	25.0	423.0	0.0757
37	4.5	19.8	533.0	0.0600
38	4.0	15.7	673.0	0.0476
39	3.5	12.5	848.0	0.0377
40	3.1	9.9	1070.0	0.0299

* American wire gage (Brown & Sharpe).

XII Natural Sines, Cosines, and Tangents*

0°–14.9°

Degs.	Function	0.0°	0.1°	0.2°	0.3°	0.4°	0.5°	0.6°	0.7°	0.8°	0.9°
0	sin	0.0000	0.0017	0.0035	0.0052	0.0070	0.0087	0.0105	0.0122	0.0140	0.0157
	cos	1.0000	1.0000	1.0000	1.0000	1.0000	1.0000	0.9999	0.9999	0.9999	0.9999
	tan	0.0000	0.0017	0.0035	0.0052	0.0070	0.0087	0.0105	0.0122	0.0140	0.0157
1	sin	0.0175	0.0192	0.0209	0.0227	0.0244	0.0262	0.0279	0.0297	0.0314	0.0332
	cos	0.9998	0.9998	0.9998	0.9997	0.9997	0.9997	0.9996	0.9996	0.9995	0.9995
	tan	0.0175	0.0192	0.0209	0.0227	0.0244	0.0262	0.0279	0.0297	0.0314	0.0332
2	sin	0.0349	0.0366	0.0384	0.0401	0.0419	0.0436	0.0454	0.0471	0.0488	0.0506
	cos	0.9994	0.9993	0.9993	0.9992	0.9991	0.9990	0.9990	0.9989	0.9988	0.9987
	tan	0.0349	0.0367	0.0384	0.0402	0.0419	0.0437	0.0454	0.0472	0.0489	0.0507
3	sin	0.0523	0.0541	0.0558	0.0576	0.0593	0.0610	0.0628	0.0645	0.0663	0.0680
	cos	0.9986	0.9985	0.9984	0.9983	0.9982	0.9981	0.9980	0.9979	0.9978	0.9977
	tan	0.0524	0.0542	0.0559	0.0577	0.0594	0.0612	0.0629	0.0647	0.0664	0.0682
4	sin	0.0698	0.0715	0.0732	0.0750	0.0767	0.0785	0.0802	0.0819	0.0837	0.0854
	cos	0.9976	0.9974	0.9973	0.9972	0.9971	0.9969	0.9968	0.9966	0.9965	0.9963
	tan	0.0699	0.0717	0.0734	0.0752	0.0769	0.0787	0.0805	0.0822	0.0840	0.0857
5	sin	0.0872	0.0889	0.0906	0.0924	0.0941	0.0958	0.0976	0.0993	0.1011	0.1028
	cos	0.9962	0.9960	0.9959	0.9957	0.9956	0.9954	0.9952	0.9951	0.9949	0.9947
	tan	0.0875	0.0892	0.0910	0.0928	0.0945	0.0963	0.0981	0.0998	0.1016	0.1033
6	sin	0.1045	0.1063	0.1080	0.1097	0.1115	0.1132	0.1149	0.1167	0.1184	0.1201
	cos	0.9945	0.9943	0.9942	0.9940	0.9938	0.9936	0.9934	0.9932	0.9930	0.9928
	tan	0.1051	0.1069	0.1086	0.1104	0.1122	0.1139	0.1157	0.1175	0.1192	0.1210
7	sin	0.1219	0.1236	0.1253	0.1271	0.1288	0.1305	0.1323	0.1340	0.1357	0.1374
	cos	0.9925	0.9923	0.9921	0.9919	0.9917	0.9914	0.9912	0.9910	0.9907	0.9905
	tan	0.1228	0.1246	0.1263	0.1281	0.1299	0.1317	0.1334	0.1352	0.1370	0.1388
8	sin	0.1392	0.1409	0.1426	0.1444	0.1461	0.1478	0.1495	0.1513	0.1530	0.1547
	cos	0.9903	0.9900	0.9898	0.9895	0.9893	0.9890	0.9888	0.9885	0.9882	0.9880
	tan	0.1405	0.1423	0.1441	0.1459	0.1477	0.1495	0.1512	0.1530	0.1548	0.1566
9	sin	0.1564	0.1582	0.1599	0.1616	0.1633	0.1650	0.1668	0.1685	0.1702	0.1719
	cos	0.9877	0.9874	0.9871	0.9869	0.9866	0.9863	0.9860	0.9857	0.9854	0.9851
	tan	0.1584	0.1602	0.1620	0.1638	0.1655	0.1673	0.1691	0.1709	0.1727	0.1745
10	sin	0.1736	0.1754	0.1771	0.1788	0.1805	0.1822	0.1840	0.1857	0.1874	0.1891
	cos	0.9848	0.9845	0.9842	0.9839	0.9836	0.9833	0.9829	0.9826	0.9823	0.9820
	tan	0.1763	0.1781	0.1799	0.1817	0.1835	0.1853	0.1871	0.1890	0.1908	0.1926
11	sin	0.1908	0.1925	0.1942	0.1959	0.1977	0.1994	0.2011	0.2028	0.2045	0.2062
	cos	0.9816	0.9813	0.9810	0.9806	0.9803	0.9799	0.9796	0.9792	0.9789	0.9785
	tan	0.1944	0.1962	0.1980	0.1998	0.2016	0.2035	0.2053	0.2071	0.2089	0.2107
12	sin	0.2079	0.2096	0.2113	0.2130	0.2147	0.2164	0.2181	0.2198	0.2215	0.2232
	cos	0.9781	0.9778	0.9774	0.9770	0.9767	0.9763	0.9759	0.9755	0.9751	0.9748
	tan	0.2126	0.2144	0.2162	0.2180	0.2199	0.2217	0.2235	0.2254	0.2272	0.2290
13	sin	0.2250	0.2267	0.2284	0.2300	0.2318	0.2334	0.2351	0.2368	0.2385	0.2402
	cos	0.9744	0.9740	0.9736	0.9732	0.9728	0.9724	0.9720	0.9715	0.9711	0.9707
	tan	0.2309	0.2327	0.2345	0.2364	0.2382	0.2401	0.2419	0.2438	0.2456	0.2475
14	sin	0.2419	0.2436	0.2453	0.2470	0.2487	0.2504	0.2521	0.2538	0.2554	0.2571
	cos	0.9703	0.9699	0.9694	0.9690	0.9686	0.9681	0.9677	0.9673	0.9668	0.9664
	tan	0.2493	0.2512	0.2530	0.2549	0.2568	0.2586	0.2605	0.2623	0.2642	0.2661
Degs.	Function	0′	6′	12′	18′	24′	30′	36′	42′	48′	54′

* Reprinted by permission from *The Engineers' Manual* by Hudson, published by John Wiley & Sons, Inc., New York.

XII Natural Sines, Cosines, and Tangents *(Continued)*

15°–29.9°

Degs.	Function	0.0°	0.1°	0.2°	0.3°	0.4°	0.5°	0.6°	0.7°	0.8°	0.9°
15	sin	0.2588	0.2605	0.2622	0.2639	0.2656	0.2672	0.2689	0.2706	0.2723	0.2740
	cos	0.9659	0.9655	0.9650	0.9646	0.9641	0.9636	0.9632	0.9627	0.9622	0.9617
	tan	0.2679	0.2698	0.2717	0.2736	0.2754	0.2773	0.2792	0.2811	0.2830	0.2849
16	sin	0.2756	0.2773	0.2790	0.2807	0.2823	0.2840	0.2857	0.2874	0.2890	0.2907
	cos	0.9613	0.9608	0.9603	0.9598	0.9593	0.9588	0.9583	0.9578	0.9573	0.9568
	tan	0.2867	0.2886	0.2905	0.2924	0.2943	0.2962	0.2981	0.3000	0.3019	0.3038
17	sin	0.2924	0.2940	0.2957	0.2974	0.2990	0.3007	0.3024	0.3040	0.3057	0.3074
	cos	0.9563	0.9558	0.9553	0.9548	0.9542	0.9537	0.9532	0.9527	0.9521	0.9516
	tan	0.3057	0.3076	0.3096	0.3115	0.3134	0.3153	0.3172	0.3191	0.3211	0.3230
18	sin	0.3090	0.3107	0.3123	0.3140	0.3156	0.3173	0.3190	0.3206	0.3223	0.3239
	cos	0.9511	0.9505	0.9500	0.9494	0.9489	0.9483	0.9478	0.9472	0.9466	0.9461
	tan	0.3249	0.3269	0.3288	0.3307	0.3327	0.3346	0.3365	0.3385	0.3404	0.3424
19	sin	0.3256	0.3272	0.3289	0.3305	0.3322	0.3338	0.3355	0.3371	0.3387	0.3404
	cos	0.9455	0.9449	0.9444	0.9438	0.9432	0.9426	0.9421	0.9415	0.9409	0.9403
	tan	0.3443	0.3463	0.3482	0.3502	0.3522	0.3541	0.3561	0.3581	0.3600	0.3620
20	sin	0.3420	0.3437	0.3453	0.3469	0.3486	0.3502	0.3518	0.3535	0.3551	0.3567
	cos	0.9397	0.9391	0.9385	0.9379	0.9373	0.9367	0.9361	0.9354	0.9348	0.9342
	tan	0.3640	0.3659	0.3679	0.3699	0.3719	0.3739	0.3759	0.3779	0.3799	0.3819
21	sin	0.3584	0.3600	0.3616	0.3633	0.3649	0.3665	0.3681	0.3697	0.3714	0.3730
	cos	0.9336	0.9330	0.9323	0.9317	0.9311	0.9304	0.9298	0.9291	0.9285	0.9278
	tan	0.3839	0.3859	0.3879	0.3899	0.3919	0.3939	0.3959	0.3979	0.4000	0.4020
22	sin	0.3746	0.3762	0.3778	0.3795	0.3811	0.3827	0.3843	0.3859	0.3875	0.3891
	cos	0.9272	0.9265	0.9259	0.9252	0.9245	0.9239	0.9232	0.9225	0.9219	0.9212
	tan	0.4040	0.4061	0.4081	0.4101	0.4122	0.4142	0.4163	0.4183	0.4204	0.4224
23	sin	0.3907	0.3923	0.3939	0.3955	0.3971	0.3987	0.4003	0.4019	0.4035	0.4051
	cos	0.9205	0.9198	0.9191	0.9184	0.9178	0.9171	0.9164	0.9157	0.9150	0.9143
	tan	0.4245	0.4265	0.4286	0.4307	0.4327	0.4348	0.4369	0.4390	0.4411	0.4431
24	sin	0.4067	0.4083	0.4099	0.4115	0.4131	0.4147	0.4163	0.4179	0.4195	0.4210
	cos	0.9135	0.9128	0.9121	0.9114	0.9107	0.9100	0.9092	0.9085	0.9078	0.9070
	tan	0.4452	0.4473	0.4494	0.4515	0.4536	0.4557	0.4578	0.4599	0.4621	0.4642
25	sin	0.4226	0.4242	0.4258	0.4274	0.4289	0.4305	0.4321	0.4337	0.4352	0.4368
	cos	0.9063	0.9056	0.9048	0.9041	0.9033	0.9026	0.9018	0.9011	0.9003	0.8996
	tan	0.4663	0.4684	0.4706	0.4727	0.4748	0.4770	0.4791	0.4813	0.4834	0.4856
26	sin	0.4384	0.4399	0.4415	0.4431	0.4446	0.4462	0.4478	0.4493	0.4509	0.4524
	cos	0.8988	0.8980	0.8973	0.8965	0.8957	0.8949	0.8942	0.8934	0.8926	0.8918
	tan	0.4877	0.4899	0.4921	0.4942	0.4964	0.4986	0.5008	0.5029	0.5051	0.5073
27	sin	0.4540	0.4555	0.4571	0.4586	0.4602	0.4617	0.4633	0.4648	0.4664	0.4679
	cos	0.8910	0.8902	0.8894	0.8886	0.8878	0.8870	0.8862	0.8854	0.8846	0.8838
	tan	0.5095	0.5117	0.5139	0.5161	0.5184	0.5206	0.5228	0.5250	0.5272	0.5295
28	sin	0.4695	0.4710	0.4726	0.4741	0.4756	0.4772	0.4787	0.4802	0.4818	0.4833
	cos	0.8829	0.8821	0.8813	0.8805	0.8796	0.8788	0.8780	0.8771	0.8763	0.8755
	tan	0.5317	0.5340	0.5362	0.5384	0.5407	0.5430	0.5452	0.5475	0.5498	0.5520
29	sin	0.4848	0.4863	0.4879	0.4894	0.4909	0.4924	0.4939	0.4955	0.4970	0.4985
	cos	0.8746	0.8738	0.8729	0.8721	0.8712	0.8704	0.8695	0.8686	0.8678	0.8669
	tan	0.5543	0.5566	0.5589	0.5612	0.5635	0.5658	0.5681	0.5704	0.5727	0.5750
Degs.	Function	0′	6′	12′	18′	24′	30′	36′	42′	48′	54′

XII   Natural Sines, Cosines, and Tangents   *(Continued)*

30°–44.9°

Degs.	Function	0.0°	0.1°	0.2°	0.3°	0.4°	0.5°	0.6°	0.7°	0.8°	0.9°
30	sin	0.5000	0.5015	0.5030	0.5045	0.5060	0.5075	0.5090	0.5105	0.5120	0.5135
	cos	0.8660	0.8652	0.8643	0.8634	0.8625	0.8616	0.8607	0.8599	0.8590	0.8581
	tan	0.5774	0.5797	0.5820	0.5844	0.5867	0.5890	0.5914	0.5938	0.5961	0.5985
31	sin	0.5150	0.5165	0.5180	0.5195	0.5210	0.5225	0.5240	0.5255	0.5270	0.5284
	cos	0.8572	0.8563	0.8554	0.8545	0.8536	0.8526	0.8517	0.8508	0.8499	0.8490
	tan	0.6009	0.6032	0.6056	0.6080	0.6104	0.6128	0.6152	0.6176	0.6200	0.6224
32	sin	0.5299	0.5314	0.5329	0.5344	0.5358	0.5373	0.5388	0.5402	0.5417	0.5432
	cos	0.8480	0.8471	0.8462	0.8453	0.8443	0.8434	0.8425	0.8415	0.8406	0.8396
	tan	0.6249	0.6273	0.6297	0.6322	0.6346	0.6371	0.6395	0.6420	0.6445	0.6469
33	sin	0.5446	0.5461	0.5476	0.5490	0.5505	0.5519	0.5534	0.5548	0.5563	0.5577
	cos	0.8387	0.8377	0.8368	0.8358	0.8348	0.8339	0.8329	0.8320	0.8310	0.8300
	tan	0.6494	0.6519	0.6544	0.6569	0.6594	0.6619	0.6644	0.6669	0.6694	0.6720
34	sin	0.5592	0.5606	0.5621	0.5635	0.5650	0.5664	0.5678	0.5693	0.5707	0.5721
	cos	0.8290	0.8281	0.8271	0.8261	0.8251	0.8241	0.8231	0.8221	0.8211	0.8202
	tan	0.6745	0.6771	0.6796	0.6822	0.6847	0.6873	0.6899	0.6924	0.6950	0.6976
35	sin	0.5736	0.5750	0.5764	0.5779	0.5793	0.5807	0.5821	0.5835	0.5850	0.5864
	cos	0.8192	0.8181	0.8171	0.8161	0.8151	0.8141	0.8131	0.8121	0.8111	0.8100
	tan	0.7002	0.7028	0.7054	0.7080	0.7107	0.7133	0.7159	0.7186	0.7212	0.7239
36	sin	0.5878	0.5892	0.5906	0.5920	0.5934	0.5948	0.5962	0.5976	0.5990	0.6004
	cos	0.8090	0.8080	0.8070	0.8059	0.8049	0.8039	0.8028	0.8018	0.8007	0.7997
	tan	0.7265	0.7292	0.7319	0.7346	0.7373	0.7400	0.7427	0.7454	0.7481	0.7508
37	sin	0.6018	0.6032	0.6046	0.6060	0.6074	0.6088	0.6101	0.6115	0.6129	0.6143
	cos	0.7986	0.7976	0.7965	0.7955	0.7944	0.7934	0.7923	0.7912	0.7902	0.7891
	tan	0.7536	0.7563	0.7590	0.7618	0.7646	0.7673	0.7701	0.7729	0.7757	0.7785
38	sin	0.6157	0.6170	0.6184	0.6198	0.6211	0.6225	0.6239	0.6252	0.6266	0.6280
	cos	0.7880	0.7869	0.7859	0.7848	0.7837	0.7826	0.7815	0.7804	0.7793	0.7782
	tan	0.7813	0.7841	0.7869	0.7898	0.7926	0.7954	0.7983	0.8012	0.8040	0.8069
39	sin	0.6293	0.6307	0.6320	0.6334	0.6347	0.6361	0.6374	0.6388	0.6401	0.6414
	cos	0.7771	0.7760	0.7749	0.7738	0.7727	0.7716	0.7705	0.7694	0.7683	0.7672
	tan	0.8098	0.8127	0.8156	0.8185	0.8214	0.8243	0.8273	0.8302	0.8332	0.8361
40	sin	0.6428	0.6441	0.6455	0.6468	0.6481	0.6494	0.6508	0.6521	0.6534	0.6547
	cos	0.7660	0.7649	0.7638	0.7627	0.7615	0.7604	0.7593	0.7581	0.7570	0.7559
	tan	0.8391	0.8421	0.8451	0.8481	0.8511	0.8541	0.8571	0.8601	0.8632	0.8662
41	sin	0.6561	0.6574	0.6587	0.6600	0.6613	0.6626	0.6639	0.6652	0.6665	0.6678
	cos	0.7547	0.7536	0.7524	0.7513	0.7501	0.7490	0.7478	0.7466	0.7455	0.7443
	tan	0.8693	0.8724	0.8754	0.8785	0.8816	0.8847	0.8878	0.8910	0.8941	0.8972
42	sin	0.6691	0.6704	0.6717	0.6730	0.6743	0.6756	0.6769	0.6782	0.6794	0.6807
	cos	0.7431	0.7420	0.7408	0.7396	0.7385	0.7373	0.7361	0.7349	0.7337	0.7325
	tan	0.9004	0.9036	0.9067	0.9099	0.9131	0.9163	0.9195	0.9228	0.9260	0.9293
43	sin	0.6820	0.6833	0.6845	0.6858	0.6871	0.6884	0.6896	0.6909	0.6921	0.6934
	cos	0.7314	0.7302	0.7290	0.7278	0.7266	0.7254	0.7242	0.7230	0.7218	0.7206
	tan	0.9325	0.9358	0.9391	0.9424	0.9457	0.9490	0.9523	0.9556	0.9590	0.9623
44	sin	0.6947	0.6959	0.6972	0.6984	0.6997	0.7009	0.7022	0.7034	0.7046	0.7059
	cos	0.7193	0.7181	0.7169	0.7157	0.7145	0.7133	0.7120	0.7108	0.7096	0.7083
	tan	0.9657	0.9691	0.9725	0.9759	0.9793	0.9827	0.9861	0.9896	0.9930	0.9965
Degs.	Function	0′	6′	12′	18′	24′	30′	36′	42′	48′	54′

XII Natural Sines, Cosines, and Tangents (*Continued*)

45°–59.9°

Degs.	Function	0.0°	0.1°	0.2°	0.3°	0.4°	0.5°	0.6°	0.7°	0.8°	0.9°
45	sin	0.7071	0.7083	0.7096	0.7108	0.7120	0.7133	0.7145	0.7157	0.7169	0.7181
	cos	0.7071	0.7059	0.7046	0.7034	0.7022	0.7009	0.6997	0.6984	0.6972	0.6959
	tan	1.0000	1.0035	1.0070	1.0105	1.0141	1.0176	1.0212	1.0247	1.0283	1.0319
46	sin	0.7193	0.7206	0.7218	0.7230	0.7242	0.7254	0.7266	0.7278	0.7290	0.7302
	cos	0.6947	0.6934	0.6921	0.6909	0.6896	0.6884	0.6871	0.6858	0.6845	0.6833
	tan	1.0355	1.0392	1.0428	1.0464	1.0501	1.0538	1.0575	1.0612	1.0649	1.0686
47	sin	0.7314	0.7325	0.7337	0.7349	0.7361	0.7373	0.7385	0.7396	0.7408	0.7420
	cos	0.6820	0.6807	0.6794	0.6782	0.6769	0.6756	0.6743	0.6730	0.6717	0.6704
	tan	1.0724	1.0761	1.0799	1.0837	1.0875	1.0913	1.0951	1.0990	1.1028	1.1067
48	sin	0.7431	0.7443	0.7455	0.7466	0.7478	0.7490	0.7501	0.7513	0.7524	0.7536
	cos	0.6691	0.6678	0.6665	0.6652	0.6639	0.6626	0.6613	0.6600	0.6587	0.6574
	tan	1.1106	1.1145	1.1184	1.1224	1.1263	1.1303	1.1343	1.1383	1.1423	1.1463
49	sin	0.7547	0.7559	0.7570	0.7581	0.7593	0.7604	0.7615	0.7627	0.7638	0.7649
	cos	0.6561	0.6547	0.6534	0.6521	0.6508	0.6494	0.6481	0.6468	0.6455	0.6441
	tan	1.1504	1.1544	1.1585	1.1626	1.1667	1.1708	1.1750	1.1792	1.1833	1.1875
50	sin	0.7660	0.7672	0.7683	0.7694	0.7705	0.7716	0.7727	0.7738	0.7749	0.7760
	cos	0.6428	0.6414	0.6401	0.6388	0.6374	0.6361	0.6347	0.6334	0.6320	0.6307
	tan	1.1918	1.1960	1.2002	1.2045	1.2088	1.2131	1.2174	1.2218	1.2261	1.2305
51	sin	0.7771	0.7782	0.7793	0.7804	0.7815	0.7826	0.7837	0.7848	0.7859	0.7869
	cos	0.6293	0.6280	0.6266	0.6252	0.6239	0.6225	0.6211	0.6198	0.6184	0.6170
	tan	1.2349	1.2393	1.2437	1.2482	1.2527	1.2572	1.2617	1.2662	1.2708	1.2753
52	sin	0.7880	0.7891	0.7902	0.7912	0.7923	0.7934	0.7944	0.7955	0.7965	0.7976
	cos	0.6157	0.6143	0.6129	0.6115	0.6101	0.6088	0.6074	0.6060	0.6046	0.6032
	tan	1.2799	1.2846	1.2892	1.2938	1.2985	1.3032	1.3079	1.3127	1.3175	1.3222
53	sin	0.7986	0.7997	0.8007	0.8018	0.8028	0.8039	0.8049	0.8059	0.8070	0.8080
	cos	0.6018	0.6004	0.5990	0.5976	0.5962	0.5948	0.5934	0.5920	0.5906	0.5892
	tan	1.3270	1.3319	1.3367	1.3416	1.3465	1.3514	1.3564	1.3613	1.3663	1.3713
54	sin	0.8090	0.8100	0.8111	0.8121	0.8131	0.8141	0.8151	0.8161	0.8171	0.8181
	cos	0.5878	0.5864	0.5850	0.5835	0.5821	0.5807	0.5793	0.5779	0.5764	0.5750
	tan	1.3764	1.3814	1.3865	1.3916	1.3968	1.4019	1.4071	1.4124	1.4176	1.4229
55	sin	0.8192	0.8202	0.8211	0.8221	0.8231	0.8241	0.8251	0.8261	0.8271	0.8281
	cos	0.5736	0.5721	0.5707	0.5693	0.5678	0.5664	0.5650	0.5635	0.5621	0.5606
	tan	1.4281	1.4335	1.4388	1.4442	1.4496	1.4550	1.4605	1.4659	1.4715	1.4770
56	sin	0.8290	0.8300	0.8310	0.8320	0.8329	0.8339	0.8348	0.8358	0.8368	0.8377
	cos	0.5592	0.5577	0.5563	0.5548	0.5534	0.5519	0.5505	0.5490	0.5476	0.5461
	tan	1.4826	1.4882	1.4938	1.4994	1.5051	1.5108	1.5166	1.5224	1.5282	1.5340
57	sin	0.8387	0.8396	0.8406	0.8415	0.8425	0.8434	0.8443	0.8453	0.8462	0.8471
	cos	0.5446	0.5432	0.5417	0.5402	0.5388	0.5373	0.5358	0.5344	0.5329	0.5314
	tan	1.5399	1.5458	1.5517	1.5577	1.5637	1.5697	1.5757	1.5818	1.5880	1.5941
58	sin	0.8480	0.8490	0.8499	0.8508	0.8517	0.8526	0.8536	0.8545	0.8554	0.8563
	cos	0.5299	0.5284	0.5270	0.5255	0.5240	0.5225	0.5210	0.5195	0.5180	0.5165
	tan	1.6003	1.6066	1.6128	1.6191	1.6255	1.6319	1.6383	1.6447	1.6512	1.6577
59	sin	0.8572	0.8581	0.8590	0.8599	0.8607	0.8616	0.8625	0.8634	0.8643	0.8652
	cos	0.5150	0.5135	0.5120	0.5105	0.5090	0.5075	0.5060	0.5045	0.5030	0.5015
	tan	1.6643	1.6709	1.6775	1.6842	1.6909	1.6977	1.7045	1.7113	1.7182	1.7251
Degs.	**Function**	**0'**	**6'**	**12'**	**13'**	**24'**	**30'**	**36'**	**42'**	**48'**	**54'**

XII Natural Sines, Cosines, and Tangents *(Continued)*

60°–74.9°

Degs.	Function	0.0°	0.1°	0.2°	0.3°	0.4°	0.5°	0.6°	0.7°	0.8°	0.9°
60	sin	0.8660	0.8669	0.8678	0.8686	0.8695	0.8704	0.8712	0.8721	0.8729	0.8738
	cos	0.5000	0.4985	0.4970	0.4955	0.4939	0.4924	0.4909	0.4894	0.4879	0.4863
	tan	1.7321	1.7391	1.7461	1.7532	1.7603	1.7675	1.7747	1.7820	1.7893	1.7966
61	sin	0.8746	0.8755	0.8763	0.8771	0.8780	0.8788	0.8796	0.8805	0.8813	0.8821
	cos	0.4848	0.4833	0.4818	0.4802	0.4787	0.4772	0.4756	0.4741	0.4726	0.4710
	tan	1.8040	1.8115	1.8190	1.8265	1.8341	1.8418	1.8495	1.8572	1.8650	1.8728
62	sin	0.8829	0.8838	0.8846	0.8854	0.8862	0.8870	0.8878	0.8886	0.8894	0.8902
	cos	0.4695	0.4679	0.4664	0.4648	0.4633	0.4617	0.4602	0.4586	0.4571	0.4555
	tan	1.8807	1.8887	1.8967	1.9047	1.9128	1.9210	1.9292	1.9375	1.9458	1.9542
63	sin	0.8910	0.8918	0.8926	0.8934	0.8942	0.8949	0.8957	0.8965	0.8973	0.8980
	cos	0.4540	0.4524	0.4509	0.4493	0.4478	0.4462	0.4446	0.4431	0.4415	0.4399
	tan	1.9626	1.9711	1.9797	1.9883	1.9970	2.0057	2.0145	2.0233	2.0323	2.0413
64	sin	0.8988	0.8996	0.9003	0.9011	0.9018	0.9026	0.9033	0.9041	0.9048	0.9056
	cos	0.4384	0.4368	0.4352	0.4337	0.4321	0.4305	0.4289	0.4274	0.4258	0.4242
	tan	2.0503	2.0594	2.0686	2.0778	2.0872	2.0965	2.1060	2.1155	2.1251	2.1348
65	sin	0.9063	0.9070	0.9078	0.9085	0.9092	0.9100	0.9107	0.9114	0.9121	0.9128
	cos	0.4226	0.4210	0.4195	0.4179	0.4163	0.4147	0.4131	0.4115	0.4099	0.4083
	tan	2.1445	2.1543	2.1642	2.1742	2.1842	2.1943	2.2045	2.2148	2.2251	2.2355
66	sin	0.9135	0.9143	0.9150	0.9157	0.9164	0.9171	0.9178	0.9184	0.9191	0.9198
	cos	0.4067	0.4051	0.4035	0.4019	0.4003	0.3987	0.3971	0.3955	0.3939	0.3923
	tan	2.2460	2.2566	2.2673	2.2781	2.2889	2.2998	2.3109	2.3220	2.3332	2.3445
67	sin	0.9205	0.9212	0.9219	0.9225	0.9232	0.9239	0.9245	0.9252	0.9259	0.9265
	cos	0.3907	0.3891	0.3875	0.3859	0.3843	0.3827	0.3811	0.3795	0.3778	0.3762
	tan	2.3559	2.3673	2.3789	2.3906	2.4023	2.4142	2.4262	2.4383	2.4504	2.4627
68	sin	0.9272	0.9278	0.9285	0.9291	0.9298	0.9304	0.9311	0.9317	0.9323	0.9330
	cos	0.3746	0.3730	0.3714	0.3697	0.3681	0.3665	0.3649	0.3633	0.3616	0.3600
	tan	2.4751	2.4876	2.5002	2.5129	2.5257	2.5386	2.5517	2.5649	2.5782	2.5916
69	sin	0.9336	0.9342	0.9348	0.9354	0.9361	0.9367	0.9373	0.9379	0.9385	0.9391
	cos	0.3584	0.3567	0.3551	0.3535	0.3518	0.3502	0.3486	0.3469	0.3453	0.3437
	tan	2.6051	2.6187	2.6325	2.6464	2.6605	2.6746	2.6889	2.7034	2.7179	2.7326
70	sin	0.9397	0.9403	0.9409	0.9415	0.9421	0.9426	0.9432	0.9438	0.9444	0.9449
	cos	0.3420	0.3404	0.3387	0.3371	0.3355	0.3338	0.3322	0.3305	0.3289	0.3272
	tan	2.7475	2.7625	2.7776	2.7929	2.8083	2.8239	2.8397	2.8556	2.8716	2.8878
71	sin	0.9455	0.9461	0.9466	0.9472	0.9478	0.9483	0.9489	0.9494	0.9500	0.9505
	cos	0.3256	0.3239	0.3223	0.3206	0.3190	0.3173	0.3156	0.3140	0.3123	0.3107
	tan	2.9042	2.9208	2.9375	2.9544	2.9714	2.9887	3.0061	3.0237	3.0415	3.0595
72	sin	0.9511	0.9516	0.9521	0.9527	0.9532	0.9537	0.9542	0.9548	0.9553	0.9558
	cos	0.3090	0.3074	0.3057	0.3040	0.3024	0.3007	0.2990	0.2974	0.2957	0.2940
	tan	3.0777	3.0961	3.1146	3.1334	3.1524	3.1716	3.1910	3.2106	3.2305	3.2506
73	sin	0.9563	0.9568	0.9573	0.9578	0.9583	0.9588	0.9593	0.9598	0.9603	0.9608
	cos	0.2924	0.2907	0.2890	0.2874	0.2857	0.2840	0.2823	0.2807	0.2790	0.2773
	tan	3.2709	3.2914	3.3122	3.3332	3.3544	3.3759	3.3977	3.4197	3.4420	3.4646
74	sin	0.9613	0.9617	0.9622	0.9627	0.9632	0.9636	0.9641	0.9646	0.9650	0.9655
	cos	0.2756	0.2740	0.2723	0.2706	0.2689	0.2672	0.2656	0.2639	0.2622	0.2605
	tan	3.4874	3.5105	3.5339	3.5576	3.5816	3.6059	3.6305	3.6554	3.6806	3.7062
Degs.	Function	0′	6′	12′	18′	24′	30′	36′	42′	48′	54′

XII   Natural Sines, Cosines, and Tangents   (*Continued*)
75°–89.9°

Degs.	Function	0.0°	0.1°	0.2°	0.3°	0.4°	0.5°	0.6°	0.7°	0.8°	0.9°
75	sin	0.9659	0.9664	0.9668	0.9673	0.9677	0.9681	0.9686	0.9690	0.9694	0.9699
	cos	0.2588	0.2571	0.2554	0.2538	0.2521	0.2504	0.2487	0.2470	0.2453	0.2436
	tan	3.7321	3.7583	3.7848	3.8118	3.8391	3.8667	3.8947	3.9232	3.9520	3.9812
76	sin	0.9703	0.9707	0.9711	0.9715	0.9720	0.9724	0.9728	0.9732	0.9736	0.9740
	cos	0.2419	0.2402	0.2385	0.2368	0.2351	0.2334	0.2317	0.2300	0.2284	0.2267
	tan	4.0108	4.0408	4.0713	4.1022	4.1335	4.1653	4.1976	4.2303	4.2635	4.2972
77	sin	0.9744	0.9748	0.9751	0.9755	0.9759	0.9763	0.9767	0.9770	0.9774	0.9778
	cos	0.2250	0.2232	0.2215	0.2198	0.2181	0.2164	0.2147	0.2130	0.2113	0.2096
	tan	4.3315	4.3662	4.4015	4.4374	4.4737	4.5107	4.5483	4.5864	4.6252	4.6646
78	sin	0.9781	0.9785	0.9789	0.9792	0.9796	0.9799	0.9803	0.9806	0.9810	0.9813
	cos	0.2079	0.2062	0.2045	0.2028	0.2011	0.1994	0.1977	0.1959	0.1942	0.1925
	tan	4.7046	4.7453	4.7867	4.8288	4.8716	4.9152	4.9594	5.0045	5.0504	5.0970
79	sin	0.9816	0.9820	0.9823	0.9826	0.9829	0.9833	0.9836	0.9839	0.9842	0.9845
	cos	0.1908	0.1891	0.1874	0.1857	0.1840	0.1822	0.1805	0.1788	0.1771	0.1754
	tan	5.1446	5.1929	5.2422	5.2924	5.3435	5.3955	5.4486	5.5026	5.5578	5.6140
80	sin	0.9848	0.9851	0.9854	0.9857	0.9860	0.9863	0.9866	0.9869	0.9871	0.9874
	cos	0.1736	0.1719	0.1702	0.1685	0.1668	0.1650	0.1633	0.1616	0.1599	0.1582
	tan	5.6713	5.7297	5.7894	5.8502	5.9124	5.9758	6.0405	6.1066	6.1742	6.2432
81	sin	0.9877	0.9880	0.9882	0.9885	0.9888	0.9890	0.9893	0.9895	0.9898	0.9900
	cos	0.1564	0.1547	0.1530	0.1513	0.1495	0.1478	0.1461	0.1444	0.1426	0.1409
	tan	6.3138	6.3859	6.4596	6.5350	6.6122	6.6912	6.7720	6.8548	6.9395	7.0264
82	sin	0.9903	0.9905	0.9907	0.9910	0.9912	0.9914	0.9917	0.9919	0.9921	0.9923
	cos	0.1392	0.1374	0.1357	0.1340	0.1323	0.1305	0.1288	0.1271	0.1253	0.1236
	tan	7.1154	7.2066	7.3002	7.3962	7.4947	7.5958	7.6996	7.8062	7.9158	8.0285
83	sin	0.9925	0.9928	0.9930	0.9932	0.9934	0.9936	0.9938	0.9940	0.9942	0.9943
	cos	0.1219	0.1201	0.1184	0.1167	0.1149	0.1132	0.1115	0.1097	0.1080	0.1063
	tan	8.1443	8.2636	8.3863	8.5126	8.6427	8.7769	8.9152	9.0579	9.2052	9.3572
84	sin	0.9945	0.9947	0.9949	0.9951	0.9952	0.9954	0.9956	0.9957	0.9959	0.9960
	cos	0.1045	0.1028	0.1011	0.0993	0.0976	0.0958	0.0941	0.0924	0.0906	0.0889
	tan	9.5144	9.6768	9.8448	10.02	10.20	10.39	10.58	10.78	10.99	11.20
85	sin	0.9962	0.9963	0.9965	0.9966	0.9968	0.9969	0.9971	0.9972	0.9973	0.9974
	cos	0.0872	0.0854	0.0837	0.0819	0.0802	0.0785	0.0767	0.0750	0.0732	0.0715
	tan	11.43	11.66	11.91	12.16	12.43	12.71	13.00	13.30	13.62	13.95
86	sin	0.9976	0.9977	0.9978	0.9979	0.9980	0.9981	0.9982	0.9983	0.9984	0.9985
	cos	0.0698	0.0680	0.0663	0.0645	0.0628	0.0610	0.0593	0.0576	0.0558	0.0541
	tan	14.30	14.67	15.06	15.46	15.89	16.35	16.83	17.34	17.89	18.46
87	sin	0.9986	0.9987	0.9988	0.9989	0.9990	0.9990	0.9991	0.9992	0.9993	0.9993
	cos	0.0523	0.0506	0.0488	0.0471	0.0454	0.0436	0.0419	0.0401	0.0384	0.0366
	tan	19.08	19.74	20.45	21.20	22.02	22.90	23.86	24.90	26.03	27.27
88	sin	0.9994	0.9995	0.9995	0.9996	0.9996	0.9997	0.9997	0.9997	0.9998	0.9998
	cos	0.0349	0.0332	0.0314	0.0297	0.0279	0.0262	0.0244	0.0227	0.0209	0.0192
	tan	28.64	30.14	31.82	33.69	35.80	38.19	40.92	44.07	47.74	52.08
89	sin	0.9998	0.9999	0.9999	0.9999	0.9999	1.000	1.000	1.000	1.000	1.000
	cos	0.0175	0.0157	0.0140	0.0122	0.0105	0.0087	0.0070	0.0052	0.0035	0.0017
	tan	57.29	63.66	71.62	81.85	95.49	114.6	143.2	191.0	286.5	573.0
Degs.	Function	0'	6'	12'	18'	24'	30'	36'	42'	48'	54'

VISUAL AIDS

The visual aids listed below and on the following pages can be used to supplement much of the material in this book. Some of them can be used in the study of different topics so that it is recommended that each one be reviewed, before use, to determine its suitability for a particular group or unit of study.

Motion pictures and filmstrips are included in the following list, the character of each being indicated by the self-explanatory abbreviations "MP" and "FS." Immediately following this identification is the name of the producer, and if different from the producer, the name of the distributor also. Abbreviations are used for names of producers and distributors, and these abbreviations are identified in the list of sources at the end of the bibliography. In most instances, the films can be borrowed or rented from local or state 16-mm film libraries. (A nationwide list of these local sources is given in *A Directory of 3660 16-mm Film Libraries*, available for $1 from the Superintendent of Documents, Washington 25, D.C.) Unless otherwise indicated, the motion pictures are 16-mm sound black-and-white films and the filmstrips are 35-mm black-and-white and silent. The length of motion pictures is given in minutes (min), that of filmstrips in frames (fr).

This bibliography is a selective one, and film users should examine the latest editions of *Educational Film Guide* and *Filmstrip Guide*, published by the H. W. Wilson Co., New York. The *Guides*, standard reference books, are available in most school, college, and public libraries. Readers should also write to manufacturers of electronic equipment, such as General Electric and Westinghouse, for copies of charts, posters, diagrams, models, and other visual aids dealing with electronics.

Adventure in Electronics (FS, GE, 36 fr color). Shows Donald Duck having his experiences with electrons, and explains the elementary principles of electronics.

Alternating Current (FS, USAF/UWF, 50 fr). An elementary introduction to the principles of alternating current. Demonstrates and explains Lenz' law, simple wave alternator, frequency, effective valve, voltage-current-time relationship, and power.

Amperes, Volts, and Ohms (MP, USN/UWF, 8 min). Explains the meaning, relationship, and measurement of amperes, volts, and ohms. (Accompanying filmstrip, same title, 23 fr.)

Basic Electricity (MP, USAF/UWF, 20 min color). An animated cartoon explaining the fundamentals of electricity, including voltage, current, resistance, magnetic fields, induction, primary and secondary coils, series and parallel circuits.

Basic Electronics (MP, USAF/UWF, 17 min color). An animated cartoon explaining the meaning of atoms and electrons, vacuum tube, cathode, rectifier tube, amplifier tube, grid, and bridge circuits.

Basic Principles of Frequency Modulation (MP, USA/UWF, 31 min). Describes what "FM" is in radio communication, how it is used, and what its advantages and limitations are.

Capacitance (MP, USN/UWF, 31 min). Demonstrates electron flow through a circuit, the charging and discharging of capacitors, variations of a charge on a capacitor in relation to time, and the behavior of capacitance with alternating current. (Accompanying filmstrip, same title, 22 fr.)

The Cathode Ray Tube: How It Works (MP, USN/UWF, 15 min). Demonstrates the construction and function of various parts of the cathode ray tube. Explains electrostatic and electromagnetic deflection and how varied currents affect the position of the spot of light on the scope.

Circuit Testing: Signal Generators (MP, USA/UWF, 26 min). Explains the theory and operation of the signal generator, including oscillating circuits, audio oscillators, radio-frequency oscillators, and frequency meters.

Coulomb's Force Constant (MP, MTP, 34 min). Describes Millikan experiment on a large scale using large plates and charged spheres, and indicates how by this method Coulomb's constant is obtained.

Coulomb's Law (MP, MTP, 28 min). Demonstrates the inverse square nature of electric force and the fact that electrical force is directly proportional to charge. Tests the inverse square law by looking for electrical effects inside a charged hollow sphere.

Current and Electromotive Force (MP, USN/UWF, 11 min). Explains electron theory, the arrangement of molecules, building up of current, conductors, electromotive force, resistance, and chemical and mechanical sources of electromotive force. (Accompanying filmstrip, same title, 38 fr.)

The Diode: Principles and Applications (MP, USOE/UWF, 17 min). Principles of electron flow across a gap; basic features of the diode tube; control of electron flow in the tube; photoelectric cells; X-ray tubes; and the diode as a rectifier. (Accompanying filmstrip, same title, 58 fr.)

Electric Fields (MP, MTP, 24 min). Discusses an electric field as a mathematical aid and as a physical entity. Demonstrates vector addition of fields, shielding effects by closed metallic surfaces, and the electric force which drives an electric current in a conductor for both straight and curved conductors.

Electric Lines of Force (MP, MTP, 7 min). Shows how to produce electric field patterns using neon sign transformer as high voltage source.

Electrodynamics (MP, EBF, 11 min). Explains the principles of current electricity and electromagnetism, including magnetic field of a coil, electromagnets, magnetic hypothesis, recalescence, induction by electric currents, and transformers.

Electromagnetic Spectrum (MP, MTP, 30 min). Explains the unity of the electromagnetic spectrum and shows, by experiments, that it arises from accelerated charges and that all phenomena are transverse polarized waves. Demonstrates Young's double slit experiment used in four different regions of the electromagnetic spectrum— X-ray, visible light (optical), microwave, and radiowave.

The Electron: An Introduction (MP, USOE/UWF, 16 min). Nature of electrons; electron flow in solid conductors; electromotive force; types and control of electron flow; electron flow and magnetic fields; and induced electron flow. (Accompanying filmstrip, same title, 40 fr.)

Electronic Research (MP, USAF, 22 min color). Describes various studies, conducted at the Air Force Cambridge Research Center, on artificial dielectrics, spherical antenna test patterns, barrier grid storage tubes, differences between consonant and vowel sounds, long-range, low-frequency radar, precision K-band antenna, radar grid transference filters, and fabrication of computer tubes.

Electronics at Work (MP, West, 20 min). Explains the six basic functions of electron tubes, and how each tube is used in industrial applications.

Electrons (MP, EBF, 11 min). Explains by animation the nature of electrons and the thesis that the fundamental unit of an electrical charge is the electron.

Electrons in a Uniform Magnetic Field (MP, MTP, 10 min). A Leybold tube (spherical cathode-ray tube with some gas to show path of electron beam) is used for fairly precise measurements for determining the mass of the electron as the electron beam is deflected by Helmholtz coils.

Electrostatics (MP, EBF, 11 min). Deals with static electricity as fundamental to an understanding of modern (1952) theories of electricity. Explains positive and negative electrification; role of insulators and conductors, movement of charges in the electroscope, the Compton electrometer, and lightning as nature's display of static electricity.

Elements of Electrical Circuits (MP, EBF, 11 min). Explains the nature of electric currents and circuits, electron motions, conductors, insulators, and factors affecting resistance. Contains animated drawings and photographic demonstrations.

Elements of Electricity (MP, USA/UWF, 15 min). Explains the breakdown of a molecule into atoms, and the relation of protons and electrons in electricity.

Franck-Hertz Experiment (MP, MTP, 25 min). Shows that kinetic energy of electrons accelerated through mercury vapor is transferred to the mercury atoms only in discrete packets of energy. The association of the quantum of energy with a line in the spectrum of mercury is established. The experiment retraced in this film was one of the earliest indications of the existence of internal energy states within the atom.

Inductance (MP, USN/UWF, 35 min). Shows how a magnetic force reacts around a coil, the nature of self-inductance, and how to increase the inductance of a coil. (Accompanying filmstrip, same title, 38 fr.)

Industrial Electronics Course (FS series, GE). Twelve filmstrips (each with a disc recording, 33⅓ rpm, 25 min) designed to give an understanding of the fundamentals and industrial applications of electronics. Titles of the 12 filmstrips are:

Harnessing the Electron	*Electronic Rectifier Equipment*
Electronic Tubes as Rectifiers	*Thy-mo-trol*
Grid Control of Electronic Tubes	*Electronic Control of A-C Power*
Fundamentals of Electricity, part 1	*Electronic Frequency Changing*
Fundamentals of Electricity, part 2	*Photoelectric Relay Systems*
Electric Relay Systems	*Electronics—Today and Tomorrow*

Interference of Photons (MP, MTP, 18 min). Demonstrates an experiment in which light exhibits both particle and wave characteristics. A very dim light source, a double slit, and a photomultiplier are used in such a way that less than one photon is in the apparatus. Characteristic interference bands of light are seen as the result of many impacts by undivided photons hitting at places consistent with the interference pattern.

Magnet Laboratory (MP, MTP, 20 min). Shows equipment used at MIT to produce strong magnetic fields and demonstrates magnetic effects of currents and the magnetism of iron.

Magnetism (MP, EBF, 16 min). Discusses the laws of polarity, the magnetic field, and terrestrial magnetism; and shows a variety of applications of magnetism to modern civilization.

Mass of the Electron (MP, MTP, 18 min). Using a cathode-ray tube encircled by a current-carrying loop of wire, measurements are taken which permit calculation of the mass of the electron.

Measurement of Electricity (MP, Coronet, 10 min color or b&w). In a dream sequence the four scientists whose names identify the basic units of electrical measure explain the volt, ampere, ohm, and watt.

Measurement with Light Waves (MP, USOE/UWF, 15 min). Principles of measurement with light waves; nature of light waves; cause of interference bands and use of these bands in ultra-precision measurement; procedures used in gage block inspection. (Accompanying filmstrip, same title, 50 fr.)

Millikan Experiment (MP, MTP, 30 min). Describes simplified Millikan experiments as photographed through the microscope. Standard spheres substituted for oil drop, X rays used, charged related to velocity of sphere across field of view of microscope. Emphasis is on presenting evidence that charge comes in natural units that are all alike.

Moving Charges (MP, MTP, 20 min color). Demonstrates some of the ways in which electrical charges can move—by being carried through conductors, through gases, and in vacuums and solutions—and how these currents can be measured.

Ohm's Law (MP, USA/UWF, 19 min). Explains the elements of electricity; electrical energy, its source, transmission, and use; composition of matter; use of force and energy; how Ohm's law functions; resistance; and the purpose and use of meters.

Oscillators (MP, USN/UWF, 13 min). Explains the basic principles of electronic oscillation.

Photons (MP, MTP, 25 min). Uses photomultiplier and oscilloscope to demonstrate that light can act as particle, explains photomultiplier, demonstrates amplification, discusses reasoning required to understand final outcome, and provides actual experimental evidence.

Principle of the Generator (MP, McGraw, 10 min). Explains by animation the elementary principles of electromagnetic induction and relates these principles to the operation of the generator.

Principles of Electricity (MP, GE, 20 min color). Explains the actions of electrons within an atom, the principles involved in the flow of current, magnetism and magnetic fields, and the meaning of volt, ampere, and ohm.

Principles of Gas-Filled Tubes (MP, USOE/UWF, 15 min). Theory of ionization applied to gas-filled tubes; control of current in circuits employing gas-filled tubes; use of the gas diode as a rectifier; action of the grid in a gas triode and application of the gas triode as a grid-controlled rectifier. (Accompanying filmstrip, same title, 36 fr.)

Principles of the Transistor (MP, McGraw, 21 min). Explains how the germanium diode and the transistor function, with details concerning the crystal lattice, "P" and "N" type germanium and hole conduction. Describes some of the present applications of the transistor and its advantages over the thermionic tube.

Project Tinkertoy (MP, USN/UWF, 28 min). A report on a joint U.S. Navy-National Bureau of Standards project to develop a new system of electronics design and manufacture using the "building-block" principle by which resistors, capacitors, tube sockets, and other parts of common design are machine assembled into functional electronic products.

RCL: Resistance, Capacitance (MP, USN/UWF, 34 min). Explains current and voltage in relation to time; voltage and current curves; the relationship of current and voltage; the measurement of voltage at source; the addition of phase components; and the effect of impedance on resonance.

Radio Antennas: Creation and Behavior of Radio Waves (MP, USAF/UWF, 12 min). Explains electric and magnetic fields, generation of electromagnetic waves, behavior of radio waves in space, ground wave, reflection and refraction, the ionosphere, and causes of fading.

Radio Receivers: Principles of Radio Receivers (MP, USAF/UWF, 17 min). Portrays the principles and operation of typical radio receivers, including crystal and tube detectors, radio and audio-frequency amplification, and the superheterodyne circuit.

Safety Precautions for Electronics Personnel (MP, USN/UWF, 18 min). Shows electrical and mechanical hazards which electronics technicians encounter in their normal work, and stresses precautions which should be employed to prevent accidents.

Series and Parallel Circuits (MP, EBF, 11 min). Explains the relationship between resistance, current, and voltage in series circuits and in parallel circuits; the advantages of each type of circuits; and a simple series-parallel combination.

Standing Waves on Transmission Lines (MP, USN/UWF, 23 min). By means of animated diagrams, laboratory demonstrations, and diverse analogies explains the causes, results, and prevention of standing waves in radio high-frequency transmission lines.

Transistors: Switching (MP, USN/UWF, 14 min). Shows examples of switching circuits in transistorized computers, explaining briefly the concept of digital computation and how transistors are used, and in more detail how a simple transistor switch works, with special attention to minority carrier storage in the base, showing how delaying effects of this storage are overcome.

The Triode: Amplification (MP, USOE/UWF, 14 min). Principles of the diode and triode; electric fields; a triode amplifier circuit; amplification of d-c. voltage changes; alternating voltages; distortion; amplification of audio-frequency signals. (Accompanying filmstrip, same title, 36 fr.)

Using Electricity Safely (FS, McGraw, 33 fr). Common-sense precautions in using and repairing electrical equipment—splices, soldering, taping, cords, switches, plugs, and sockets.

Vacuum Tubes (MP, EBF, 11 min). Explains the three functions of the vacuum tube—amplifier, rectifier, and oscillator.

Vacuum Tubes: Electron Theory and the Diode Tube (MP, USAF/UWF, 16 min). Explains electron behavior in matter, electron sources in vacuum tubes, symbols of tubes, functioning of tube in a circuit, and effect of plate voltage changes, space charge, and diode and duodiode as reflectors.

Volt Ohmmeter Operation (MP, USN/UWF, 15 min). Shows how to operate a volt ohmmeter (Weston and other types) to measure ohms and volts.

Voltaic Cell, Dry Cell, and Storage Battery (MP, USA/UWF, 18 min). Explains the principles of a voltaic cell, a dry cell, and a storage battery.

What Is Electricity? (MP, West, 20 min). Animation explains the movement of electrons, flow of current, and other information about electricity.

Film Sources

Coronet—Coronet Instructional Films, Chicago 1, Ill.

EBF—Encyclopaedia Britannica Films, Wilmette, Ill.

GE—General Electric Co., 1 River Road, Schenectady 5, N.Y.

McGraw—McGraw-Hill Book Co., Text-Film Dept., 330 W. 42nd St., New York 36, N.Y.

MTP—Modern Talking Picture Service, 3 E. 54th St., New York 22, N.Y.

*USA—U.S Department of the Army, Washington, D.C.

*USAF—U.S. Department of the Air Force, Washington 25, D.C.

*USN—U.S. Department of the Navy, Washington 25, D.C.

*USOE—U.S. Office of Education, Washington 25, D.C.

UWF—United World Films, Inc., 1445 Park Ave., New York 29, N.Y.

West—Westinghouse Electric Corp., Pittsburgh 30, Pa.

* Films distributed by United World Films, Inc.

INDEX